SAP PRESS e-books

Print or e-book, Kindle or iPad, workplace or airplane: Choose where and how to read your SAP PRESS books! You can now get all our titles as e-books, too:

- By download and online access
- For all popular devices
- And, of course, DRM-free

Convinced? Then go to www.sap-press.com and get your e-book today.

Plant Maintenance with SAP S/4HANA®: Business User Guide

 **PRESS**

SAP PRESS is a joint initiative of SAP and Rheinwerk Publishing. The know-how offered by SAP specialists combined with the expertise of Rheinwerk Publishing offers the reader expert books in the field. SAP PRESS features first-hand information and expert advice, and provides useful skills for professional decision-making.

SAP PRESS offers a variety of books on technical and business-related topics for the SAP user. For further information, please visit our website: *www.sap-press.com*.

Karl Liebstückel
Configuring Plant Maintenance in SAP S/4HANA
2020, 763 pages, hardcover and e-book
www.sap-press.com/5102

Bhattacharjee, Narasimhamurti, Desai, Vazquez, Walsh
Logistics with SAP S/4HANA: An Introduction (2nd Edition)
2019, 589 pages, hardcover and e-book
www.sap-press.com/4785

Jawad Akhtar
Production Planning with SAP S/4HANA
2019, 1010 pages, hardcover and e-book
www.sap-press.com/4821

Jawad Akhtar
Quality Management with SAP S/4HANA
2020, 950 pages, hardcover and e-book
www.sap-press.com/4924

Stoil Jotev
Asset Accounting with SAP S/4HANA
2020, 337 pages, hardcover and e-book
www.sap-press.com/5028

Karl Liebstückel

Plant Maintenance with SAP S/4HANA®

Business User Guide

Editor Meagan White
Acquisitions Editor Emily Nicholls
Copyeditor Ruth Saavedra
Cover Design Graham Geary
Photo Credit Shutterstock.com: 785685529/© nd3000; iStockphoto.com: 941796818/© Morsa Images
Layout Design Vera Brauner
Production Hannah Lane
Typesetting SatzPro, Krefeld (Germany)
Printed and bound in the United States of America, on paper from sustainable sources

ISBN 978-1-4932-2020-5
© 2021 by Rheinwerk Publishing, Inc., Boston (MA)
3rd edition 2021

Library of Congress Cataloging-in-Publication Data
Names: Liebstückel, Karl, author.
Title: Plant maintenance with SAP S/4HANA : business user guide / Karl
Liebstückel.
Other titles: Instandhaltung mit SAP. English
Description: 1st edition. | Bonn ; Boston : Rheinwerk Publishing, 2020. |
Translation of: Instandhaltung mit S/4HANA.
Identifiers: LCCN 2020035397 (print) | LCCN 2020035398 (ebook) | ISBN
9781493220205 (hardcover) | ISBN 9781493220212 (ebook)
Subjects: LCSH: Plant maintenance--Data processing. | SAP HANA (Electronic
resource)
Classification: LCC TS192 .L5513 2020 (print) | LCC TS192 (ebook) | DDC
658.2/0285--dc23
LC record available at https://lccn.loc.gov/2020035397
LC ebook record available at https://lccn.loc.gov/2020035398

Contents at a Glance

Dear Reader,

Many years ago, at my previous publishing company, we used a rather unwieldy ERP system (I won't name names!) to store our book-related data. Because ours was a small satellite office, part of my job whenever we hired someone new for the editorial team was to train them on our software. While we did have internal documentation for our main system tasks like creating a record for a new book, assigning ISBNs, and generating P&L statements, knowing exactly which buttons to press, and when, was hardly intuitive. I often wished for a book like this one that I could simply hand to new hires!

Author Karl Liebstückel has decades of experience both in operating PM systems and in teaching others to use them, and that knowledge jumps off each page. For complex PM tasks, there's no better teacher. I always picture our readers with the book next to their computer or terminal, well-worn and maybe a little smudged, though I know a number of you are likely reading it on an e-reader or tablet. Whatever the format, I hope this book makes your day-to-day work just a little bit easier!

What did you think about *Plant Maintenance with SAP S/4HANA: Business User Guide*? Your comments and suggestions are the most useful tools to help us make our books the best they can be. Please feel free to contact me and share any praise or criticism you may have.

Thank you for purchasing a book from SAP PRESS!

Meagan White
Editor, SAP PRESS

meaganw@rheinwerk-publishing.com
www.sap-press.com
Rheinwerk Publishing · Boston, MA

Contents

1 Introduction to Plant Maintenance with SAP S/4HANA 27

2 Organizational Structures 55

4   Work Order Cycle

5　Preventive Maintenance

6   Other Business Processes

7 Integrating Applications from Other Departments

8   Plant Maintenance Controlling   437

9   New Information Technologies for Plant Maintenance   495

10   Usability   569

Appendices

Foreword

As the world becomes more and more dynamic, complex, and data driven, maintenance has to face a permanent change in economic and technical challenges. Essentially, all asset-intensive industries are facing disruptive challenges from changing business models and higher cost pressures. Yet what does this mean for asset management?

The big imperatives are still the same: It is still important to balance cost, risk, and performance in accordance with International Organization for Standardization (ISO) 55001 and other new management standards. Moreover, the requirement to focus on reducing costs and being more efficient, to optimize capital expenditure, to avoid incidents, and to cope with revenue objectives and ever-evolving regulatory compliance challenges, remains unchanged.

What has changed is the massive amount of data on assets generated by plants for the purpose of being used for more effective asset management. The generated data can be shared in real time across the ecosystem, enabling new collaborative business models and, further, resulting in true operational excellence. By means of artificial intelligence and machine learning, we have the ability to process massive amounts of data faster than ever before.

This data provides a wealth of insights potentially transforming asset management with ways of helping companies to make use of their assets more effectively. Asset managers need ways to enable information transparency throughout the entire lifecycle of an asset and within the ecosystem of operators, equipment manufacturers, and service providers. Cloud-based networks facilitate efficient collaboration among all business partners throughout the complete asset lifecycle.

This requires a seamless digital representation of physical assets, allowing the digitalization of key processes—a digital twin. Plant operators as well as decision-makers can use this digital twin to easily access to all relevant information in order to reinvent their business models, business processes, and the ways people work.

At SAP, we call this *intelligent asset management*, and it will truly be the future of asset management. SAP can help you develop an environment in which you will be able to manage asset-related information and processes throughout the complete asset lifecycle. SAP Intelligent Asset Management combines solutions based on SAP S/4HANA with applications based on SAP Cloud Platform.

Now, customers in different fields and industries worldwide use SAP Intelligent Asset Management solutions. Solutions like ours enable them to support holistic asset management, which is integrated within the processes of logistics, human resources, purchasing, production, and plant and occupational safety, as well as to manage the entire lifecycle of their physical assets.

In this book you will read about how you can realize intelligent asset management provided by the solutions from SAP. I am sure that with the help of this book you will be able to take up a great deal of essential information from which a successful realization in your company will highly benefit.

Boris Mohr
Director, Intelligent Asset Management, SAP SE

About This Book

Genius is one percent inspiration and ninety-nine percent perspiration.
—Thomas A. Edison

Slowly but surely, a new plant maintenance concept is establishing itself in the minds of decision makers. This concept moves away from the notion of plant maintenance as purely a cost driver and toward the realization that goal-oriented, modern plant maintenance can be a success factor and provide a competitive advantage for your company. In other words, the trend is moving away from terms like *cost factor* and toward descriptions and components that ensure machine availability, increase production, and ensure plant safety. At the same time, in many industries, more than 40% of enterprise costs are either directly or indirectly attributable to plant maintenance. Even selling your company's internal plant maintenance services to outside companies may be a possibility. Thus, the plant maintenance area can contribute to the increase in revenue.

Many enterprises are only now slowly realizing that, in plant maintenance, the transition from cost factor to success factor can be accomplished only with the support of modern communication and information technology. In most other enterprise areas, this idea has already been taken for granted. The chosen IT solution should, ideally, have the following features:

- Be embedded in the heterogeneous network of enterprise processes
- Flexibly support all plant maintenance-specific business processes—from the elimination of malfunctions via preventative plant maintenance up to new plant maintenance strategies such as condition-based maintenance or reliability-centered maintenance
- Be oriented toward future challenges in the enterprise and the market
- Integrate modern technologies such as cloud computing, the Internet, and mobile devices
- Be easy to use because, in contrast to other enterprise areas such as purchasing or accounting, your users in plant maintenance may not be familiar with the daily IT tools of the trade.

Moreover, decision makers have increasingly realized how important plant maintenance is for the implementation of Industry 4.0 concepts. Irrespective of the topic discussed in the context of Industry 4.0, the role of plant maintenance for these topics—

and, in particular, the data-technical integration of plant maintenance—is always emphasized and underlined. This includes, for example:

- Machine-to-machine communication
- Autonomous production systems
- Human-to-machine communication
- Augmented reality
- Cyber-physical systems
- Smart factories
- Spare parts procurement via 3D printing
- Digital factories

One of SAP's responses to these requirements is *SAP S/4HANA Asset Management*. Illustrating the different uses for plant maintenance departments, this book is based on this current release level. This book gives you an overview of the functionalities and opportunities for a wide range of applications of SAP S/HANA Asset Management. It imparts not only a sense of the current range of functions but also gives an impression of the multitude of possible options.

As a result, each company must find its own solution in plant maintenance; this is why a pure description of functions is insufficient here. Based on my thirty-plus years of experience of plant maintenance with SAP and my work on more than eighty customer projects, in this book, I will show you how you can use SAP S/4HANA Asset Management functionality in your enterprise and also how not to use it.

In the book, customer examples illustrate what other companies have done. I also provide numerous practical tips that will be equally useful whether you are a beginner or an advanced user of a previous release of SAP ERP.

Unfortunately, widespread prejudice exists that usability is not necessarily a major feature of SAP applications. I have always been especially concerned not to let this prejudice become the final verdict. Usability is particularly significant in plant maintenance. Therefore, I devote an entire chapter to a range of measures that will help you to increase usability and thus user acceptance of the SAP system in your enterprise. Furthermore, I will present the results of a study we conducted at the university, which clearly proved that such measures yield an effective advantage in business processes to improve usability and demonstrated the extent to which they do so.

You can expect the following highlights: numerous tips and tricks for daily operations and advice on what you should (and should not) do in the course of your daily work.

Target Audience

This book is addressed to you directly. So, who are *you*? And what can you expect from this book?

- You are a *project lead* responsible for a project involving plant maintenance with SAP. In reality, you are also a technical expert, a maintenance planner, a workshop manager, an IT expert, and a member of the organizational team, among other things. This book gives you lots of advice on project management, IT strategy, and the other strands of your job.

- You are a *member of the project team* and are interested in creating a particular kind of system for plant maintenance with SAP. Therefore, your actual daily activities mean that you are also a maintenance planner, a workshop manager, an IT expert, a company engineer, a technical expert, a group leader, and a member of the organizational team, among other things. You too will find a lot of helpful advice on business processes and procedures in this book.

- You are a *manager* and have to decide whether or not to implement plant maintenance with SAP. In your daily work, you are a technical leader, a maintenance manager, a facility manager, an IT manager, and an organizational manager, among other roles. This book will give you specific information about what the SAP system can and cannot do.

- You are a *key user*, which means that you help your colleagues in their daily work of executing business processes, and you therefore need more background information on the system than the average user. This book will give you a lot of information about why something may or may not happen in the system, what you can do about it, and what you should not do.

- You are a *consultant*. This book will be useful to you whether you work in management consulting and need strategic advice or are a specialist consultant and are looking for application information. You'll obtain this information here.

- You are interested in plant maintenance with SAP on a general level. This book offers you an overview and a basic understanding of the subject matter as well as a certain level of detail.

Whom does this book not address? What will you not find here?

- If you are a *developer* who is looking for help with programming (for example, for interfaces or add-ons), this book not for you.

- If you are an *end user* and need a user guide for your enterprise's SAP system, this book will only partly fulfill your requirements. Individual installed systems are often too multifaceted to include all possible variations in a single book.

- If you are an *(internal or external) consultant*, *key user*, or *member of the project team* and are hoping for in-depth explanations and tips on customizing from this book, you will not find such information here. For this topic, refer to the separate book,

Configuring Plant Maintenance in SAP S/4HANA, SAP PRESS, 2020, *https://www.sap-press.com/5102.*

What This Book Can and Cannot Do

This book does not include customizing information or programming information, nor is it end-user documentation (or SAP documentation). In this book, however, I'll try to provide the following for you:

- I'll give you a basic understanding of the philosophy of SAP in plant maintenance.
- I'll describe the functionality of the SAP system in order to illustrate its options while making you aware of the limits of this functionality.
- I'll use reference processes and typical examples (such as that of the structuring of technical systems) to demonstrate how you can map your plant maintenance processes in the SAP system.
- I'll give you information on whether and where you can adapt the system to your own needs by cross-references to customizing. The current customizing settings can be found in the book we mentioned earlier, *Configuring Plant Maintenance in SAP S/4HANA.*
- I'll give you arguments that will enable you to decide whether or not to implement plant maintenance with SAP.
- I'll provide you with advice on making usability a central feature of your SAP system.
- I'll give you many useful tips and tricks for your SAP plant maintenance system.

One thing that I have learned from my experiences with past projects: Every enterprise has its own idea of how the SAP system should be used. For example, every enterprise will map its technical systems differently, every enterprise will set up its business processes differently, every enterprise needs to connect to different systems, and so on. Therefore, you should regard the information presented in this book as a basic starting point for your own ideas on how to adapt the system to your enterprise's individual needs and thus to create your SAP plant maintenance system.

Structure of This Book

This book is divided into ten chapters.

Chapter 1 lays out the business foundations and gives you a basic understanding of SAP's commitment to the area of plant maintenance. In this chapter, you'll also learn how maintenance strategies have developed over the years, what stages of development SAP has gone through in the plant maintenance area, and what SAP's position is today.

Organizational structures are the basis of everything in an SAP system. **Chapter 2** explains generic SAP organizational units and demonstrates the maintenance-specific organizational units that are required for other procedures.

A requirements-oriented approach to the structuring of technical systems is a prerequisite for executing business processes in plant maintenance with SAP. SAP provides various elements for mapping your own plant structure, and like every other enterprise, you'll have to decide which resources you want to use for which purposes. **Chapter 3** describes the options and limitations that apply when it comes to the structuring of technical systems; I'll give a lot of advice and make recommendations. I'll also provide tips on what you need to consider before you actually start to work in the system.

Chapter 4 forms the core of the book. The focus here, as before, is on the uniqueness of the work order cycle within each enterprise. SAP provides resources that you, and every enterprise, can tailor to suit individual requirements. This chapter shows the options and limitations of SAP S/4HANA Asset Management and also contains recommendations on how you can best use the system and what preparations you'll need to make before starting to work in the system.

Chapter 5 presents the range of possibilities of preventive plant maintenance which SAP S/4HANA offers you. You'll learn about different kinds of task lists. Various configuration levels of maintenance plans are shown, starting with a simple time-based single-cycle plan through a performance-based strategy plan up to condition-based maintenance.

Building on the basic work order cycle of Chapter 4, **Chapter 6** will show other business processes for adjustment of standard processes (i.e., simplified order processing or external processing). Further enhancements are introduced, such as calibration of measuring instruments or refurbishment of spare parts.

Your plant maintenance concept is constantly interacting with (and thus also exchanging data with) other departments in your enterprise. This interaction is reflected in the system in the comprehensive and in-depth integration between plant maintenance and applications used in other departments. These applications can be in SAP S/4HANA, in other SAP systems, or in non-SAP systems. **Chapter 7** illustrates the integration options in the system, analyzes the interfaces, and again provides recommendations and tips.

Two types of controlling are available in plant maintenance: Operational controlling controls ongoing business processes, and analytical controlling is used to prepare for decisions. Therefore, in **Chapter 8**, I'll show you the options for budgeting maintenance activities, on the one hand, and the options and limitations of the resources provided by SAP for the analytical area, on the other.

Modern information and communication technologies such as cloud computing, the Internet, and mobile architectures have become established in plant maintenance, as in almost every other area. In **Chapter 9**, you'll see state-of-the-art technologies, focusing particularly on their prerequisites, options, and limitations in plant maintenance. In addition, there will be an assessment of mine on what we can expect from these technologies in the future.

In **Chapter 10**, I'll first present the options that the SAP system provides for improving usability. We'll then go on to conclude the book with the results of several empirical laboratory tests. At the SAP Laboratory at the Würzburg-Schweinfurt University of Applied Sciences, we set up real-world conditions and tested how long it takes to execute business processes when every effort is made to increase usability and when usability measures are not implemented. I myself was astonished by the results, which I'll share with you in this chapter.

The Appendix contains a wealth of additional information, such as overviews in tabular form, suggestions for further reading, and much more.

Online Material for This Book

At *https://www.sap-press.com/5180*, you will find the *overviews* from Appendix B for download.

To make it easier for you to use this book, particular information is highlighted using the following special icons:

[!]

Caution

Boxes with this icon contain important information about the topic under discussion. This icon is also used to warn you about potential sources of error or stumbling blocks.

[+]

Practical tip

This book contains lots of tips and recommendations that I have gathered from my own professional experience. This kind of information is contained in boxes with this icon.

What's New to This Book?

This book, based on the 4th edition of *Plant Maintenance with SAP: Business User Guide*, was completely rewritten for SAP S/4HANA concerning issues like the following:

- Screenshots were newly edited with Belize-theme.
- Amended menu paths have been adjusted.
- Terminology was updated.

Regarding the functionality of the core system, there are only minor differences from SAP ERP to SAP S/4HANA. In cases of significant differences (i.e., maintenance planning schedule) it is explicitly pointed out and clarified.

Chapter 9 has been completely revamped, with the newest information technologies for plant maintenance. Among others, there you will find new features like the following:

- The ten most important SAP Fiori apps for plant maintenance
- The new mobile SAP solution for plant maintenance: SAP Asset Manager
- Cloud-based advanced settings for SAP Intelligent Asset Management with its most important components

Acknowledgments

I would like to thank everyone who contributed to the success of this book:

- My English editors, Meagan White and Emily Nicholls, as well as my German editor, Eva Tripp, for their encouraging support as well as for their constructive suggestions for improvements.
- My beloved wife, Brigitta Liebstückel, not only for her loving and moral support while I wrote this book, but also, and in particular, for spending such a lot of time for translating many passages of the book and for proofreading the whole book.

Now, I hope that working with this book helps you obtain many ideas and a great deal of inspiration for your own enterprise.

Finally, true to the spirit of Thomas A. Edison's quote (which, from my point of view, is the best quote of all), I wish you the energy, patience, and stamina required to implement these ideas in your enterprise.

Chapter 1

Introduction to Plant Maintenance with SAP S/4HANA

This chapter takes a look at the increasing significance of plant maintenance and the associated change in perspective, which has also given rise to new terminology. It then outlines the environment of SAP's Plant Maintenance component.

In the past few years, plant maintenance has become more and more important for the following business, economic, and technological reasons:

- **Business factors**
  - Rising acquisition values for technical systems
  - A disproportionate increase in costs resulting from losses
  - A higher, modified requirements profile for maintenance activities
  - The need for real-time collaboration with customers and vendors
  - Reduced vertical integration
- **Economic factors**
  - An increasing proportion of maintenance costs attributable to the gross national product (GNP)
  - Continuous growth in the number of people employed in the maintenance sector
  - More stringent environmental regulations and occupational health and safety regulations
  - Globalization of product markets
  - Expansion of the services sector
- **Technological factors**
  - Increased innovation speed
  - Increased automation
  - Increasingly interlinked, complex technical systems

This chapter will closely examine these influencing factors, all of which interact, and the associated changes to plant maintenance. Furthermore, this chapter will introduce the many changes that the maintenance components in the SAP system have undergone. It will also provide an overview of the application system of SAP S/4HANA, introduce the SAP HANA database, and discuss the three main user interfaces for SAP S/4HANA.

1.1 Plant Maintenance Today: New Ideas Need New Space

More and more companies are abandoning the outdated view that plant maintenance is a necessary evil or simply a cost factor. The ever-increasing pressure to be competitive in terms of quality and productivity is driving companies toward plant maintenance, which today occupies a much higher position in a company's priority list of objectives than ever before. This extends to the realization that a company can sell its plant maintenance services in the market and thus can contribute to increased revenue in addition to reduced costs.

Market globalization is increasingly leading to close collaboration with customers and vendors. Vertical integration is becoming lower and lower. Thus, in the automotive industry in 2015, vertical integration dropped considerably, to just 23%, and to 10% in individual cases, such as for the Porsche Cayenne. That is, the automotive industry produces just 10%–25% of the end product itself, and everything else comes from upstream production stages: the suppliers. As a result, dependency on the availability of technical systems at upstream production levels has increased proportionately.

In the past, a company could take internal countermeasures against malfunctions within the production flow of deeply structured production processes, but these countermeasures are entirely inconceivable for globalized production flows. Consequently, at the present time, two objectives, *prevention of malfunctions* and *increased or guaranteed availability of technical systems*, are coming increasingly to the fore of maintenance objectives.

Preventive maintenance is another goal of today's plant maintenance and can be achieved by changing the design of the technical system or machine. Another important aspect of preventive maintenance for production employees is to share in the responsibility (keyword: total productive maintenance [TPM]) of ensuring that no unscheduled outages occur, if possible. First-line maintenance tasks (on-call services for fault clearance) can also support the process.

In recent years, machines and technical systems have undergone extensive development in terms of their structures and the technology deployed. However, this development also means that recording the condition of individual components or assemblies has become more difficult because modern technical systems have considerably more weak points than previous systems. In addition, design engineers no longer tend toward oversized developments but, rather, favor space-saving, lightweight technical systems. As a result, however, components are more numerous and more sensitive to signs of wear and defects.

Plants and machinery are constructed in a much more modular manner today than previously. Thus, maintenance is applied differently to individual components of a system (component maintenance) and no longer refers to the complete system. Other goals may include the following:

- Increased, optimum use of the lifecycle of technical systems and devices
- Improved quality of finished products
- Improved operating safety
- Optimized operating procedures
- Future-oriented cost planning
- Lower restart costs
- Compliance with legal requirements, in particular environmental regulations
- Compliance with manufacturer guidelines, so you can make a claim under warranty if required

However, other objectives may also interest you, depending on your industry, the objects to be maintained, the size of your company, your company's organization, and other influencing factors. If, for example, you are a maintenance service provider, customer satisfaction will be of primary importance to you. If you work in real estate, maintenance tasks may contribute to strengthening your negotiating position when selling real estate. Therefore, each company should develop clear maintenance objectives and communicate these to everyone involved (for example, employees, customers, and so on).

Two unavoidable consequences resulted from this change within plant maintenance: New maintenance terminology had to be coined for organizations with responsibilities both nationally and internationally, and companies had to react to these challenges by changing their maintenance strategies.

1.2   New Plant Maintenance Terminology

In 2018, the German Institute for Standardization (Deutsches Institut für Normung [DIN]) published a new version of the German standard DIN 31051—Fundamentals of Maintenance—to replace the older version from 1985 and 2003. The older version had to be revised because EN 13306 was published in 2001 (current version EN 13306: 2018-02) and compiled new terminology for plant maintenance. Maintenance is divided accordingly in the current version of DIN 31051:2018-09 into four basic measures (see Figure 1.1).

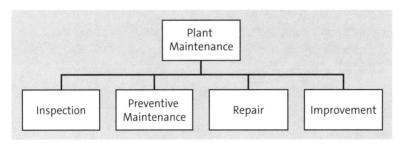

Figure 1.1 Plant Maintenance Terminology

Plant maintenance includes "combinations of all technical and administrative measures as well as of management measures throughout the lifecycle of a unit, which are aimed at preserving or restoring its functional state so that it can perform the required function." Maintenance essentially is comprised of the following four tasks: *inspection*, *maintenance*, *repair*, and *improvement*, each of which is described in more detail in this book. Let's look at each of them briefly:

- **Inspection**
  To ensure both the high availability and operating safety of machines, technical systems, and equipment, regular inspections are required to determine their technical condition and to define the necessary maintenance tasks. The new DIN 31051 defines inspection as all tasks for determining and assessing the actual condition of a unit, including identifying the cause of wear and tear and deducing the consequences necessary to ensure its future use. In contrast, the old DIN 31051 defined inspection as all tasks for determining and assessing the actual condition. The inspection includes the following measures in particular:
  - Checking
  - Measurement
  - Observation
  - Assessment
  - Deriving consequences

- **Preventive maintenance**
  Whereas the old DIN 31051 defined preventive maintenance as all tasks for preserving the target condition, the new DIN 31051 defines maintenance as all tasks for delaying the reduction of the wear reserve. Preventive maintenance tasks include the following tasks in particular:
  - Visual inspection
  - Adjustment
  - Replacement
  - Supplement

- Lubrication
- Preservation
- Cleaning
- Functional testing

To obtain the required functional efficiency and availability of machines, technical systems, and equipment, you must implement maintenance tasks regularly, based on the manufacturer guidelines, the maintenance plans, and customer needs, while taking into account the changing operation-specific processes and conditions.

- **Repairs**

  The old DIN 31051 defined repairs as all tasks for restoring the target condition. In contrast, the new DIN 31051 defines as repairs all physical tasks that are carried out to restore the functioning of a faulty unit. Via maintenance and repairs, nonfunctioning components, assemblies, and so on in machinery, plants, and equipment, both unscheduled (fault clearance) and scheduled (planned shutdowns), are replaced, and full functionality is thus restored. Repairs thus consist of the following activities in particular:

  - Unit exchange
  - Restoration of functions
  - Breakdown resolution

- **Improvement**

  New to DIN 31051 are improvement tasks, defined as the combination of all technical, administrative, and management tasks to improve the reliability, maintainability, and/or safety of a unit without changing its original function. The constant improvement of the plant serves to increase the operational and functional safety of machines, plants, and equipment. At the same time, a corresponding potential for improvement is identified, solutions are designed, and specified measures are implemented. Inspections are comprised of the following tasks in particular:

  - Elimination of weak points
  - Improvement in machinery and plant design
  - Optimized business processes
  - Acceleration of the exchange of information

Further Resources

For more information on these four measures, see DIN 31051:2018-09: Fundamentals of Maintenance, issued by Deutschen Institut für Normung (DIN) (German Institute for Standardization), Berlin/Vienna/Zurich: 2018.

Table 1.1 summarizes and compares the old and new versions of DIN 31051.

Activity	DIN 31051:1985-01	DIN 31051:2018-09
Inspection	Tasks for determining and assessing the actual condition	Tasks for determining and assessing the functional condition with determination of the causes of wear and tear and derivation of the necessary tasks
Preventive maintenance	Tasks for maintaining the target condition	Tasks for delaying the reduction of the wear reserve
Repair	Tasks for restoring the target condition	Tasks carried out to restore the functioning of a faulty unit
Improvement		Tasks to improve the reliability and/or maintainability and/or safety of a unit without changing its original function

Table 1.1 Old and New DIN 31051

In 2014, the International Organization for Standardization (ISO) published several asset management standards, including the following three standards:

- ISO 55000 deals with the basic principles of asset management, providing general definitions, explaining benefits for users, and introducing the asset management system. Furthermore, ISO 55000 describes the relationship between asset management and the asset management system.
- ISO 55001 forms the core of the ISO series and describes all critical requirements for asset management systems. ISO 55001 provides the basis for certification and is thus comparable to ISO 9001 in quality management.
- ISO 55002 contains descriptions for implementing an asset management system.

So, in contrast to the German standardization, the ISO standards provide a comprehensive definition of the asset management concept and are not limited to plant maintenance only.

Table 1.2 provides an overview of topics related to ISO 55000 and others.

Area	Tasks
Corporate organization	- Corporate organization and its context - Stakeholders' expectations - Goal of the asset management system
Management	- Management and responsibility - Strategy and specifications
Planning	- Opportunities and risks - Objectives and the meeting of objectives

Table 1.2 Spheres of Activity in ISO 55000

Area	Tasks
Support	▪ Resources, skills, communication, information, and documentation
Operational tasks	▪ Operational planning and control ▪ Change management ▪ External assignment
Performance assessment	▪ Monitoring, assessment, analysis, and evaluation ▪ Internal audits ▪ Management review
Improvement	▪ Corrective measures ▪ Preventive measures ▪ Continuous improvement

Table 1.2 Spheres of Activity in ISO 55000 (Cont.)

1.3   Maintenance Strategies over Time

Not only have responsible organizations thus responded to changing business conditions, but also, the companies themselves have adopted new challenges posed by their changed maintenance strategies (see Figure 1.2), as follows:

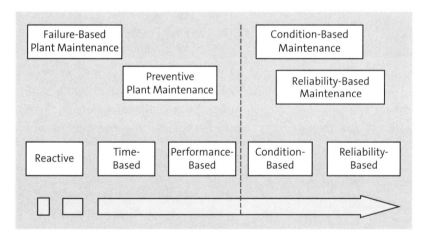

Figure 1.2 Plant Maintenance Strategies over Time

▪ **From reactive to preventive maintenance**
New market and technology challenges are reflected in the development of maintenance strategies and concepts. The classic reactive maintenance, which provides for the repair of the plant after downtime, has been successively replaced by preventive maintenance focused on proactive maintenance and inspection tasks. Finally, the "firefighting strategy" had to be replaced with the increased linking of plants, since

the failure of one machine could stop the entire production line and thus result in high standstill costs.

- **Time-based or performance based?**
  Preventive maintenance can be performed in a time-based (that is, calendar-based) or performance-related (that is, counter-based) manner. Why is this distinction so important, especially against the backdrop of the possible use of IT? Performance-related maintenance requires significantly more administrative effort than time-based maintenance.

  With time-related maintenance, you define maintenance plans only with fixed or sequential cycles. SAP S/4HANA Asset Management can thus calculate all maintenance dates and automatically generates an order for the calculated date.

  However, performance-based maintenance requires a counter (kilometers, operating hours, quantities, and so on) and only works correctly if meter readings are recorded at regular intervals. Organization, planning, and recording of meter readings thus lead to an administrative burden that should not be underestimated. The maintenance planning and control system can correctly calculate the updated maintenance schedules only if the current meter readings are available regularly.

- **Ratio of planned to executed maintenance orders**
  For a long time, the ratio of executed to planned maintenance orders was at 90:10 in many companies that followed the "firefighting strategy." For many companies, this ratio may still apply, but numerous companies are already utilizing more and better planning and may thus have reached a ratio of 70:30 or even of 50:50. If you've reached a better ratio in your company, you can be proud of your organization.

- **Condition-based maintenance**
  With this technique, maintenance activities are executed if a measuring point on a technical object has reached a certain condition. Condition-based maintenance requires regular inspections of a plant, including the recording of inspection results, or the presence of upstream systems that constantly monitor the condition of a plant and trigger a notification in SAP S/4HANA Asset Management in the event of an emergency (for example, exceeding or falling below predetermined value limits). Possible upstream systems may be, for example:
  - Mobile data acquisition systems
  - Process control systems
  - Central building control systems
  - Supervisory control and data acquisition systems

- **Reliability-based maintenance**
  This determines the maintenance tasks, operating rules, and structural adjustments that are necessary for the desired reliability of a technical system. Reliability-centered maintenance is a method of analysis that contains rules for the decisions and is based on the analysis of the functions of a machine. Possible malfunctions

and their causes are derived from this analysis. A failure impact assessment is carried out for each cause. This collection of information is called an *information worksheet* and is largely a failure mode and effects analysis (FMEA). A decision diagram is then used for any cause of a failure in the information sheet to check whether a condition-related, preventive, or reactive task is recommended. If none of these measures are useful, design changes or amended operating rules are considered.

1.4   Plant Maintenance over Time in SAP

The history of plant maintenance in SAP dates back to 1986, when the first version of plant maintenance in SAP was put on the market with *RM-INST* within the SAP R/2 system. Subsequent releases of RM-INST appeared in 1988 (4.3) and 1991 (5.0).

In 1994, the first version of the *Plant Maintenance (PM)* module of SAP R/3 was put on the market. SAP R/3 releases then underwent various name changes: from SAP R/3 via SAP R/3 Enjoy and mySAP.com to SAP R/3 Enterprise. The term for plant maintenance remained constant up to the mySAP.com release: PM. In SAP R/3 Enterprise, however, SAP introduced the concept of asset lifecycle management (ALM).

As SAP 2005 launched the first SAP ERP release on the market, we had to adapt yet again to a new term for plant maintenance: *SAP Enterprise Asset Management (SAP EAM)*. The release names changed often since then: First was mySAP ERP 2005, then the *my* disappeared, and the release was renamed SAP ERP 2005. A short time later, SAP replaced the year with the continuous release number; it has been SAP ERP 6.0 since then.

In 2016 when SAP introduced the first SAP S/4HANA version with logistic functions to the market, they came up with a new term for the plant maintenance application: *SAP S/4HANA Asset Management*. This should not be confused with asset accounting, for fixed asset accounting.

Alas, there is no uniform terminology. The definition of terms for the plant maintenance application in SAP S/4HANA is not as consistent as it sounds at first. SAP media on this subject (presentations, online documentation, F1 help, customizing, roadmaps) use different names for the same product. You'll find terms and abbreviations like the following:

- SAP Asset Management
- SAP Digital Asset Management
- SAP S/4HANA Asset Management
- SAP Enterprise Asset Management (SAP EAM)
- SAP Maintenance Management
- SAP Maintenance and Service Management
- SAP Plant Maintenance (SAP PM)

Each of these terms is used synonymously. For a book author, this synonymous use of different labels for identical product is confusing, and so will it be for the reader. This is why a term has to be chosen which excludes any confusion about the product associated with. For the present book, we decided to use the most frequently used term in SAP S/4HANA publications, which is *SAP S/4HANA Asset Management*.

1.5   SAP S/4HANA Application System

In 2016, SAP S/4HANA was released as a successor to SAP ERP 6.0. Just like SAP ERP, SAP S/4HANA is a complete enterprise resource planning (ERP)-system comprised of all enterprise-specific business processes and functions. Unlike the previous SAP ERP system, SAP S/4HANA is exclusively offered on an SAP HANA database. There are no versions available for other database systems.

SAP S/4HANA is offered both on-premise (referred to as SAP S/4HANA) and in the cloud (referred to as SAP S/4HANA Cloud). The utilization of a hybrid scenario is quite conceivable. In this case certain applications are installed on-premise, whereas others will be used in the cloud.

SAP S/4HANA (remember, this means the on-premise edition) is delivered once a year. For SAP S/4HANA Cloud, there is an update every three months (see Figure 1.3).

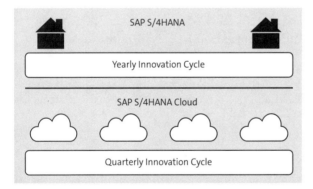

Figure 1.3 SAP S/4HANA Innovation Cycle

[+]
All Following Descriptions Refer to the On-Premise Version
In SAP S/4HANA Cloud, only a few possibilities are made available for adjusting the system to the needs of your business. You merely may consume the SAP-defined standard.

In contrast, in SAP S/4HANA, you are given the opportunity to activate business functions, to customize, for additional programming or modification.

The following sections will give you an overview of the functionality available in SAP S/4HANA and the use of enhancement packages.

1.5.1   SAP S/4HANA Overview

SAP S/4HANA offers the following range of functions (as of September 2020, see Figure 1.4):

- Finance (financial accounting, annual accounts, cost center accounting, profitability analysis)
- Human resources (with time recording)
- Sourcing and procurement (with procurement process, contract administration, invoice management)
- Supply chain (production planning, inventory management, warehouse management)
- Manufacturing (with production orders, quality management)
- Marketing
- Sales (with customer order processing and contract management)
- Service (with service handling, service contracts, and spare parts management)
- Asset management (with plant maintenance)
- Research and development (with product development and project management)

	SAP S/4HANA Finance	SAP S/4HANA Human Resources *SAP SuccessFactors* *SAP Fieldglass*	SAP S/4HANA Sourcing and Procurement *SAP Ariba* *SAP Fieldglass*	SAP S/4HANA Manucaturing	SAP S/4HANA Supply Chain
Suite	• Financal Services Network	• Core Human Resourses and Payroll • Talent Management • Time and Attendance Management • Human Captial Analytics	• Supplier collaboration • Business Network • Guided End-User Buying • External Workforce Management		
Products	• Financal Planning and Analysis • Accouting and Financal Close • Treasury Management • Receiveables Management • Invoice Management and Accounts Payable			• Constrained Production Planning • Production Scheduling	• Extended Warehouse Management • Advanced ATP
Digital Core — SAP S/4HANA Enterprise Management	• Accouting and Closing Operations • Acccouting • Cost Management and Profitablity Analysis	• Time Recording	• Operational Purchaseing • Collaborative Sourcing and Contract Management • Invoice and Payables Management • Supplier Management • Procurement Analytics	• Production Orchestration and Execution • Quality Management	• Inventory and Basic Warehouse Managament • Production Planning
	• Order and Contract Management	• Service Management* • Service Master Data Managment* • Service Parts Management* • Service Agreement Management*		• Maintenance Management	• Product Development and Project Control* • Production Engineering
Products	• Sales Planning and Performance Management		• Billing and Revenue Innovation Management (BRIM)	• Asset Operations and Maintenance* • Environment, Health, and Safety	• Enterprise Portfolio and Project Management • Commercial Project Management • Complaint Product Lifecycle Management
Suite	*SAP Sales Cloud* SAP S/4HANA Sales	*SAP Customer Experience* SAP S/4HANA Service	*SAP Marketing Cloud* SAP S/4HANA Marketing and Commerce	SAP S/4HANA Asset Management	SAP S/4HANA Research and Development

*(Partally) Compatibility Scope   Industries

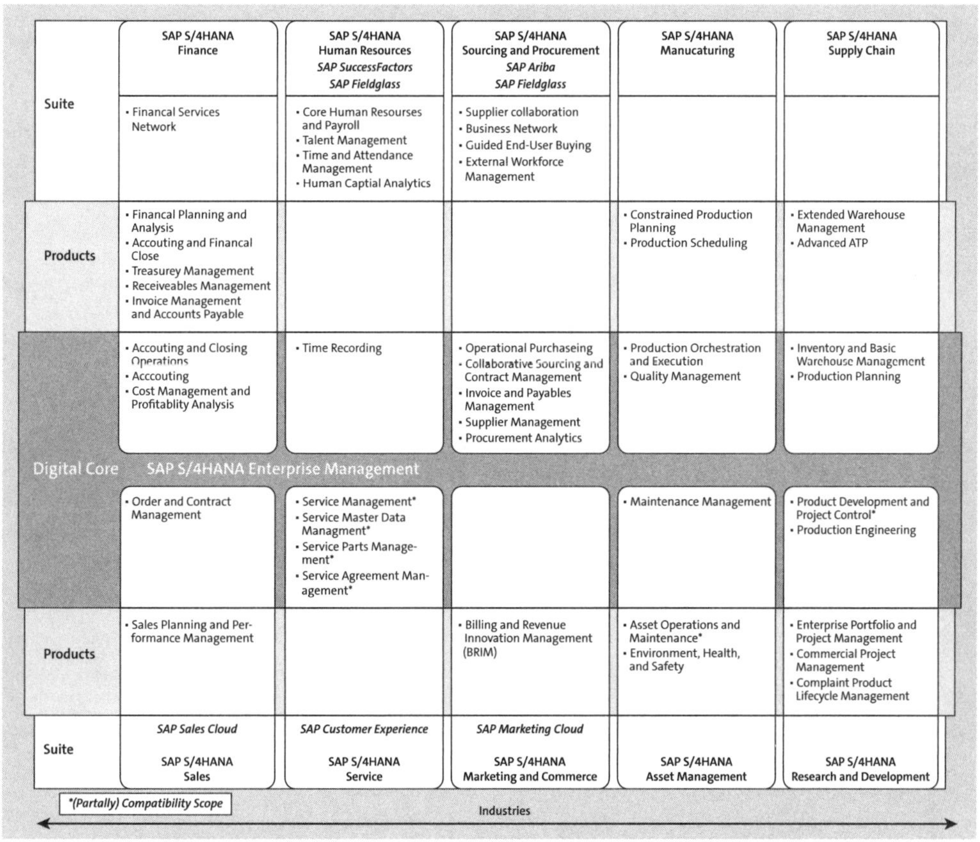

Figure 1.4 SAP S/4HANA Overview

These applications correspond to the inner dark area in Figure 1.4, often referred to as the *SAP S/4HANA core*.

This range of functions may be supplemented with additional features via interfaces in different places, as follows. This is the *SAP S/4HANA suite*.

- SAP SuccessFactors for human resources department
- SAP Ariba for purchasing department
- SAP Customer Service for sales and service department

1.5.2   Enhancement Packages

Enhancement Packages for SAP S/4HANA are delivered once a year on average. In the past, further developments were exclusively delivered within the scope of a release update, creating a challenge for the customers that they could only tackle by means of migration projects, which meant quite an effort for them.

In contrast to the former release updates, Enhancement Packages ensure careful further development of the SAP system, without causing efforts like migration projects.

Each Enhancement Package contains enterprise extensions or enterprise business functions. With Transaction SFW5 (Switch Framework), they can be activated separately if needed (see Figure 1.5). Some of the functions are reversible; some are not.

Name	Description	Planned Status	Dependen...	Document...	Software Component
LOG_EAM_CI_1	Enhancement Package 2 - Enterprise Asset Management	Business func. will remain activat...		i	S4CORE
LOG_EAM_CI_10	Enterprise Asset Management Teil 10 (Reversible)				S4CORE
LOG_EAM_CI_12	Enterprise Asset Management Teil 12 (Reversible)	✓			S4CORE
LOG_EAM_CI_13	Enterprise Asset Management Teil 13 (Reversible)				S4CORE
LOG_EAM_CI_2	Enhancement Package 3 - Enterprise Asset Management	Business func. will remain activat...		i	S4CORE
LOG_EAM_CI_3	Enterprise Asset Management: Continuous Improvements	Business func. will remain activat...		i	S4CORE
LOG_EAM_CI_4	Enterprise Asset Management Part 4	Business func. will remain activat...		i	S4CORE
LOG_EAM_CI_5	Enterprise Asset Management Part 5	Business func. will remain activat...		i	S4CORE
LOG_EAM_CI_6	Enterprise Asset Management Part 6 (Reversible)	✓		i	S4CORE
LOG_EAM_CI_7	Enterprise Asset Mgmt Part 7	Business func. will remain activat...			S4CORE
LOG_EAM_CI_8	Enterprise Asset Management Part 8 (Reversible)	✓			S4CORE
LOG_EAM_CI_9	Enterprise Asset Management Part 9 (Reversible)	✓			S4CORE
LOG_EAM_CI_9_ORD_OPER_COMP	EAM, Reassign / Copy Order Components and Copy Operations (...	✓			S4CORE
LOG_EAM_GEF	EAM, Geographical Enablement Framework Integration			i	S4CORE
LOG_EAM_LINEAR_1	EAM, Linear Asset Management 1	Business func. will remain activat...		i	S4CORE
LOG_EAM_LINEAR_2	EAM, Linear Asset Management 2 (Reversible)	✓		i	S4CORE
LOG_EAM_MAM	Business function for Mobile Asset management Enhancement p...			i	S4CORE
LOG_EAM_MPOINT_MASS_DEACT	EAM: Mass Deactivation of Measuring Points and Counters (Reve...	✓		i	S4CORE
LOG_EAM_MPS1	Maintenance Plan Scheduling Using Preselection 1 (Reversible)	✓		i	S4CORE
LOG_EAM_OLC	Operation Account Assignment	Business func. will remain activat...		i	S4CORE
LOG_EAM_OLC_2	Operation Account Assignment 2 (Reversible)	✓		i	S4CORE
LOG_EAM_PAM	EAM: Pool Asset Management	Business func. will remain activat...		i	S4CORE
LOG_EAM_PRINT	Enterprise Asset Management Printing	Business function is obsolete and...			S4CORE
LOG_EAM_QM_CODE_DEACT	EAM/QM, Deactivation of Codes (Reversible)	✓			S4CORE
LOG_EAM_SHIFTFACTORS	EAM, Shift Factors for Multiple Counter Plans	Business func. will remain activat...		i	S4CORE

Figure 1.5 Business Functions

For plant maintenance the following business functions mainly come into use:

- /EAMPLM/LOG_EAM_WS (Worker Safety)
- LOG_EAM_CC (Configuration Control Innovations)
- LOG_EAM_CI_1 (e.g., digital signatures)
- LOG_EAM_CI_2 (e.g., new BAPIs and BAdIs)
- LOG_EAM_CI_3 (e.g., inspection rounds)
- LOG_EAM_CI_4 (e.g., inspection round enhancements)
- LOG_EAM_CI_5 (e.g., mass changes for order operations)
- LOG_EAM_CI_6 (e.g., call horizon in days)
- LOG_EAM_CI_7 (e.g., follow order)
- LOG_EAM_CI_8 (e.g., mass availability check)
- LOG_EAM_CI_9 (e.g., authorization groups for maintenance strategies)
- LOG_EAM_CI_9_ORD_OPER_COMP (Copy Order Operations and Components)
- LOG_EAM_CI_10 (e.g., maintenance packages is lists)
- LOG_EAM_CI_11 (e.g., notification mass change enhancements)
- LOG_EAM_CI_12 (e.g., additional texts for non-stock material and external operations)
- LOG_EAM_CI_13 (e.g., end date and reasons for maintenance plans)
- LOG_EAM_LINEAR_1 (Linear Asset Management)
- LOG_EAM_LINEAR_2 (Linear Asset Management part 2)
- LOG_EAM_MPOINT_MASS_DEACT (Mass Deactivation of Measuring Points and Counters)
- LOG_EAM_MPS1 (Maintenance Plan Scheduling with Selection)
- LOG_EAM_OLC (Costs and Accounting on Operation Level)
- LOG_EAM_OLC_2 (Costs and Accounting on Operation Level part 2)
- LOG_EAM_PAM (Pool Asset Management)
- LOG_EAM_PRINT (Print Functions)
- LOG_EAM_QM_CODE_DEACT (Deactivating Codes
- LOG_EAM_SHIFTFACTORS (Shift Factors for Multiple Counter Plans)
- LOG_EAM_SIMP (e.g., flexible order layout)
- LOG_EAM_SIMPLICITY (1-8, Simplified Management of EAM Functions)
- LOG_EAM_VE_INT (Integration with SAP 3D Visual Enterprise)
- EA-PLM (Electronic Parts Catalogs)
- LOG_EAM_POM (Project Oriented Maintenance)
- LOG_EAM_POM_2 (Logbook Innovations)

- LOG_EAM_ROTSUB (Refurbishment & Subcontracting)
- LOG_EAM_ROTSUB_2 (Refurbishment & Subcontracting part 2)
- LOG_MM_SERNO (Serial Numbers in Purchasing with Integration in Inventory Management & Shipping)
- LOG_PP_SRN_CONF (Shift Report and Notes)
- LOG_PP_SRN_02 (Shift Report and Notes part 2)

Activating LOG_EAM_CI Business Functions

It is advisable to activate enterprise business functions LOG_EAM_CI.

They contain small round-offs, making your tasks easier and smarter in the day-to-day business.

You may do so unhesitatingly, as there are no dependencies with other applications.

1.6   SAP HANA Database

SAP has never marketed a product as much as SAP HANA (HANA stands for *high-performance analytic appliance*), a database technology that SAP introduced in 2010. SAP HANA involves a combination of hardware and software to enable higher performance compared to traditional applications by using in-memory technology.

In-memory technology means that the data is stored not on a hard disk but in the computer's memory, thus making access much faster. SAP HANA was developed by SAP to enable large databases (big data) to be browsed more efficiently.

SAP HANA combines techniques from the hardware and software sectors. On the software side, SAP HANA constitutes a hybrid of the column-oriented functioning of in-memory databases and the row-oriented functioning of relational databases (see Figure 1.6).

Due to the direct access option to characteristics or key figure values in columns, the fields can be accessed much faster, because only individual rows, instead of large volumes of data records—as in the case of row-oriented access—are read.

On the hardware side, the system tries to move as much as possible from the hardware memory to the CPU cache and from the disk storage to the main memory to take advantage of the faster access speed in each case (see Figure 1.7).

Country	Plant	Planner group	Orders
USA	Dallas	100	485
USA	Dallas	101	590
Germany	Hamburg	200	635
Germany	Hamburg	201	345

Row-oriented database

Row 1	US	3000	100	485
Row 2	US	3000	101	590
Row 3	DE	1000	200	635
Row 4	DE	1000	201	345

Column-oriented database

Column1	Column2	Column3	Column4
US	3000	100	485
US	3000	101	590
DE	1000	200	635
DE	1000	201	345

Figure 1.6 Row- and Column-Oriented Databases

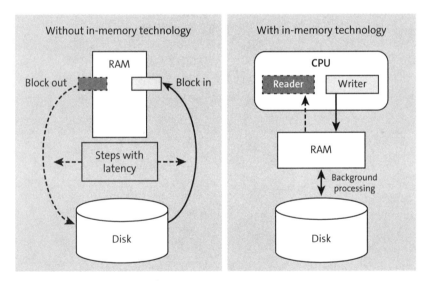

Figure 1.7 SAP HANA Principles

SAP HANA was initially designed for analytical applications (such as profitability analysis, SAP Business Warehouse [SAP BW], or SAP BusinessObjects). Over time, SAP HANA was successively made available for all applications, especially with the release of SAP HANA for SAP Business Suite and, thus, for SAP ERP in 2013. Unlike SAP ERP, which can also be operated on other databases (anyDB), SAP S/4HANA runs exclusively on a HANA database.

1.7   User Interfaces

Via which user interfaces can SAP S/4HANA be accessed? SAP's statement on the matter is:

> All innovations of SAP S/4HANA have to been made available for the access via user interface of SAP Fiori in order to ensure a uniform desktop for all devices. A customer using the on-premise edition of SAP S/4HANA is still able to use the conventional desktop.

There are two important statements behind this:

- You may only access SAP S/4HANA Cloud via the SAP Fiori interface
- With SAP S/4HANA, you may access it via SAP GUI or SAP Business Client (as well as SAP Fiori).

If you are using SAP GUI, you will notice hardly any difference between SAP S/4HANA and SAP ERP at the desktop. Accessing plant maintenance, for example, you will find the same routing, files, and transactions as with SAP ERP (see Figure 1.8). This is good news for all of you who are considering changing to SAP S/4HANA for this reason. Don't let yourself get confused: SAP S/4HANA is just a conventional ERP system. With your familiar SAP GUI, you can access the complete functionality of SAP S/4HANA.

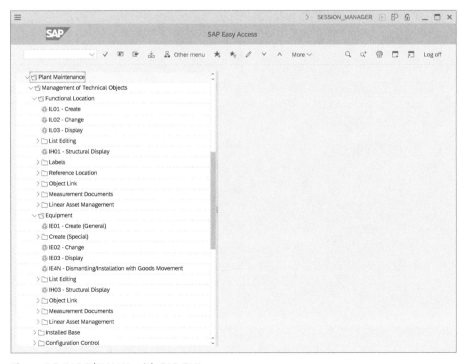

Figure 1.8 SAP S/4HANA with SAP GUI

Let's now look at the three UIs: SAP GUI, SAP Business Client, and SAP Fiori.

1.7.1   SAP GUI

Many readers are likely familiar with the desktop and functionality of SAP GUI. Now I would like to introduce to you some specialities regarding the access to SAP S/4HANA (see Figure 1.9).

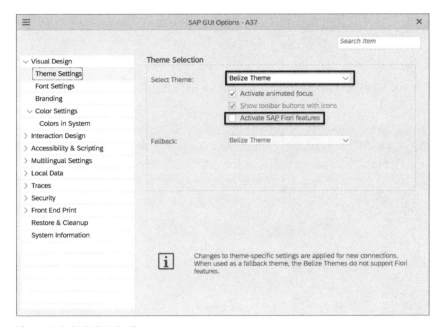

Figure 1.9 SAP GUI Options

As of SAP GUI 7.50, SAP offers the Belize theme. It shows a strong resemblance to the SAP Fiori interface and prettys up the SAP system with a contemporary look. But you can use any other theme for accessing S/4HANA (e.g., the frequently used Signature).

Admittedly, SAP GUI holds a disadvantage with the Belize theme. There are no graphic icons available, only lettered function keys, which makes working a bit cumbersome.

As of SAP GUI 7.60, then, graphic icons are again provided. This is why I recommend that you use this version.

Another recommendation of mine is not to set the switch **Activate SAP Fiori features**. This places important functions like execute and save to the bottom right, making working with the program rather uncomfortable, as all the rest of the functions are placed at the top of the screen. If you don't set the switch, the functions are automatically placed in the usual place at the top of the screen along with all the other functions.

SAP GUI 7.60 without SAP Fiori Features
Using SAP GUI 7.60 with the Belize theme will make your work as comfortable as it could be, except for activating the Fiori features, however.

1.7.2   SAP Business Client

For several years now, SAP has offered SAP Business Client as an alternative. This is a rich client which has to be installed as a desktop application like SAP GUI. It allows the use of portal services, application content, and tasks directly from the backend. The following sections look at your connection options for SAP Business Client and then move on to its general functions.

Connection Options

In contrast to SAP GUI, in SAP Business Client, you have not one, but three different connection options.

First, you can set up a simple *SAPLOGON connection*. If you use this option to log on, the system access is nearly the same as for SAP GUI connections (see Figure 1.10).

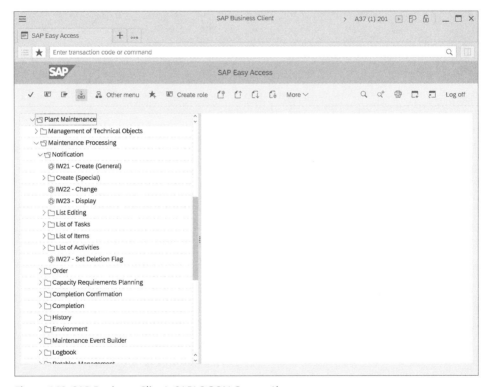

Figure 1.10 SAP Business Client: SAPLOGON Connection

Second, you can set up an original SAP Business Client connection. If you use this option to log on, you'll be able to choose between various options (for example, **Last Opened** or assigned **Work Centers**; see Figure 1.11). Depending on your selection, you can access assigned functions: For example, if you select a work center, you'll navigate to the respective task list.

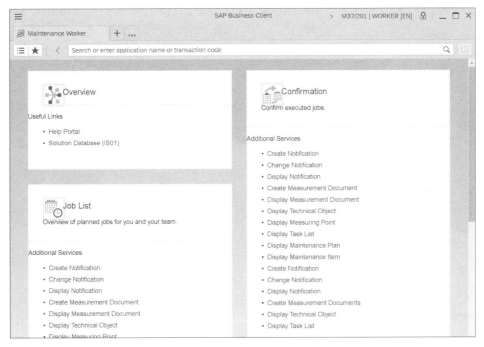

Figure 1.11 SAP Business Client: Business Client Connection

Third, you can call the page with the SAP Fiori apps assigned to you (see Figure 1.13). For more information on SAP Fiori, refer to Chapter 9, Section 9.1.2. This looks exactly like accessing your SAP Fiori launchpad with the browser.

General Functions

The following is an overview of the most important SAP Business Client functions:

- **Using standard SAP transactions**
  In SAP Business Client, you can call and execute all standard SAP transactions.

- **Tabs**
  As you can see in the top bar in Figure 1.10, SAP Business Client uses a tab technology to display all called functions in a single window. As a result, you can access several functions in parallel, without having to open a new window in each case.

- **Search**
  SAP Business Client has three different search options (in the bar below the tabs):

  - Enterprise search: Search in enterprise data.

  - External search engines and encyclopedias: Search via external search engines (such as Google or Yahoo) and encyclopedias (such as Wikipedia).

  - Desktop search: Search in the desktop documents.

- **Roles, task lists, overviews, and reports**
  SAP Business Client also has access to portal roles. Thus, task lists and overviews

form the initial screen, comprised of a menu-like collection of functions that are assigned to a single or composite role. Figure 1.11 shows an example of the initial screen for the *maintenance worker* role.

- **Side panels**

  An important enhancement of SAP Business Client with respect to SAP GUI is the use of side panels. Side panels display additional information about an application in a page area. Such information can be, for example:

  - Key figures, for example, mean time to repair (MTTR) or mean time between repair (MTBR)

  - Analyses from the SAP BW, for example, damage analyses or costs analyses

  - Reports from controlling, for example, cost center reports or internal order reports

  - Graphics from SAP 3D Visual Enterprise

  - Object services

Figure 1.12 shows an example equipment master record with the associated damage analysis in relation to damage codes.

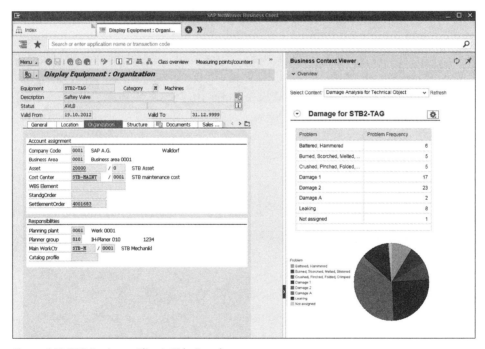

Figure 1.12 SAP Business Client: Side Panel

To use the side panels comprehensively, you must activate the business functions LOG_EAM_SIMP, LOG_EAM_SIMPLICITY, and LOG_EAM_SIMPLICITY_2 through LOG_EAM_SIMPLICITY_9.

Useful Side Panel Information

You can use the side panel in SAP Business Client to display useful additional information about the technical object (for example, damage analyses or key figures).

For more plant maintenance-specific SAP Business Client functions (for example, the Asset Viewer or confirmation of unplanned tasks), refer to the respective chapters.

1.7.3   SAP Fiori

SAP Fiori is SAP's latest user experience (UX) that provides access to SAP systems. SAP Fiori will run on all devices, i.e., accessible not only via desktop or notebook, but on mobile devices like tablets and smartphones as well. Therefore, SAP Fiori is an alternative to SAP GUI, to SAP Business Client, or to SAP's mobile solutions.

The number of SAP Fiori apps offered by SAP is growing rapidly. You can find the current status in the SAP Fiori apps reference library (*https://fioriappslibrary.hana.ondemand.com*). As of June 2020, it currently shows more than 1,800 SAP Fiori apps for SAP S/4HANA. In the area of asset management, there are approximately 200 SAP Fiori apps, including many apps from project management, materials management, and quality management, which all have points of contact with plant maintenance (e.g., apps for inventory in embedded Extended Warehouse Management (EWM) in SAP S/4HANA and for usage decisions in an inspection lot). Approximately 50 SAP Fiori apps are currently available for actual maintenance topics. You'll learn about the most important of these in Chapter 9, Section 9.1.2.

SAP Fiori offers a frontend design with *tiles* that allow for the process of selecting functions and apps (the SAP Fiori launchpad, see Figure 1.13). Users may create their own frontend out of tiles they are entitled to use, which is similar to favorites in SAP GUI.

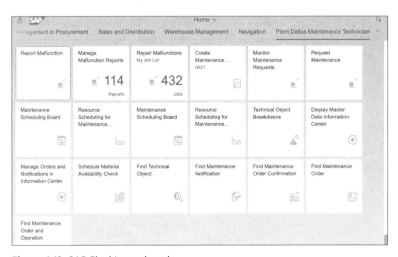

Figure 1.13 SAP Fiori Launchpad

When users click one of these functions or apps, the browser shows the screens as an SAPUI5 frontend (SAPUI5 is based on HTML5). Let's now look at the types of apps and some primary characteristics of SAP Fiori apps.

Types of SAP Fiori Apps

SAP Fiori apps can be distinguished by three features (see Figure 1.14):

- **Content**
  Transactional apps, analytical apps, and factsheet apps (This is the distinction preferred by SAP.)
- **Dynamicity**
  Static apps and dynamic apps (only listing apps)
- **Results**
  Real apps with added value, real apps without added value, and pseudo apps

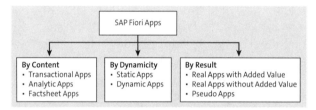

Figure 1.14 SAP Fiori Apps: Types

SAP Fiori Apps Based on Content

According to content, which is the distinction SAP prefers, there are three different kinds of SAP Fiori apps (see Figure 1.15), as follows:

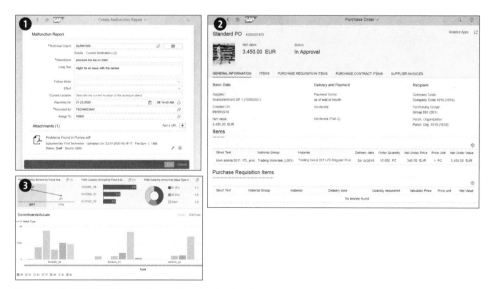

Figure 1.15 SAP Fiori Apps: According to Content

❶ Transactional apps

These apps execute certain business processes (e.g., setting up a purchase order, recording a confirmation). These apps can tally 1:1 with a transaction in SAP GUI. In addition, a couple of functions can be combined in one app.

❷ Factsheet apps

These apps provide the most important information for one object (e.g., supplier, material master, customer) within one screen display.

❸ Analytical apps

These apps can be used to produce evaluations, key figures, statistics, and diagrams for your business processes.

SAP Fiori Apps Based on Dynamicity

SAP Fiori apps that issue lists can be subdivided into static and dynamic apps, as follows:

- **Static apps**

  These apps operate like list transactions in SAP GUI. You enter your selection criterion (e.g., plant) in an upstream selection screen, and the list will show the relevant findings. If you want to change the selection criteria (e.g., another or an additional plant), you return to the selection screen, widen your selection, and subsequently see the new (static) findings.

- **Dynamic apps**

  These apps show the selection area and findings in a template. If you change the selection, the findings are adjusted dynamically. Figure 1.16 shows the My Purchasing Document Items app, for an example.

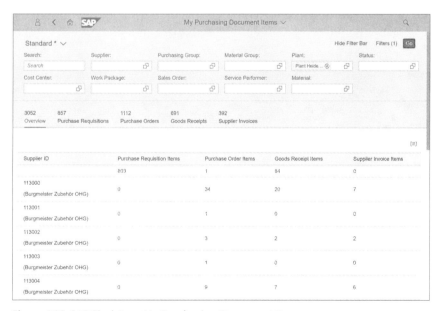

Figure 1.16 SAP Fiori App: My Purchasing Document Items

SAP Fiori Apps Based on Results

Additionally, SAP Fiori apps can be classified according to the result, such as "real" SAP Fiori apps with added value, real SAP Fiori apps without added value, and pseudo SAP Fiori apps.

First, let's define what we mean by a real SAP Fiori app with added value. In essence, these apps use SAPUI5 technology and add value in comparison to using SAP GUI. Added value can mean a number of things, including the following:

- Extracting a single function out of a complex function (e.g., Release Maintenance Orders app and Approve Purchase Orders app)
- Pooling a couple of transaction into just one (e.g., Post Incoming Invoices app)
- Providing functions that don't exist in SAP GUI (e.g., dynamic apps)
- Preparing and consolidating statistics for graphic representation
- Showing results on the SAP Fiori launchpad (see Figure 1.19 later in this section for an example)

Next, real SAP Fiori apps without added value indicates that the app uses SAPUI5 technology but doesn't add any additional value for the user. For example, Figure 1.17 shows the Create Purchase Requisition app, which uses SAP Fiori technology but doesn't provide any added value compared to Transaction ME51N in the SAP GUI.

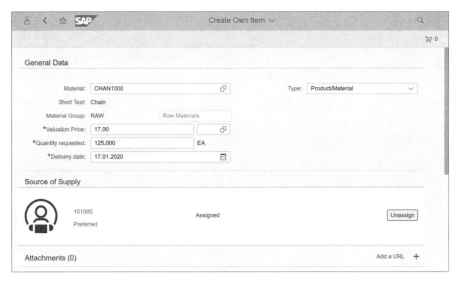

Figure 1.17 SAP Fiori App: Create Purchase Requisition

Finally, "pseudo" SAP Fiori apps refer to SAP Fiori apps that neither use SAPUI5 nor provide any additional value for the user. For example, Figure 1.18 shows the Create Supplier Invoice app, which doesn't use SAPUI5 and only displays Transaction MIRO in an additional window with a Web Dynpro surface. Therefore, there is no additional value for the user.

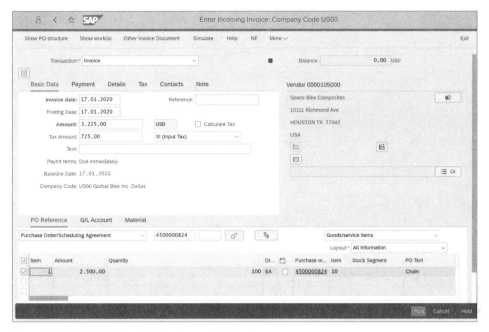

Figure 1.18 SAP Fiori Pseudo App: Incoming Invoice

Characteristics of SAP Fiori

Value-adding apps basing on SAPUI5 facilitate users' work in the following ways:

- The surface is responsive, which means it identifies the terminal device and accessing data and aligns itself to the device.

- The operation is coherent. In all apps, all functions and all devices of the operation are unified. All processes share and are controlled by the same data.

- Just like in SAP GUI, there is a role-based allocation. This is why each user will only find the specific functions personally assigned to him on his SAP Fiori launchpad.

- Just like in SAP GUI, numerous possibilities for personalization are available (e.g., selection variants, field selection).

- Each SAP Fiori app may be used on mobile devices, which enables users to access their data or tasks from anywhere at any time.

- Provision is made for developing specific customer requirements, which means users may integrate their own, self-developed apps within the SAP-provided development workbench (e.g., SAP Web IDE toolkit).

Moreover, these characteristics of SAP Fiori are useful in day-to-day-business:

- If it's necessary or relevant, important key figures will be shown on the SAP Fiori launchpad (see Figure 1.19).

- You can send emails (e.g., to send a list or link for a document) from within each app.

- All lists may be exported to Microsoft Office.

Figure 1.19 SAP Fiori Apps with Key Figures

On the other hand, in everyday business, some aspects can be rather off-putting:

- SAPUI5 surfaces contain a lot of empty space, so they aren't compact, which is also why screen pictures are needlessly big and blind.
- Because SAP GUI uses tab strips, information is assigned according to relevant headlines and then allotted to tab strips. This tab strip technique isn't available at HTML5. Instead of tab strips, information is shown one item below the other in SAP Fiori. In many cases, this creates very long screens that require a lot of scrolling to get the information you want.
- Positioning of functional keys isn't standardized yet.

In Chapter 9, Section 9.1.2, I'll show you what kind of SAP Fiori apps are available for plant maintenance.

1.8   Summary

The following are the major takeaways regarding plant maintenance with SAP in general:

- SAP S/4HANA is the successor to SAP ERP 6.0 as well as a complete ERP system within which all enterprise-specific business processes and functions are included.
- SAP S/4HANA is exclusively offered on the SAP HANA database. Versions for other databases are not available.
- SAP S/4HANA is offered on-premise as well as in the cloud, as follows:
  - In SAP S/4HANA Cloud there are only a few possibilities to adjust the system to your demands. You can only consume the standard defined by SAP.
  - SAP S/4HANA provides a variety of possibilities for activating business functions, for customizing, for add-ons, or for modifications.
- Via activating business functions, you may expand the scope of functions step by step.
  - You should activate the functions LOG_EAM_CI.

- They contain small round-offs, making your tasks easier and smarter in the day-to-day business.
- You may do so unhesitatingly, as there are no dependencies with other applications.
- You have three options for accessing your SAP S/4HANA system:
  - SAP GUI, the most widely used version
  - SAP Business Client with additional possibilities, but hard to configure
  - SAP Fiori, most heavily promoted by SAP and made for casual users, but it should be assessed whether a certain app really provides any additional benefit

Chapter 2
Organizational Structures

This chapter provides information about the essential elements for maintenance processing in the SAP system: the general organizational units, maintenance-specific organizational units, and work center.

An organizational structure is comprised of the following areas: the general SAP organizational units (for example, controlling area, company code, plant, storage location), the maintenance-specific organizational units (for example, location or plant section), and finally, the maintenance work centers (for example, mechanical workshop, electrical workshop, measurement, and control). This chapter will cover the definition of each of these elements.

2.1 SAP Organizational Units

Organizational units form the basis of all master data and business processes in SAP ERP. In the following sections, you'll learn about the most important organizational units from a maintenance perspective.

[+]

Organizational Units in the SAP Project

If you implement SAP S/4HANA Asset Management, the general organizational units in the SAP system (for example, the company code, controlling area, and plant) are usually already defined. These units were defined when areas of SAP S/4HANA, such as controlling, material management, and so on, were implemented. Therefore, you can only influence the design if SAP S/4HANA Asset Management is implemented from the outset or if you define separate organizational units from a pure maintenance perspective.

2.1.1 The Plant from a Maintenance Perspective

The plant is, without doubt, the most important organizational unit for plant maintenance. A plant fulfills several maintenance functions:

- A plant is responsible for planning maintenance activities. In this context, this plant is known as a *planning plant*. To convert a plant to a planning plant, you use the customizing function **Maintain Planning Plant**.

- All of the technical objects to be maintained are physically present in a plant (functional location, equipment, and serial number). In this case, this plant is known as a *maintenance plant*. A plant becomes a maintenance plant if you create a technical object there. To assign the planning plant responsible for the maintenance plant, you use the customizing function **Assign Maintenance Planning Plant**.

- You require a plant with a storage location in which you can store spare parts.

- Furthermore, some technical objects (serial numbers) can be stored in a plant with a storage location.

2.1.2   Maintenance-Specific Organizational Units

Additional maintenance-specific organizational units (either maintenance plant-specific or planning plant-specific) play an important role within a plant (see Figure 2.1).

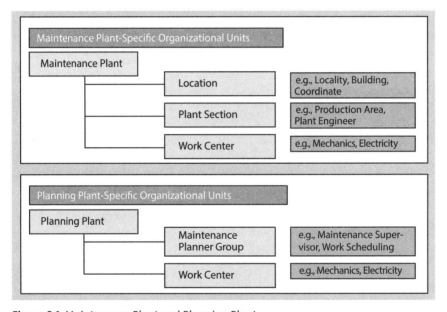

Figure 2.1 Maintenance Plant and Planning Plant

Technical objects (functional location and equipment) also contain all of the maintenance and planning plant-specific data, which is then copied to notifications and orders. This data is explained in more detail later in this chapter.

Work centers perform maintenance tasks or are responsible for such tasks. Work centers relate either to the planning plant or to the maintenance plant (Section 2.2).

A *planner group* is responsible for planning maintenance tasks and also relates to a planning plant. You maintain planner groups using the customizing function **Define Planner Groups**.

Using Planner Groups

You can set up maintenance planner groups, for example, if you want to map work scheduling or individual maintenance planners known by name.

You must use a label to indicate the physical *location* of a technical object. You always define a location with reference to a maintenance plant. Furthermore, to maintain locations, you use the customizing function **Define Location**.

Naming Locations

In practice, either building numbers (for example, F141 or WDF21) or, if they exist, plant coordinates (for example, A01 or K15) are among the most commonly used locations.

You define the responsibilities associated with operating a (production) facility as a *plant section*. To maintain plant sections, you use the customizing function **Define Plant Sections**.

Responsibilities for the Plant Section

In practice, either the plant engineer responsible for the asset or the production area belonging to the asset have proven themselves as plant sections.

2.1.3 Other General Organizational Units

In addition to the maintenance-specific organizational units, other general organizational units are also relevant for SAP S/4HANA Asset Management.

You assign a company code to the plant (see Figure 2.2). The *company code* is the smallest organizational unit for which a complete, self-contained set of accounts can be drawn up for the purposes of external reporting ("the company"). These accounts record all relevant transactions and generate balance sheets and profit and loss statements.

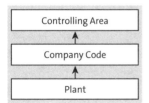

Figure 2.2 General Organizational Units

When you assign a technical object to a maintenance plant, the technical object is automatically assigned the plant's company code in the background.

The *controlling area* is an organizational unit within a company for which a self-contained cost accounting can be performed. A controlling area may include one or more company codes.

When you assign a technical object to a maintenance plant, you not only create its company code, but you also determine its controlling area. Similarly, when you assign a work center to a plant, you also assign its controlling area.

[+]

Controlling Areas Involved

From a plant maintenance perspective, ideally, the controlling area of the technical object and the controlling area of the work center are identical.

You may now be wondering why using controlling areas is a good idea. We'll explain why in the next section.

2.1.4 Plant-Specific and Cross-Plant Maintenance

For business processes in plant maintenance, you need to differentiate between order planning and execution in the same plant and order planning and execution in different plants, both of which we'll cover in the following sections.

Plant-Specific Maintenance

In practice, the most frequently encountered situation is where the maintenance requirement is planned in the plant in which it originates, the orders are fulfilled by workshops in the same plant, and the spare parts are stored within the same plant. In Figure 2.3, this plant is known as Plant 1000. The following applies here: maintenance plant = planning plant = spare parts storage.

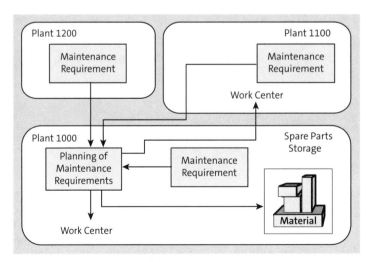

Figure 2.3 Plant and Plant Maintenance

Cross-Plant Maintenance

In contrast to plant-specific maintenance, other situations may involve more than one plant, for example:

- You may have a plant (for example, plant 1200) where an asset is maintained (the maintenance plant) but all other functions (planning, order execution, and spare parts storage) are the responsibility of another plant (for example, plant 1000).
- You may have a plant (for example, plant 1100) where additional partial functions (order execution) are also the responsibility of this plant but other partial functions (order planning and spare parts storage) are the responsibility of other plants (for example, plant 1000).

Cross-plant maintenance is not difficult if the maintenance plant of the technical object and the plant of the executing work center are in the same company code.

The same applies if the plants are in different company codes but belong to the same controlling area, which is also a standard scenario.

However, a problem arises if the plants belong to different controlling areas. This case involves a customer-vendor relationship rather than a standard scenario. Therefore, in this case, the maintenance plant (customer) has to trigger purchase orders, and the plant of the work center (vendor) triggers a sales order and its associated invoice. The billing document is entered in turn as an incoming invoice in the maintenance plant—a tedious process overall. How can we simplify the process?

[+]

Plants in Different Controlling Areas

If you implement cross-plant maintenance and your plants are in different controlling areas, the following approach is recommended:

- In the work center plant, create a cost center for the actual maintenance plant.
- Assign all of the technical objects to the work center plant (as a maintenance plant) and to this cost center.
- Process all maintenance orders in the work center plant.
- Manually issue periodic invoices (for example, monthly) from the work center plant whereby the customer maintenance plant is debited the amount and the cost center is credited the same amount.

This procedure saves you from having to create purchase orders, sales orders, and individual invoices as well as posting individual incoming invoices.

2.2   Work Centers

From a maintenance perspective, a work center represents either an individual person (for example, the engineer M. Huber) or a workshop, thus, a group of persons. In practice, the following workshops are the most commonly used:

- Mechanical workshops
- Electrical workshops
- Measurement and control
- Machine centers
- Welding workshops
- Paint shops
- Cleaning lines
- Building services engineering

No Individual Persons as Work Centers

Avoid using individual persons as work centers. You could jeopardize your chances of capacity planning. Furthermore, work center data requires a great deal of maintenance. For person-specific responsibilities, use partner functions (see Chapter 3, Section 3.11.7).

If you nevertheless record work centers for each person, please note the legal regulations for each country. In Germany, for example, you can only do this if you have given your employee representatives a written company agreement in which, among other things, you state that the information will not be used to compare employee performance.

In plant maintenance, work centers are used as the following:

- Responsible work center in the equipment master record and functional location master record
- Responsible work center in a maintenance item
- Responsible work center in the header of a task list
- Performing work center in the operations of a task list
- Responsible work center in the notification
- Responsible work center in the order header
- Performing work center in the operations of an order

Need for Work Centers

Work centers are the individual master records that you must create in order to use SAP S/4HANA Asset Management. You can implement business processes, for example, without technical objects (functional locations, equipment, and so on), but not without work centers.

You can use Transaction IR01 to maintain work centers. In this transaction, you would first assign a work center number and then assign the work center to a plant.

Choice of Work Center Numbers

Frequently, you have to specify the work center in maintenance processing. Therefore, you should keep work center numbers as short as possible (for example, M for mechanical workshop, E for electrical workshop, and so on).

The work center contains information that is essential for maintenance processing (see Figure 2.4).

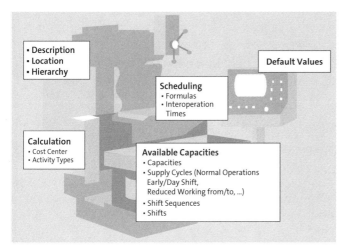

Figure 2.4 Work Center: Content Overview

Work centers contain basic data. You maintain this data on the **Basic Data** tab (see Figure 2.5).

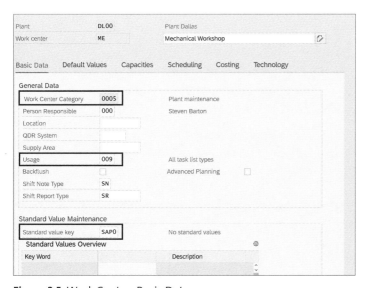

Figure 2.5 Work Center: Basic Data

Characteristics of the Task List Usage

When maintaining basic data for a work center, make sure that you set the task list usage to 004 (maintenance tasks lists) or 009 (all task list types), so that the work center can be used in maintenance processing.

Furthermore, the standard value key must be set to "SAP0," so that standard values such as setup times or machine times are not required later.

Work centers contain default values that are copied into the operations or referenced when creating maintenance task lists and maintenance orders. Referencing means that the data cannot be changed in the maintenance task list. You maintain default values on the **Default Values** tab. The most important default value is the control key (see Figure 2.6), via which you can subsequently control the following in the order:

- Whether the operation is to be part of costing
- Whether the operation is to be scheduled
- Whether the operation is to generate capacity requirements
- Whether a confirmation is expected for the operation
- Whether the operation should be processed externally
- Whether service specifications are to be set up in the operation

You maintain the control key in customizing using the function **Maintain Control Key**.

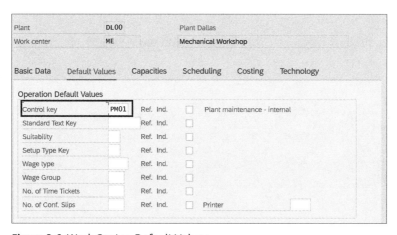

Figure 2.6 Work Center: Default Values

Using the Control Key

Using the control key, you can control in detail the business functions that an operation should have (cost, print, confirm, assign externally, schedule, and so on).

You require at least two control keys, namely, a key for internal processing and a key for external processing. You can use other control keys as required.

You should always define the control key in the work center as a default value so that you do not always have to manually enter it in the task list and order.

Work centers contain scheduling data required for lead-time scheduling. You maintain scheduling data on the **Scheduling** tab (see Figure 2.7).

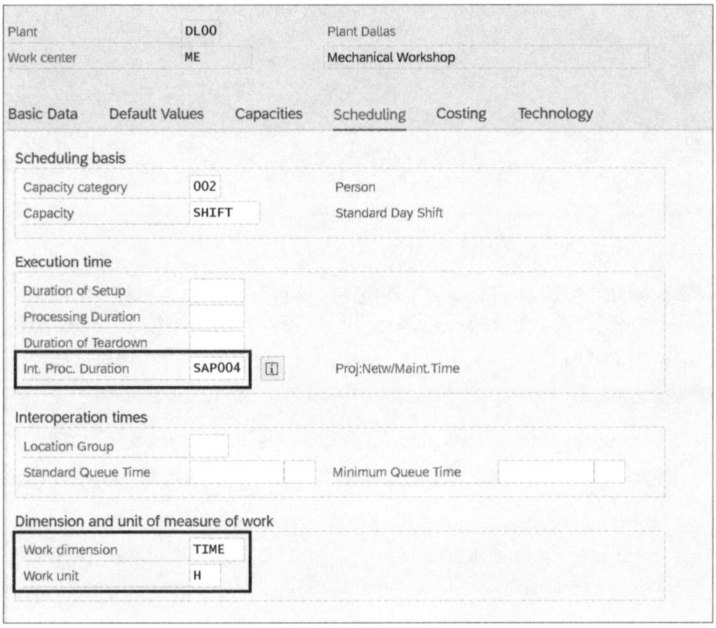

Plant	DL00	Plant Dallas	
Work center	ME	Mechanical Workshop	

Basic Data   Default Values   Capacities   Scheduling   Costing   Technology

Scheduling basis

Capacity category	002	Person	
Capacity	SHIFT	Standard Day Shift	

Execution time

Duration of Setup			
Processing Duration			
Duration of Teardown			
Int. Proc. Duration	SAP004	🛈	Proj:Netw/Maint.Time

Interoperation times

Location Group				
Standard Queue Time			Minimum Queue Time	

Dimension and unit of measure of work

Work dimension	TIME
Work unit	H

Figure 2.7 Work Center: Scheduling

Formula for the Duration of Internal Processing

If you want to schedule the orders later, your work center requires a formula in the **In. Proc. Duration** (duration of internal processing) field. This formula must point to the **DAUNO** field, that is, to the duration from the operation. The formula SAP004 is defined in the standard SAP version.

You can check or define the formula for the duration of internal processing using the customizing function **Define Formula Parameters for Work Centers**.

Work centers contain available capacity data required for capacity planning. Available capacity specifies which service provides capacity for each workday. A capacity is always assigned to a work center and, in plant maintenance, is generally expressed in hours per week. The capacity data is maintained on the **Capacities** tab (see Figure 2.8).

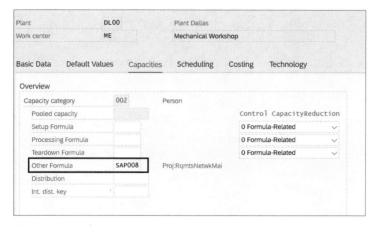

Figure 2.8 Work Center: Capacities

[+]

Formula for the Requirements of Internal Processing

If you subsequently want to execute capacity planning for your work center, your work center requires a formula in the field **Requirements of Internal Processing**. This formula must point to the **ARBEI** field, that is, the work from the operation. In the standard system, this formula is SAP008.

You can check or define this using the customizing function **Define Formula Parameters for Work Centers**.

In the work center, the available capacity is maintained on the **Capacities** tab by clicking the **Capacity** button. Figure 2.9 shows which information you can specify for the available capacity.

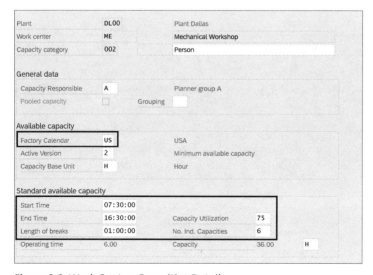

Figure 2.9 Work Center: Capacities Detail

Most required details, for example, the **Start Time**, **End Time**, **Length of Breaks**, **No. Ind.Capacities** (number of craftsmen) fields, are not critical and are easily determined.

If you work in different time periods with different staff assignments, you can maintain intervals and also define multilayer models.

The rate of capacity utilization is critical: This rate specifies (in %) the portion of gross capacity available to the craftsmen (net) for planned orders. Several factors can lower the capacity utilization rate, such as:

- Additional, necessary personal time (restroom breaks, unplanned breaks, work meetings, and so on)
- Illness
- Leave
- Unplanned orders

The proportion of unplanned orders can only be roughly estimated and is thus a critical factor in maintenance.

Rates of Capacity Utilization in Practice

Without considering unplanned orders, a rate of capacity utilization of between 65% and 75% is most common in practice.

To account for unplanned orders, you have two options:

- You can consider them in the capacity utilization rate, which is then reduced according to the proportion of unplanned orders to a value between 30% and 50%.
- You can reserve some personnel beyond the number of individual capacities specified in the available capacity (that is, the number of craftsmen) and deploy them only for unplanned orders, so that the data specified in the available capacity is available only for planned orders.

Work centers contain costing data that enables you to cost operations; this data is maintained on the **Costing** tab (see Figure 2.10).You can check or define this using the Customizing function **Define Formula Parameters for Work Centers**.

Prerequisites for Costing

If you subsequently want to perform costing for your work center, your work center requires the following:

- A cost center
- An activity type
- A formula in the field **Requirements for Internal Processing**. This formula must point to the ARBEI field, that is, the work from the operation. In the standard system, the formula SAP008 is used.

Chapter 7, Section 7.1.8, provides information on how to define the associated allocation record in controlling.

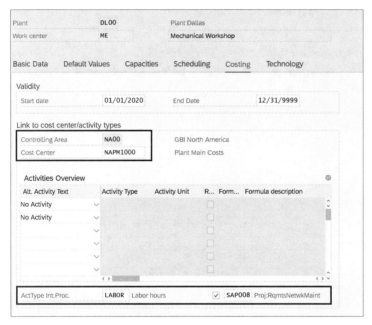

Figure 2.10 Work Center: Costing

2.3 Summary

Following are the major features of SAP S/4HANA Asset Management organizational structures:

- With organizational units, you define your enterprise's organizational structure in general and your plant maintenance structures in particular. They provide a basis for all master data and business processes.

- In SAP S/4HANA Asset Management projects, the general organizational units in the SAP system (e.g., the company code, controlling area, and plant) are usually predefined.

- The plant is the central and most important organizational unit in logistics.

- In SAP S/4HANA Asset Management, you have to define *maintenance planning plants* and *maintenance plants*. SAP S/4HANA Asset Management supports plant-specific maintenance and cross-plant maintenance.

- From an SAP S/4HANA Asset Management perspective, a *work center* represents either an individual person or a group of persons.

- In SAP S/4HANA Asset Management, work centers are used in many locations like notifications, orders, task lists, and maintenance plans.

Chapter 3
Structuring of Technical Systems

This chapter introduces you to the structuring elements of SAP S/4HANA Asset Management. I'll show you the purposes for which you can and cannot use each resource and provide you with numerous tips on aspects you should observe in the structuring of technical systems.

Technical systems must be suitably structured so you can use SAP S/4HANA Asset Management to map business processes in plant maintenance and subsequently process them. My experience with previous projects has shown that every company has its own idea of how it wants to map its technical systems in SAP S/4HANA Asset Management, and each company does it differently—no two companies that I have encountered have used the same approach in structuring their technical systems. As a result, each company develops its own requirements within the implementation project, especially in relation to the following questions:

- Which structuring elements should be used?
- How deep should the structure be?
- As of which structure level should a particular element be used?
- Which information should you store?
- Which functions should you use?
- At which levels should the assets be mapped?

If you are considering implementing SAP S/4HANA Asset Management and want to map your technical systems there, then before doing so, you should ask yourself these questions and answer them to the best of your current knowledge. This chapter will begin with an in-depth look at a number of these important questions.

Next, the chapter will cover the most important elements of the technical system: function locations, equipment, serial numbers, links, object networks, linear assets, materials, bills of materials (BOMs), classes, and characteristics. The chapter will also cover the product structure browser, the asset viewer, and a number of other additional functions available to you when working with technical objects.

3.1 Actions before Mapping Your Technical Systems in the SAP System

In this section, we'll first outline the questions that you should answer before you start structuring your technical systems, and then we'll provide tips on how to answer the questions.

When trying to find the answers, the following principle should apply: as much as is necessary, but as little as possible. For you, this principle means that you should find out what your business and technical requirements are and look for the easiest way to map these requirements in SAP S/4HANA Asset Management.

Throughout the rest of this book, I'll use lots of examples to show you how to apply this principle.

3.1.1 Question 1: Which Structuring Resources Should Be Used?

SAP S/4HANA Asset Management provides you with a broad range of potential structuring resources: functional locations, reference functional locations, equipment, object links, serial numbers, maintenance assemblies, materials, and different types of bills of materials (BOMs). Let's look at these structural elements in more details:

- **Functional locations**
  These represent a complex, generally multilevel structure for technical systems, where you create each element of the technical system structure as a functional location. Therefore, functional locations are used to establish a vertical asset structure. Functional locations usually represent immovable, functional units. Examples include process plants in the chemical and pharmaceutical industries, power plants, production lines, buildings, conduits, infrastructure, and computer networks.

- **Reference functional locations**
  These are solely templates for generating "real" functional location structures or for subsequently passing on data to "real" functional locations. Reference functional locations cannot be the subject of business processes (for example, malfunction reports). Rather, they are used as a reference template.

- **Equipment**
  This represents movable, individual aggregates (inventories). Examples include machines, pumps, and engines; production resources/tools (PRTs); fleet objects (cars, trucks, forklift trucks, and industrial trucks); and IT inventories (PCs, printers, monitors, notebooks, and projectors). Equipment categories that are moved infrequently (for example, pumps) are intended to be installed on functional locations. Other equipment categories (for example, fleet objects) are, due to their constant movement, not installed on functional locations.

- **Object links**
  These are established between different technical objects (pieces of equipment or

functional locations). Such links exist, for example, between individual production units, between production plants and supply systems, and between supply systems and disposal systems. You use object links to form an *object network*. In this way, your technical systems can have a horizontal structure. Object links cannot be the subject of business processes (for example, malfunction reports). Rather, they are used for information and visualization purposes only.

- **Linear assets (linear asset management)**
  These are technical systems with a linear infrastructure, whose properties and conditions can change from section to section (dynamic segmentation). Examples of linear assets include pipelines, road networks, rail networks, power lines, pipes, and so on. You can create linear assets as technical objects (for example, functional locations, equipment) and store linear data there.

- **Material**
  Unlike a piece of equipment, a material does not represent an individual item but, rather, a type of object, for example, the type *pump normal 400 – 100* or the type *three-phase normal engine SM/I, 220/380V, 50Hz, 0.18kW*. A material includes a specific amount of the corresponding type; you require materials for spare parts and for pieces of equipment and maintenance assemblies (PM assemblies) that are suitable for storage.

- **PM assembly**
  This serves to provide a functional location or piece of equipment with a deeper structure. Thus, for example, a forklift truck could be comprised of the following PM assemblies: *lift type*, *chassis*, *brake system*, and *drive assembly*. Furthermore, you can assign a maintenance assembly to a notification, order, or maintenance plan in order to specify the location of any damage that occurs.

- **Serial numbers**
  You can create serial numbers for a material number, and a material number can have several serial numbers. A serial number is an individual item and corresponds to a piece of equipment. The serial number function enables you to place the equipment in storage. In terms of usage, a material serial number corresponds to a piece of equipment.

- **Equipment BOM**
  This generally is comprised of a list of spare parts and is assigned directly to a piece of equipment. As a result, only this piece of equipment can use this BOM.

- **Functional location BOM**
  This generally is comprised of a list of spare parts and is assigned directly to a functional location. As a result, only this functional location can use this BOM.

- **Material BOM**
  This also is comprised of a list of spare parts. However, you can make it available for any number of pieces of equipment or functional locations by using an indirect assignment.

You could now use all of these resources, but you should avoid doing so if possible. Instead, consider the following principle: as much as is necessary, but as little as possible.

As Few Resources as Possible for Structuring

Use as few different structuring resources as possible. The more structuring resources you use, the more difficult it becomes to decide, in individual cases, how to classify a particular object and the more errors may occur: Is this a piece of equipment, or is it perhaps an assembly or maybe even a material?

If you follow this principle, not only will you be able to define and record your technical systems more easily, but you'll benefit from a positive effect on how you map and implement your business processes. Section 3.2 through Section 3.11, introduce you to structuring resources and describe the options available as well as the functions associated with each of these resources. I'll not only provide you with information on the resources that you can use for specific purposes but also point out especially when you should not use any resources. This valuable information will then enable you to decide which resources on offer make the most sense for you to use.

3.1.2 Question 2: How Deep Should the Structure Be?

In concrete terms, several questions concern the depth of the structure: How many structure levels do you form in SAP S/4HANA Asset Management for your technical systems? Do you prefer a detailed structure for technical systems in which you structure down to the last spare part? Or do you prefer a rough structure in which you form only the first three to four levels for your technical systems? Each company must find its own answer to these questions.

Unfortunately, this book cannot provide you with one general recipe for success. I can only highlight the advantages associated with both options (see Table 3.1).

Detailed Technical System Structure	Rough Technical System Structure
Better able to detect weak points	Less time and effort required to record and maintain technical system data
Better able to detect cost drivers	Fewer maintenance plans
More accurate definition of default values	Easier assignment for notifications and orders
	Fewer notifications and orders

Table 3.1 Detailed Versus Rough Technical System Structures

If your structure is as detailed as possible, you'll then be able to subsequently perform analyses that are accurate and specific, for example, to detect weak points or cost drivers. Detailed structures enable you to accurately define default values such as cost centers, addresses, maintenance planner groups, or main work centers. Accurate default values increase user acceptance and accelerate business processes.

However, all of these advantages come with some disadvantages: the great deal of time and effort required to record and maintain the master data, more maintenance plans, a higher volume of orders, and possible problems when assigning notifications and orders.

The disadvantages of a detailed technical system structure are directly related to the possible advantages of a rough technical system structure: less time and effort required to record and maintain technical system data, fewer maintenance plans to be recorded, simple assignment of notifications and orders, and fewer notifications and orders.

Let's take a look at a numerical example to clarify the problem associated with the quantity structure: Normally, levels in a hierarchy are related by a multiplier of 4 to 6 from level to level, so if you structure a functional location in a lower level, on average, 4 to 6 functional locations exist in the sublevel.

What does this mean for you? Let's assume that you have 50 technical systems and, on average, 5 items in the next structure level, 5 more items on the next level, and so on. This setup would then result in the number of technical objects shown in Table 3.2. You can see how many technical objects you could have for each structure level, regardless of whether the objects are pieces of equipment, functional locations, or something else.

Number of Structure Levels	Resulting Number of Technical Objects
1	50
2	300
3	1,500
4	7,500
5	37,500
6	187,500
7	937,500
8	4,687,500

Table 3.2 Number of Technical Objects

Therefore, the number of technical objects experiences not linear growth but, rather, exponential growth, depending on the number of structure levels. This simple example clarifies the meaning of exponential growth in numerical terms.

[+]

> **Structuring Broadly or Deeply?**
>
> From my experience in various projects, the following strategy is recommended with regard to the structuring of technical systems and has already been tried and tested by many users:
>
> ■ First, use a rough structure to map your technical systems across the entire area.
>
> ■ Later on, break down only those parts of this structure requiring further detail (not all of it).
>
> For example, you can refine the structure wherever you feel the information value of the weak point analysis is insufficient or wherever you have identified cost-intensive technical systems.
>
> The approach whereby you map deep structures across the entire area from the outset potentially leads to the problem of having to remove some structure levels. This approach in turn, if at all possible, requires a great deal of time and effort and has many disadvantages.

3.1.3 Question 3: Which Criteria Should Be Applied to the Structuring of Technical Systems?

Once again, there is no clear-cut answer to this question. Answering this question depends on your requirements, especially in relation to manageability, reporting, and so on. In principle, you can structure your technical systems according to the following criteria:

■ Spatial criteria (for example, technical systems in building A, building B, and so on)

■ Functional criteria (for example, all pumps receive one superior structure)

■ Production-oriented, procedure-oriented, or process-oriented criteria (for example, production line C, chemical installation D, power supply E, air conditioning unit F, and so on)

3.1.4 Question 4: On Which Structure Level Should a Particular Resource Be Used?

In practice, the most frequently used structuring sequence is functional location → equipment → bill of materials (see Figure 3.1).

The question "At which structure level should a particular resource be used?" can be broken down into three subquestions, as discussed in the following sections.

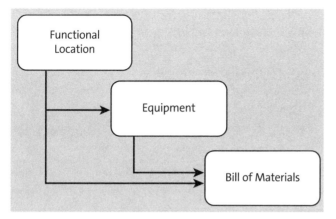

Figure 3.1 Structuring Sequence

Question 4.1: Where Is the Boundary between a Functional Location and a Piece of Equipment?

The answer to this question will help you determine which functions you want to map in the system and whether you can fulfill these functions better with functional locations or pieces of equipment. Previously, functional locations and pieces of equipment differed greatly from each other. However, with each release, these technical objects have become more and more similar, and today, both have almost the same functions. However, the following key differences remain between functional locations and pieces of equipment:

- The fundamental difference between functional locations and pieces of equipment is illustrated by the fact that functional locations are designed to map complex, multilevel structures for technical systems, while pieces of equipment are supposed to map individual units. Conversely, as a result, multilevel structures for technical systems can basically be mapped even with pieces of equipment, but this approach quickly reaches its limits. The mapping of individual devices using functional locations is also only possible to a limited extent.

- Functional locations cannot be stored, whereas equipment can be stored using serial numbers.

- Pieces of equipment represent movable inventories; that is, they are installed in different technical systems over time and thus can document a usage history.

- Special vehicle data can be maintained for equipment only.

- The equipment has an internal and external number assignment, while the functional location number is only assigned externally.

- You can subsequently change the number of a functional location, while the number of a piece of equipment is always permanently assigned.

- The *refurbishment* business process (see Chapter 6, Section 6.4) works only with equipment (more precisely, material serial numbers) but not for functional locations.

- The *subcontracting* business process (see Chapter 6, Section 6.5) works only with equipment (more precisely, material serial numbers) but not for functional locations.

- The *calibration of test equipment* business process (see Chapter 6, Section 6.6) works only with equipment but not for functional locations.

- The *pool asset management* business process (see Chapter 6, Section 6.8) works only if the pool is created as a functional location and the devices to be lent are created as pieces of equipment.

Table 3.3 illustrates clear comparisons between the different properties of equipment and functional locations.

	Equipment	Functional Location
Mapping complex structures	In certain cases	Yes
Mapping individual devices	Yes	In certain cases
Internal number assignment	Yes	No
External number assignment	Yes	Yes
Changing numbers	No	Yes
Usability period	Yes	No
Usage history	Yes	Yes
Refurbishment	Yes	No
Subcontracting	Yes	No
Calibration	Yes	No
Pool asset management	Yes	Yes

Table 3.3 Differences between Pieces of Equipment and Functional Locations

[+]

Complex Structures and Individual Devices

You can map multilevel structures for technical systems via a hierarchy of functional locations and individual devices such as machines or vehicles as pieces of equipment.

Question 4.2: Where Is the Boundary between a Functional Location and a BOM?

This question is also best answered by looking at the relevant functions:

- Functional locations represent individual aggregates and thus permit an individual history. However, the items in a BOM are represented by material numbers and thus represent an aggregate type, and as a result, functional locations do not permit an individual history or cost monitoring, and so on.

- Functional locations can act as reference objects in notifications, orders, and maintenance plans, whereas BOMs cannot act as reference objects.

- Functional locations are not suitable for storage, whereas BOM items are suitable for storage.

Table 3.4 compares the characteristics of BOMs and functional locations.

	BOM Item	Functional Location
Individual aggregates	No	Yes
Reference object of notifications, orders, and maintenance plans	In certain cases	Yes
Storage-capable	Yes	No

Table 3.4 Differences between BOM Items and Functional Locations

Functional Location or BOM Item?

If you require an individual history for functional units, you should map these as functional locations. If you do not require any individual history for parts in storage, you should map these parts as material numbers in the BOM.

Question 4.3: Where Is the Boundary between a Piece of Equipment and a BOM?

Now that you know equipment can be stored using serial numbers, only the two following functional differences remain between equipment and BOMs:

- Pieces of equipment represent individual inventories and thus permit an individual history and cost monitoring. However, the items in a BOM are represented by material numbers and thus represent an aggregate type and do not permit individual histories.

- Pieces of equipment can be reference objects in notifications, orders, and maintenance plans, whereas BOMs cannot be reference objects.

Table 3.5 compares the characteristics of pieces of equipment and BOMs.

	BOM item	Equipment
Individual history	No	Yes
Reference object of notifications, orders, and maintenance plans	In certain cases	Yes
Storage-capable	Yes	Yes

Table 3.5 Differences between Pieces of Equipment and BOMs

[+]
Equipment or BOM Item?

If you require an individual history for inventories, you should map them as pieces of equipment; if you do not require individual histories for inventories, you should map them as material numbers or in the BOM.

3.1.5   Question 5: How Are Numbers Assigned?

Essentially, two types of number assignment exist for IT systems:

- **Internal number assignment**
  You determine a number range interval, and when required, the SAP system assigns the next available number.
- **External number assignment**
  When required, you manually assign the number of a technical object.

Now, let me explain how numbers are assigned to functional locations and equipment.

Question 5.1: How Are Numbers Assigned to Functional Locations?

You always assign an external number to a functional location in accordance with the structure indicator. You can manually assign the functional location number according to the specifications made using the structure indicator.

You define the structure indicator in customizing and determine the following (see Figure 3.2):

- How many levels the asset structure should have
- How many decimal places the numbers at each level should have and according to which rule the number of functional locations should be created:
  - **A**: letters
  - **N**: numeric characters
  - **X**: alphanumeric characters

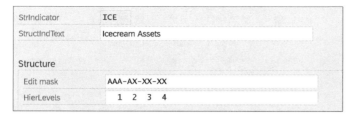

Figure 3.2 Functional Location: Structure Indicator

A common misconception is that SAP systems only permit generic numbers, for example:

- 1. level: ICE
- 2. level: ICE-M1 total
- 3. level: ICE-M1-01 total

This idea is incorrect because the SAP system permits you to break away from the naming convention, for example:

- 1. level: ICE
- 2. level: ICE-M1 total
- 3. level: P1001 total

[+]

Numbering Functional Locations

If you are already using other systems (for example, computer-aided design [CAD] or Document Management System [DMS]) that use the functional location number, you can also use the existing number in SAP S/4HANA Asset Management and assign non-generic numbers.

Take time to carefully consider the numbering you wish to use and discuss with other users and experts the best way to manage it.

Even though you can subsequently change the number of the functional locations under certain conditions (for example, if you activate alternative labeling), this process can be time-consuming.

Avoid using organizational abbreviations in functional location numbers (for example, company code, plant, and cost center). If reorganization were necessary, then you would have to rename the functional locations.

Question 5.2: How Are Numbers Assigned to Pieces of Equipment?

You can assign the numbers internally or externally. Table 3.6 provides an overview of the advantages and disadvantages associated with each procedure. You must decide for yourself which procedure is most suitable for your company.

Advantages	Disadvantages
<ul><li>Easy to retain</li><li>Good information value when manually editing documents</li><li>Easy to synchronize with different systems</li><li>Conclusions made using the number</li></ul>	<ul><li>Lengthy preparation time</li><li>Considerable effort required to agree on a common assignment with other plants</li><li>The defined key "bursts," that is, it eventually contains an insufficient number of characters</li><li>Assignment frequently difficult or impossible if no boundaries exist</li><li>Unable to change numbers</li></ul>

Table 3.6 External Equipment Numbers: Advantages and Disadvantages

3.1.6 Question 6: Which Information Should You Store?

The master records of the technical objects have predefined, allocated data. You can differentiate between the following data types:

- Data that you want or have to store because of your requirements
- Data that should be stored because of the mapping in the SAP system (for example, the cost center)

However, the principle *as much as is necessary, but as little as possible* must also apply here. Establishing a data graveyard for its own sake, of interest to no one and viewed by no one, does not make sense and requires considerable time and effort to record and maintain its data.

Data and Information

Only collect data that is also information (i.e., useful) for you.

Furthermore, SAP offers flexible options for configuring master data:

- You can define the layout of the master record yourself (number, sequence, tab name, and tab contents).
- The definition of the layout can be divided into object types (vehicles, technical systems, pumps, PCs, and so on).
- The field selection option enables you to differentiate important information from unimportant information and to hide fields that you do not require.

Defining Your Own Layouts

You should avail yourself of the option to determine the layout of the master data and design your own layouts for your master data: For example, you can place the most important information on the first tab and hide unimportant fields.

3.1.7   Question 7: How Is the Master Data Incorporated into the SAP System?

Two options for incorporating master data into the SAP system are always available: manual or automatic.

If you switch from another maintenance planning and control system to SAP S/4HANA Asset Management, or if the technical system data exists in another electronic form, you should try to automatically incorporate this data into the SAP system. For this purpose, SAP provides the standard tools Transaction IBIP (Plant Maintenance Batch Input) and Transaction LSMW (Legacy System Migration Workbench).

If the data is not in electronic form, you require a plan for data retrieval. These aspects are discussed in the book *Configuring Plant Maintenance in SAP S/4HANA*, SAP PRESS, 2020, *https://www.sap-press.com/5102*.

3.1.8   Question 8: Is It Easy to Delete Data Records?

SAP archiving is the only way to remove functional locations or pieces of equipment that have been set up once they are in the system. Complex and onerous requirements have to be fulfilled in order to delete this kind of information. This is because the following dependencies, among other things, are checked when deleting:

- Whether notifications still exist
- Whether orders still exist
- If so, whether purchase requisitions, purchase orders, invoices, or material withdrawal documents for the orders still exist
- Whether measurement documents were recorded
- Whether confirmation documents still exist

[+]

Deleting Master Records

You cannot delete a piece of equipment or a functional location that has been in use for any time.

What other alternatives do you have now? Obsolete functional locations and pieces of equipment should be reassigned to a "scrap yard" (Section 3.2).

3.1.9   Question 9: Which of the Available Functions Should Be Used?

SAP S/4HANA Asset Management provides you with a range of functions within each structuring resource that you will not find in such scope and scale in any other maintenance planning and control system. The functions are described in more detail in Section 3.2 through Section 3.11 and are compared in Appendix B, Section B.1.

This functional diversity presents you with many options but also carries the risk of overloading the system and placing excessive demands on your users.

Deleting Functions

You can take the list of all functions of the master data and delete the ones you do not want to use, both physically from the system and also from your mind.

3.1.10   Question 10: Which Strategy Should You Pursue When Recording Master Data?

The tenth and final question applies to the strategy for recording master data, that is, the steps or scope in which the master data should be transferred to the system: all master data from all plants at once or completely for one plant or for one area only?

These questions have no standard answers. Each company must find its own way here, on the basis of its general conditions (size, structure, competencies, organization, technical system types, and so on).

Following this preparatory work and these prerequisites, absolutely nothing should prevent you from structuring your technical systems in SAP S/4HANA Asset Management.

The following sections explain each of the technical objects. I'll differentiate between the individual object types, describe the range of functions available, and outline possible areas of use for each object.

3.2   Functional Locations and Reference Functional Locations

The previous section provided a general definition of functional locations: Functional locations represent a complex, generally multilevel, immovable asset structure. Therefore, functional locations are used to establish a vertical asset structure. Practical examples include the following:

- Process plants in the chemical, pharmaceutical, and food industries
- Power plants such as coal-fired power plants, hydroelectric power plants, or nuclear power plants
- Production lines in discrete manufacturing
- Complex machines such as automated systems or flexible production cells
- Real estate
- Power systems, gas systems, water systems, and heating systems
- Pipeline systems
- Infrastructure such as roads, public places, tracks, tunnels, and bridges

- Computer networks
- Complex vehicles such as locomotives, high-speed trains, and tractors
- Aircraft

Figure 3.3 shows an example of a process-oriented technical system structure.

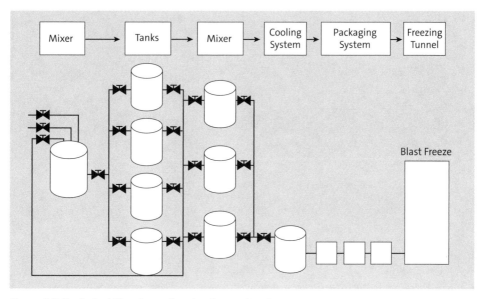

Figure 3.3 Technical Structure of an Ice Cream Asset

How do you decide when to create a functional location in SAP S/4HANA Asset Management for certain items? You should create functional locations in the following cases:

- When you want to manage individual data from a maintenance perspective (technical data such as performance data or organizational data such as the work center)
- When you want to create notifications, orders, or maintenance plans
- When you want to manage an asset pool
- When you have documentation obligations and must provide evidence of maintenance tasks performed
- When you want to collate and analyze technical data (such as causes of damage, measurement readings, or counter readings)
- When you want to verify costs
- When you require different perspectives for the technical systems (for example, one perspective for electrical engineering and one perspective for measurement and control)

You can define the technical system from Figure 3.3 in SAP S/4HANA Asset Management (called via Transaction IH01), as illustrated in Figure 3.4.

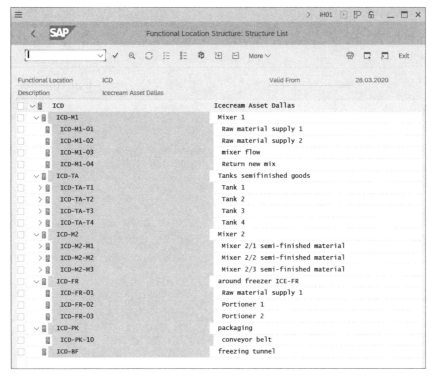

Figure 3.4 Transaction IH01 Structural Display of Ice Cream Asset

Let's now look at the process for creating functional locations and reference functional locations, as well as some alternative labeling considerations.

3.2.1 Creating Functional Locations: Single Entry

If you want to create only one new functional location, call Transaction IL01. Then, choose a suitable structure indicator and assign a new number.

Functional location numbers can have a maximum of 30 characters, and if alternative labeling is activated (Section 3.2.4), the maximum is 40 characters.

[+] **Highest Functional Location: Plant**

If you use SAP S/4HANA Asset Management in several plants, we generally recommend that you create the plant itself as a functional location and as the first level. However, avoid using the SAP plant number.

Why? When you assign the functional location number at the client level, the system cannot simultaneously manage functional location ICE in both plant 01 and plant 02. Therefore, we recommend that you create functional locations 01 and 02 for plants 01 and 02, respectively, and the numbers 01-ICE and 02-ICE for the actual technical systems.

For all other levels, the following applies: Based on the number assigned, the system will try to arrange the new functional location within an existing technical system structure.

Setting Superior Functional Locations

If the system cannot automatically assign the new functional location to a superior functional location, you must manually enter any superior functional location in the initial screen in Transaction IL01 to avoid problems when subsequently maintaining data.

Figure 3.5 shows you the initial screen for the single entry of functional locations.

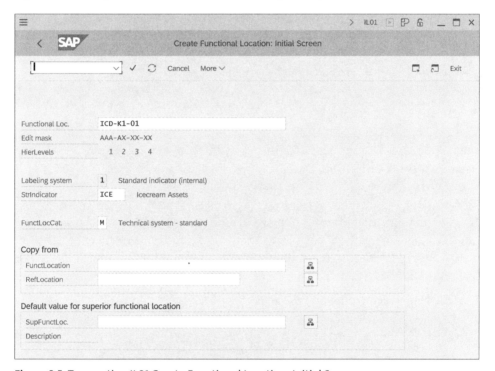

Figure 3.5 Transaction IL01 Create Functional Location: Initial Screen

Setting Up a Scrap Yard

Since deleting master data from SAP S/4HANA Asset Management can be difficult, if not impossible, you should create a "scrap yard" in addition to the "real" functional locations and reassign all obsolete functional locations and pieces of equipment to this location.

Figure 3.6 shows a sample layout of a functional location.

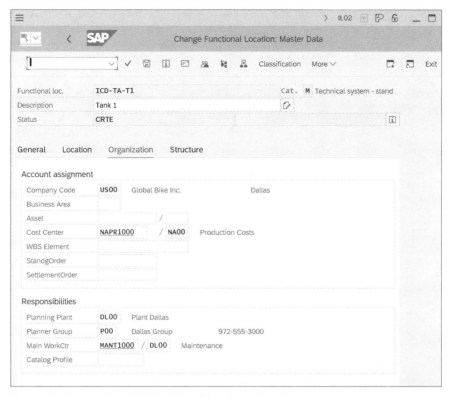

Figure 3.6 Transaction IL02 Functional Location: Layout

The layout of the master records (functional location, equipment, and serial number) can be configured relatively flexibly. You can use the customizing function **Set View Profiles for Technical Objects** to define multiple tabs, and you can assign up to four screen groups to each tab.

The following screen groups are available:

- General data (size, weight, and inventory number)
- Reference data (vendor, acquisition value, and acquisition date)
- Manufacturing data (manufacturer, year of construction, and month of construction)
- Location data (maintenance plant, location, and room)
- Address (zip code, town, telephone number, and fax number)
- Account assignment (cost center, technical system, and company code)
- Responsibilities (planner group and main work center)
- Structuring (superior functional location and position)
- Equipment (installed equipment)

- Customer/vendor data
- Standard class (full screen or subscreen)
- Partner (partner function, name, and address)
- Long text
- Warranty (customer warranty or vendor warranty)
- Documents (full screen or subscreen)
- User data with their own fields
- Log book data
- Linear data for functional locations and characteristics

Hiding Fields

You can use the screen control to adjust the individual fields; that is, you can hide unnecessary fields, or you can declare important fields as mandatory fields. In this case, use the customizing function **Define Field Selection for Functional Locations**.

In many application scenarios, you may need to display the functional locations and pieces of equipment in the sequence in which they appear in the production steps. If you only use numeric functional location numbers, you can achieve this sequence by using the number assignment. However, if you use alphabetical or alphanumeric characters, SAP S/4HANA Asset Management sorts the functional locations and pieces of equipment alphabetically and not in the sequence in which they appear in the process steps.

Thus, for example, in Figure 3.7, the sequence M1 · TA · M2 · FR · PK · BF can be found in the second level of the ice cream plant; you achieve this sequence by assigning position numbers in ascending order to the functional locations and pieces of equipment, in this case 10 · 20 · 30 · 40 · 50 · 60. The **Position** field itself has four alphanumeric characters (see Figure 3.7).

Figure 3.7 Transaction IL02 Functional Location: Position Number

[+]

Using the Position Field

You can use the **Position** field in the **Structuring** screen group to arrange your functional locations and pieces of equipment. Pay attention to standard conventions because, for example, the value "20" is sorted before "3." The best option is to use 4-digit position numbers (for example, "0001" instead of "1" or "0030" instead of "30").

The **Work center** field in the **Location Data** screen group and the **Main WorkCtr** field in the **Responsibilities** screen group are often confused (see Figure 3.8 and Figure 3.9).

Figure 3.8 Transaction IL02 Functional Location: Main Work Center

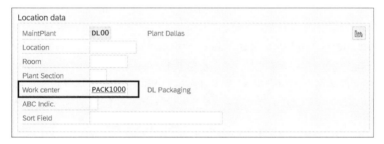

Figure 3.9 Transaction IL02 Functional Location: Work Center

Assign a *main work center* to a functional location if, in maintenance processing, you want this work center to be proposed in notifications and/or orders as the executing maintenance workshop.

Assign a *work center* to the functional location if you want the planned maintenance orders to subsequently appear in the planning table of the production planners (Transaction CM21), to show machine unavailability, for example.

[!]

Work Center versus Main Work Center

The *work center* represents the functional location as a production resource (a production work center in SAP S/4HANA production planning and control). The *main work center* corresponds to a maintenance workshop.

In the **ConstType** field in the **Structuring** screen group, enter a material number with which all similar objects are grouped together (see Figure 3.10). You'll then have access to the same BOMs and general maintenance task lists, for example. For more information, refer to Section 3.6 for materials, Section 3.7 for BOMs and Chapter 5, Section 5.3, for task lists.

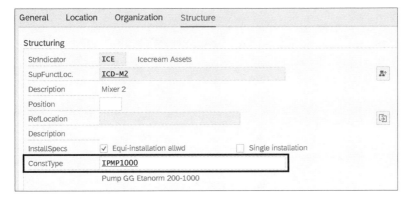

Figure 3.10 Transaction IL02 Functional Location: Construction Type

---

Construction Types as Links

Use the **ConstType** field if you want to create a link to a material number, to the BOM for this material, or to general maintenance task lists.

3.2.2   Creating Functional Locations: Collective Entry

If you want to record several functional locations at once or if you want to copy a functional location structure that you created previously, use Transaction IL04 (Create Functional Location – List Entry). Figure 3.11 shows you how you can copy the existing structure ICE to a structure known as ICB to use as a copy reference. For this purpose, click the **Copy reference** button and determine which objects are to be copied from the template.

The system now generates a completely new functional location structure, ICB, containing all of the functional locations. Before you save structure ICB, the system displays the complete list so that you can make any necessary corrections.

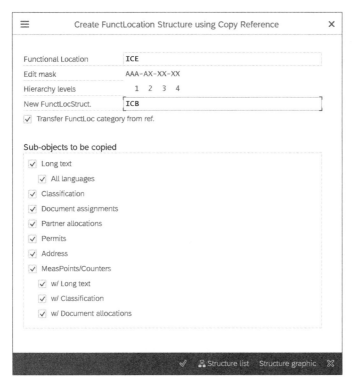

Figure 3.11 Transaction IL04 Create Functional Location: List Entry

3.2.3   Reference Functional Locations

Reference functional locations do not represent technical systems that actually exist but solely serve the purpose of acting as a template for real functional locations. As a result, you can copy functional location structures from reference structures. Unlike a copy with a functional location structure as a reference, changes to the reference structure are transferred to the resulting functional location structures.

However, the reference functional location contains much less information than a functional location. A reference functional location contains the following information:

- Responsibilities (planner group, main work center)
- Structuring (superior reference functional location, position)
- Standard class
- Texts
- Documents

3.2.4   Alternative Labeling

Alternative labeling systems can be used for different purposes. You can assign several numbers to a functional location structure or each individual location within the structure for different perspectives (as shown in Figure 3.12, for example, your own naming conventions versus your customer's naming conventions).

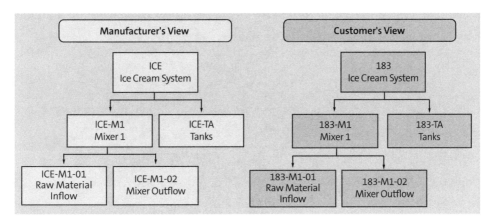

Figure 3.12 Alternative Labeling for Complete Systems

You can create primary and secondary functional location structures (as shown in Figure 3.13, for example, a primary structure for the power supply and a secondary structure for building services).

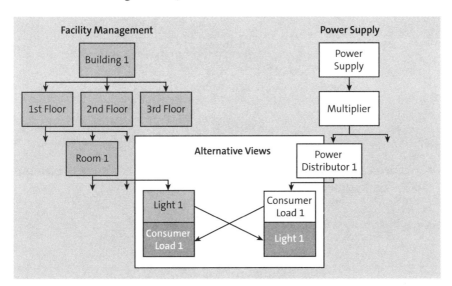

Figure 3.13 Alternative Labeling for Individual Functional Locations

You assign several numbers at the lowest level, thus where the same physical location is involved, and the functional location appears in several lists (Transaction IL05). The primary functional location structure is always displayed in the structural display (Transaction IH01 [Functional Location Structure List]).

You can change a functional location number, which is necessary, for example, in the following cases:

- If you have assigned an incorrect number
- If you scrap a technical system but use some of its parts in another technical system
- If part of a technical system is used in another technical system (see Figure 3.14)

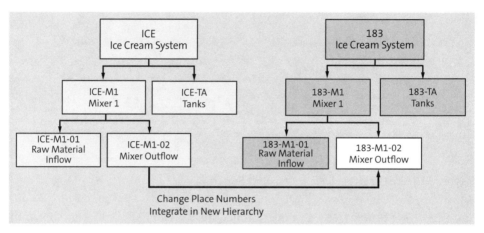

Figure 3.14 Alternative Labeling to Change Functional Location Number

Activating Alternative Labeling

You activate alternative labeling via the customizing function **Activate Alternative Labeling**, and you can then change the number of the functional location. Once you activate alternative labeling, however, you cannot deactivate it.

You use the customizing function **Define Labeling Systems for Functional Locations** to define the different perspectives that you want to manage for functional locations.

Within a functional location, you can now view or change the functional location number using **More · Extras · Alternative Labels · Overview** (see Figure 3.15).

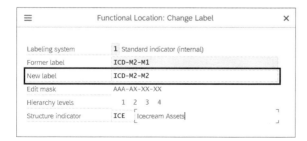

Figure 3.15 Transaction IL02 Functional Location: Changing Number

3.3 Equipment and Serial Numbers

Equipment represents movable, individual aggregates (inventories). For example, equipment could include the following:

- Machines
- Means of production (pumps and engines)
- Production resources/tools (PRTs)
- Test equipment (scales and gauges)
- Fleet objects (cars, trucks, forklift trucks, and industrial trucks)
- IT inventories (PCs, printers, monitors, notebooks, and projectors)
- Robots

For which devices do you now create an equipment master record in SAP S/4HANA Asset Management? You create a piece of equipment in the following scenarios:

- You install devices on functional locations, and you want to maintain a usage history.
- You want to store the devices.
- You want to manage individual data from a maintenance perspective (technical data such as performance data or organizational data such as the work center).
- You want to create notifications, orders, or maintenance plans.
- You have documentation commitments and must provide evidence of maintenance tasks performed.
- You want to collate and analyze technical data (such as causes of damage, measurement readings, or counter readings).
- You want to verify costs.
- You want to refurbish a device.
- You want to subcontract an external supplier (subcontracting).
- You manage devices in a pool, and you want to support the borrowing process.
- You want/need to perform calibrations or checks.

A piece of equipment can be configured in exactly the same way as a functional location. As a result, an equipment master record could look like Figure 3.16.

The following sections show you how to install equipment in functional locations and how you can store them. You'll also get to know the purpose of equipment hierarchies and, finally, a summary comparison of equipment and functional locations.

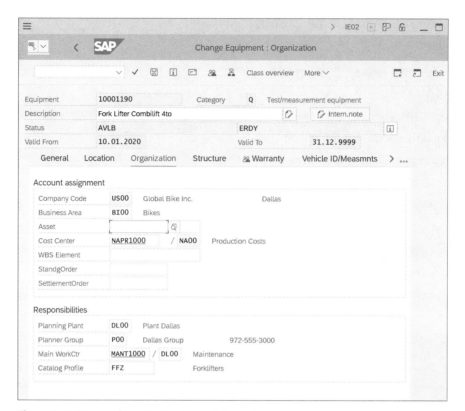

Figure 3.16 Transaction IE02 Equipment: Layout

3.3.1 Installing Equipment on Functional Locations/Dismantling Equipment from Functional Locations

On the one hand, some equipment categories have, from their design perspective, a layout that enables them to be installed at functional locations, which applies, for example, to pumps, engines, or robots. However, other equipment categories (for example, vehicles, tools, and so on) do not have this layout.

On the other hand, however, you may also have functional locations where you want to prevent the installation of equipment, for example, if you have created a plant as a functional location. Some functional locations constitute installation positions and are thus intended for the installation of equipment.

Consequently, certain prerequisites must be fulfilled so that you can install a piece of equipment at a functional location.

In the master record of the functional location, you must select the **Equi-installation allwd** checkbox in the **Structuring** screen group (see Figure 3.17).

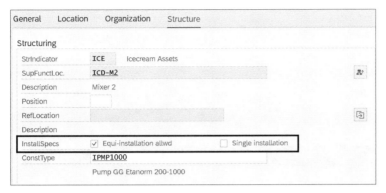

Figure 3.17 Transaction IL02 Functional Location: Allow Equipment Installation

Furthermore, if you only want one piece of equipment to be installed at a certain time, also select the **Single installation** checkbox.

From an equipment perspective, you must use the customizing function **Define Installation at Functional Location** to define which equipment categories can and cannot be installed (see Figure 3.18). If these prerequisites are fulfilled, you can install the equipment from an equipment perspective (Transaction IE02 [Change Equipment]) or from a functional location perspective (Transaction IL02 [Change Functional Location]).

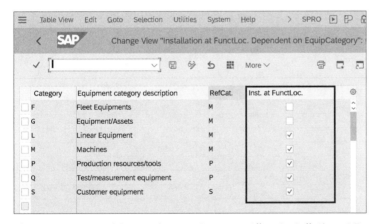

Figure 3.18 Customizing Equipment Category: Allow Installation at Functional Location

If you restructure from an equipment perspective, use the function **More · Structure · Change Installation Location**. There, you dismantle the equipment in the old location in the first step and install it in the new installation location in the second step (see Figure 3.19).

Change Equipment Installation Location
Functional loc.
ICD-TA-T1
Superord.Equip.
Position
Inst/DismTime
03-29-2020
06:19:10
Inst. w. DataTransfer

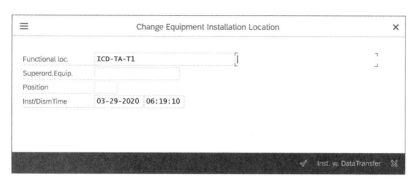

Figure 3.19 Transaction IE02 Equipment: Install at Functional Location

Furthermore, if you have used the customizing function **Usage History Update** to activate the usage history for each equipment category, the history is automatically updated. The history lists the functional locations and the time periods in which a piece of equipment was installed. In Transactions IE02/IE03 (Change Equipment/View Equipment) you can use the menu function **More • Extras • Usage List** to view this history from an equipment perspective, or you can use Transaction IL07 (Multilevel Functional Location List) to view this history from a functional location perspective. Figure 3.20 shows the usage list from an equipment perspective.

IE02
Display Equipment: Equipment List
More
Exit
S Valid From | Valid To | Plng Plant | Functional Location | FunctLocDescrip. | SuperEq.
03-29-2020 | 12-31-9999 | HD00 | ICE-TA-T1 | Tank 1
06-08-2019 | 03-29-2020 | HD00 | ICE-TA-T1-02 | Tank 1 Drain
01-27-2019 | 06-08-2019 | HD00 | 10000-B01-2 | Pump Block 2
01-27-2019 | 01-27-2019 | HD00

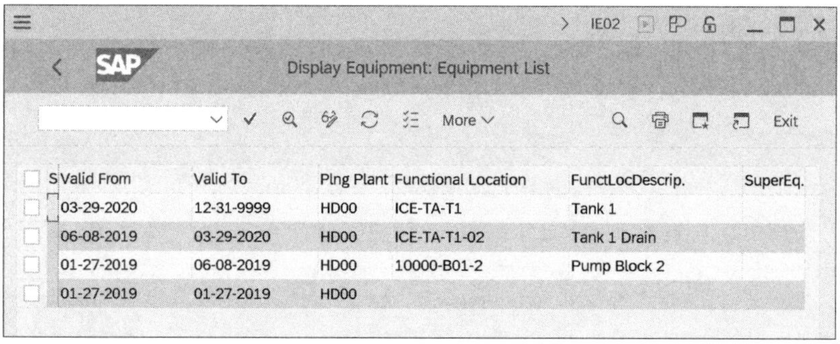

Figure 3.20 Transaction IE02 Equipment: Usage List

3.3.2 Placing Equipment in Storage/Removing Equipment from Storage

If you want to use the function for placing equipment in storage or removing it from storage, certain prerequisites must be fulfilled.

You must add the material/serial number segment to the equipment master. You do this by activating the **Serial Number** segment in the equipment master under **More • Edit • Special Serial No. Functions** and assigning the equipment a material number (see Figure 3.21).You can assign the material master in the **General Plant Parameters** group in the **Serial no. profile** field (see Figure 3.22).

Enter a level in the **SerLevel** field to determine whether the serial number and equipment number are to be synchronized.

You maintain the serial number profile using the customizing function **Define Serial Number Profiles**. Here, you determine whether specifying serial numbers for goods movements is mandatory, whether only existing serial numbers must be moved, or whether you can create new serial numbers for equipment that you place in storage/remove from storage.

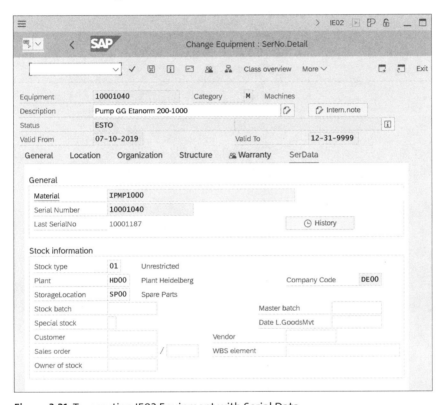

Figure 3.21 Transaction IE02 Equipment with Serial Data

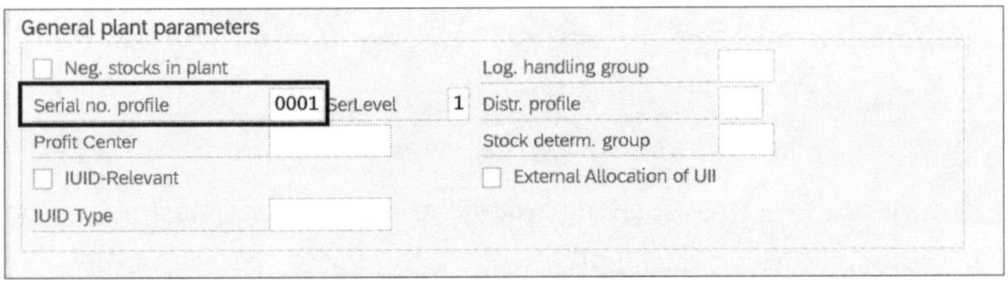

General plant parameters			
☐ Neg. stocks in plant		Log. handling group	
Serial no. profile	0001 SerLevel 1	Distr. profile	
Profit Center		Stock determ. group	
☐ IUID-Relevant		☐ External Allocation of UII	
IUID Type			

Figure 3.22 Transaction MM02 Material: Assign Serial No. Profile

If these prerequisites are fulfilled, you can place the piece of equipment or the material/serial number in storage. You can move the equipment using general inventory management transactions (for example, Transaction MIGO) or using Transaction IE4N

(Equipment Installation with Goods Movement)—a special SAP S/4HANA Asset Management transaction (see Figure 3.23).

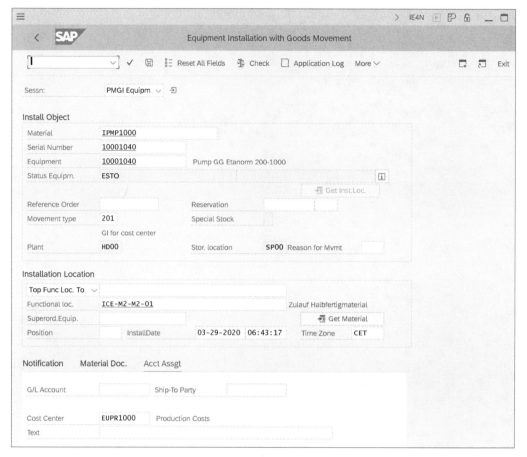

Figure 3.23 Transaction IE4N Install Equipment with Goods Issue

You can now use one of the following two processes:

- You can place equipment in storage while simultaneously removing it from the functional location.

- You can remove equipment from storage while simultaneously installing it at a functional location.

Now, the equipment in stock is displayed in inventory management, for example, Transaction MMBE (Stock Overview) (see Figure 3.24).

To display a list containing all equipment installed, use the menu path **More · Environment · Equipment/Serial No.** (see Figure 3.25).

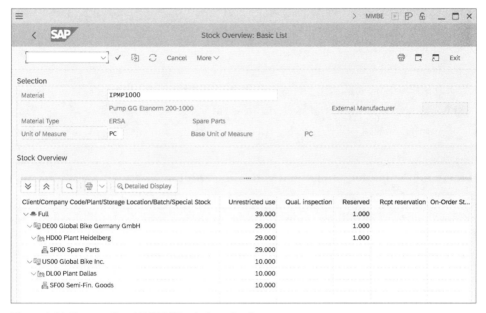

Figure 3.24 Transaction MMBE (Stock Overview)

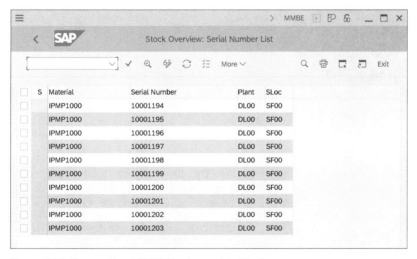

Figure 3.25 Transaction MMBE Equipment in Stock

3.3.3 Equipment Hierarchies

In addition to the cases where a single piece of equipment is installed on a functional location or removed from a functional location, in practice, you may have a case where, not just one piece of equipment, but rather an entire equipment group comprised of several pieces of equipment, is replaced. Typical examples include the following:

- Roller conveyors comprised of several pieces of equipment, for example, racks, rolls, and drive motors

- (Motor) bogies for rail vehicles comprised of several pieces of equipment, for example, suspension systems, wheels, motors, and gear wheels

- Painting stations, which include several pieces of equipment, such as the painting station itself, a circulating pump, and an agitator

- Robots that consist of several pieces of subequipment, such as designs, robotic arms, and tools

If, for example, you have a problem with one of the bogie's wheels, the wheel is not usually replaced, but rather the entire bogie is replaced. Equipment hierarchies may reflect such combinations where the entire piece of equipment (bogie) is comprised of subequipment (motor, wheel, and so on) (see Figure 3.26).

Figure 3.26 Bogie

You could map this bogie as an equipment hierarchy, similar to the hierarchy shown in Figure 3.27 (Transaction IH03 [Equipment Structure List]).

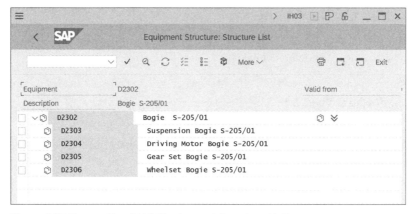

Figure 3.27 Transaction IH03 (Equipment Structure List)

Equipment Group as Equipment Hierarchy

If you always consider an entire equipment group, you should work with equipment hierarchies.

An order OR notification history is always updated on the equipment that is specified in the order or notification—not directly updated for the superior equipment. Therefore, you should check whether equipment hierarchies fulfill your reporting and analysis requirements.

3.3.4   Functional Comparison between Pieces of Equipment and Functional Locations

In this section, we'll recapitulate the differences between a piece of equipment and a functional location.

A piece of equipment provides the following options:

- You can serialize a piece of equipment by assigning it a material and a serial number. As a result, inventory management is possible for the piece of equipment.

- You can install equipment at functional locations or on other pieces of equipment.

- In fleet management, a vehicle can be a piece of equipment, which then has special vehicle data.

- A piece of equipment installed at a functional location can save its usage history. The system writes an equipment usage period for each installation location, which enables you to trace the entire usage history.

- In addition to the standard tabs for the equipment master record, you can, if required, call additional tabs (**Sales Data**, **PRT Data**, **Configuration Data**) from the menu, without having to make the relevant settings in customizing.

Equipment Features

When using equipment, the following features should be noted:

- When structures are created, pieces of equipment do not automatically find their location in the structure; locations must be assigned manually for each master record.

- You can no longer change the equipment number after it's created.

- You cannot analyze equipment hierarchies on the basis of the superior piece of equipment.

The functional location provides the following options:

- You can change the label of a functional location after it is created if you have activated the alternative labeling function.

- Additional labeling is also possible for functional locations.
- As a result of the structure indicator, functional locations automatically find their location in the structure when you create them (in accordance with the top-down principle).
- The strictly hierarchical structure enables data to be summarized (for example, costs) at any hierarchy level.
- A functional location can be a piece of real estate in Flexible Real Estate Management with SAP S/4HANA (RE-FX with SAP S/4HANA; for more information, see Chapter 7, Section 7.1.9).
- You can define a functional location in investment management with SAP S/4HANA. Therefore, orders can automatically be assigned to an investment program (for more information, see Chapter 8, Section 8.3.3).

Functional Location Features

Functional locations also have some features that you should note:

- You must create at least one structure indicator, but you usually create several structure indicators in customizing.
- Functional locations are usually installed in superior functional locations. However, they can also exist as individual objects.
- A functional location installed at another functional location cannot save the history of its installation locations. Instead, it can only show its current installation location.
- Automatic assignment no longer works when you restructure functional location structures that have different structure indicators. As with pieces of equipment, you must manually assign the superior functional location.

3.4   Links and Object Networks

For the sake of completeness, we should also mention that SAP S/4HANA Asset Management functions are available to map links between different technical objects or systems (pieces of equipment or functional locations). Such links exist:

- Between production units
- Between production plants and supply systems
- Between supply systems and disposal systems

You can use object links to form an object network, and as a result, your technical systems can have a horizontal structure.

You can only define links between two pieces of equipment (Transaction IN07 [Create Object Link for Equipment]) or between two functional locations (Transaction IN04 [Create Functional Location Object Link; see Figure 3.28); the link itself can also be a piece of equipment or a functional location, but this is not necessary. You cannot establish a link between a piece of equipment and a functional location.

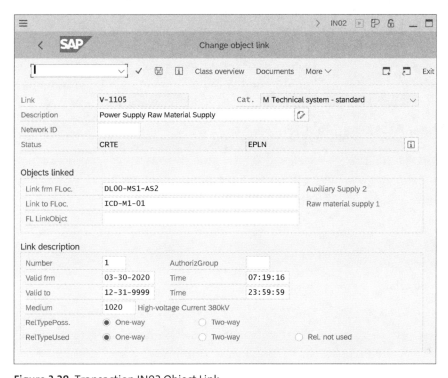

Figure 3.28 Transaction IN02 Object Link

You form an object network by creating several individual, logically consecutive object links. You can display an object network by viewing the graphic for a list of functional location links (Transactions N15/16 [Object Network for Functional Locations]; see Figure 3.29) or the graphic for a list of equipment links (Transactions IN18/19 [Object Network for Equipment]).

Figure 3.29 Transaction IN15/IN16 Object Network

[!] **Should You Use Object Links?**

In practice, link and network mapping play a minor role in the SAP system for the following reasons:

- Object links cannot be integrated in business processes; that is, you cannot write any notifications, orders, maintenance plans, and so on, to an object link.

- Suitable, industry-specific systems (such as geographic information systems [GISs], network monitoring systems, and measuring and control technology systems) are generally used and coupled with the SAP system (see Chapter 7, Section 7.3).

3.5   Linear Asset Management

Linear assets (*linear asset management*) are technical systems with a linear infrastructure, whose condition and properties can change from section to section (dynamic segmentation). Examples of linear assets include the following:

- Pipelines
- Road networks
- Railway networks
- Overhead cables
- Pipes

From these examples, you can see that this functionality, among other things, would be of particular interest to the oil and gas industry, to utility companies (electricity, gas, and water), to road maintenance companies, to public authorities, or to rail operators.

Before we go into more detail, we'll first explain some aspects of linear asset management and the underlying problems using the practical example of a highway (see Figure 3.30).

The example is based on the following information:

- First, the total length of the highway (e.g., highway A81) is 293 km.

- The highway should be divided into several sections, for example, from interchange to interchange or from junction to junction (such as junctions 002 and 003, which are separated by a distance of 13 km).

- The highway has specific properties that can change over its course, such as change of road surface (for example, from tar to asphalt for 11.5 km), speed restrictions in places (for example, to 120 km/h), or varying number of lanes (between two and four).

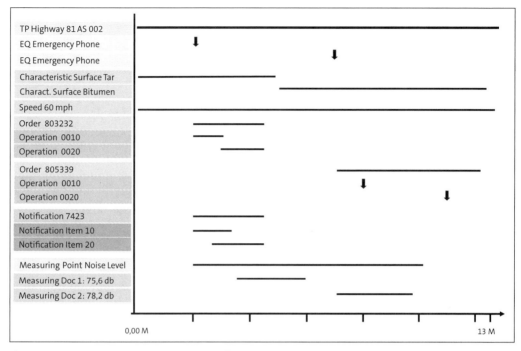

Figure 3.30 Linear Asset Management: Highway Example

- Stationary equipment such as emergency phones, toll plazas, bridges, parking lots, or rest areas (with emergency telephones at 3 km and 7 km) are located along the route.

- On 11/30, a maintenance order must be performed in the section 2 to 4.5 km.

- Operation 10 concerns the quarterly grass cuttings in section 2.1 to 2.7 km.

- Operation 20 concerns the twice-yearly cleaning of the lateral boundary indicators in section 2.7 to 4.5 km.

- Various necessary repair measures are described in a notification sent on 11/15, which concerns the section 2.5 to 5 km.

- Notification item 10 describes various holes in the road surface for the section 2.0 to 2.6 km.

- Notification item 20 describes corroded surfaces in the central guardrail for the section 2.3 to 4.8 km.

- The noise level is measured in the section 2.0 to 10.0 km.

- On 11/23, a noise level of 75.6 decibels was measured in the section 3.5 to 5.0 km.

You can store the linear data for your technical objects, as follows:

- General linear data such as starting point, end point, length, and unit of measurement

- Offset data such as horizontal or vertical offset with respect to a starting point and the unit of measurement
- Marker data such as marker type, distance between two markers, and the unit of measurement

You can assign linear data to the following objects:

- Equipment
- Functional locations
- Measuring points
- Measurement documents
- Notifications
- Notification items
- Orders
- Confirmations
- Maintenance items

[+] **Fully Integrated Processing**

In contrast to links, linear asset management is integrated consistently in the maintenance business processes. You can thus record linear data, not only in the master data, but also in planning (maintenance plans, notifications, orders) and in the confirmation.

To enable you to use linear asset management to its full potential, you must fulfill some conditions.

- In the classification system customizing, you have used the function **Maintain Object Types and Class Types** to create an organizational area, for example, the organizational area L for linear objects.
- In customizing for linear asset management, you have used the function **Define Offset Types** to define offset types, for example, the horizontal offset and the vertical offset.
- In customizing for linear asset management, you have used the function **Organizational Area for Characteristics with Linear Data** to assign the equipment and functional locations an organizational area, for example, the organizational area L for linear data.
- To enable recording linear data for measuring points and measurement documents, you have defined a measuring point type using the function **Define Measuring Point Types** and have set the indicator **Linear System** there.
- Using the function **Set View Profiles for Technical Objects**, you have defined view profiles for functional locations and one for equipment and have assigned the field groups for linear data there.

- To enable storing linear data for functional locations, you have used the function **Define Type of Functional Location** to define a functional location type, and you have assigned the view profile, where you also have set the indicator **Linear System**.

- To enable storing linear data for equipment, you have used the function **Maintain Equipment Category** to define an equipment category, where you also assigned the view profile and have set the indicator **Linear System**.

If you now want to create a linear functional location, first call Transaction IL01 (Create Functional Location). Next, choose a suitable structure indicator and assign a new number.

If you want to create a linear piece of equipment, call Transaction IE01 (Create Equipment). Assign an equipment number or let the system assign a number.

In either case, make sure that you select the equipment category or functional location type that is defined as a linear object.

After the view profiles have been correctly set and assigned, you can start maintaining the linear data (see Figure 3.31), as follows:

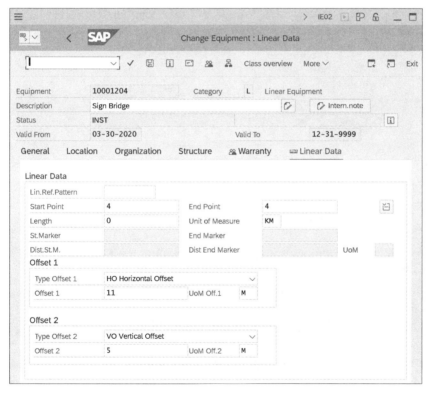

Figure 3.31 Transaction IE02 Equipment: Linear Data

- **Starting point**

  In the **Starting Point** field, which determines the beginning of a section, enter the value "4" for our example.

- **End point**

  In the **End Point** field, you also enter the value "4" and thus define that the end of the section is to be identical to the starting point because our example involves a stationary system.

- **Length and unit of length**

  If, instead of stationary equipment, linear objects are involved, such as sections, you can enter the **Length** and the **Unit of Measure** here (for example, 0 km).

- **Offset**

  In the dropdown menu of the **Type Offset 1** field in the **Offset 1** area, select the **HO** option for horizontal offset. Next, in the **Offset 1** field, enter the value "11." For the **Type Offset 2** field in the **Offset 2** area, select the **VO** option for vertical offset. Then, in the **Offset 2** field, enter the value "5." With these settings, the device will be offset 11 m from the side of the road (horizontal offset) at a height of 5 m (vertical offset).

If you have also assigned a suitable class, you can now also maintain the stored characteristic values (see Figure 3.32).

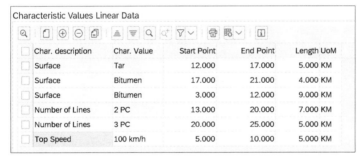

Char. description	Char. Value	Start Point	End Point	Length UoM
Surface	Tar	12.000	17.000	5.000 KM
Surface	Bitumen	17.000	21.000	4.000 KM
Surface	Bitumen	3.000	12.000	9.000 KM
Number of Lines	2 PC	13.000	20.000	7.000 KM
Number of Lines	3 PC	20.000	25.000	5.000 KM
Top Speed	100 km/h	5.000	10.000	5.000 KM

Figure 3.32 Transactions IL02/IE02 Linear Asset Management: Characteristics

[+]

Dynamic Segmentation

What is special about maintaining linear characteristics is that you can assign the same characteristic with the same or different values with length specification. Thus, the surface changes in the example shown apply to three sections (bitumen on the section 3 to 12 km, tar on the section 12 to 17 km, and bitumen on the section 17 to 21 km), while a speed restriction of 100 km/h applies only on the section 5 to 10 km. This functionality is called *dynamic segmentation*.

Figure 3.33 shows a completed linear technical system structure, which has been called via Transaction IH01.

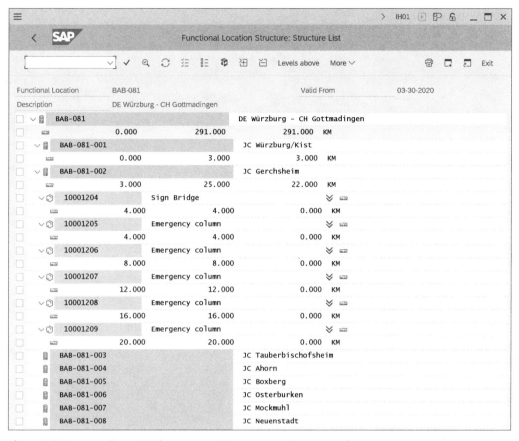

Figure 3.33 Transaction IH01 Linear Asset Management: Structure List

You can also graphically display such a linear technical system structure over the course of the route. To do so, call Transaction IL07 (Multilevel Functional Location List). Select the correct filter on the initial screen (see Figure 3.34).

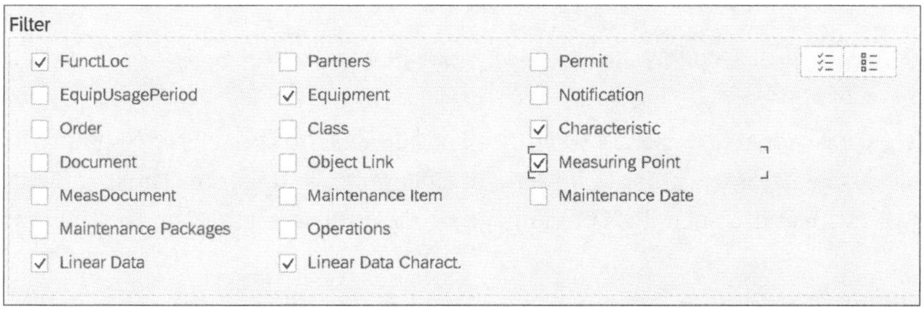

Figure 3.34 Transactions IL07/IE07 Linear Asset Management: Multilevel List Filter

Now, on the multilevel list click the **Linear Data** button, and you call up the graphic linear technical system structure (see Figure 3.35).

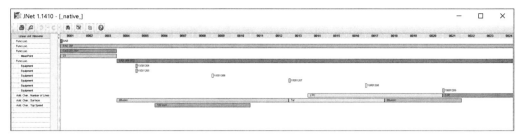

Figure 3.35 Linear Asset Management: Graphic

Instead of individual transactions, you can also use the list of transactions to directly maintain the linear data for multiple objects. To do so, proceed as follows:

- First, call Transaction IL05 (Change Functional Location – List) for the maintenance of functional locations or Transaction IE05 (Change Equipment – List) for the maintenance of equipment.
- Now narrow the selection and then start the list.
- Call the linear data by clicking the **Linear Data** button.
- You can maintain all linear data in the list that is displayed (see Figure 3.36).

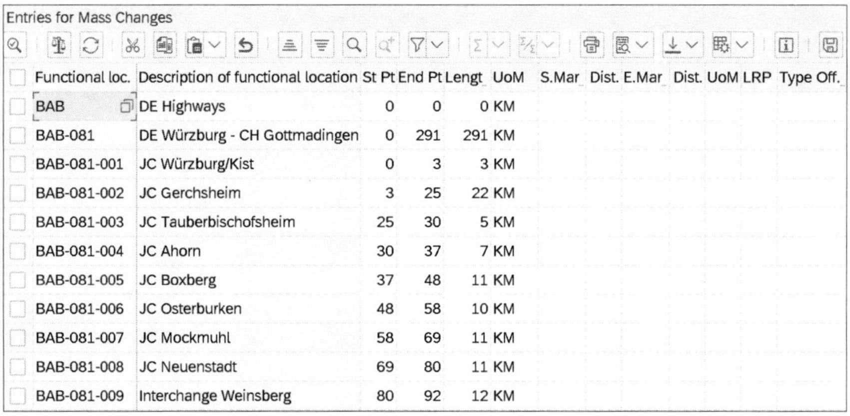

	Functional loc.	Description of functional location	St Pt	End Pt	Lengt	UoM	S.Mar	Dist.	E.Mar	Dist. UoM	LRP	Type Off.
	BAB	DE Highways	0	0	0	KM						
	BAB-081	DE Würzburg - CH Gottmadingen	0	291	291	KM						
	BAB-081-001	JC Würzburg/Kist	0	3	3	KM						
	BAB-081-002	JC Gerchsheim	3	25	22	KM						
	BAB-081-003	JC Tauberbischofsheim	25	30	5	KM						
	BAB-081-004	JC Ahorn	30	37	7	KM						
	BAB-081-005	JC Boxberg	37	48	11	KM						
	BAB-081-006	JC Osterburken	48	58	10	KM						
	BAB-081-007	JC Mockmuhl	58	69	11	KM						
	BAB-081-008	JC Neuenstadt	69	80	11	KM						
	BAB-081-009	Interchange Weinsberg	80	92	12	KM						

Entries for Mass Changes

Figure 3.36 Transactions IL05/IE05 Linear Asset Management: Mass Change

Linear reference patterns are created so you can assign descriptive reference points to real technical objects or documents (orders, notifications, and so on). Thus, you can then send a notification, such as "The damage occurred 10 km after the Jagsttal rest area."

You maintain linear reference patterns using Transactions IK81 (Create), IK82 (Change), and IK83 (Display). The following are relevant as pattern types:

- General markers (for example, 10, 20, 30, … km)
- Distinctive functional locations (for example, the Weinsberg interchange)
- Distinctive pieces of equipment (for example, the Jagsttal service area)

3.6   Material and PM Assemblies

The material master contains information about materials that a company designs, procures, produces, and stores and then sells and integrates data from the various areas of a company, for example, purchasing or accounting. Unlike a piece of equipment or a functional location, a material master record does not describe just one thing but, rather, describes similar items. As a result, a material master record generally represents several similar spare parts, assemblies, raw materials, and so on.

From a maintenance perspective, material master records are used for the following purposes:

- Some material master records are purchased as spare parts and then stored.
- Some material master records are purchased as equipment and then placed in storage as material/serial numbers.
- Some material records are construction types that only encompass similar pieces of equipment or functional locations so that shared functions can be executed, for example, management of shared BOMs or general maintenance task lists.
- Some material master records serve as maintenance assemblies for substructures of pieces of equipment or functional locations.
- Some material master records fulfill the same function as spare parts, the only difference being that they are not placed in storage, but rather, they are procured each time as non-stock items (for example, because they are too expensive, too large, or rarely used).
- Some material master records are used as operating resources for maintenance tasks, but not as spare parts (for example, tools or protective clothing).

The material master record has a hierarchical structure (see Figure 3.37) that resembles the organizational structure of your company. Some material data is valid at all organizational levels, and some is valid only at certain levels.

- At the *client level*, the following applies: General material data that is valid for the entire company is saved at this level. This data includes, among other things, the material group, the base unit of measure, the material short texts, and the conversion factors for alternative units of measure.
- All of the data that is valid in a specific plant and in the associated storage locations is saved at the *plant level*. This data includes, for example, accounting data, purchasing data, material requirements planning (MRP) data, and forecast data.
- All data that refers to one particular storage location is saved at the *storage location level*. This data primarily concerns storage location stock.

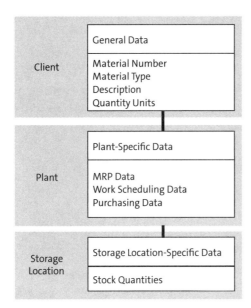

Figure 3.37 Material Master: Structure

You must create a material master record, identified by a unique material number, for each material used by your company. As with equipment, you can assign an external or internal number.

You can group materials that have the same basic characteristics together by assigning them to one common material type. As a result, you'll have the ability to manage different materials in a uniform manner, according to your company's requirements.

You use the material type to determine the following:

- Which user departments (purchasing, production, sales and distribution, accounting, and so on) can maintain the material master record
- Whether the material number can be assigned internally or externally
- The number range interval from which the material number originates
- Which screens appear and in which order
- Which user department-specific data is available for entry
- Whether quantity and value changes are updated
- The procurement type of a material, that is, whether the material is produced in-house or procured externally
- Which accounts are posted to if a material is placed in storage or removed from storage

Figure 3.38 provides an overview of potential material types.

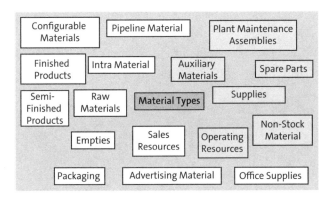

Figure 3.38 Material Master: Material Types

From a maintenance perspective, the following material types, which have a darker background in Figure 3.38, are of practical relevance:

- Auxiliary materials are those materials that form part of a finished product but are insignificant and barely seen in the finished product (for example, screws, adhesive, and welded joints).

- Expendable supplies are not part of the finished product but are required for the production process (for example, lubricant, power, grease, oil, and so on).

- Spare parts are used to replace defective parts and can be purchased and placed in storage.

- Maintenance assemblies are not standalone objects but, rather, logical elements that divide the technical objects in plant maintenance into clearly defined units. A forklift truck, for example, can be a technical object; the lifting plant, gear shift, chassis, and so on, can be its associated maintenance assemblies.

- Operating resources are required for maintenance tasks (for example, tools and devices, test equipment, protective clothing, and safety devices). Unlike expendable supplies, these resources do not perish but, rather, wear out with use over time.

- Non-stock materials are not held in storage but are procured as required and used immediately. Non-stock materials occur when, for example, the parts are too expensive, are rarely required, or are difficult to store (too large, too heavy, or too bulky). The master record of non-stock materials is comprised of purchasing data only.

[!]

Defining Your Own Material Types

You can determine which material types you require with which controls for your company using the **Define Attributes of Material Types** function.

Since, in the example, several departments in a company work with the same material and each department uses different information about the material, the data in a material master record is arranged by user department (see Figure 3.39).

The **Basic Data** and **Classification** views are at the client level; that is, the views are valid for all plants and storage locations. In the case of the **Accounting** view, you can choose whether you want to manage all of the data together at the company code level for all plants assigned to a company code or separately at the plant level for each plant.

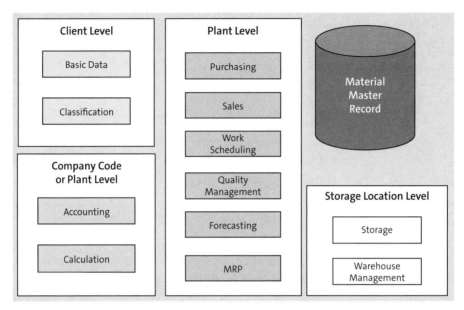

Figure 3.39 Material Master: Views

The **Purchasing, Material Requirements Planning Sales and Distribution, Work Scheduling, Quality Management** and **Forecast** views are at the plant level; that is, the views are valid for all storage locations which are assigned to the plant.

The **Storage** and **Warehouse Management** views are at the storage location level.

The maximum value of the material master consists of over thirty screens. Since these screens usually only have to be maintained in a rudimentary manner from a maintenance perspective, you should adapt the layout of the material master record. Doing so restricts the selection of views (see Figure 3.40).

Figure 3.40 Transaction MM02 Material Master: View Selection

Furthermore, the screen templates contain only fields that you can actually use and which provide information (see Figure 3.41).

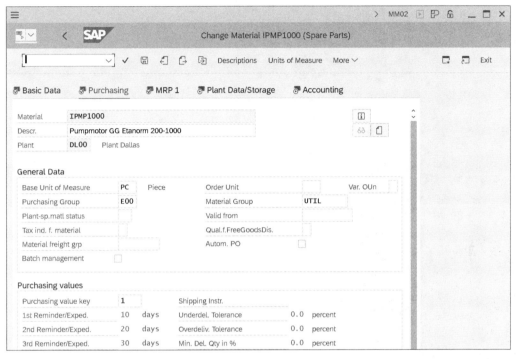

Figure 3.41 Transaction MM02 Material Master: Layout

Adjusting the Layout of the Material Master Record

You should not use the default layout of the material master record provided by SAP in the standard system because it contains too many views, too many screen groups, and too much data.

You should define your own layout with selected views, selected screen groups, and selected data. You can define your own layouts using the customizing functions found under **Configuring the Material Master**.

This book will not describe the material master in any further detail, but I recommend you read my book *Configuring Plant Maintenance in SAP S/4HANA*, SAP PRESS, Boston 2020, *http://www.sap-press.com/5102*.

3.7   Bills of Materials

A BOM is essentially a complete, formally structured list of all components that belong to a product or assembly. BOMS contain the material numbers of the individual components as well as their quantities and units of measure (see Figure 3.42). Components can be parts or assemblies that can or cannot be kept in storage. Assemblies, in turn, can have BOMs that describe them in greater detail, which results in a multilevel BOM structure.

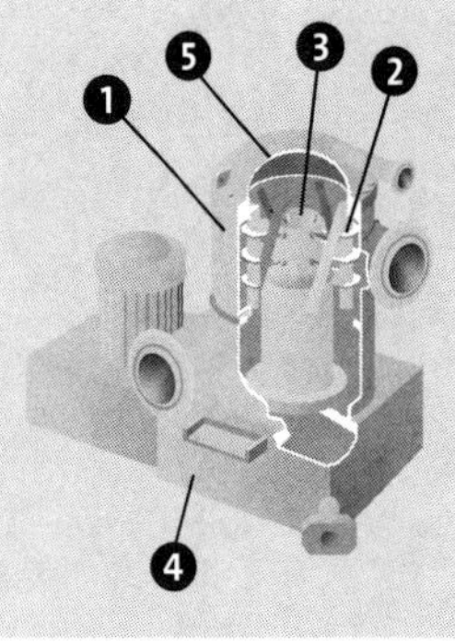

Item Number	Description	Material Number	Quantity	Quantity Unit
❶	Spiral Casing	T-B00	1	ST
❷	Blade Wheel	100-200	1	ST
❸	Shaft	100-300	1	ST
❹	Outrigger	100-600	2	ST
❺	Pressure Lid	100-400	1	ST

Figure 3.42 Design Drawing and Derived BOM

In SAP S/4HANA, BOMs are used not only in plant maintenance, but also in other areas:

- In production as production BOMs
- In controlling as costing BOMs
- In sales as sales order BOMs

In plant maintenance, you can primarily use BOMs for the following two purposes:

- **Structure description**
  You can use a BOM to describe the structure of a technical object or material and then use it to pinpoint the location of damage or the location where maintenance tasks are performed for a technical object.
- **Spare parts assignment**
  You can use the BOM to describe the assignment of spare parts for a technical object or material.

[!] **Spare Parts BOMs**

In practice, maintenance BOMs are primarily used as spare parts BOMs.

From a plant perspective, you must distinguish between three different BOM categories (see Figure 3.43):

- **Equipment BOMs**
  You create an equipment BOM for exactly one piece of equipment (Transaction IB01 [Create Equipment BOM]), and therefore, you can only use the BOM in connection with this piece of equipment.

■ **Functional location BOMs**
The same also applies for a functional location BOM (Transaction IB11 [Create Functional Location BOM]).

■ **Material BOMs**
You can indirectly make a material BOM (Transaction CS01 [Create Material BOM]) available for several pieces of equipment and/or functional locations by using the **ConstType** field in the master record for the piece of equipment or functional location in the **Structuring** screen group. As a result, all pieces of equipment and functional locations for which a material number is entered in the **ConstType** field can access the material BOM (see Figure 3.44).

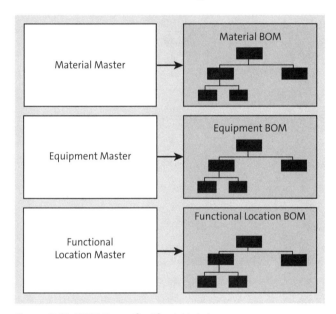

Figure 3.43 BOM Types for Plant Maintenance

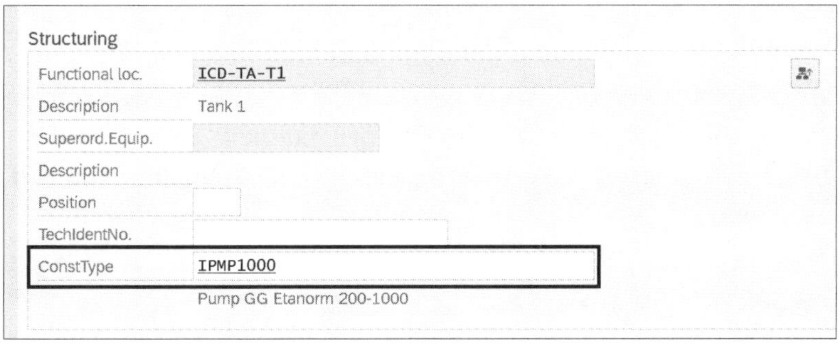

Structuring		
Functional loc.	ICD-TA-T1	
Description	Tank 1	
Superord.Equip.		
Description		
Position		
TechIdentNo.		
ConstType	IPMP1000	
	Pump GG Etanorm 200-1000	

Figure 3.44 Transaction IE02/IL02 Construction Type

Consequently, two BOM assignment procedures exist: *direct assignment* and *indirect assignment* (see Figure 3.45).

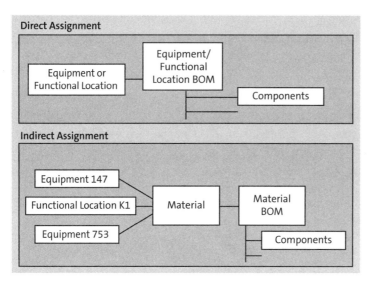

Figure 3.45 Direct and Indirect BOM Assignment

[!] **Using BOMs**

If you use BOMs in plant maintenance, note the following:

- Pieces of equipment and functional locations can have both directly and indirectly assigned BOMs.

- BOMs for pieces of equipment and functional locations are triggered simultaneously in maintenance processing.

- If you use BOMs, you should create material BOMs as much as possible and assign them as construction types to your pieces of equipment and functional locations.

- Record those parts that are the same for the relevant equipment or functional location category as a material BOM. Record those parts in which a piece of equipment or functional location has a different category as an equipment BOM or a functional location BOM.

In the upper part of Figure 3.46, you'll see a structure list for a piece of equipment (Transaction IH04 [Equipment Structure]) in the form of a multilevel spare parts BOM, which was assigned indirectly by construction type IPMP1000 to piece of equipment E16000. The last four items are spare parts from the directly assigned equipment BOM.

[!] **No Usage of Other BOM Categories**

The BOM categories usually found in other applications, such as variant BOMs or multiple BOMs, which are used, for example, in production, are practically insignificant in plant maintenance.

IH04
Equipment Structure: Structure List
Expand whole
More
Exit
Equipment E16000
Valid from 03-30-2020
Description Pump GG Etanorm 200-1000
E16000 Pump GG Etanorm 200-1000
IPMP1000 Pump GG Etanorm 200-1000
H-1000 Casing Pump normal suction L
G-1000 Transmission Pump normal suction L
M-1000 Motor Pump normal suction L
S-1000 Support Leg Pump normal suction L
W-1000 Shaft Pump normal suction L
FLDG16000 Flat Gasekt 45/65 mm L
GMDG1000 rubber seal 35mm L
WH1000 Shaft protection sleeve 1000/250 L
DSRG1000 Spacer ring 50mm L

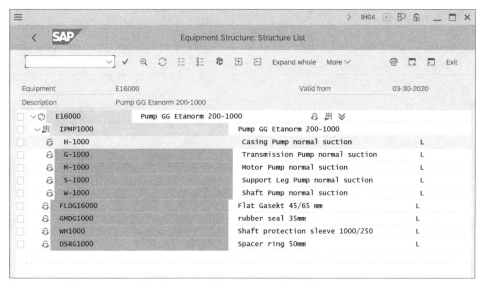

Figure 3.46 Transaction IH03 Equipment Structure with BOMs

The where-used list (Transaction CS15) is the mirror image of a BOM—thus, not from the top to the bottom like a BOM, but from the bottom to the top. The where-used list shows you the BOMs that contain a specific spare part or assembly.

As shown in Figure 3.47, in the **BOMcat** column, material FLDG16000 Flat Gasket is in equipment BOMs (BOM category **E**), in material BOMs (BOM category **M**), and in functional location BOMs (BOM category **T**).

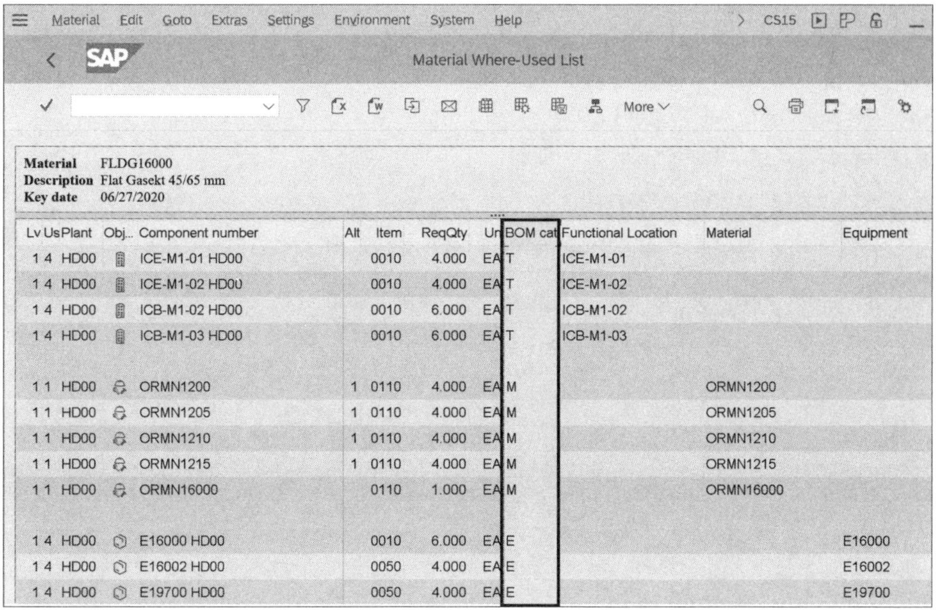

Material Edit Goto Extras Settings Environment System Help
CS15
Material Where-Used List
More
Material FLDG16000
Description Flat Gasekt 45/65 mm
Key date 06/27/2020
Lv Us Plant Obj... Component number Alt Item ReqQty Un BOM cat Functional Location Material Equipment
1 4 HD00 ICE-M1-01 HD00 0010 4.000 EA T ICE-M1-01
1 4 HD00 ICE-M1-02 HD00 0010 4.000 EA T ICE-M1-02
1 4 HD00 ICB-M1-02 HD00 0010 6.000 EA T ICB-M1-02
1 4 HD00 ICB-M1-03 HD00 0010 6.000 EA T ICB-M1-03
1 1 HD00 ORMN1200 1 0110 4.000 EA M ORMN1200
1 1 HD00 ORMN1205 1 0110 4.000 EA M ORMN1205
1 1 HD00 ORMN1210 1 0110 4.000 EA M ORMN1210
1 1 HD00 ORMN1215 1 0110 4.000 EA M ORMN1215
1 1 HD00 ORMN16000 0110 1.000 EA M ORMN16000
1 4 HD00 E16000 HD00 0010 6.000 EA E E16000
1 4 HD00 E16002 HD00 0050 4.000 EA E E16002
1 4 HD00 E19700 HD00 0050 4.000 EA E E19700

Figure 3.47 Transaction CS15 Material Where-Used List

3.8   Classification

In the SAP system, a *class* represents a group of similar objects that are described based on the *characteristics* that they have in common. From a maintenance perspective, a class system offers you the following options:

- Using classes, you can technically describe any objects (for example, equipment, functional locations, and materials) using the characteristics beyond the master records fields.
- You can group similar objects, from a technical viewpoint, into classes.
- Whenever necessary, the SAP system provides you with search functions to help you find objects by using classes and characteristics.
- You can use classes to describe *dynamic segmentation* in objects under linear asset management (Section 3.5).

The class system structure is comprised of three steps. In the first step, you describe the properties of an object, which are represented by characteristics, in Transaction CT04 (Characteristics). The individual characteristics are created centrally in SAP S/4HANA.

In a characteristic, you may define, for example, any of the following properties (see Figure 3.48):

- The name and the keywords (multilingual)
- The status (released, locked, and so on)
- The value assignment (one value or multiple values)
- Whether intervals are allowed
- The data type (character, date, numeric)
- The number of characters
- Whether negative values are allowed
- A table of allowed values
- The link to a database field
- Whether the characteristic is to be restricted to certain class types

In the second step, you define the classes in Transaction CL02 and store the objects to be classified there. You then assign characteristics to the classes you created (see Figure 3.49).

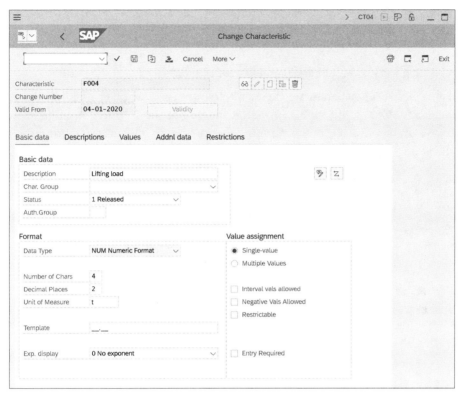

Figure 3.48 Transaction CT04 Maintain Characteristic

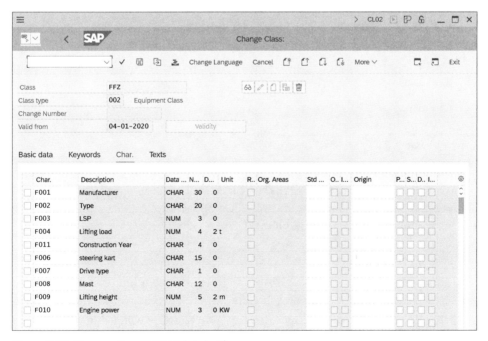

Figure 3.49 Ttransaction CL02 Maintain Class

The class types are preassigned by SAP, and they define the object type for which a class is to apply (for example, 001 Material, 002 Equipment, 003 Functional Location, and so on).

You can assign any alphanumeric name to your classes.

The **Same Classification** parameter checks whether the class has objects with the same characteristic values (see Figure 3.50). Select the **Do not check** radio button because, otherwise, unintentionally long runtimes or performance problems can occur during classification.

Figure 3.50 Transaction CL02 Class: Same Classification

The most important elements within a class are the characteristics that define the technical properties of the class. In our example, class FFZ (forklifts) contains technical properties such as a lifting load and lifting height.

On the **Keywords** tab, you can specify objects of this class. In the forklift example, you can use this class for industrial trucks, wheel loaders, or hand pallet truck.

Classification provides you with a wide range of options that go beyond the scope of this book. Examples include the following:

- Using object dependencies to derive characteristics
- Using variant configuration to define complete characteristic value tables
- Transferring characteristic values from the relevant functional location or piece of equipment
- Defining value tables

[+] **Using a Class System**

If you have carefully considered your class system and have a manageable number of characteristics (less than one page of characteristics works best), a high level of acceptance may be achieved among your users. Your SAP S/4HANA Asset Management system will become an operating resources database, and additional records or parallel systems will be superfluous.

Setting up a class and characteristics system can be time consuming, requiring both an organizational effort to create a concept and a technical effort to record the data in the system. You can considerably reduce this time and effort by using a predefined class system such as *eCl@ss*.

Class System Template

At *https://www.eclass.eu/en/index.html*, you will find a template for a complete class system, including all of the characteristics and keywords. eCl@ss is a hierarchical system for grouping materials, products, and services according to product-specific idiosyncrasies described using characteristics. As of Version 11.0 (2020), eCl@ss is comprised of more than 45,000 classes in 4 hierarchical levels, more than 19,000 characteristics, and more than 55,000 keywords. eCl@ss is available in 17 languages. While eCl@ss may be much more than you will ever require, you can easily choose elements you require from a template rather than starting from scratch.

Furthermore, you can also use the relevant data transfer programs from SAP for classification and transfer of characteristics in order to transfer the classification of eCl@ss. These programs are available in Transaction SXDA (with business objects BUS3060, BUS1003, and BUS1088) or in Transaction LSMW (under the data transfer objects 0130, 0140, and 0150).

Not only well-known companies and associations from all industries (for example, Audi, BASF, Cognis, DB, E.ON) are involved in the development of eCl@ss, but SAP is also represented as a full member of the steering committee.

The third step is to assign objects, that is, to actually classify them: Once you create the classes that you require for the classification, you can assign individual objects to these classes. The objects are described using the characteristics contained in the class.

You can assign the objects using a central transaction (Transaction CL20N [Assign Objects to Classes]), or you can classify the objects directly in the master record itself, which is normally the case. For example, you classify the equipment using Transaction IE02 (Change Equipment) (see Figure 3.51), classify the material using Transaction MM02 (Change Material Master), or classify functional locations using Transaction IL02 (Change Functional Location).

Figure 3.51 Transaction IE02 Equipment: Classification

Setting a Standard Class

When assigning a class to a functional location or a piece of equipment, always select the checkbox for the standard class, which is the only way to ensure that the class-related object statistics of the plant maintenance information system (PMIS) are updated. For more information about PMIS, see Chapter 8, Section 8.2.3.

Whenever necessary, SAP S/4HANA provides you with search functions that allow you to find objects with certain technical characteristics again. The following usage scenarios are typical for search functions:

- You require a list of all pumps that cross certain performance boundaries.
- An engine has failed, and you require an equivalent replacement.
- A spare part on the technical system is defective, but the original spare part is no longer in storage, so you look for an alternative.
- Since the delivery procedure from the warehouse is to be changed, you require a list containing the maximum payload of all of your industrial trucks.

You can use the following transactions for the search functions:

- Transaction CL30N (Find Objects in Classes), which enables you to find objects within a class according to characteristic restrictions
- Transaction CL6BN (Object List), which enables you to create a complete object list for a class
- Transactions IE05 (Equipment List Change) and IH08 (Equipment List Display), which enable you to create a list of equipment with organizational (for example, cost center, plant) and technical restrictions (a class with characteristic value assignments) (see Figure 3.52)

S	Equipment	Object Description	Valid To	PlPl	Construction Year	Drive type	Engine power	LSP	Lifting height	Lifting load	Manufacturer	Mast	Type	steering kart
	10001002	Gabelstapler Linde 4,5 to	12-31-9999	HD00	2009	1	125 KW	300	2.80 m	7.50 t	LINDE		TRIPLEX ETV-A 32	MANUALLY
	10001114	Gabelstapler Linde 4,5 to	12-31-9999	HD00	2009	1	125 KW	300	2.80 m	7.50 t	LINDE		TRIPLEX ETV-A 32	MANUALLY
	10001115	Gabelstapler Linde 4,5 to	12-31-9999	HD00	2009	1	125 KW	300	2.80 m	7.50 t	LINDE		TRIPLEX ETV-A 32	MANUALLY
	10001116	Gabelstapler Linde 4,5 to	12-31-9999	HD00	2009	1	125 KW	300	2.80 m	7.50 t	LINDE		TRIPLEX ETV-A 32	MANUALLY
	10001117	Gabelstapler Linde 4,5 to	12-31-9999	HD00	2009	1	125 KW	300	2.80 m	7.50 t	LINDE		TRIPLEX ETV-A 32	MANUALLY
	10001118	Gabelstapler Linde 4,5 to	12-31-9999	HD00	2009	1	125 KW	300	2.80 m	7.50 t	LINDE		TRIPLEX ETV-A 32	MANUALLY
	10001119	Gabelstapler Linde 4,5 to	12-31-9999	HD00	2009	1	125 KW	300	2.80 m	7.50 t	LINDE		TRIPLEX ETV-A 32	MANUALLY
	10001120	Gabelstapler Linde 4,5 to	12-31-9999	HD00	2009	1	125 KW	300	2.80 m	7.50 t	LINDE		TRIPLEX ETV-A 32	MANUALLY
	10001121	Gabelstapler Linde 4,5 to	12-31-9999	HD00	2009	1	125 KW	300	2.80 m	7.50 t	LINDE		TRIPLEX ETV-A 32	MANUALLY
	10001122	Gabelstapler Linde 4,5 to	12-31-9999	HD00	2009	1	125 KW	300	2.80 m	7.50 t	LINDE		TRIPLEX ETV-A 32	MANUALLY
	10001123	Gabelstapler Linde 4,5 to	12-31-9999	HD00	2009	1	125 KW	300	2.80 m	7.50 t	LINDE		TRIPLEX ETV-A 32	MANUALLY
	10001189	Fork Lifter Linde 4,5 to	12-31-9999	HD00	2009	1	125 KW	300	2.80 m	7.50 t	LINDE		TRIPLEX ETV-A 32	MANUALLY
	10001190	Fork Lifter Combilift 4to	12-31-9999	DL00	2018	1	55 KW	400	2.50 m	5.50 t	CATERPILLAR	FRONT	906M	MIDDLE

Figure 3.52 Transaction IE05: Equipment List with Characteristics

- Transactions IL05 (Functional Location List Change) and IH06 (Functional Location List Display), which enable you to create the same list for functional locations
- Transaction IQ08 (Serial Number List Change), which enables you to create the same list for serial numbers
- Transaction IE20 (Replace Equipment), which enables you to find a replacement piece of equipment with the same properties as the original piece of equipment

3.9   Product Structure Browser

This section introduces you to a function that is often unknown, even among experienced users: Transaction CC04 (Product Structure Browser). The product structure browser is a general tool from the product data management area in logistics that enables you to set up, manage, and display complex product structures. Since the product structure browser enables you to manage not only functional locations and pieces of equipment, but practically all logistics objects (documents, BOMs, maintenance task lists, classifications, and so on), you can use the browser not only in plant maintenance but also in engineering/design, production, and so on.

From a maintenance perspective, the product structure browser (see Figure 3.53) is similar to the display format for the structural display (Transactions IH01 and IH03).

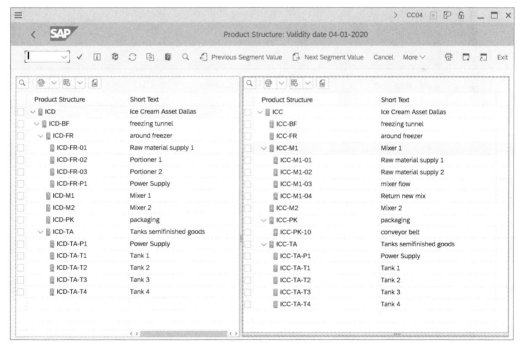

Figure 3.53 Transaction CC04 (Product Structure Browser)

However, some considerable differences exist between the two display formats. The advantages of the product structure browser compared to the structural display are as follows:

- You can use drag and drop to move technical objects (for example, install a piece of equipment on another functional location).
- You can create new technical objects or implement existing technical objects in the structure.
- You can change existing objects in the structure (for example, renumber a functional location).
- You can display functional locations, pieces of equipment, and BOMs as well as documents, classes, and characteristics.
- You can change the status of technical objects (flag for deletion, inactive/active flag).
- You can generate a workflow task for a technical object and send technical objects.

[+] **Using the Product Structure Browser**

The product structure browser is a suitable resource for displaying and changing object structures. However, note that the changes are immediately posted to the database.

3.10 Asset Viewer

With the Asset Viewer, SAP Business Client provides a similar function as the structural display or product structure browser (see Figure 3.54). The Asset Viewer enables you to display information in addition to the mere structure of the technical systems, for example:

- Whether document links exist
- What notifications exist
- What orders exist
- What maintenance task lists, maintenance items, and maintenance plans were created
- What classes and characteristics are defined
- Whether measuring points and counters exist

From the Asset Viewer, you can interactively execute specific functions for a technical object:

- You can create a notification or an order.
- You can display information about the object.
- You can install, dismantle, or modify a piece of equipment.

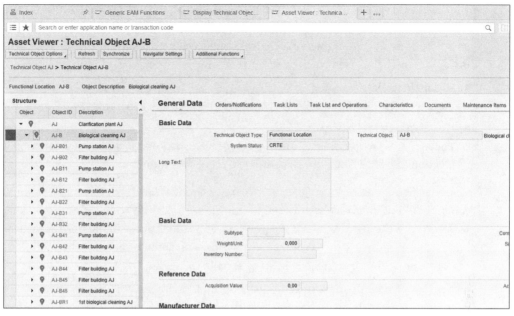

Figure 3.54 Asset Viewer

To use the Asset Viewer comprehensively, you must activate the business functions LOG_EAM_SIMP and LOG_EAM_SIMPLICITY*.

> **Useful Additional Information in the Asset Viewer in SAP Business Client**
> You can use the Asset Viewer in SAP Business Client to view not only the asset structure, but also any additional information (for example, maintenance plans, orders, and so on). From the Asset Viewer, you can also create new master data (for example, maintenance task lists or maintenance plans) and new transaction data (for example, notifications and orders).

3.11 Generic Functions

This section will introduce some additional functions available to you when you're working with technical objects. Let's start with data transfer and then move on to mass changes, measuring points, documents, address management, warranties, partners, permits, and statuses.

3.11.1 Data Transfers

Data is automatically transferred within structures or across objects. If you use reference functional locations, functional locations, and pieces of equipment to structure your technical systems, the hierarchical structures that you create frequently have the same master record data. For easier, more straightforward maintenance when creating structures, and during engineering change management, you have the option of using the data transfer function with which you can execute the following actions:

- **Hierarchical data transfer**
  Transfer data in superior objects to lower-level objects in a hierarchy.

- **Horizontal data transfer**
  Transfer data across objects (from a reference functional location to a functional location or from a functional location to a piece of equipment).

If you change data within an object structure (reference functional location structure, functional location structure, or equipment hierarchy), this change is automatically transferred to the lower-level objects (see Figure 3.55). In the case of the horizontal data transfer (see Figure 3.56), the data is automatically transferred between two different object types. In this case, you have two options in turn:

- You can change the data in the reference functional locations. These changes are then automatically transferred to all functional locations derived from these reference functional locations.

- You can change data in functional locations on which pieces of equipment have been installed. The data changes are then automatically transferred to the pieces of equipment.

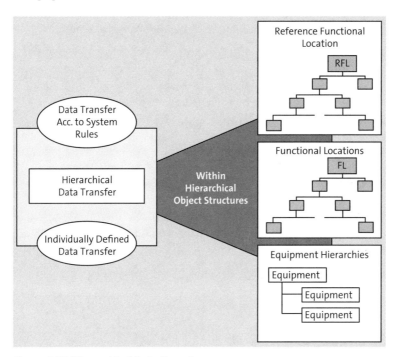

Figure 3.55 Hierarchical Data Transfer

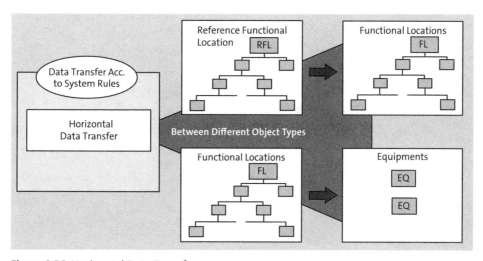

Figure 3.56 Horizontal Data Transfer

Paying Attention to Data Origin Indicators

By structuring the functional locations and pieces of equipment in an intelligent manner, you can avoid extensive data maintenance, for example, if cost centers or responsibilities change.

Each field of a technical object has an indicator (see Figure 3.57) to show whether this field references its content from a superior object or from a reference functional location or whether the field is individually maintained.

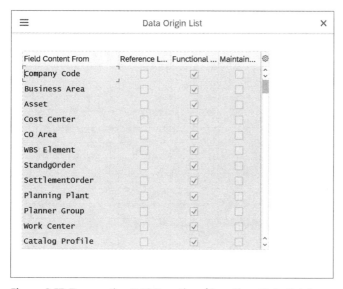

Figure 3.57 Transaction IL03 Functional Location: Data Origin

[+]

Changing Data Origin

In the case of a hierarchical data transfer, you can manually change the indicator for each field at any time. In the case of a horizontal data transfer, you can only determine this indicator when the data is transferred, that is, only when the equipment is installed at the functional location.

[+]

Data Origin and Individual Maintenance

If you manually maintain a field once at a lower level, this field is assigned the **Individual Maintenance** indicator. Consequently, if data is changed at a higher level, the object itself and its lower-level objects remain unchanged.

3.11.2   Mass Change of Pieces of Equipment and Functional Locations

In addition to data transfer, you can also change specific field contents in a targeted manner in several pieces of equipment or functional locations. To do this, use the relevant list change transaction, such as Transaction IE05 or Transaction IL05, and select the master records that you want to change. To access the mass change function itself, choose **More · Goto · Perform Mass Change**. A dialog box opens, where you can enter the fields to be changed and the new field contents (see Figure 3.58).

If you select the **Execute** or **Execute in the Background** option, the field contents are changed in all of the objects you selected. In order for this function to work, the inheritance indicator must be set to **Individually maintained**. Conversely, as a result, an inheritance indicator set correctly to **Superior Functional Location** or **Superior Equipment** has precedence over the mass change function.

Unfortunately, not all fields can be changed using the mass change function. Fields such as **Authorization Group**, **Cost Center**, and **Operational Area** can be changed, while the **Technical Identification Number**, **Sort**, and **Construction Type** fields cannot.

[!]

Prerequisite

The LOG_EAM_SIMP business function must be activated in order for you to use the mass change function to change functional locations and equipment.

[+]

Mass Processing of Equipment and Functional Locations

The mass processing function enables quick and easy changes to the field contents of several technical objects at the same time. Note, however, that hierarchically inherited field contents are not changed and that this function cannot be used for all fields.

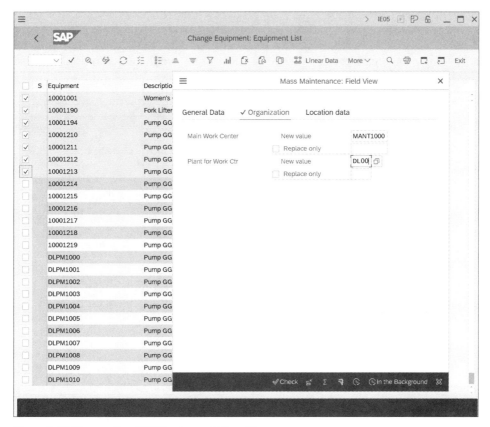

Figure 3.58 Transaction IE05 Equipment Mass Change

3.11.3 Measuring Points and Counters

Three scenarios exist where recording measurement documents and counter readings makes sense:

- **State of a technical object**
  Here, the aim is to document the state of a technical object at any given time, which is important if detailed evidence of the correct state of a technical object must be provided by law. This evidence may include critical values recorded for environmental protection purposes, hazardous working areas that are monitored for industrial hygiene and safety reasons, and the condition of equipment in clinics as well as measurements of emissions and pollution for objects of all types.

- **Performance-based maintenance**
  In the case of counter-based maintenance, maintenance activities are always performed if the counter of the technical object has reached a particular counter reading. (For more information on this topic, see Chapter 5, Section 5.5 and Section 5.6.)

- **Condition-based maintenance**
  In the case of condition-based maintenance, maintenance activities are always

performed if one of the measuring points of a technical object exceeds or falls below a threshold value. (For more information on this topic, see Chapter 5, Section 5.8.)

Measuring points mark those locations at which the current condition of a technical system is described, for example:

- Temperature
- Rotation speed pressure
- Level of contamination
- Viscosity

At individual measuring points, you can specify target values as well as upper and/or lower limits. Figure 3.59 shows a measuring point for a location where the operating temperature is measured.

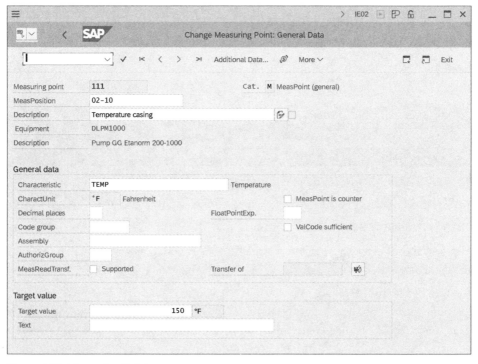

Figure 3.59 Measuring Point

If a measuring point is involved to which a linear object is assigned, the linear data also appears (see Figure 3.60).

At measuring points, *measurement documents* are recorded that contain discontinuous values, for example, an internal engine temperature of 150°F is recorded in a measurement document at 10:25, a temperature of 155°F is recorded at 11:05, a temperature of 145°F is recorded at 12:10, and so on.

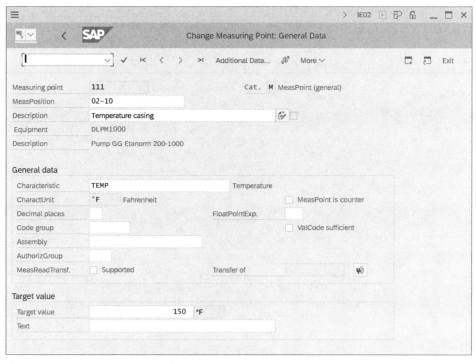

Figure 3.60 Measuring Point with Linear Data

Measuring points are always in technical objects, that is, in pieces of equipment or functional locations. Figure 3.61 shows measurement readings fluctuating over time.

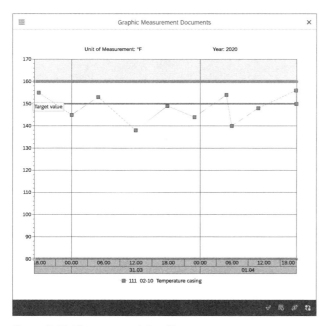

Figure 3.61 Measurement Readings

Counters mark those locations in the SAP system where you can represent object wear, consumption, or reduction of a working supply, for example, a kilometer counter, an operating hours counter, the number of pieces, a quantity produced in tons, and so on. Figure 3.62 shows you a counter for measuring operating hours.

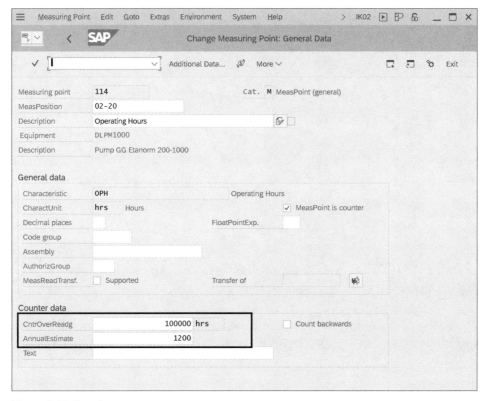

Figure 3.62 Counter

The following two values are particularly important when counters are used for performance-based maintenance:

- **Counter overflow reading**
  The counter overflow reading in the **CntrOverReadg** field is the first value that a counter cannot display. For example, in the case of a five-digit counter, this value would be 100,000.

- **Annual estimate**
  The system uses the annual estimate in the field **Annual Estimate** to forecast the next maintenance date based on the current counter reading.

Detailed explanations are provided in Chapter 5, Section 5.5.

Counter readings are recorded for counters. These readings contain values that continuously rise or continuously fall. For example, in the case of a forklift truck, 1,250 operating hours were recorded on January 20, 1,274 operating hours were recorded on January 25, and 1,295 operating hours were recorded on February 1. Counters are always in technical objects, that is, in pieces of equipment or functional locations. Figure 3.63 shows an example of counter reading development over time.

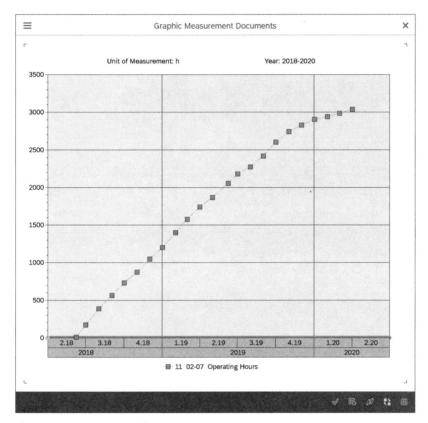

Figure 3.63 Counter Readings

You can also transfer measurement documents from one measuring point to another measuring point. Both measuring points can be in the same technical system hierarchy (functional location structure, installed equipment), but they do not have to be. You can also establish a separate measuring point hierarchy. Figure 3.64 shows you a measurement documents transfer oriented toward a functional location structure.

If the measurement document concerns measurement readings, the absolute readings are transferred. If the measurement document concerns counter readings, however, the differences between the counter readings are transferred.

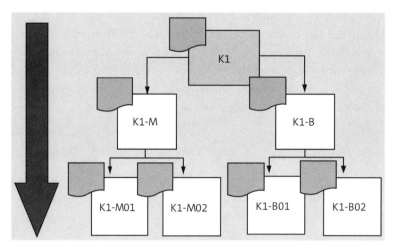

Figure 3.64 Measurement Documents Transfer

Using Counters and Measuring Points

Both the counter definition and regular recording of counter readings form the basis of performance-based, preventive maintenance.

Both the measuring point definition and regular recording of measurement readings form the basis of condition-based maintenance.

3.11.4 Documents

In your company, you may want to link the technical objects to documents, for example:

- Design drawings
- Work instructions
- Checklists
- Images
- Inspection instructions
- Exploded drawings
- Measuring and control technology profiles
- 3-D models

In Figure 3.65, for example, you can view a 3D model.

When linking objects to documents, you have two options: via document master records or via object links, each of which the following sections will discuss.

Figure 3.65 3D Model

Document Master Records

You can manage your drawings in the SAP system as document master records (Transactions CV01N through CV04N). You can then establish a link to the original in the document master record. To enable assigning the document to a technical object, you must embed the **Linked Documents** screen group (see Figure 3.66) or establish the link in the document master record using the view profile (customizing function **Set View Profiles for Technical Objects**), which you assigned to your functional location category or equipment category.

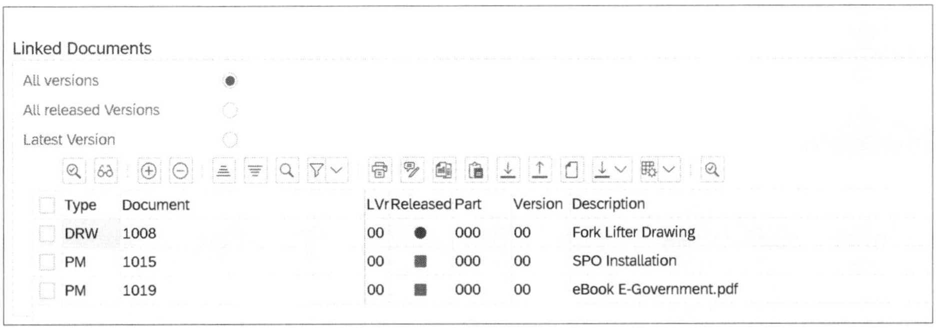

Linked Documents

All versions ●
All released Versions ○
Latest Version ○

	Type	Document	LVr	Released	Part	Version	Description
☐	DRW	1008	00	●	000	00	Fork Lifter Drawing
☐	PM	1015	00	■	000	00	SPO Installation
☐	PM	1019	00	■	000	00	eBook E-Government.pdf

Figure 3.66 Links to Document Master Records

It is now very easy to add a new document and have a document master record automatically created in the background. Use the function key ⬚ to create a new document. A window opens in which you can enter a description for the document to be added (see Figure 3.67).

Then Windows Explorer opens, and you select the original document (see Figure 3.68).

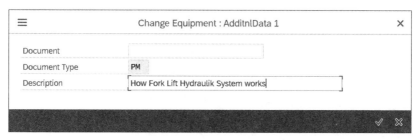

Figure 3.67 Description of a New Document

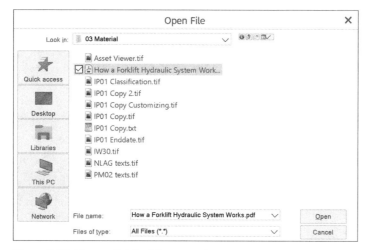

Figure 3.68 Choose Original Document

If more than one vault is available for the original document, a window for selecting the vault appears in which the original document is to be stored (see Figure 3.69).

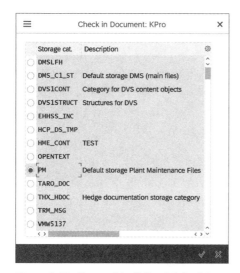

Figure 3.69 Choose Vault for Original Document

As a result, the system creates a new document master record and assigns it to the equipment (see Figure 3.70).

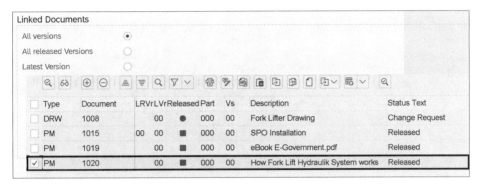

Figure 3.70 New Document Assigned

If you work with document master records, you can assign the same document to several technical objects, or a technical object can have several document links.

Object Service Attachment

In addition to the document master records, you can also use object services to assign documents to your technical objects. You can access object services under **More · System · Services for Object** or by clicking the ▣∨ button (**Object Services**). Then choose ▯∨ (**Create · Attachment**) in the toolbar displayed (Figure 3.71).

Figure 3.71 Object Service Toolbar

You can now define the following information as attachments:

- PC files such as PDF documents, images, or Office files
- Internal notes
- External URL addresses

An attachment list will be generated (see Figure 3.72) from which you can call the original documents again at any time.

In practice, choosing between document master records and object services can be difficult. Table 3.7 compares the most important similarities and differences.

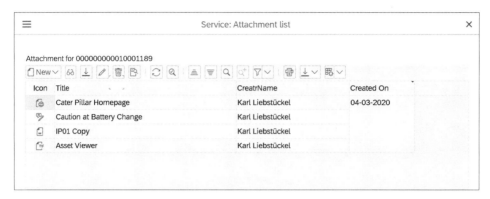

Figure 3.72 Attachment List

	Document Master Records	Object Links
Document Master	Document master records required or automatically created	No document master records required
Handling	Simple handling	Simple handling
Storage	Original document linked or copied to SAP database	Original document copied to SAP database
Linking	N:M link possible (that is, an object with several documents and a document to several objects)	Only 1:M link possible (that is, an object with several documents, but not a document to several objects)
Find	Several transactions for searching documents and objects (e.g., Transactions IE05, IL05, and CV04N)	Difficult to find, no transaction for searching documents and assignment to objects
Authorization	Several authorization objects (e.g., document type, status, and activity)	No authorization objects (everyone can create, delete, etc.)

Table 3.7 Differences between Document Master Records and Object Services

[+]

Document Master Record or Object Service?

When asked whether you should use document master records or object services, I have a clear recommendation: use document master records. The authorization concept, the possibility of multiple assignment, and the search options speak for this. The argument that used to speak for object services is also obsolete: now it is as easy to add a document with an automatically generated document master record as an object service.

3.11.5 Address Management

The SAP system deploys uniform address management, which also integrates the objects in plant maintenance (see Figure 3.73):

- Functional locations
- Equipment
- Notifications
- Orders
- Purchase requisitions for non-stock materials

If you define an address in a technical object, this address is then transferred to the notification. The address is also transferred to the order; here, you can then choose to define a separate order address if this differs from the object address. You can use the customizing function **Define Access Sequence for Determining Address Data** to define which of these addresses is to be used as the ship-to address for non-stock materials (NLAG in Figure 3.73); you can also define a separate ship-to address for each item.

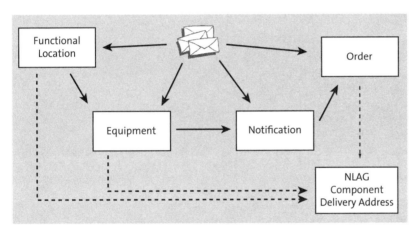

Figure 3.73 Central Address Management

Figure 3.74 shows a window in which an address has been maintained for a functional location.

Using Address Management

If you deploy typical plant maintenance and the postal addresses of the objects are identical to the plant address, you do not have to define any object addresses.

However, if your objects are spread across and throughout regions (for example, electric utilities, water utilities, gas utilities, telecommunications, infrastructure), we recommend that you transfer the address information to the relevant technicians and external companies.

Figure 3.74 Address of a Technical Object

3.11.6   Warranties

A warranty is a commitment from a manufacturer, vendor, or salesperson to a customer that services are guaranteed for a particular period of time, without the customer being billed. A warranty always refers to a technical object (functional location, equipment, or serial number). You can cover the following warranties (see Figure 3.75):

- Manufacturer and vendor warranty (warrantee, inbound)
- Customer warranty (warrantor, outbound)

[+]   **Do You Require Only a Vendor Warranty?**

If you yourself are not a warrantor and thus require only a vendor warranty, which is mostly the case in maintenance, you can hide the customer warranty by deleting the entry **Warranty Type 1 = Customer Warranty** in the customizing function **Change Warranty Types**.

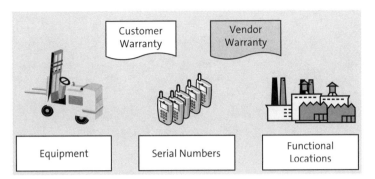

Figure 3.75 Warranties

To manage warranties for a technical object, you must assign the **Warranties** screen group in the view profile (customizing function **Set View Profiles for Technical Objects**).

Warranties are usually time dependent (see Figure 3.76). The **Check Status** indicator shows that a warranty claim exists.

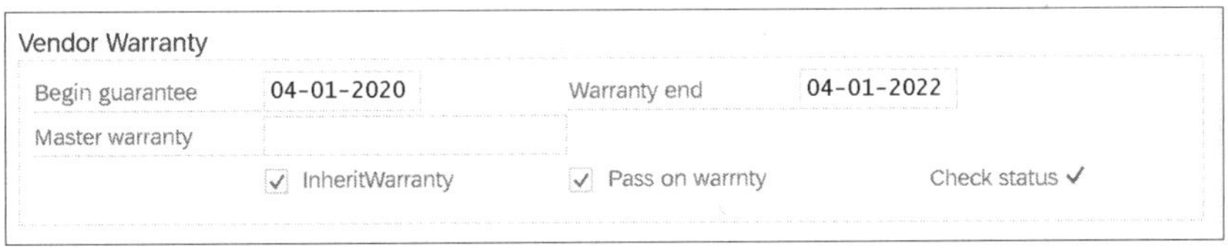

Vendor Warranty			
Begin guarantee	04-01-2020	Warranty end	04-01-2022
Master warranty			
	✓ InheritWarranty	✓ Pass on warrnty	Check status ✓

Figure 3.76 Time-Dependent Warranty

Your warranty may also depend on a certain level of performance (for example, mls, hours of operation). Time-dependent and performance-dependent warranty counters can be defined in master warranties, which you maintain using Transactions BGM1 through BGM3 (Maintain Warranties) (see Figure 3.77).

Time-dependent and performance-based warranty counters differ as follows:

- **Time-dependent warranty counters**
  For a time-dependent warranty counter, you must create a characteristic in the class system that has a unit of the *time* dimension. The system can use the warranty start date to determine whether the counter is still valid on the key date of the check.

- **Performance-based warranty counters**
  When using a performance-based warranty counter, the relevant technical object must have a counter (for example, kilometer counter, operating hours counter). Furthermore, the counter reading must have been recorded for this counter at the start of the warranty.

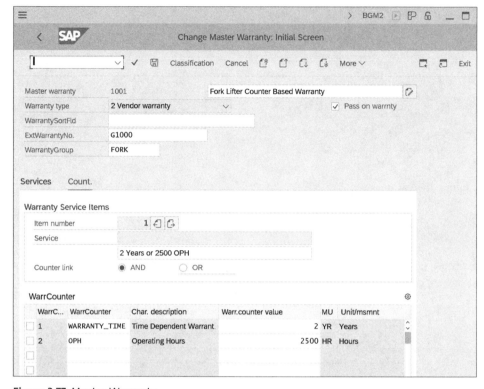

Figure 3.77 Master Warranty

Figure 3.78 shows you a vendor warranty that has been defined for a technical object; this vendor warranty references a master warranty. The **Check Status** indicator shows that a warranty claim no longer exists.

Figure 3.78 Counter-Dependent Warranty

[+]   **Warranties for Technical Objects**

You can define a warranty for a technical object and perform a warranty check based on the defined warranty. You can use the warranty check to determine whether the technical object is still under warranty. Furthermore, warranty inheritance enables you to view the warranty data of the superior technical object.

3.11.7 Partners

SAP S/4HANA Asset Management knows by default only a few organizational objects that you can assign to a technical object. Essentially, these organization objects are the maintenance planner group and the main work center.

By defining partners, you can considerably expand these competencies and responsibilities and specify them in greater detail. You can assign any number of partners to a technical object. A partner (business partner) is either an internal or external organizational unit, as follows:

- **Internal partners**
  Internal partners can be, for example, departments, cost centers, or persons who are involved in processing maintenance tasks.

- **External partners**
  External partners can be, for example, vendors, manufacturers, or service providers that play an important role for a technical object.

A partner can be an individual or a legal entity.

You must be able to distinguish between the following terms (see Figure 3.79):

- **Partner type**
  Partner types are predefined by SAP and always contain a database table (customer, contact person, vendor, user, personnel number, organizational unit, and position).

Partner Type	Predefined e.g., LF = Vendor Master Record
Partner Function	Freely Definable e.g., HS = Vendor AL = System Supplier SV = Service Provider
Partner Determination Procedure	Freely Definable e.g., HS Mandatory AL Mandatory SV Optional
Technical Object	HS: 4711 Stevens Inc. AL: 6576 Smith & Associates SV: 4812 Miller Systems Inc. SV: 4813 Johnson Services

Figure 3.79 Partner Management

- **Partner function**

  You can freely define partner functions with reference to a partner type in customizing (**Define Partner Determination Procedure and Partner Function**). For example, you can define partner functions such as the manufacturer, plant vendor, and service provider and refer all functions to the Vendor database table.

- **Partner determination procedure**

  You can freely define a partner determination procedure, which is a grouping of partner functions that specifies which partner functions are permitted or must always be specified. For example, you can determine that the manufacturer and vendor must always be specified for a piece of equipment, but also that the service provider is an optional specification.

To make this assignment to a technical object, use the customizing functions **Assign Partner Determination Procedure to Equipment Category** or **Define Category of Functional Locations**.

Figure 3.80 shows you potential functions that can be assigned to a technical object.

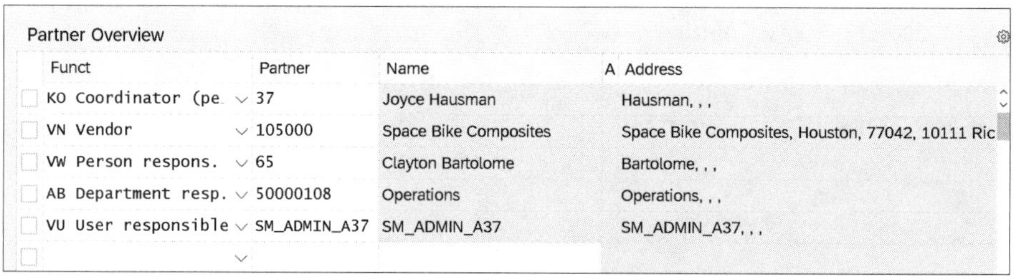

Partner Overview				⚙
Funct	Partner	Name	A Address	
☐ KO Coordinator (pe. ∨	37	Joyce Hausman	Hausman, , ,	^
☐ VN Vendor ∨	105000	Space Bike Composites	Space Bike Composites, Houston, 77042, 10111 Ric	
☐ VW Person respons. ∨	65	Clayton Bartolome	Bartolome, , ,	
☐ AB Department resp. ∨	50000108	Operations	Operations, , ,	
☐ VU User responsible ∨	SM_ADMIN_A37	SM_ADMIN_A37	SM_ADMIN_A37, , ,	
☐	∨			

Figure 3.80 Technical Object: Partner Overview

3.11.8   Permits

For some technical objects, certain regulations or conditions must be taken into account when using them or when performing maintenance work. You can define these regulations for a technical object as permits. Important permits in plant maintenance include:

- Fire permits
- Notifications of environmental protection
- Welding permits
- Drivers' licenses
- Fire protection permits
- Vat access permits
- Activation authorizations
- Technical inspection certificates
- Explosion protection zones

To define permits, use Transaction IPMD and then assign the technical object via **More ·
Goto · Permits** (see Figure 3.81).

Figure 3.81 Technical Object: Assigning Permits

When you assign permits for the technical objects, you also define whether an order is
to be placed, must be placed, or must not be placed when an order is released (**OR** column) or when an order is technically complete (**OC** column).

Furthermore, you can define whether the relevant approval is to be printed on the
order paper (**Print** column) and whether the permit is to be transferred to the processing data (for example, an order or notification) (**Proposal** column).

Permits as Approvals

You can use permits to determine that an order is not released or technically complete
until authorized users have added their electronic signatures.

3.11.9 System Status and User Status

The technical objects and the complete processing with notification and order are
linked to SAP's general status management. Here, you have to distinguish between the
system status and the *user status*.

For certain business processes, the system sets the system statuses internally and automatically as part of its general status management. Typical system statuses for technical objects include:

- CRTE: created
- AVLB: available
- INAC: inactive
- DLFL: deletion flag set
- EFRE: equipment free (not installed)
- INST: equipment installed
- ASEQ: equipment in hierarchy
- ESTO: placed in storage

The business processes that you can execute for each of these object statuses is also defined in status management. If, for example, you set a piece of equipment to inactive, then you inform the business processes which of them are still permitted (green traffic light), which will trigger a warning message (yellow traffic light), and which are prohibited (red traffic light) (see Figure 3.82).

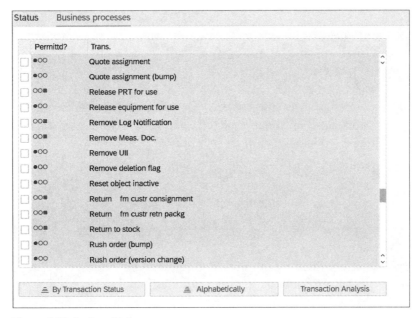

Figure 3.82 System Status

Since you cannot change the system statuses directly (they are automatically set by the system), you can only display them.

In addition to the predefined system status, you can freely define user statuses that fulfill your requirements. To assign a user status to a technical object, you must fulfill the following requirements:

- You have defined a status profile with the necessary status.
- You have assigned the status profile to the equipment category or the functional location category.

To define a status profile with the necessary status, you use the customizing function **Define User Status**. You can define any number of statuses within the status profile (see Figure 3.83).

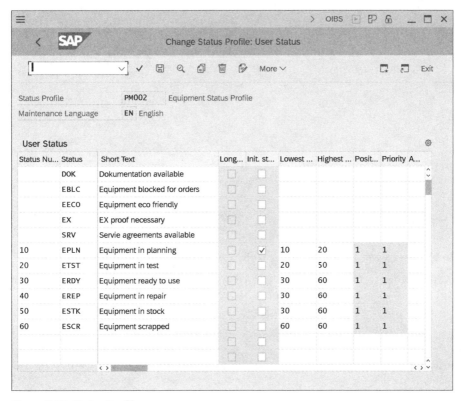

Figure 3.83 Status Profile

To assign your status profile to an equipment category or functional location category, you use the customizing function **Assign User Status Profile to Equipment Category** or **Define Category for Functional Locations**.

Using the User Status Efficiently

You can use the user status to control, in detail, which business processes should be permitted or prohibited for your technical objects.

[+]

If these prerequisites are fulfilled, click the 🛈 button to navigate to the status within the technical objects and set the status you require (see Figure 3.84).

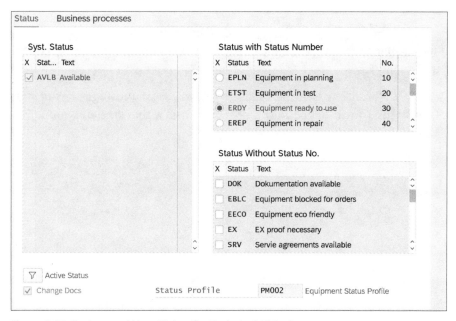

Figure 3.84 System and User Status for Technical Object

If several system statuses and user statuses exist, the following sequence generally applies with regard to determining which business processes are permitted:

- If only one status prohibits a business process, then the process is prohibited.
- If none of the statuses prohibits the business process, but at least one permits it while issuing a warning message, then the process is permitted with a warning message.
- The business process is permitted only if all of the statuses permit it.

You can check this using the **Transaction Analysis** button on the **Business Processes** tab (see Figure 3.85).

[+]
Automating Status Assignment
You can set up the user status in customizing in such a way that it is automatically set or deleted when the system status is changed. In this way, you can further restrict the permitted business transactions of a system status in a clever way, without the user having to carry out additional data maintenance.

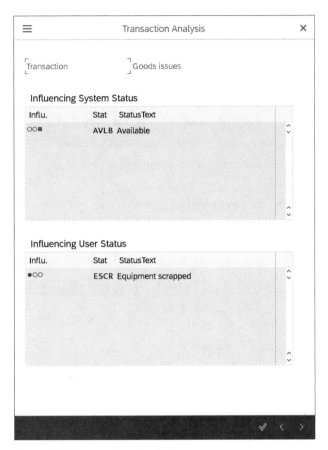

Figure 3.85 Transaction Analysis

3.12   Summary

SAP S/4HANA Asset Management provides a broad range of potential structuring elements. In this chapter you learned about their most important functions and how to use them.

But before you map your technical systems to SAP, you should ask yourself some questions and answer them to the best of your current knowledge (e.g., which resources should be used or how deep to structure technical assets).

The most important technical objects are without any doubt functional locations and equipment. You have learned the differences between these two elements:

- Functional locations represent a complex, generally multilevel structure for technical systems, where you create each element of the technical system structure as a functional location. Therefore, functional locations are used to establish a vertical asset structure. Functional locations usually represent immovable, functional units.

- Equipment represents movable, individual, and physical inventories. Examples include machines, pumps, engines, production resources/tools, fleet objects and IT inventories. Some of them are used to be installed at a functional location.

In this chapter you learned about the functions of other structuring elements as well and how to use them:

- Reference functional locations as templates for generating "real" functional location structures or for subsequently passing on data to "real" functional locations
- Equipment hierarchies as an entire equipment group comprised of several pieces of equipment
- Object links between different technical objects (pieces of equipment or functional locations), though they are used for information and visualization purposes only
- Linear assets for technical systems with a linear infrastructure, whose properties and conditions can change from section to section (dynamic segmentation)
- Materials for spare parts, non-stock materials, or PM assemblies that are suitable for storage
- Serial numbers for storing equipment in stock
- BOMs for assigning spare parts to a technical object or material

In SAP S/4HANA Asset Management, some functions are used in several locations or for several objects. Therefore, they have a generic character. These functions are:

- Classification for defining technical characteristics for technical objects
- Product structure browser for changing technical structures in a graphical way
- Asset viewer for viewing technical structures with additional information
- Data transfer (hierarchical and horizontal)
- Mass change for equipment, serial numbers, and functional locations
- Measuring points for condition-based maintenance and counters for performance-based maintenance
- Documents as document master record or as object service
- Address management for technical objects and processing objects
- Warranties (time-dependent and counter-dependent)
- Partners for assigning partners with different roles to technical objects
- Permits for assigning technical or business requirements to technical objects
- Status management with system and user status

In this chapter you learned how to use these generic functions—mostly explained on the basis of only one object as an example, but the example represents other objects as well.

Chapter 4

Work Order Cycle

This chapter represents the heart of this book. The SAP system holds a large toolbox for the purpose of custom-tailoring it to individual enterprise-specific needs. This chapter highlights the options and limitations of the system for the work order cycle. Valuable recommendations on how to make best use of the system are completed with suggestions on what kind of preparations you'll have to consider before getting started.

After having already seen many companies from the inside, I can, in good conscience, state that each company has its own idea about what the work order cycle in plant maintenance should be like and how it must be mapped in the SAP system. As a result, you—like all other user companies before you—will have to consider how you can map your day-to-day activities in SAP S/4HANA Asset Management and how SAP should support you in accomplishing tasks. No book on Earth can do this work for you; however, I believe that you'll find this chapter quite helpful. Chapter 6 and Chapter 7, being based on this chapter, will show more business processes for your day-to-day business.

The next section gives you a few tips about what you should do before you map the work order cycle in SAP S/4HANA Asset Management. Once you've walked through those questions, this chapter moves on to the key elements of the work order cycle: notification, planning, controlling, processing, and completion.

4.1 Actions to be Taken before Mapping the Work Order Cycle in SAP S/4HANA

Similar to the structuring of technical systems, the following principle should also apply in your search for all answers for business processes: "as much as is necessary, but as little as possible."

You'll quickly notice that SAP S/4HANA Asset Management offers a great number of functions that you can use. Find out what your business and technical requirements are and look for the easiest way to map these requirements in SAP S/4HANA Asset Management. In this chapter, I'll show you numerous examples of how you can implement this principle.

Gaps: Omitting What Is Unnecessary

The full functionality of SAP S/4HANA Asset Management does not have to be, and should not be, implemented all at once.

Let's now look at the questions you should ask yourself before mapping the work order cycle in SAP S/4HANA.

4.1.1   Question 1: Which Functions Should You Use?

Appendix B, Section B.2 includes an overview of SAP S/4HANA Asset Management functions that you can use to process your work order cycle. Later, this chapter will discuss in detail what the keywords specifically mean. Section B.2 includes a table with three columns to indicate priority. Assess the relevant functions according to their significance in your company and decide for yourself.

Prioritizing Functions

In principle, you should provide users with solutions where they are needed the most. We recommend a three-tier prioritization:

- Priority A: absolutely necessary, must be implemented immediately in the first expansion phase
- Priority B: could have additional benefits, could be implemented in a subsequent expansion phase
- Priority C: will not be necessary according to present knowledge, and therefore not introduced.

First, deal with the functions with priority A. Remove the functions with priority C from the list and banish them from your thoughts.

4.1.2   Question 2: Should You Use a Notification and/or an Order?

You can and must decide which of the following objects you want to use to support your business processes:

- Only the notification
- Only the order
- Both the notification and the order

The answer to this question generally depends on the functions and information that the individual objects have to offer and how important these functions are to you.

Notification

What are the basic differences between a notification and an order?

- **Purpose**

  A notification is used to request and document a maintenance activity, whereas an order is used to plan and implement a maintenance task.

- **Information contained**

  A notification therefore mainly contains technical information, while an order essentially contains processing information.

- **Integration points**

  A notification has practically no integration points with other SAP applications and therefore does not contain information about any costs, whereas the order, as a highly integrated object, has many links to other areas of SAP S/4HANA, such as warehouse management, purchasing, and controlling.

This quite different orientation is reflected in the different functions (see Appendix B, Section B.2) and the different information contained in both objects.

A notification has the following characteristics:

- **Header data**

  Each notification has header data that includes information used to identify and manage the notification, such as technical object or responsible work center. The header data applies to the complete notification.

- **Notification item**

  You enter and maintain the data in a notification item for the purpose of identifying in more detail the problem or damage that occurred or the data for the executed action. A notification can have several items. However, most notifications in practice only consist of one item, which is created automatically when you record a damage code or a cause of the damage.

- **Actions**

  Actions document the work performed for a notification and are particularly important in inspections to provide evidence of the work performed and the results established (e.g., oil level checked or noise level checked). Actions can relate either to the header or to an item of the notification.

- **Tasks**

  Task data describes activities that still have to be performed and may only have resulted from implementing the maintenance activity (i.e., creating a report or changing a maintenance plan). Tasks can relate either to the header or to an item of the notification.

Figure 4.1 shows an overview of the structure of a notification with the relevant information.

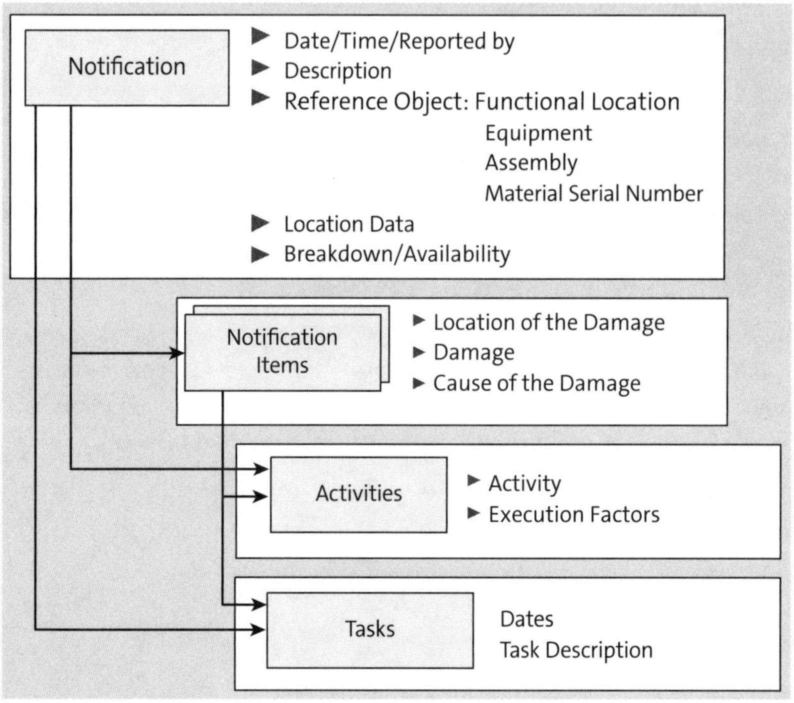

Figure 4.1 Notification: Structure and Content

Order

The order has a different structure from the notification:

- **Header data**
  Header data is information that is used to identify and manage the order; this data applies to the complete order, such as technical object or responsible work center.

- **Object list**
  If the order involves several objects (for example, for an inspection round), you can enter these objects in the object list. The object list contains all objects for which the order is executed (functional locations, equipment, assemblies, and notifications).

- **Operations**
  You can use operations to describe the work that you want to be performed when the order is being implemented (e.g., unlock system or change engine oil). Operations are carried out either by your own employees or by external companies.

- **Material list**
  The material list contains spare parts that are required and consumed when an order is being executed. These spare parts can either be stock material for which a reservation is subsequently generated or non-stock material for which a purchase requisition is created.

- **Production resources/tools**

  To execute an order, you may require production resources/tools (PRTs), for example, tools, protective clothing, and hand pallet trucks. However, unlike a material, PRTs are not consumed.

- **Settlement rule**

  In the settlement rule, you specify the cost object (for example, cost center) to which the costs must be charged. The settlement rule either applies to the complete order, or you can assign different assignments to the operations.

- **Cost data**

  Cost data informs you about how high the estimated, planned, and actual costs are in the value categories for this order, which cost elements are relevant for the order, which key figures of the plant maintenance information system are updated using the value categories, and how these key figures are updated by the actual costs of the order. You obtain cost information for individual operations and as the total for the complete order.

Figure 4.2 shows an overview of the structure of an order with the relevant information.

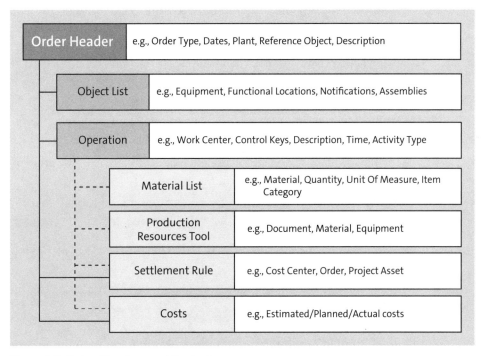

Figure 4.2 Order: Structure and Content

Deciding between an Order or a Notification

Decide as early as possible whether you want to use notifications and/or orders. If your company is like approximately 80% of all companies using SAP, you will use both notifications and orders. The rest only use orders. In some individual cases (mainly in the initial phase), companies can opt to use notifications only.

4.1.3   Question 3: Which Information Should You Store?

The third question applies to the following types of business information that you store in the system:

- Information that you absolutely must store to actually be able to process a notification or an order (for example, reference object)
- Information that you reasonably want to store in SAP S/4HANA Asset Management (for example, the cost center)

As Much as Is Necessary, but as Little as Possible

The principle "as much as is necessary, but as little as possible" must also apply to the stored information. A data graveyard, which is only created for its own sake and is of no interest to anyone, is not seen or analyzed by anyone, and only signifies time and effort in terms of entering and maintaining data, makes no sense. Thus, only enter data that is also information for you.

SAP S/4HANA Asset Management also enables you to configure notifications and orders flexibly:

- You can define the *layout* of screen templates yourself based on the notification or order type (number, sequence, name, and content of tabs).
- The *field selection* option enables you to differentiate important information from unimportant information or to hide fields that you do not require.

The LOG_EAM_SIMP business function must be activated in order for you to use a flexible screen layout for orders.

Designing Your Own Layouts

Use this option to define the appearance of notifications and orders and design your own layouts: For example, you can place the most important information on the first tab and hide unimportant fields.

You'll find the explanations about how to do this in Section 4.2 and Section 4.3.

4.1.4   Question 4: How Can You Ensure That Users Accept the System?

Although this question also applies essentially to the structuring of technical systems, the topics *user acceptance* and *usability* are much more important in relation to maintenance processing, since work is performed in these areas on a daily basis.

No one can guarantee that the system will be accepted by the users or will be considered user-friendly. However, you can increase the likelihood of user acceptance by reading Chapter 10 and implementing the suggestions made there.

4.1.5   Question 5: What Role Does Business Process Modeling Play?

Business process modeling (e.g., with BPML [Business Process Modeling Language] or EPC [event-driven process chains]) plays an important role when SAP systems are being implemented—regardless of the application. Proper analysis and documentation of the previous maintenance processes (actual analyses) and a detailed planned concept of the business processes indicating how they must subsequently be performed with the support of the SAP system are basic prerequisites for the implementation and are the basis for customizing SAP S/4HANA Asset Management.

A full and correct business process modeling is definitely worth the time and effort. You will find further information on this topic in the book *Configuring Plant Maintenance in SAP S/4HANA*, SAP PRESS, 2020, *https://www.sap-press.com/5102*.

4.1.6   Question 6: When Should You Include the Other User Departments?

You should include other user departments in the company as soon as possible. If you choose order processing, numerous questions will arise that affect the business processes and require permits. Order processing applies particularly if you want to integrate warehouse management, purchasing, and controlling. In this context, for example, you must answer the following questions:

- What information must the automatically generated purchase requisitions contain?
- Who creates the purchase order?
- Where is the acceptance of services performed entered?
- How are notifications made for goods receipts?
- Is the material delivered to or collected from the warehouse?
- Who calculates the final costing and when?
- Are the orders settled automatically?
- What does the costing sheet look like for maintenance orders?

Experience shows that such coordination processes with the relevant user departments take longer than you would initially think.

[+] **Doubling the Planned Time**

A good rule of thumb is to double the time planned for coordination with the relevant user departments. Specify the coordination process as early as possible. Specifically, define who must look after which aspect and when and who must make which decisions, and finally, check the "homework" in terms of sustainability.

We'll now look at the work order cycle in detail. Starting with this task will make it easier to describe other business processes such as breakdown maintenance or follow-up entries using abstract concepts based on this process (see Chapter 5 and Chapter 6).

The work order cycle for a planned repair task is characterized by the fact that the required resources (work centers, materials, external companies, and so on) can be planned but are only identified when the need arises. This business process occurs, for example, in the following cases:

- If the casing on a pump has to be resealed
- If the lift chain on a forklift truck has to be replaced
- If a door in a building has to be replaced
- If a pressure control valve in the process plant has to be changed
- If test equipment has to be recalibrated

The work order cycle could be performed in the following five steps (see Figure 4.3):

1. **Notification**
   In step **❶**, enter the notification of specific damage or any other request (such as a request for a modification).

2. **Planning**
   In step **❷**, the order is created and planned from the notification. Typical planning tasks include creating operations, reserving spare parts, appointing external companies, or planning operating times. The account assignment rules are also defined in this step.

3. **Controlling**
   In step **❸**, you transfer the order to controlling, where you check the corresponding availability (in particular material availability), provide the required capacities, and print out the shop papers.

4. **Execution**
   The processing phase in step **❹** involves withdrawing spare parts from the warehouse and the actual processing of the order.

5. **Completion**
   After you complete these tasks, the required actual times are confirmed as complete in step **❺**. Technical completion confirmations in relation to how the damage was

handled and the condition of the asset are also entered here. In a final step, the order is settled by controlling. The information is updated in the history.

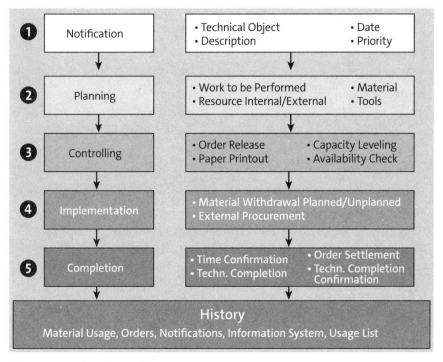

Figure 4.3 Work Order Cycle: Steps

The following sections go through these five steps, and in doing so, I'll explain the functions that SAP S/4HANA Asset Management offers.

4.2 Notification

Notifications are the maintenance processing tool that you use in exceptional operational situations to perform the following activities:

- Describe the technical emergency situation associated with an object
- Request required repair work in the maintenance department
- Document the work performed

Notifications thus document maintenance tasks and make them available for analysis in the long term. In this section, we'll first focus on entering notifications in SAP S/4HANA Asset Management itself. As part of this process, this section covers notification types and content, flexible reference objects, object information, notification items, catalogs, classification, partners, addresses, documents, printing, and statuses.

4.2.1   Creating a Notification

Notifications are either entered directly by the relevant requester (for example, a production employee) or transferred to plant maintenance using the usual means of communication (for example, by telephone or form) and entered there.

You can create notifications in the SAP system in several different ways:

- **SAP dialog transactions**
  You can use the SAP dialog transactions (Transactions IW21 [Create Maintenance Notification] and IW24 [Create Malfunction Report] through IW26 [Create Maintenance Request]), which are directly available in SAP S/4HANA Asset Management.

- **SAP Fiori app**
  You can use an SAP Fiori app provided by SAP (e.g., Request Maintenance) or developed by yourself (see Chapter 9, Section 9.1.2).

- **Your own web transactions**
  In addition, you can also develop your own Web transactions, the data of which is transferred by Business Application Programming Interfaces (BAPIs) to the SAP system (see Chapter 10, Section 10.4.2).

- **Mobile systems**
  For mobile plant maintenance, for example, you can use SAP Work Manager or SAP Asset Manager (see Chapter 9, Section 9.2.2 and Section 9.2.3), which enables you to create notifications in a decentralized manner, which are then transferred to the backend system.

- **Upstream systems**
  Procedures are used in which the notification data is created in upstream systems (such as geographic information systems [GIS], process control systems, and diagnostic systems). This data is then transferred to SAP S/4HANA Asset Management via an interface (for example, the plant maintenance-production control system [PM-PCS] interface) and the notification is created there (see Chapter 7, Section 7.3.1).

4.2.2   Notification Types

In earlier releases, SAP offered three predefined notification types in the standard system:

- **Activity report**
  For documenting performed actions

- **Malfunction report**
  For information about malfunctions and problems that occur

- **Maintenance request**
  For requesting tasks to be performed

You can now define notification types as you wish according to your own requirements. You should define the notification types based on the functions in which the notification types differ in customizing. You can define, for example, the following settings for each notification type in customizing:

- Number ranges
- Partner determination procedures
- Print controls
- Status profiles

One of the most important functions, however, is the option to define your own screen layout for each notification type. The structure displayed in Figure 4.1 containing all the data of a notification is reflected in the layout of the M1 notification type delivered by SAP (see Figure 4.4).

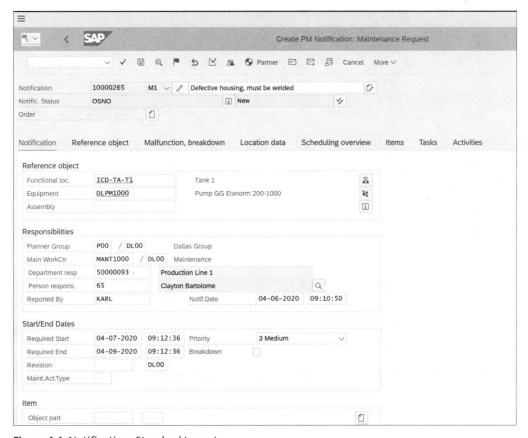

Figure 4.4 Notification: Standard Layout

This notification type consists of eight tabs, some with subtabs. Thus, for example, the **Items** tab still contains subtabs for items, causes of damage, tasks, and actions. Each tab has up to five field groups.

However, this type of screen layout would be overly complex for a production employee, for example, who merely wants to report damage.

Designing Your Own Layouts for Notifications

Design suitable screen layouts for your notification types. Adapted and simplified screen layouts increase user acceptability. Use the **Screen Structure for Extended View** or **Screen Structure for Simplified View** customizing function for this purpose.

An entry screen could look like the one configured for you as notification type M0 (see Figure 4.5).

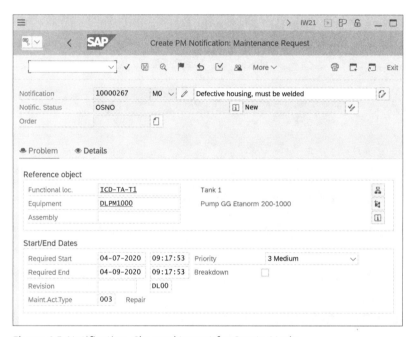

Figure 4.5 Notification: Changed Layout for Create Mode

Different Layouts for Entering and Changing

You can even set up the screen layout in such a way that a different layout appears when you change data compared to when you enter data. In this case, use the activity type for the screen structure in the customizing function.

When do you need this option? You may, for example, want to provide a production employee with a screen that is as basic as possible for entering a notification. However, if the maintenance employee subsequently calls the same notification at a later stage, he or she should be able to update the notification with additional required information.

If the same notification is called in change mode, for example, its screen could then have tabs and field groups like those shown in Figure 4.6.

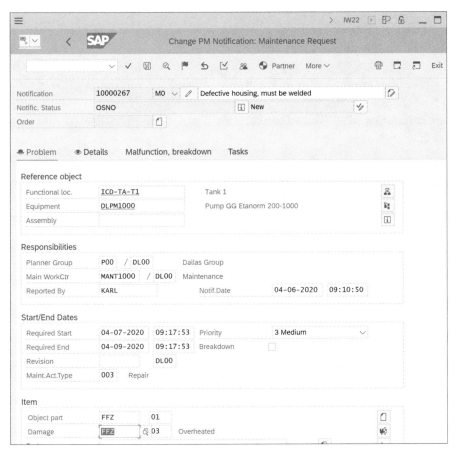

Figure 4.6 Notification: Changed Layout for Change Mode

For a long time, you could not change the notification type retroactively in the SAP system. For example, let's say you wanted to create a normal maintenance request with notification type M1 but accidentally selected notification type M2 for malfunction reports. In earlier releases, to solve the problem, you had to complete the notification with the wrong notification type and create a new notification with the correct notification type.

Now, you can change the notification type retroactively (see Figure 4.7). To do so, call the notification in change mode (e.g., Transaction IW22 or IW28) and click on the change icon ✎ for the notification type. Now, you can select a notification type from the dropdown list.

However, a prerequisite is that the change of the notification types as **Extended** is enabled for the change of the **Notification Type from** and **Notification Type to** for the **Allowed Change of Notification Type** customizing function.

Figure 4.7 Notification: Change Notification Type

If the notification type was changed, it will be recorded as system status NTCH (notification type changed), which means that at a later stage you may search purposefully for notifications that were changed earlier.

4.2.3   Notification Content

The following *screen groups* or tabs are available as possible notification content:

- Reference objects (equipment, functional location, assembly, material serial number)
- Responsibilities (planner group, main work center)
- Items and causes (damage, cause of damage, object part)
- System availability (system availability before, after)
- Malfunction data (breakdown, start, end, duration of breakdown)
- Start/end dates (priority, required start, required end)
- Item overviews (assembly, text)
- Activities for notification header and notification item
- Tasks for notification header and notification item
- Causes for notification header and notification item
- Notifications and object addresses
- Partner overviews (partner role, partner, address)
- Warranties (start and end of warranty)
- Locations (maintenance plant, cost center, business area)
- Scheduling overviews (date of notification, completion, technical control)
- Maintenance plans (maintenance task list, maintenance plan)

The most important information in the notification is the object in question itself, the reference object.

4.2.4   Flexible Reference Objects

You can enter notifications as reference objects for all technical objects, thus for functional locations, pieces of equipment, assemblies, or material serial numbers. If you assign a lower-level object to a notification, the higher-level objects are also entered automatically. Thus, if you enter an assembly, for example, the equipment and functional location are also automatically included in the notification.

You can also enter notifications without specifying a technical object, which is the case in the following situations:

- If a malfunction report refers to an object that is not listed under a number in the system
- If the faulty object cannot be located precisely yet
- If a notification refers to a new object to be provided as part of an investment measure

You have the following options to specify the type of technical object to be entered:

- **For a notification type**
  In customizing via the function **Screen Areas in Notification Header**
- **For a user**
  Within the notification by selecting **More · Extras · Setting · Default Values**
- **For an individual notification**
  Within the notification by selecting **More · Extras · Setting · Reference Object**

When you receive a new notification from a requester and you need to decide whether the maintenance task is to be performed or not, finding out concise information about the object can be useful. You can use the object information, which you'll learn about next, for this purpose.

4.2.5 Object Information

You can display concise information relating to the reference object, that is, object information, in a dialog box (see Figure 4.8).

This information involves the following:

- Structure data (for example, object hierarchy)
- Technical characteristics of classification
- Previous cases of damage and number of processing days
- Previous notifications and/or orders, or ones that are still open, which were created or completed for the object
- Maintenance plans and documents
- Warnings when limits are exceeded

You can call more detailed data such as an individual notification, for example, for all this information from the dialog box. You can also go to the information system to compile statistics and reports.

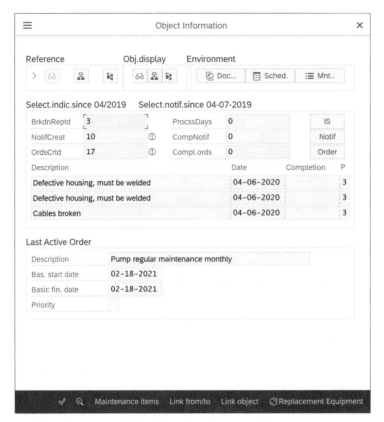

Figure 4.8 Notification: Object Information

[+] **Object Information as a Concise Overview**

Object information gives you concise information about the reference object and contributes to your decision about whether and when a task must be performed. You can define the content of the object information in customizing using the function **Define Object Information Key** and then assign the object information to your notification type using the customizing function **Assign Object Information Keys to Notification Types**.

4.2.6   Notification Items

You would generally use notification items to specify the information of the notification header in more detail, for example, specifying several locations of damage where damage has occurred (notification header: forklift truck; notification items: lifting frame, brake system, and operator's compartment) (see Figure 4.1).

However, since the items are not subsequently transferred when an order is created, user companies rarely use notification items. This pattern is also reflected in empirical studies: A survey among members of the "Maintenance and Service Management" DSAG working group (a German-speaking SAP user group) showed that the average number of items is less than 1.1. If you now consider that an item is generated automatically when you record a damage code or a cause of the damage, the reverse scenario here means that not even every tenth notification has manually created items.

Notification Items: Hardly Used

Notification items are rarely used in practice. Damage and requests are usually specified in the long text or using catalogs.

[!]

4.2.7   Catalogs and Catalog Profiles

In addition to organizational information (such as deadlines, responsibilities, or cost centers), you can also store technical information about problems, malfunctions, damage, causes, and solutions or troubleshooting in a notification. This information is part of the notification and is included in the history. The special feature here compared to all other information is the fact that you can formalize this information in catalogs and therefore make it available for analyses.

You generally use a maximum of five catalogs in plant maintenance (see Figure 4.9):

- Damage
- Causes of damage
- Object parts
- Tasks
- Actions

Each catalog has the following three-tier structure: catalog → code group → codes.

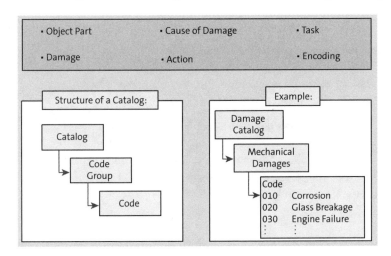

Figure 4.9 Notification: Catalog Structure

A code exists for each set of findings. Furthermore, the codes, in turn, are grouped together to form code groups according to particular characteristics.

[!]

Categorization Criteria for Catalogs

Companies normally use the following as categorization criteria for code groups in catalogs:

- Functional criteria (for example, mechanical damage, electrical causes of damage, or hydraulic object parts)

- Object-related criteria (for example, damage to engines, causes of damage to pumps, or object parts for forklift trucks)

You maintain catalogs in Customizing using the function **Maintain Catalogs** or via Transaction QS41. Figure 4.10 shows, for example, what the codes for forklift trucks might look like in the catalogs for *damage*, *damage causes*, and *object parts*.

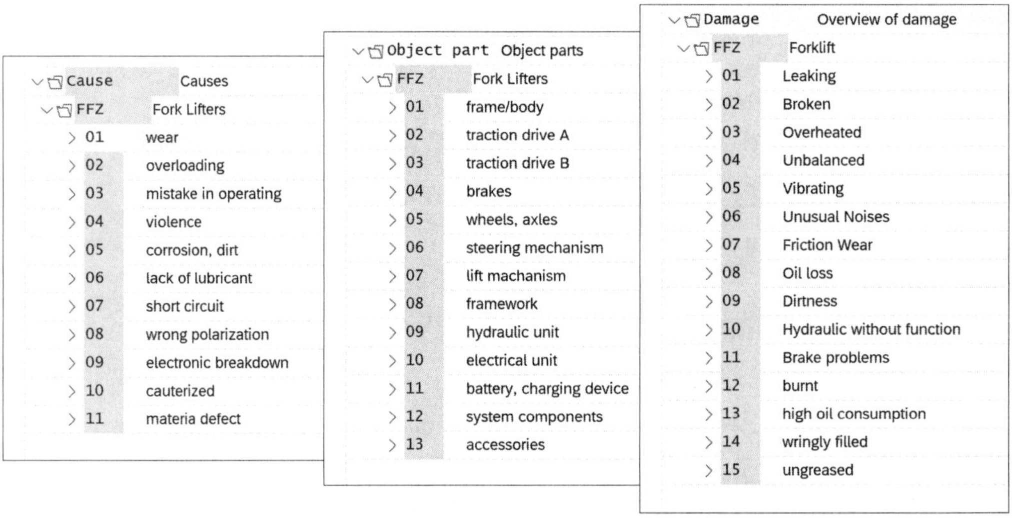

Figure 4.10 Notification: Catalog Example for Fork Lifters

[+]

Catalog Groups Limited to 25 Entries

We recommend that you define clear damage, cause, and object part codes. A maximum of 25 codes should be available to the user. Otherwise, finding the necessary code will be too time-consuming for your users, and data quality and system acceptance will suffer as a result. Therefore, the principle "as much as is necessary, but as little as possible" applies here also.

You cannot delete codes that you have already used. The LOG_EAM_QM_CODE_ DEACT business function enables you to deactivate these codes and lock them for further usage. To do so, select the **Disabled** checkbox in the **Change Code** view in customizing.

For disabled codes, the following applies:

- You cannot assign disabled codes to a notification. The input help does not display disabled codes. If you enter a disabled code manually, the system returns an error message.

- However, codes are still available as selection criteria in reports after they have been disabled. In the input help of the reports, the respective codes are marked as disabled.

In the catalog profile (see Figure 4.11), you can, on the basis of functional factors, specify which code groups must be used for a certain reference object or notification type.

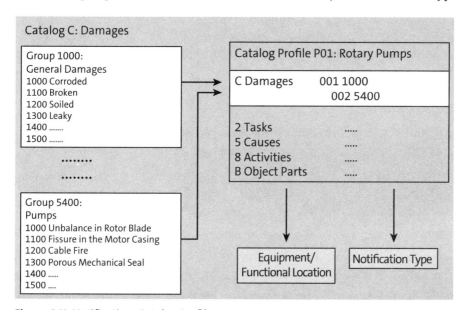

Figure 4.11 Notification: Catalog Profile

You can assign a catalog profile to the following objects:

- To equipment in the **Responsibilities** screen group (see Figure 4.12)

- To a functional location, also in the **Responsibilities** screen group

- To a notification type in customizing via the customizing function **Chance Catalogs and Catalog Profile for Notification Type**

Figure 4.12 Equipment: Catalog Profile

If you have now perhaps entered a catalog profile for the technical objects and notification type, the following sequence applies: equipment → functional location → notification type. Despite this sequence, however, you can individually change or assign the catalog profile in a notification by selecting **Extras · Settings · Catalog Profile · Selection**.

Using the Catalog Profile

You can use a catalog profile to make a basic number of codes available that are useful for the reference object; all other codes are "sorted." Using a catalog profile increases accuracy and user acceptance.

4.2.8   Classification

Earlier in this section we discussed the various options you can use to store information in a notification. If these options are not sufficient or if you require different information, you can also classify notifications.

Chapter 3, Section 3.8, explained the basic principles of classification. To classify notifications, you need to meet the following requirements:

- You have created the required characteristics.
- You need classes with class type 015 (error records).
- You have used the customizing function **Change Catalogs and Catalog Profile for Notification Type** to activate the **Active Class** switch and assign a catalog profile.
- You have assigned a classification to the catalog profile, in turn, using the customizing function **Define Catalog Profile** and set the **Classification Screen** switch.

When you have fulfilled these prerequisites, you can classify the notification on the item detail screen (see Figure 4.13).

Additional Information by Classifying a Notification

You can use the classification to add additional information to your notifications without any programming or modifications. In this case, however, you must define classes of class type 015 (error records) and their assignment in the customizing for the catalog profile.

Figure 4.13 Notification: Classified

4.2.9   Partners

The same process that is described for master data in Chapter 3, Section 3.11.7, also applies for notifications. You can assign and define as many partners as freely as you wish to a notification. For example, partner information could include the following:

- Contact person at the plant
- Service company
- Organizational unit responsible
- Vendor
- Person responsible in controlling
- Technician
- Maintenance supervisor's office

You must create a partner determination procedure to use partners (customizing function **Define Partner Determination Procedure**) and assign a notification type (customizing function **Assign Partner Determination Procedure to Notification Type**).

Now, when you create a notification and enter a reference object assigned to the partner, the system will try to transfer the partners from the reference object. If the partner roles in the partner determination procedure of the reference object and partner determination procedure of the notification are identical, the partner is transferred from the reference object to the notification.

Thus, for example, a vendor (partner determination procedure YEQ, partner role LI, vendor number 1000) is assigned to the equipment. This vendor is now transferred to the notification if the partner determination procedure of the notification (for example, YMD) also contains the LI partner role. Incidentally, the same process also applies for the partner transfer from the reference object to the order and from the notification to the order (see Figure 4.14).

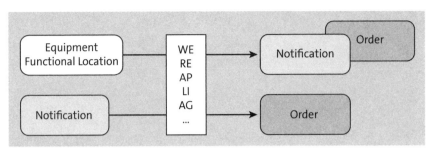

Figure 4.14 Notification: Partner Transfer

[+]

Additional Responsibilities Due to Partner Roles

By default, SAP S/4HANA Asset Management only knows a few organizational units that you can assign to a maintenance task—the planner group and the work center responsible. By defining partners, you can considerably expand these areas and the people responsible and specify more detail. To do this, you must define partner roles and partner determination procedures and their assignment to the notification type.

4.2.10   Addresses

If you have stored an address for the reference object, this address is transferred to the notification. However, if the notification processing does not take place at this address (i.e., because the reference object was brought to a central workshop), you can change this address and store an individual notification address (see Figure 4.15).

Figure 4.15 Notification: Address

4.2.11   Documents

You can assign related documents during the processing of maintenance notifications (see Figure 4.16). You can create new documents, assign existing documents, and change or cancel document assignments. You can navigate to the view of the respective document info records and call the original files of the assigned documents.

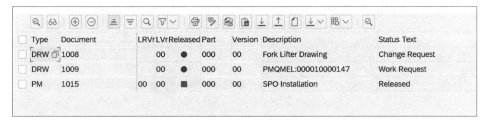

Type	Document	LRVr	LVr	Released	Part	Version	Description	Status Text
DRW	1008		00	●	000	00	Fork Lifter Drawing	Change Request
DRW	1009		00	●	000	00	PMQMEL:000010000147	Work Request
PM	1015	00	00	■	000	00	SPO Installation	Released

Figure 4.16 Notification: Documents Assigned

To enable assigning of documents to a notification, you need to define the relevant document types using the customizing function **Define Document Types** for the PMQMEL object and also use the customizing function **Set Screen Templates for Notification Type** to assign the screen **092 DMS links** to the notification type.

4.2.12   Printing

The SAP system enables you to output notifications on different media in different layouts. The following notification papers, for example, can be printed:

- **Notification overview**
  A notification overview is a complete printout of a notification to enable the parties involved (technicians, employees of work scheduling and production, and so on) to get an overview of the notification.

- **Activity report**
  You could use an activity report as the basis for the work. An activity report contains a list with possible activities, tasks, and so on. The person who corrects the malfunction can only confirm the work he or she has performed by checking it off in this list.

- **Breakdown analysis**
  A breakdown analysis could be a printout of the specifications about the breakdown duration and system availability.

[+]

Choices When Printing

You can decide how many and which notification papers you want to print, the layout you want these notification papers to have, and which notification papers are to be output on which output medium.

The following media are relevant as output media:

- Local printers
- Network printers
- Fax machines
- Email addresses
- PC downloads

Notification Printing and/or Shop Paper Printing

However, often shop papers, rather than notification papers, are printed. Notification papers are normally only used to enhance the shop papers or if sales order processing is not active.

Section 4.4 discusses further details about *printing* (prerequisites, functions, customizing) in conjunction with an order.

4.2.13   System and User Statuses

Like for master data, for notifications, you can assign a user status to them, and a system status can be set by the system, depending on the functions performed.

You must have defined a status profile for the *notification* object type (customizing function **Define User Status for Notifications**) and must have assigned this status profile to the notification type (**Assign User Status to Notification Types**).

In the notification itself, you then set a status by going to the status, clicking the button, and setting the required status under the Status tab (see Figure 4.17).

[+]

Permitting or Prohibiting Functions with User Status

You can use user status to explicitly control which business transactions will be permitted or prohibited in your notifications.

You can set up user statuses in customizing in such a way that, when the system status is changed, the user status is automatically set or deleted. As a result, you're able to further restrict the permitted business transactions of a system status in a clever way, without the user having to carry out additional data maintenance.

At this point, I've explained the most important functions of notifications, and we can conclude the notification phase. Let's now come to the planning phase, which represents the transition to the order and the commissioning of the maintenance workshops.

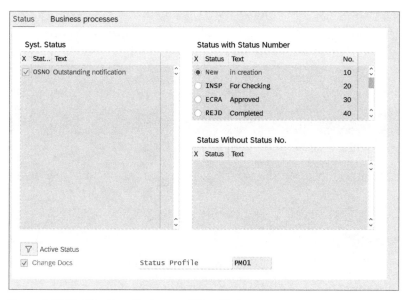

Figure 4.17 Notification: System and User Status

4.3 Planning

Many of the functions we discussed for notifications (refer to Section 4.2) are also available for processing orders, as follows:

- **Flexible reference object**
  You can also assign technical objects flexibly in the order, either as a default value per order type via customizing (using the function **Set Up Order Types**) or as a user-specific value (within the order via **Extras • Settings • Reference Object**).

- **Object information**
  In the order, you can also use the object information to obtain concise information about the object environment if you have created object information keys in customizing and assigned these to the order type (customizing functions **Define Object Information Key** and **Assign Object Information Key to Order Types**).

- **Status management**
  The order also contains system statuses that are automatically assigned by the system when business functions are executed, for example, REL (released) or MACM (material availability confirmed). You can also assign user statuses manually in the order if you have defined a status profile for the *order* object type (customizing function **Define User Status Profile for Orders**) and have assigned this to the order type (**Assign User Status to Order Types**).

- **Partners**
  You can also assign partners in the order if you have defined a partner determination procedure and have assigned it to the order type (via the customizing functions

Define Partner Determination Procedure and **Assign Partner Determination Procedure to the Order**). In the order, the same rules apply for transferring partners as those that are described for the notification.

- **Address**
  If you have stored an address for the reference object and/or in the notification, this address is copied to the order as the object address or as the order address. However, you can change the order address or manually create an order address if one has not yet been created automatically.

The following section will focus on the order functions that are not available in the notification.

4.3.1   Creating an Order

Six options are available for you to create an order (see Figure 4.18):

❶ **Automatically generating an order from a maintenance plan**
  In this scenario, you have defined a maintenance plan that automatically generates an order at periodic intervals on the basis of the information stored there (for example, reference object, order type, maintenance task list). Chapter 5 discusses this option in more detail.

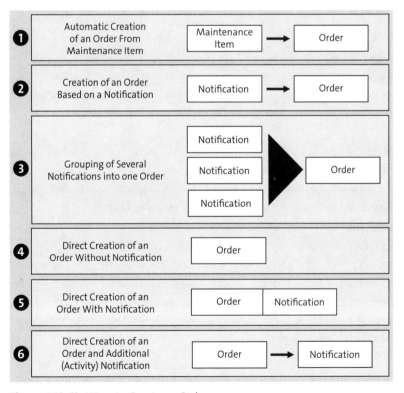

Figure 4.18 Six Ways to Create an Order

❷ Creating an order based on a notification

In this scenario, you have received an individual notification from a requester (for example, from production), and you now create an order from this notification. As shown in Figure 4.19, you see a notification from which you can create an order by clicking the button.

IW22
Change PM Notification: Maintenance Request
Partner
More
Exit
Notification
10000275
M0
Electric problems
Notific. Status
OSNO
New
Order

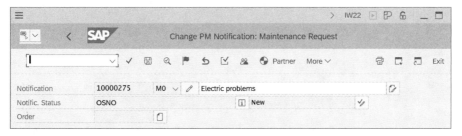

Figure 4.19 Transaction IW22: Creating Order from Notification

❸ Combining several notifications into one order

In this scenario, you have received several notifications that are to be processed within a single order (for example, several malfunction reports that refer to the same asset). You have the option to create an order from the notification list (Transaction IW28 [Change Notification List], see Figure 4.20); the notifications are entered automatically in the object list. You can select several notifications and combine them into a single order by selecting **More • Notification • Generate Order**.

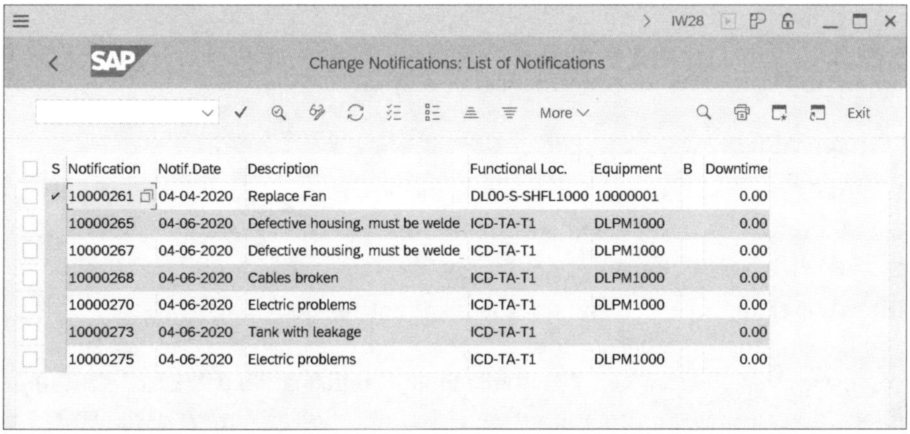

IW28
Change Notifications: List of Notifications
More
Exit
S Notification Notif.Date Description Functional Loc. Equipment B Downtime
10000261 04-04-2020 Replace Fan DL00-S-SHFL1000 10000001 0.00
10000265 04-06-2020 Defective housing, must be welde ICD-TA-T1 DLPM1000 0.00
10000267 04-06-2020 Defective housing, must be welde ICD-TA-T1 DLPM1000 0.00
10000268 04-06-2020 Cables broken ICD-TA-T1 DLPM1000 0.00
10000270 04-06-2020 Electric problems ICD-TA-T1 DLPM1000 0.00
10000273 04-06-2020 Tank with leakage ICD-TA-T1 0.00
10000275 04-06-2020 Electric problems ICD-TA-T1 DLPM1000 0.00

Figure 4.20 Transaction IW28: Combining Several Notifications to an Order

❹ Directly creating an order without a notification

In this scenario, you want to create an order directly without a notification: You use Transaction IW31 (Create Maintenance Order) for this purpose. The order header contains information similar to that of a notification (see Figure 4.21): description, reference object, dates, and people responsible.

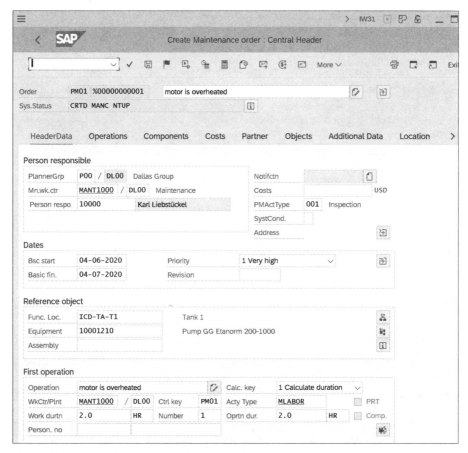

Figure 4.21 Transaction IW31: Create an Order Directly

❺ **Directly creating an order including a notification**
Similar to the previous option, in this scenario, you want to create an order directly, but you would also like to add information such as damage, cause of damage, or breakdown to it. For more information, see Chapter 6, Section 6.1.1.

❻ **Directly creating an order with a subsequent notification**
You have created an order without a notification, but when completing the order, you realize that you also want to enter technical confirmation data of a notification in addition to time confirmation data. If a notification is not yet assigned to an order, you can create a new notification for the order at any time from the order by clicking the **Notifctn** button.

4.3.2   Order Types

You can define order types as you wish to meet your own requirements. You should define the order types based on the functions where these differ in customizing. You can define settings for each order type in customizing, such as:

- Number range
- Default values (for example, for external processing or for using maintenance task lists)
- Priorities
- Costing and order settlement
- Availability check
- Scheduling
- Print control
- Interface for Internet catalogs
- Confirmation procedure
- Object information
- Partner determination procedure
- Status profile
- Screen layout

If you want to access different number ranges or if you require different screen layouts or want to settle the orders differently, for example, you have to set up different order types.

[+]

Order Types in Plant Maintenance

Experience has shown that you normally require the following order types at a minimum:

- An order type for repairs
- An order type for preventive maintenance
- An order type for calibrations (if used)
- An order type for investment measures

[+]

Agreement among Order Types across Areas

When you define your order types, you must consult with your colleagues from controlling (internal orders), production (production orders), service management (service orders), and project management (networks) since those areas use the same order tables.

4.3.3 Content of Orders

You define the layout of the orders in customizing using the customizing function **Define View Profiles** or **Assign View Profiles to Order Types**.

[+]

Designing Your Own Layouts for Orders

Design suitable screen layouts for your order types; you can also base these on the type of activity (adding, changing, displaying). Adapted and simplified screen layouts increase user acceptability.

Figure 4.22 displays an adapted order layout that consists of only one tab with a few field groups. By clicking the 🔒 button, you can always switch between the adapted layout and the standard layout defined by SAP.

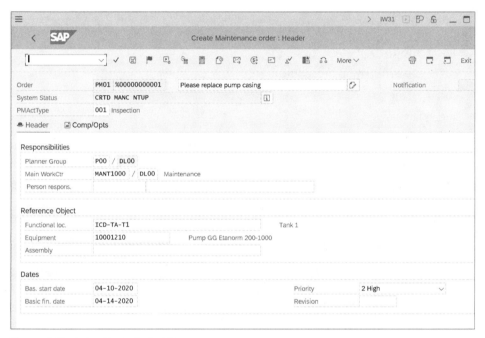

Figure 4.22 Order: Basic Order View

4.3.4   Order Operations

In the order operations (see Figure 4.23), you describe the maintenance activities to be performed. If the short text is not sufficient for your description, a separate long text is available for every operation. In addition to the description, the operation contains the standard time, work center, number of people involved, and other control information.

You must differentiate between the columns **Work** and **Duration** for the standard times. The **Work** column represents the scope of work, in other words, the volume of work to be completed per operation. The values entered in that column are included in the costing and the capacity requirements planning. In contrast, the **Duration** column represents the lead time of the individual operations; the relevant values are included, in turn, in scheduling.

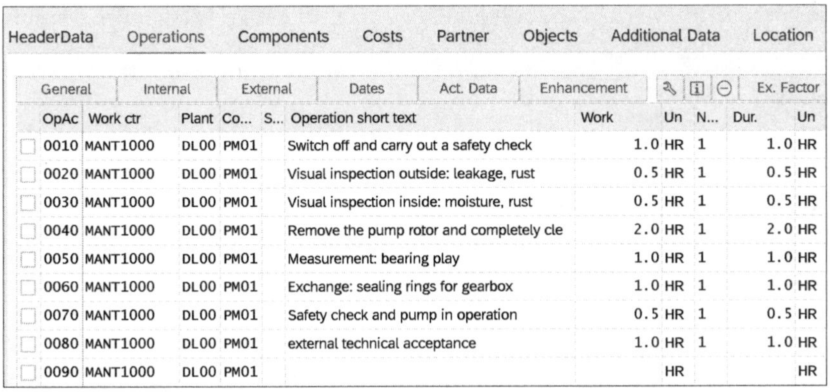

OpAc	Work ctr	Plant	Co...	S...	Operation short text	Work		Un	N...	Dur.	Un
☐ 0010	MANT1000	DL00	PM01		Switch off and carry out a safety check		1.0	HR	1	1.0	HR
☐ 0020	MANT1000	DL00	PM01		Visual inspection outside: leakage, rust		0.5	HR	1	0.5	HR
☐ 0030	MANT1000	DL00	PM01		Visual inspection inside: moisture, rust		0.5	HR	1	0.5	HR
☐ 0040	MANT1000	DL00	PM01		Remove the pump rotor and completely cle		2.0	HR	1	2.0	HR
☐ 0050	MANT1000	DL00	PM01		Measurement: bearing play		1.0	HR	1	1.0	HR
☐ 0060	MANT1000	DL00	PM01		Exchange: sealing rings for gearbox		1.0	HR	1	1.0	HR
☐ 0070	MANT1000	DL00	PM01		Safety check and pump in operation		0.5	HR	1	0.5	HR
☐ 0080	MANT1000	DL00	PM01		external technical acceptance		1.0	HR	1	1.0	HR
☐ 0090	MANT1000	DL00	PM01					HR			HR

The tab row above the table reads: HeaderData | Operations | Components | Costs | Partner | Objects | Additional Data | Location, and below: General | Internal | External | Dates | Act. Data | Enhancement | Ex. Factor

Figure 4.23 Order: Operations

Another important control element is the *control key*. We recommend using the default value from the performing work center, but you can also change the control key. For more information on the control key, refer to Chapter 2, Section 2.2.

4.3.5 Responsibilities

Different options allow you to define the people responsible at both the header level (see Figure 4.24) and the operation level in the order:

- **Planner group**
  You can define a planner group at the order header level (**Planner Grp** field). A planner group is either an individual person or a group (for example, work scheduling) responsible for planning the relevant order.

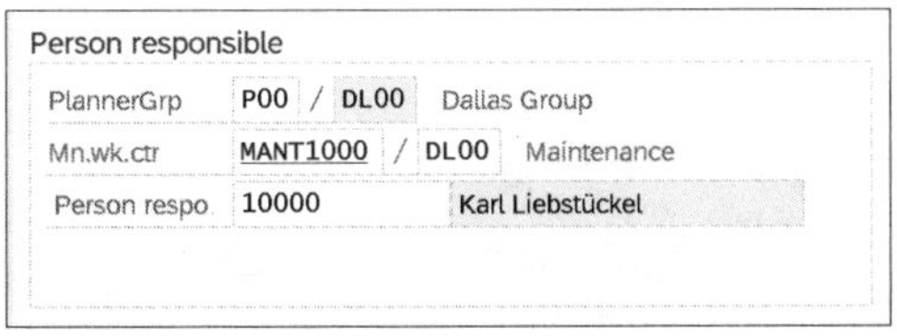

Person responsible

PlannerGrp	P00 / DL00	Dallas Group	
Mn.wk.ctr	MANT1000 / DL00	Maintenance	
Person respo	10000	Karl Liebstückel	

Figure 4.24 Order: Responsibilities

- **Main work center**
  You must define a main work center at the order header level (**Mn.wk.ctr** field). Here, you specify the workshop that holds the primary responsibility for implementing the order.

- **Person responsible**
  You can also name a person responsible (**Person respo.** field). This person is usually from the responsible work center and serves as the central contact person during execution of the order. That person would answer any questions that arise, for

example. You must have used the customizing function **Assign Partner Determination Procedure to Order** to define an *order* role.

- **Work center**
  You assign a work center to each operation (**WkCtr/Plt** field), thus the workshop executing the operation. You can include several workshops in an order in this way.

- **Processor**
  You can also assign, to each procedure, a person who should perform the procedure (see Figure 4.25), which is usually a person from the work center.

Figure 4.25 Order Operation: Personal Number

- **Several persons**
  You can also assign several persons to a procedure if the procedure involves several technicians. Enter the number of persons involved, which you indicate for the requirements assignments (see Figure 4.26). However, you must have used the customizing function **Assign Partner Determination Procedure to Order** to define a *split creation* function role and have assigned a control key to the relevant operation, for which in turn, the function **Determine Capacity Requirements** has been activated.

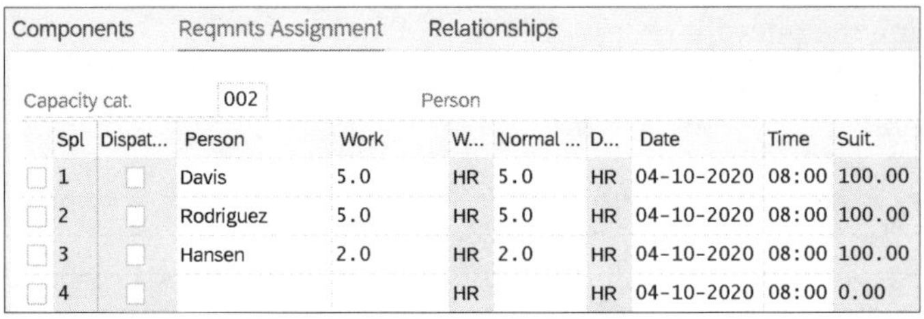

Components		Reqmnts Assignment		Relationships						
Capacity cat.		002		Person						
Spl	Dispat...	Person	Work	W...	Normal	D...	Date	Time	Suit.	
1		Davis	5.0	HR	5.0	HR	04-10-2020	08:00	100.00	
2		Rodriguez	5.0	HR	5.0	HR	04-10-2020	08:00	100.00	
3		Hansen	2.0	HR	2.0	HR	04-10-2020	08:00	100.00	
4				HR		HR	04-10-2020	08:00	0.00	

Figure 4.26 Order Operation: Several Persons

[+]

Responsibilities for the Order

As the person responsible, you can assign a planner group, main work center, and person responsible to the order at the header level. You can assign the latter if this person is assigned to the order type as a partner in customizing.

As the person responsible for executing the order, you can assign a work center, person, or several people at the order level, the latter if *splits* is assigned to the order type as the role in customizing.

You can also assign any number of other people responsible to the order using partner determination procedures.

4.3.6 Scheduling

Scheduling involves calculating the scheduled dates at the operation level and the header level, based on the basic dates manually defined in the order and taking into account the durations at the operation level.

[+]

When Scheduling Does Not Make Sense

Scheduling in the SAP system only makes sense if you have saved standard times. If you do not have standard times, you should not activate scheduling initially. You can ensure that standard times are set up by using a control key for which the **Schedule** option is not activated.

SAP S/4HANA Asset Management basically supports two different types of scheduling: lead time scheduling and network scheduling (see Table 4.1).

Lead Time Scheduling	Network Scheduling
Carries out either forward or backward scheduling	Carries out forward and backward scheduling
Assumes sequential processing of the order	Can take into account sequential processing and dependencies: ■ Relationships ■ Network structures
Determines dates of the order	Determines the earliest and latest dates of an order: ■ Buffer

Table 4.1 Scheduling Types

Lead time scheduling is executed either as forward scheduling or backward scheduling. Based on the basic start date and by adding the operation durations, forward scheduling involves calculating the earliest scheduled start and end dates at both the header and operation levels. In contrast, backward scheduling involves calculating the latest scheduled start and end dates at the header and operation levels based on the basic end date and by subtracting the operation durations.

Both forward and backward scheduling are executed for network scheduling, taking relationships into account in particular; the basic start date is used as the basis for calculating the earliest scheduled dates, while the latest scheduled dates are calculated based on the basic end date. The difference between the earliest and latest date results in the buffer and is shown for each operation and at the header level.

To perform scheduling, you must fulfill the following prerequisites:

- The relevant duration must be entered in all operations.
- You have assigned a control key to the operation. Furthermore, the **Schedule** option is activated for this control key.
- You have assigned a formula for the *internal processing duration* to the work center. This formula must point to the **DAUNO** field, that is, the duration from the operation. In the standard system, the formula is SAP004.
- If you want to execute lead time scheduling, you can use the customizing function **Set Scheduling Parameters** to assign the scheduling type (forward, backward) to the order type in the plant.
- If you want to execute network scheduling, you must define a graphics profile in customizing using the function **SAP NetWeaver · Application Server · Frontend Services · Bar Chart · Define Graphics Profiles**, which you make available in turn for maintenance orders using the customizing function **Create Default Value Profiles for General Order Data**. You must also use the customizing function **Default Values for Maintenance Task List Data and Profile Assignments** to assign it to the *plant/order type* combination.

[+]

Do Not Adjust Basic Dates

In the **Set Scheduling Parameters** customizing function, you will find a setting option for adjusting the basic dates. Set this option to **Do Not Adjust Basic Dates**. Otherwise, the basic dates you entered manually will be overwritten by the **Scheduled dates** during scheduling; in other words, the dates you entered manually will be lost, and you will not be able to restore them.

Based on these prerequisites, the system first calculates the scheduled dates as the lead time scheduling at the header level (see Figure 4.27) and for the individual operations.

Dates							
Bsc start	04-10-2020		Priority	2 High		⌄	🗓
Basic fin.	04-14-2020		Revision				
SchedStart	04-10-	08:00	Actual start		00:00	☑	Shift
Sched.Fin.	04-11-2020	10:48	Actual Finish		00:00	☐	Ind:Relshp
SchedType	1 Forwards	⌄	Reference Date	04-10-2020		☑	AutoSched.
Rel. view		⌄	Start in past	0		☑	Breaks
Version		⌄	Adjust dates	2		☑	Cap.reqmts
Cal. Sel.	0 From Work Cente. ⌄		Calendar ID				

Figure 4.27 Order: Scheduling Dates

> **Forward Scheduling**
>
> Forward scheduling is the normal case for lead time scheduling in plant maintenance.

You switch from lead time scheduling to network scheduling by maintaining the relationships by choosing **More • Goto • Graphics • Network Structure** in the order and navigating to the network structure table. There, you activate the **Link** mode by clicking the 🕂 button. You can then maintain different types of relationships (see Figure 4.28), as follows:

❶ Finish-start relationship
You would use a finish-start relationship to connect the end of an operation with the start of a follow-on operation. Since you can define finish-start relationships for several follow-on operations from one operation, you can process the follow-on operations in parallel.

❷ Start-start relationship
You would use a start-start relationship to connect the start of two operations to each other; these operations thus must start simultaneously.

❸ Finish-finish relationship
You would use a finish-finish relationship to connect the end of two operations to each other; these operations thus must end simultaneously.

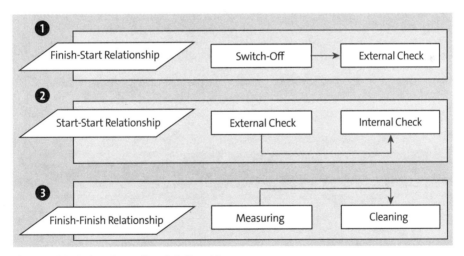

Figure 4.28 Order: Operation Relationships

> **Creating Finish-Start Relationships Automatically**
>
> In the order, you can automatically create finish-start relationships in the system for all operations by selecting **Order • Functions • Dates • Create Relationships**.

As a result, you create a graphical network structure (see Figure 4.29).

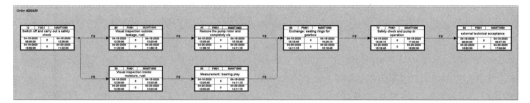

Figure 4.29 Order: Network Structure

The graphical network structure illustrates the logical dependency of the individual operations. In contrast, a bar chart (called in the order by selecting **More** · **Goto** · **Graphic** · **Bar Chart**) displays the dates and duration of the operations (see Figure 4.30).

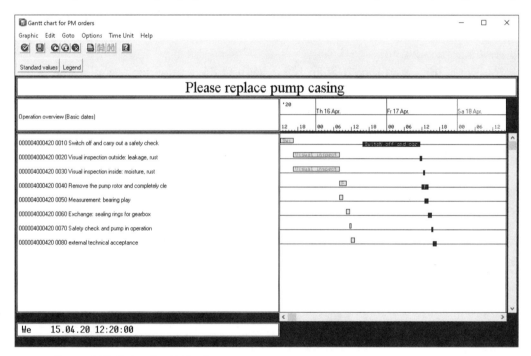

Figure 4.30 Order: Gantt Chart

4.3.7 Material Planning

When planning the required material, you must determine whether the material is stock material or non-stock material.

The planning process for the stock material takes place as follows (see Figure 4.31): The stock materials (item category **L**) that you schedule for the order are reserved in storage ❷. For each order type, you must determine in customizing whether the material reservation must become effective immediately or only when the order is released ❸.

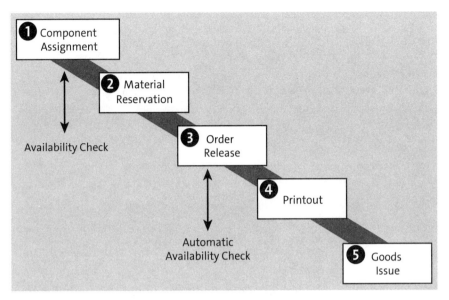

Figure 4.31 Order: Processing Stock Material

The respective customizing function is **Change Documents, Collective Purchase Requisitions, Define MRP Relevance**. Then, activate the **Reservation/Purchase Requisition** option. However, you can change the relevant indicator in the material item of the order when you process the order.

❶ **Component assignment**
The component assignment in the order enables you to perform an availability check straight away.

❷ **Material reservation**
The component assignment creates a material reservation automatically.

❸ **Order release**
When you release the order, the system automatically performs an availability check.

❹ **Print**
When you print the shop papers, you can also print out corresponding documents for the workshop and warehouse (for example, a material staging list and material withdrawal slips).

❺ **Goods issue**
You enter planned goods issues with a reference to the reservation and unplanned goods issues by entering the order number.

[!]

Creating Reservations Automatically

Note that you cannot suppress the activation of a reservation for stock material; material reservations are thus created in any case. With the customizing function **Change Documents, Collective Purchase Requisitions, Define MRP Relevance** and by activating the **Reservation/Purchase Requisition** option, you can only control when the reservation becomes effective, either immediately or when the order is released.

[+]

No Separation between Reservation and Purchase Requisition

Importantly, you also cannot create any separation between a reservation for stock material and a purchase requisition for non-stock material. Therefore, if you have activated the **Reservation/Purchase Requisition** option via the Customizing function **Change Documents, Collective Purchase Requisitions, Define MRP Relevance** and have set the **Immediate** option, the reservations become effective immediately, and purchase requisitions are created. Thus, you cannot, for example, create purchase requisitions immediately and only let the reservations become effective when the order is released. This process is only possible if you manually change this in each case in the order.

The planning process for non-stock material is done by following these six steps (see Figure 4.32):

❶ Component assignment

The component assignment in the order (item category N) enables you to specify additional purchasing information. The component that you assign can optionally have a material number. If you assign a material number, you can describe the material by manually entering a short text.

❷ Purchase requisition

The system creates a purchase requisition based on this information—either directly when you save the order or when you release it (by activating the **Reservation/Purchase Requisition** option via the customizing function **Change Documents, Collective Purchase Requisitions, Define MRP Relevance**).

❸ Purchase order

In purchasing, purchase orders are created from the purchase requisitions. The purchase order items are assigned to the order in this case.

❹ Order release

Goods receipts with reference to the order can be entered as soon as the order is released.

❺ Goods receipt
When you enter the goods receipts, the purchase order value is debited on the order when the goods receipt is valuated.

❻ Invoice receipt
The order is automatically debited or credited when an invoice is received or if differences occur in the invoices.

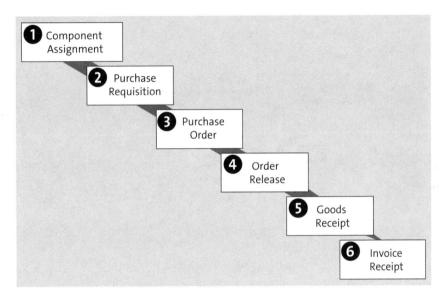

Figure 4.32 Order: Processing Non-stock Material

You have the following options for the actual planning operation:

- **Manual entry**
  You can manually assign a material to an operation from the general material list.

- **Structure list**
  You can select spare parts from the structure list of the reference object (**List** button). If you have assigned the order a functional location, equipment, and an assembly, all direct and indirect bills of materials (BOMs) (if available) will be displayed in the structure list.

- **Maintenance task list**
  If you use a maintenance task list in the order, and spare parts are assigned to the maintenance task list, these are transferred to the order.

- **Material where-used list**
  If you processed orders for the reference objects in the past and used spare parts in this case, you can display these using the material where-used list (via the 🔲 button) and transfer items from this into the existing order.

189

Material Where-Used List for Material Planning

The longer equipment or a functional location has already been in use, the more meaningful the history of the exchanged spare parts and, therefore, the more helpful the material where-used list for component planning.

Figure 4.33 shows an overview of these options.

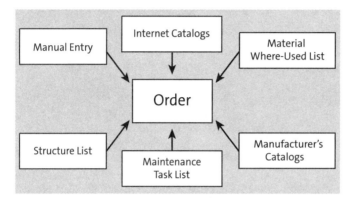

Figure 4.33 Order: Component Planning Options

In the customizing function **Set Scheduling Parameters**, use the **Adjust Dates** switch to specify the following for each plant and order type:

- Whether all material components are required on the start date of the order
- Whether individual material components are required on the start date of the individual operation

Do Not Adjust Basic Dates, Requirements Dates at Operation Level

Set the parameter **Adjust dates** to **Do not adjust basic dates, Dependent requirements on operation dates**. In the previous section on scheduling, we explained why you should not adjust the basic dates. You should schedule the dependent requirement at the operation level, since all materials will otherwise be made available at the start of the order processing, which would increase warehouse stocks unnecessarily.

Alternatively, you can assign a requirement date to each component manually (see Figure 4.34). If the component is a non-stock material, the requirement date is simultaneously the required delivery date, which is communicated to the supplier.

General Data
Component
Plant
DL00
Stor. location
Batch
Sort String
Goods Recipient
Unloading Point
Reqmt Date
06/27/2020 08:00:00
Offset
Manual Requirement Date
Reservation
3690 1
Movement type
261

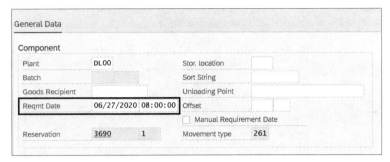

Figure 4.34 Order: Component Requirement Date

The LOG_EAM_CI_3 business function must be activated in order for you to assign a requirement date manually. Figure 4.35 displays a fully planned material list.

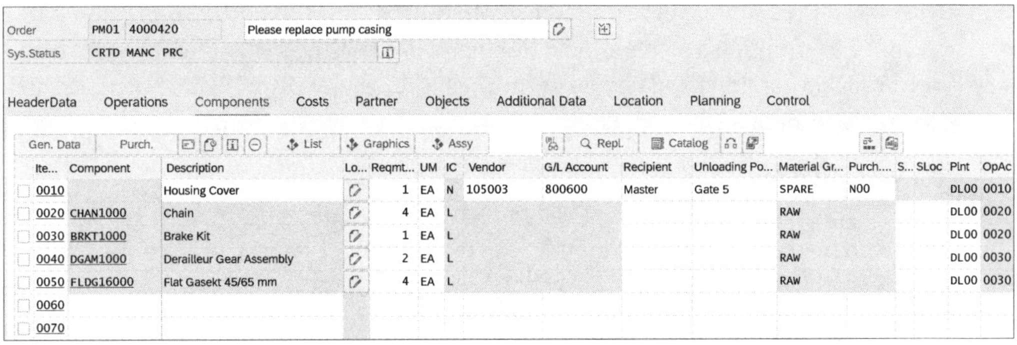

Order PM01 4000420 Please replace pump casing
Sys.Status CRTD MANC PRC
HeaderData Operations Components Costs Partner Objects Additional Data Location Planning Control
Gen. Data Purch. List Graphics Assy Repl. Catalog
Ite... Component Description Lo... Reqmt... UM IC Vendor G/L Account Recipient Unloading Po... Material Gr... Purch.... S... SLoc Plnt OpAc
0010 Housing Cover 1 EA N 105003 800600 Master Gate 5 SPARE N00 DL00 0010
0020 CHAN1000 Chain 4 EA L RAW DL00 0020
0030 BRKT1000 Brake Kit 1 EA L RAW DL00 0020
0040 DGAM1000 Derailleur Gear Assembly 2 EA L RAW DL00 0030
0050 FLDG16000 Flat Gasekt 45/65 mm 4 EA L RAW DL00 0030
0060
0070

Figure 4.35 Order: Component List

The components are used (such as lubricants, for example) or integrated (such as assemblies, for example) during the processing of the order.

The operation overview and the component overview previously included only a selection of fields predefined by SAP. Purchasing data was sorely missed. If you activate business function LOG_EAM_CI_5, you can maintain all purchasing data in the operation overview and the component overview (for example, vendor, material group, goods recipient, unloading point, or purchasing group).

There is another new feature within the business function LOG_EAM_CI_8: If you activate it, you are shown the supplier's name, material group text, and general ledger account short text—in the overview as well as on the detail screen (see Figure 4.36).

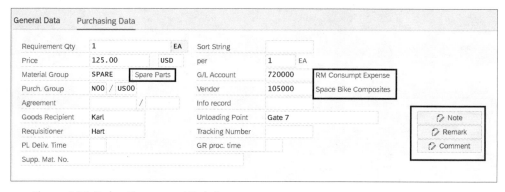

Figure 4.36 Order: Component Details

Previously, you could only add a single long text for the non-stock item, which then was transferred to the purchase requisition as item text. The business function LOG_ EAM_CI_12 brings in another innovation here: If you activate it, up to four text types are available for individual text entry. By means of several customizing functions, text types can be defined for purchase requisitions, such as the following:

- Which types of text you want to use
- Which text type of the non-stock item should be copied to which text type of the purchase requisition
- Which labelling texts should appear on the function keys

Figure 4.36 shows possible text types (e.g., note, remark, comment), which you can then call up individually using a pushbutton.

The business function LOG_EAM_CI_9_ORD_OPER_COMP brings another innovation. With this business function, you can use the following new functions when processing maintenance orders in the corresponding transactions and in the simple order view:

- You can copy operations and sub-operations. Use the function key ▦ at the operation list for this.
- You can copy materials that you have entered for an operation. Use the function key ▦ at the component list for this.
- You can move individual materials from one operation to another operation. Use the function key ⬚ at the component list for this.

4.3.8   Electronic Parts Catalogs

In the following, you will see how you can use the technology of electronic parts catalogs for the procurement of spare parts—directly from the planning of the maintenance order.

> **Link Catalogs Directly to SAP S/4HANA**   [+]
>
> The option of selecting spare parts via catalogs is available as a direct link to the maintenance order in SAP S/4HANA Asset Management.

Prerequisites for the direct connection of the order to catalogs are as follows:

- Activating the enterprise extension EA-PLM with the switch framework (Transaction SFW5).

- Assigning one or more catalogs to the order types (customizing function **Interface for Procurement Using Catalogs (OCI) · Define Catalogs** and **Assign Catalog to Order Type**)

You can use the catalogs for your material planning in Transaction IW31/IW32 (Maintain Order) on the **Components** tab or in Transaction IW3K (Change Order Component Overview) using the **Catalog** button. If you have assigned several catalogs to the order type in customizing, a popup window appears in which you select the catalog. The system then jumps directly to the selected catalog. There, you select the required parts by marking them, fill your shopping basket by using the **Add** function, and transfer them to SAP S/4HANA Asset Management using the **Check out** function (see Figure 4.37).

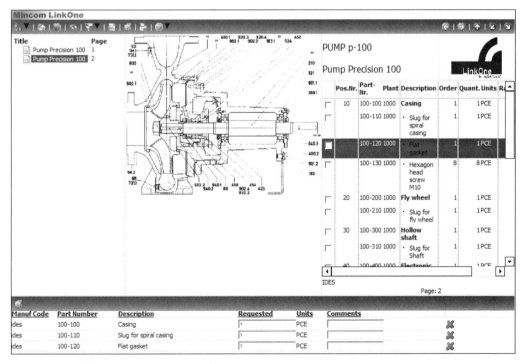

Figure 4.37 Order: Electronic Parts Catalog

If you have files with manufacturer catalogs in your network or on your local workstation, you can also select spare parts from these catalogs using the same technology and transfer them to the order.

Use Predefined or Own Conversion Modules

When the shopping basket is transferred to SAP S/4HANA Asset Management, it is checked whether the selected spare part possibly corresponds to an inventory-managed material number. The customizing function **Define Conversion Modules** allows you to define how this check is to be carried out (e.g., checking the manufacturer material number or checking the text). If the existing conversion modules do not perform the check you want them to do, you may develop and save your own conversion modules.

The advantages of catalogs compared to manual material planning are obvious:

- Faster identification of the required spare part
- Avoidance of content errors due to images
- Avoidance of data errors due to higher data quality
- Fixed specification of materials that can be ordered
- Fixed sources of supply
- Reduction of the number of suppliers with which orders can be placed
- Reduction of purchase orders channeled past the system because of high user acceptance
- Higher process efficiency because of easier processing
- Reduction of material master records of stock material

Furthermore, compared to BOMs, the advantages of working with catalogs are obvious: In addition to some previously mentioned plus points such as visualization, there is no necessity for creating and maintaining a BOM. Above all, the change management of many companies is either incomplete or quite complex.

However, the effort you have to put into creating, changing, and using the catalogs is offset by the advantages.

Take Advantage of Catalogs

Using catalogs means, in effect, prevention of effort (e.g., for the management of material masters and BOMs). The purchase order processes are less prone to errors (e.g., through visualization) and become more complete (e.g., through high user acceptance). Also, it would be very welcome to get your suppliers to look after their entries in the catalogs themselves. This way, facts and figures stay updated with no bother to you.

In addition to the components, you may also need PRT, which we'll discuss next.

4.3.9   Production Resources/Tools

In contrast to components, PRT, such as protective clothing, hand pallet trucks, drawings, and so on, are not used when the order is being executed but are, instead, required for processing the order and are returned (to stock) at the end.

You can assign three different types of PRT to an operation (see Figure 4.38):

	PRT Assignments to Operation						
Item	Cat	Production resources/tools	Plnt	Co...	Description	Qty	Unit
0010	M	PPFH1700	DL00	1	Milling Head	1	PC
0020	M	DRMS1250	DL00	1	Torque Wrench	1	PC
0030	D	1015 PM 000 00		1	SPO Installation	1	EA
0040	E	E16900		1	Tension meter		

Figure 4.38 Order: Production Resource Tools

- **Material**
  If the required production resource/tool is listed as a material number

- **Document**
  If the required production resource/tool is a document that is stored as a document master record

- **Equipment**
  If the required production resource/tool is listed as an equipment master record

The production resource/tool list is called via the ⚒ button on the operations overview screen.

4.3.10   Documents

You can assign related documents during the processing of maintenance orders (see Figure 4.39).

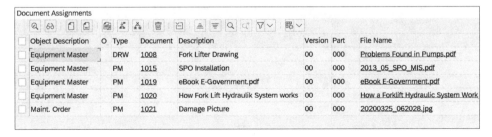

	Object Description	O	Type	Document	Description	Version	Part	File Name
	Equipment Master		DRW	1008	Fork Lifter Drawing	00	000	Problems Found in Pumps.pdf
	Equipment Master		PM	1015	SPO Installation	00	000	2013_05_SPO_MIS.pdf
	Equipment Master		PM	1019	eBook E-Government.pdf	00	000	eBook E-Government.pdf
	Equipment Master		PM	1020	How Fork Lift Hydraulik System works	00	000	How a Forklift Hydraulic System Work
	Maint. Order		PM	1021	Damage Picture	00	000	20200325_062028.jpg

Figure 4.39 Order: Documents

Other options available to you are as follows:

- You can create new documents, assign existing documents, and change or cancel document assignments.

- You can navigate to the view of the respective document info records and call the original files of the assigned documents.

- You can also show the assigned documents for the maintenance notifications and the *equipment*, *functional location*, and *assembly* reference objects.

- Functions for filtering, searching, and sorting are available within the document list.

Prerequisites for using documents are as follows:

- You must activate the LOG_EAM_CI_6 business function before you can assign documents to an order or order operation.

- You must also use the customizing function **Define Document Types** to define the relevant document types for the object PMAUFK (order) or PMAFVC (operation).

4.3.11   Object List

An object list is used when you must perform certain activities not only on one object, but on a whole range of objects (i.e., an inspection round) or when you have several notifications that you want to process as part of a single order. You can use the object list in the order for these cases.

You can add the following objects to an object list (see Figure 4.40):

- Functional locations
- Equipment
- Material serial numbers
- Notifications

Figure 4.40 Order: Object List

Costs for Object Lists

The accruing costs are only updated by default on the reference object in the order header, and the relevant cost center is debited in the order settlement. If you want to settle the costs proportionally on all affected cost centers, use the customer exit **Create Customer-Specific Settlement Rule** (IWO10027).

Unfortunately, no default option is available to distribute the costs in the history.

4.3.12   Costing and Estimated Costs

In costing, costs are automatically calculated based on the allocation records that you stored in the system and on the amounts specified in the resource planning. The planned costs (and also the actual costs that subsequently accrue) are not planned manually.

The planning of resources lead to the accrual of planned costs on the order. You can display the costs there via two different methods (see Figure 4.41):

- **According to the cost elements**
  The costs displayed according to the cost elements show all cost elements included in the costing. More like a controlling-orientated view, this display shows a comparison of planned and actual costs.

- **According to the value categories**
  The costs displayed according to the value categories summarize several cost elements into value categories. Normally, this display more clearly lays out costs for maintenance purposes and displays a comparison of estimated, planned, and actual costs.

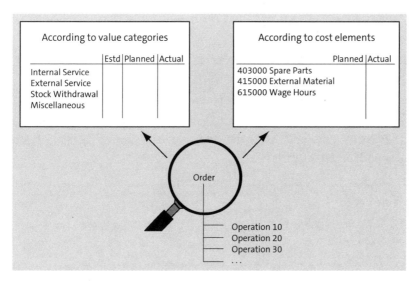

Figure 4.41 Order: Cost Overviews

The costs of an order are calculated at two summarization levels at which you can also display the costs:

- **At the operation level**
  The costs displayed at the operation level show all costs involved in the respective operation—either on the basis of cost elements as a planned/actual comparison or on the basis of maintenance categories as a comparison of estimated/planned and actual costs (see Figure 4.42). To display the costs at the operation level, you activate the customizing function **Costs at Operation Level** per plant and order type. Orders whose costs are displayed at the operation level obtain the status ACAS (activity account assignment). In other words, you can use this status to select the orders in question.

- **At the header level**
  The costs displayed at the header level summarize all costs at the operation level and show all costs involved in the order—either on the basis of cost elements as a planned/actual comparison or on the basis of maintenance categories as a comparison of estimated/planned and actual costs. The costs at the header level are always displayed, irrespective of whether you have activated costs at the operation level.

Overview	Costs	Quantities			
Group/Description		Estimated Costs	Planned Costs	Actual Costs	Currency
∨ ⬚ Operation Co		590.00	500.00	0.00	USD
∨ ⬚ 0010					
⬚ Internal Labor		100.00	50.00	0.00	USD
⬚ Non-stock Material		490.00	450.00	0.00	USD

Figure 4.42 Order: Cost on Operation Level

To ensure that the system can determine the costs based on your resource planning, you must meet the following prerequisites:

- You must use the **Costing** function to assign a control key to the operations that are to be included in the costing.

- You must assign work to the operations that you want to be included in the costing.

- You must use Transaction KP26 to define a fixed price (**Fixed Price** option) and/or variable price (**Variable Price** option) for the version you use, for the fiscal year, for the cost center, and for the activity type.

[!]

Fixed or Variable Prices

Since costing is based on full costs in plant maintenance, you are free to split the price at a fixed and variable price or not.

- You must use the customizing functions of controlling to maintain the costing variant, valuation variant, and costing sheet. (For more information, refer to Chapter 7, Section 7.1.8)

- You must use the customizing function **Assign Costing Parameters and Results Analysis Keys** to assign a planned costing variant and an actual costing variant to the order type for each plant.

- In the work center, you must maintain the following data on the **Costing** tab: cost center, activity type, and formula key.

- The formula key must point to the **ARBEI** field (the work from the operation). In the standard system, the formula is SAPO08.

- Transfer prices (either a standard price or a moving average price) must be defined for the materials whose costs are to be calculated.

- You have entered a value for non-stock materials and external activities.

- To display the costs at the operation level, you have activated the customizing function **Costs at Operation Level** per plant and order type. This customizing function is available if you have activated business functions LOG_EAM_OLC and LOG_EAM_OLC2.

- If you have subsequently activated the costs at operation level, you have used Transaction OLI5N to run the report RIPMCO01 to rebuild existing order costs.

Preliminary costing of an order occurs automatically when you save or is triggered during order processing when you click on the ▦ button.

Figure 4.43 shows the costs displayed at the cost element level. You can display these costs by selecting the **Costs** tab and executing the **Planned/Actual Report** function.

Plan Version 0 Plan/Act - Version

Cumulative Data
Legal Valuation
Company Code Currency/Object Currency

Cost Element	Cost Element (Text)	Σ	Total Plan Costs Σ	Total Actual Costs Currency	Σ	Plan/actual variance	Plan/act. var(%)
740000	Consumables		450.00	0.00 USD		450.00-	100.00-
720000	Raw Material Consumption Expense		1,198.50	0.00 USD		1,198.50-	100.00-
700000	External Labor		690.00	0.00 USD		690.00-	100.00-
800000	Internal Labor		325.00	0.00 USD		325.00-	100.00-
Debit			2,663.50 ▪	0.00 USD	▪	2,663.50-	
		▪ ▪	2,663.50 ▪ ▪	0.00 USD	▪ ▪	2,663.50-	

Figure 4.43 Order: Cost Overview on the Cost Element Level

If the order was costed, the system sets the status of the order to **PRC** (pre-costed). If costs also exist at the operation level, the system sets the status **ACAS** (activity assigned).

Figure 4.44 shows the costs displayed according to value categories.

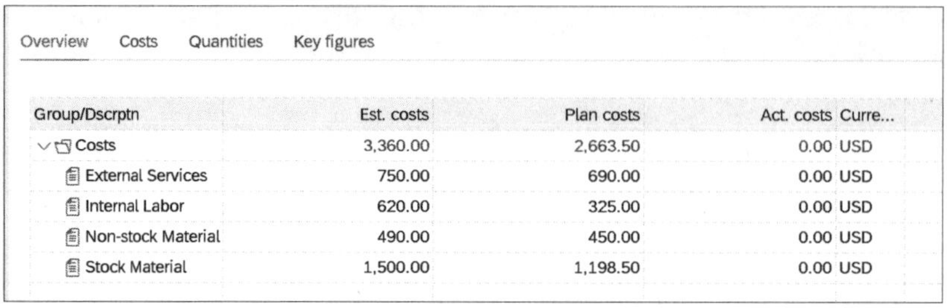

Overview Costs Quantities Key figures			
Group/Dscrptn	Est. costs	Plan costs	Act. costs Curre...
⌄ 🗂 Costs	3,360.00	2,663.50	0.00 USD
📄 External Services	750.00	690.00	0.00 USD
📄 Internal Labor	620.00	325.00	0.00 USD
📄 Non-stock Material	490.00	450.00	0.00 USD
📄 Stock Material	1,500.00	1,198.50	0.00 USD

Figure 4.44 Order: Cost Overview on the Value Category Level

Planned and actual costs are costed automatically. You can also enter estimated costs. However, estimated costs are not calculated; instead, they are specified manually because they are solely based on a maintenance planner's empirical values and not on planned resources. Three different methods are available for entering estimated costs:

- At the operation level, estimated costs can be differentiated for each value category. (The total for all operations is then shown at the header level for each value category and as a total.)

- At the header level, estimated costs can be differentiated for each value category. (The total is then created automatically.)

- As the total for the entire order.

In the following cases, the exclusivity principle applies:

- If you have activated the **Costs** function at the operation level, you can perform the cost estimation either at the operation level or as a total for the entire order. However, a cost estimation at the header level for value categories is not possible.

- If you have not activated the **Costs** function at the operation level, you can perform the cost estimation either at the header level for the individual value categories or as a total for the entire order; a cost estimation at the operation level is not possible.

By clicking the ⇌ button, you can copy the planned costs into the estimated costs at any time until the order is released. What lies behind this function? This function is intended for users who want to freeze the planned costs of an order at any given time (often with the order release). Using this function, you can define planned costs, for example, at the level that exists at the time of the order release, and thus subsequent plans change the planned costs but not the estimated costs.

[+]

Estimated Costs versus Upper Value Limits

Neither determining planned costs nor assigning estimated costs prevents certain value limits from being exceeded. If you want to prevent the exceeding of value limits, assign an order budget. If you have then activated the availability check in customizing, warnings or error messages appear when certain value limits are reached or are exceeded.

Chapter 3, Section 3.11.8, explained how you can assign permits to a functional location or to equipment. With this assignment, you were able to select the **Proposal** column (that is, permit proposed for the processing) and also force the permit to be granted either when the order was released (**OR** column) or when it was technically completed (**OC** column). If this is the case, you must now grant these permits within the order processing before the order can be released or completed (see the **OR** and **OC** columns in Figure 4.45).

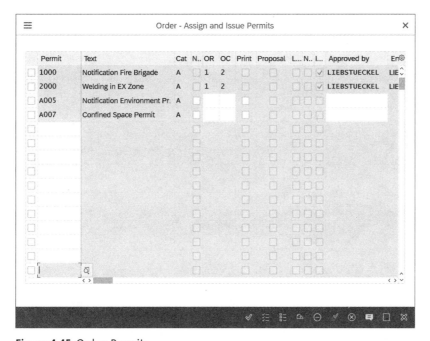

Figure 4.45 Order: Permits

In addition to the permits proposed automatically from the object master record, you can also manually assign additional necessary permits for this order only.

You can grant permits via the 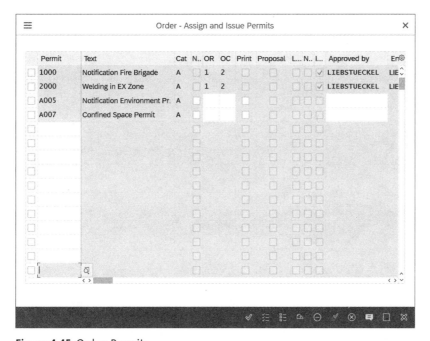 button; you can undo granted permits via the button. In the overview, the system will show who granted the permit and when.

Using Permits Where It Makes Sense

You can use permits to ensure that an order is not released, or is not technically completed, until the required permits have been granted according to the dual-control or multiple-control principle.

You can use the SAP authorization concept to ensure that different people can grant permits, release an order, or technically complete an order.

4.3.13 Order Hierarchy

When one or more suborders are created for an order, you have an *order hierarchy*. An order hierarchy is a multilevel structure of orders and suborders to separate comprehensive orders or combine several orders.

You can create a suborder for a superior order in Transaction IW36 (see Figure 4.46).

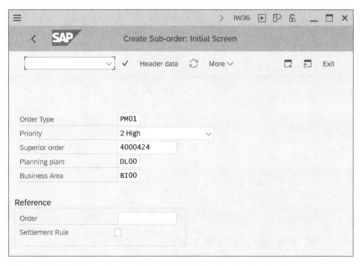

Figure 4.46 Order: Transaction IW36 (Create Suborder)

In practice, the creation of suborders rivals the creation of operations. As you saw earlier, you can perform certain planning operations on operations, as in the following operations, for example:

- Work specifications and work centers
- Materials
- PRT
- Scheduling

However, the operations are bound by the specifications of the order header. The suborder, in contrast, is planned completely separately, which means that:

- You can assign an independent reference object to a suborder.
- The suborder can be budgeted independently.
- The suborder can be approved independently.

All of these functions exceed the functions of an operation.

[+] **When Suborders Are Useful**

You should create suborders rather than operations within order processing if you have tasks that require the following:

- A separate reference object
- A separate order budget
- Independent approval

In the main order, you can view the order structure (by choosing **More · Extras · Suborders · Overview**) and the cost summarization (by choosing **More · Extras · Suborders · Cost Overview**) using special reports. Figure 4.47 displays an incrementally summarized cost overview.

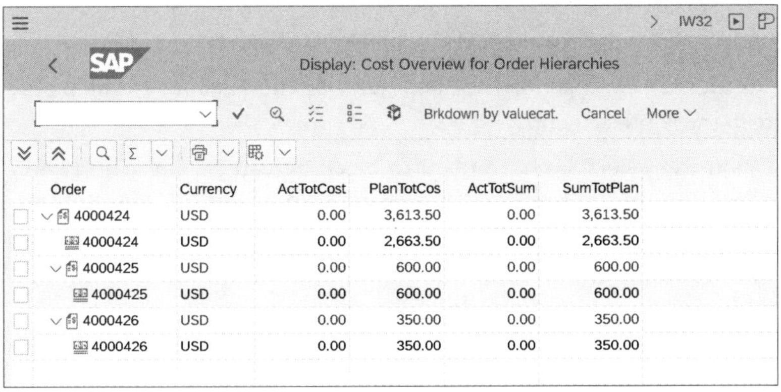

Order	Currency	ActTotCost	PlanTotCos	ActTotSum	SumTotPlan
∨ 4000424	USD	0.00	3,613.50	0.00	3,613.50
4000424	USD	0.00	2,663.50	0.00	2,663.50
∨ 4000425	USD	0.00	600.00	0.00	600.00
4000425	USD	0.00	600.00	0.00	600.00
∨ 4000426	USD	0.00	350.00	0.00	350.00
4000426	USD	0.00	350.00	0.00	350.00

Display: Cost Overview for Order Hierarchies — IW32

Figure 4.47 Order: Suborder Cost Overview

4.3.14   Object Services

Chapter 3, Section 3.11.4, explained the options available as part of object services when discussing the special functions for technical objects.

Of course, object services are also available for orders. However, note the following aspect of object services that applies to orders only: If you have assigned the *attachment* object service to an order and the order therefore has a list of attachments, the 🖉 button will be clearly available in the order header (see Figure 4.48). When you call the relevant order, you can immediately tell whether an attachment list has been assigned to it. To display the attachment list, click on the button.

Order	PM03 4000424	Electric Cable broken
Sys.Status	CRTD ESTC ACAS MANC PRC	

Figure 4.48 Order: Attachment List

Attachment List Button

The **Attachment List** button in the order header indicates directly whether documents have been assigned to an order using the object service.

[!]

The LOG_EAM_CI_3 business function must be activated in order for you to display the **Attachment List** button.

4.3.15   Do Not Execute Orders

At the end of the planning phase, you might decide that you do not want to execute an order, for example, because your colleagues from production think that the costs are too high or because the problem has already been solved or because the order has been entered twice by mistake. In this case, you can close the order using the **Do not Execute** function up to the release of the order.

Various options are available that you can use to not execute orders:

- To stop a single order, use Transaction IW32 and select **Order • Functions • Complete • Do Not Execute** in the context menu.
- In list editing, you can select several orders to block by using Transaction IW38, selecting the orders, and selecting **Order • Completion • Do Not Execute** in the context menu. You can use the mass change function if the **LOG_EAM_CI_7** business function is enabled.

The following consequences arise from not executing an order:

- The order can no longer be changed.
- The order cannot be updated.
- The order will have the **CLSD** (closed) status.
- The deletion flag will be set for purchase requisitions.
- Reservations will be deleted.
- Capacity loads will be reduced or capacities will be released.
- If a notification was assigned to the order, the notification will not be closed. You have to close notifications manually or assign them to another order.

4.3.16   To Be Printed Before Order Is Released

For a long time, in the SAP system, orders could not be printed until they were released. However, you might need to print individual order documents or even an entire order before the order is ready to be released. For example, you may want to inform your technicians, or you need to provide spare parts that require some time to be picked, or production requires a written quotation.

Business function LOG_EAM_CI_7 is available for this purpose. In the customizing function **Define Printer**, enable the **Allow Print Before Release** function in **User-Specific Print Control**.

The actual print function then corresponds to the normal print function for released orders.

We can leave the subject of planning the order now and move on to the SAP system options that you would normally use when the actual order processing is immediately imminent: controlling.

4.4 Controlling

Controlling is comprised of the functions mass change, availability check (material, PRT, staff), capacity requirements planning, order release, shop paper printing, and paging. The following sections will cover each of these functions in turn.

4.4.1 Mass Change of Orders and Operations

As part of your daily business, you'll certainly encounter scenarios in which you need to assign the same information to several orders. This duplicated information is necessary, for example, in the following cases:

- You want to draw up a weekly timetable and need to schedule several orders on the same dates.
- You are down several employees in one workshop and need to shift orders to another workshop.
- Controlling has created new settlement orders to which several plant maintenance orders are to be assigned.
- You have hired a new planner to whom you want to assign a new worklist.

In scenarios like these, proceed as follows to perform a mass change of orders:

- Start Transaction IW38 to execute a list change for orders and restrict the worklist (for example, by order type or date).
- In the list displayed, select the orders you want to change simultaneously.
- Choose **More · Order · Carry Out a Mass Change**.
- Enter the relevant new information (for example, the main work center or date) and then implement the changes.

Proceed as follows to perform a mass change of operations:

- Start Transaction IW37 to execute a list change for operations and restrict the worklist (for example, by work center or date).
- In the list displayed, select the operations you want to change simultaneously.
- Choose **More · Operation · Carry Out a Mass Change**.

Enter the relevant new information (for example, the main work center or date) and then implement the changes (see Figure 4.49).

Prerequisites

You have to activate the business function LOG_EAM_CI_5 so that you can change the mass of operations. You also need the values OR (order) and OV (operation) for the authorization object I_MASS.

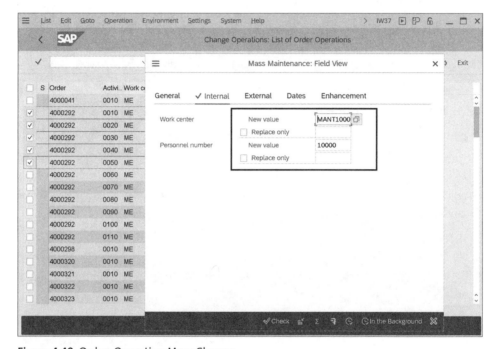

Figure 4.49 Order: Operation Mass Change

Reducing Maintenance Effort with Mass Changes

The **Mass Change** function provides an easy, reliable, and fast way of changing the field contents in several orders simultaneously.

4.4.2   Capacity Requirements Planning

In capacity requirements planning, you compare the available capacity with the capacity requirement. You maintain the available capacity in the work center (see Chapter 2, Section 2.2), and the capacity requirement is determined by the standard times of the operations in the order. However, capacity planning does not always make sense.

When Capacity Planning Makes Sense

Essentially, capacity planning only makes sense if the predictable order volume is sufficiently large and the standard times are reasonably accurate. Unlike in production, these prerequisites are frequently not fulfilled in plant maintenance. Either no exact specifications exist for the standard times and/or you have a large number of unplanned orders.

In most production departments, inexact standard times are not normally a problem, since similar production orders always recur. In plant maintenance, however, standard times mainly apply only to the areas of preventive maintenance and inspection. All other tasks more or less only occur once, and the estimates concerning the required time are correspondingly inexact.

This prerequisite also does not present a problem in the majority of production departments, with the exception of rush orders. In plant maintenance, however, we may encounter emergency maintenance and short-term repairs, and we cannot plan in advance when and how often these situations will occur. Only periods of preventive maintenance are known and can thus be planned as can longer-term repairs.

Capacity Requirements Planning for Plannable Volumes of More Than 60%

[+]

If you have a plannable order volume of less than 60% due to unplanned repairs and emergency maintenance and can only enter inexact details for the standard time, simply deactivate capacity requirements planning. You can deactivate capacity requirements planning by using a control key for which the **Capacity Requirements** function is not activated.

However, if you have exact standard times, the proportion of planned orders is high, and you think that capacity requirements planning could help you, remember that capacity requirements planning always consists of three levels (see Figure 4.50):

❶ **Capacity requirement**
The capacity requirement specifies what capacity is required for individual orders at any given time. Capacity requirements are determined during the lead time scheduling and scheduled at the work centers.

❷ **Capacity leveling**
Now compare these requirements with the available capacity and then carry out a capacity leveling, that is, a leveling of overloads and underloads by taking corresponding measures such as shifting the date of an order, for example.

❸ **Available capacity**
Available capacity has already been described in detail in Chapter 2, Section 2.2.

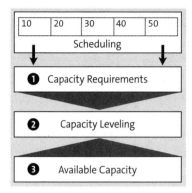

Figure 4.50 Capacity Planning

Capacity requirements are created based on orders—more specifically, specifications in the operations in the **Work** field. To generate capacity requirements, you must fulfill the following prerequisites:

- In the work center, you have entered a formula for calculating the capacity requirement for internal processing. This formula must point to the ARBEI field, that is, the work from the operation. In the standard system, the formula is SAPO08.

- In the case of operations, you use a control key for which the **Capacity Requirements** function is activated.

- You have scheduled the order (see the section on scheduling).

You can use capacity overviews (for example, Transaction CM01) to view a comparison of available capacity and capacity requirements, in table format (as shown in Figure 4.51).

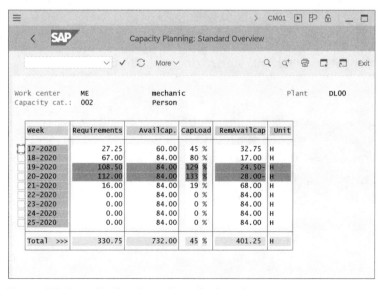

Figure 4.51 Capacity Planning:– Capacity Overview

You can obtain the following information, in particular, from the capacity overviews:

- Current available capacity
- Amounts of capacity loads
- Overload situation
- Available capacity

If the capacity overview clearly shows that the available capacity is not sufficient, you must take capacity-leveling measures (see Figure 4.52):

- You can increase (temporarily or permanently) the available capacity by scheduling additional shifts, workdays, or manual workers.
- You can reschedule individual orders at other work centers if these still have remaining available capacities.
- You can move the date of individual orders forward or backward.
- You can assign individual orders to external companies.

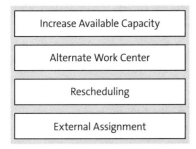

Figure 4.52 Capacity Planning: Capacity Leveling

[+]

First Choice: Postponing Orders

The most common and thus least complicated procedure used to level capacity overloads or underloads in plant maintenance involves postponing orders or bringing them forward.

4.4.3 Availability Checks in General

An availability check means that you let the system check whether the resources you plan for the requirements date are available in sufficient quantities or numbers.

You can perform an availability check for materials, available capacities, and PRT. You control this for each plant and order type using the customizing function **Availability Check for Materials, PRTs, and Capacities**.

You can use all three availability checks to determine how the system should behave if the requested resource is not available in sufficient quantities or numbers:

- Release based on a user decision
- Automatic release despite insufficient availability
- No release

[+] **Allowing Users to Decide**

When performing an availability check, always let the user decide what should happen when a resource is not available.

Prerequisites for performing availability checks are an active availability check and a defined overall profile that controls how the capacity requirements planning is to be performed. The overall profile consists of several individual profiles such as a control profile, time profile, and evaluation profile. You can set up these profiles in customizing using the detail functions under **Production · Capacity Requirements Planning · Capacity Leveling and Enhanced Evaluation**.

If you have not yet checked the capacity availability, the order is given the **CANC** status (capacity availability not checked); if the capacity check is unsuccessful, the system sets the status in the order to **MSCP** (capacity shortage).

4.4.4   PRT Availability Check

Where a check of PRT is concerned, you can control whether only the status or also the inventory is checked. You can only check the inventory, however, if you list the PRT as material master. You cannot check equipment or documents. However, we won't discuss these aspects in more detail here because this check is seldom used.

If the check for available PRT is performed but unsuccessful, the system sets the status of the order to MSPR (PRT availability shortage).

4.4.5   Material Availability Check

Three types of availability checks exist: static, dynamic, and global:

- During a *static availability check*, the system checks whether the relevant material is available in sufficient quantities at the plant on the current date (today). This type of check is not suitable for a modern material availability check.

- A *dynamic availability check* determines whether the required material is sufficiently available in the plant for the requirements date (that is, when the order is being implemented). Figure 4.53 illustrates how the current warehouse stock (based on the current date and taking into account safety stocks) is likely to change until the requirements date due to stock movements (planned goods receipts, planned goods issues, planned stock transfers). The available to promise (ATP) quantity is determined for the requirements date. This type of availability check is used by SAP S/4HANA Asset Management.

- A dynamic availability check is initially performed for a *global availability check*. If the result of this check is negative, you can use alternative strategies. You can check, for example, whether the material is available in another plant, whether spare material is available, or whether the required material can be delivered at short notice by potential vendors. This type of availability check is used in production planning and detailed scheduling (PP-DS) in SAP S/4HANA.

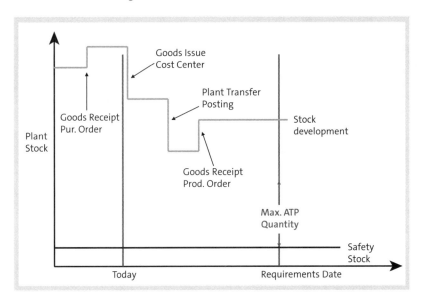

Figure 4.53 Order: Dynamic Material Availability Check

However, since we are dealing with SAP S/4HANA Asset Management here, this section will only discuss the procedure used for the dynamic availability check.

Prerequisites to be met to perform a material availability check are as follows:

- First, you must enter a checking group on the **MRP 3** tab in the material master, for example, 02 (individual requirements). From the perspective of plant maintenance, this checking group defines only a group of several materials which has to be checked following the same procedure. You maintain the checking group by using the customizing function **Define Checking Group**.

- You then must define a checking rule (for example, PM: plant maintenance) using the customizing function **Define Checking Rules**. This checking rule also has no initial effect but, rather, merely represents a grouping of procedures.

- You must define the actual scope of the check from the combination of checking group and checking rule using the customizing function **Define Scope of Check**. Here, you define, for example, which stock types and planned goods receipts and issues must be taken into account for the check.

- Finally, you must define the actual checking control for each plant and order type using the customizing function **Define Checking Control**.

When you have fulfilled all of these prerequisites, you can then check whether the materials you planned are available for the requirements date. These checks occur at different levels:

- You can check the availability of an individual material within an individual order (Transaction IW32, 🕒 button at the material level).

- You can check the availability of all materials within an individual order (Transaction IW32, 🕒 button at the header level).

- When you release the order, the system automatically triggers an availability check again. If all materials are available, the order is released. If all materials are not available, the system response is based on your setting for the **Material Release** option in the customizing function **Define Checking Control**. The order is either implemented or rejected, or you determine whether the order should be released or not.

You can now display the results of a material availability check as follows:

- You can display the result for an individual order within Transaction IW32 by choosing **More · Order · Functions · Availability · Availability List**.

- In Transaction IW38, you can display the result of several orders by choosing **More · Goto · List of Available Material** (see Figure 4.54).

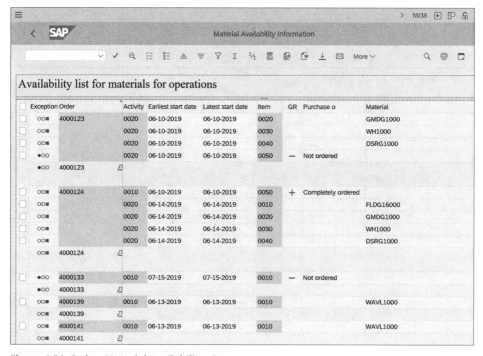

Figure 4.54 Order: Material Availability List

If you have not yet performed the availability check, the order has the **MANC** status (material availability not checked). If the availability check was performed with the result that the material is available, the system sets the status to **MACM** (material confirmed) in the order. If the availability check was performed with the result that the material is unavailable, the status is set to **MSPT** (missing part).

If you activate the business function LOG_EAM_CI_8, in addition to the individual check described above, the collective availability check is available, i.e., you can check the availability of multiple orders at the same time.

To do this, proceed as follows: Either you start Transaction IW38A (Material Availability Check) and an availability check is then carried out for all orders found in the selection, or you start Transaction IW38 (Order List) and mark the orders to be checked. To do this, start the menu function **More · Environment · Material Availability Check**.

Result: You receive information as to whether materials are available or not, whether availability could not be checked due to missing customizing settings, etc. (see Figure 4.55).

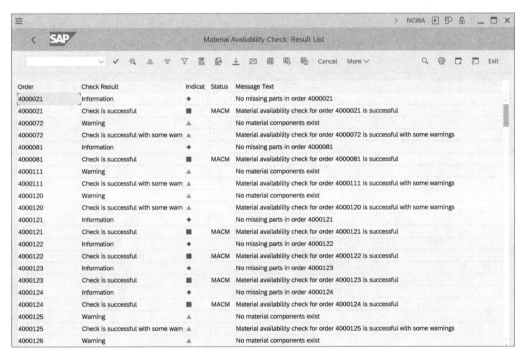

Figure 4.55 Order: Collective Material Availability Check

4.4.6   Order Release

As long as the order still has the **CRTD** (created) status, you cannot print shop papers, withdraw material, or confirm times. You cannot post a goods receipt for ordered spare parts either. This status changes when the order is released, after which you can then perform the following activities:

- The reservation is effective, and you can withdraw the material.
- You can print shop papers.
- You can confirm the order.
- You can move goods.
- You can settle the order.

When you release an order, the system checks whether the required materials and production resources/tools are available and whether the required permits are granted. When the order is finally released, the material reservations are relevant for materials planning and can be withdrawn, and the purchase requisitions are created.

Also note that you can no longer change the cost estimation after the order is released.

Various options are available that you can use to release orders:

- You can release an individual order (Transaction IW32, ⚑ button).
- You can use the **Put in process** function (Transaction IW32, 🖪 button); the order is released, and the shop papers are simultaneously printed.
- You can simultaneously release several orders from list processing (Transaction IW38, select the orders and click the ⚑ button).
- You can also release orders immediately when they are created. This option is available when the system creates orders automatically, that is, for orders that are generated using a maintenance plan (see Chapter 5) or that you create from a notification.

[+]

Releasing Orders Automatically

To ensure that orders that result from maintenance plans or notifications are immediately released when they are created, use the customizing function **Configure Order Types** to set the **Release immediately** indicator for the required order types.

When the orders are released, the system sets the status in the order to **REL**.

4.4.7 Shop Paper Printing

Generally, when notifications and orders are used, only the order is printed.

[+]

Freedom of Choice with Shop Paper Printing

You have considerable freedom of choice in relation to the following:

- How many shop papers you want to print out
- Which shop papers you want to print out

> - The titles you wish to assign to shop papers
> - The layout of these shop papers
> - Which shop paper is to be output and on which output medium

For example, you could print the following documents as shop papers (see Figure 4.56):

- **Operation control tickets**
  An operation control ticket provides the maintenance engineer responsible with a complete overview of the maintenance order. You could also print the permit details here.

- **Job tickets**
  A job ticket, which accompanies the order, provides the manual worker performing the task with a complete overview of the order.

- **Material staging lists**
  A material staging list shows the warehouse clerk which materials for this order have been scheduled for each operation. This list, for example, could be printed directly in the warehouse.

- **Material withdrawal slips**
  A material withdrawal slip authorizes the manual worker to retrieve the materials required for the order from the warehouse. A material withdrawal slip is printed for each material component.

- **Time tickets and completion confirmation tickets**
  Time tickets and completion confirmation tickets are printed out only for those operations for which this is specified by their control keys. The number of time/completion confirmation tickets specified there is printed out for each operation for each manual worker involved in processing an order. The manual worker enters the time that he or she needed to perform the relevant operation.

- **Object lists**
  An object list contains all functional locations, equipment, notifications, and so on involved in the order if an object list is to be processed in the order (for an inspection round, for example).

Shop Paper Printing with Documents

Documents are frequently stored for technical objects, which must be printed out completely or partially together with the shop papers. Unfortunately, SAP does not provide a standard solution for this. However, some manufacturers have started to develop and distribute a fee-based add-on for this purpose, for example, SEAL Systems AG (*www.sealsystems.com*) and the Prometheus Group (*www.prometheusgroup.com*).

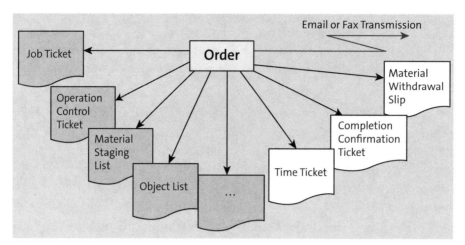

Figure 4.56 Order: Shop Papers

The following *output media* are available:

- Local printers
- Network printers
- Fax machines
- Email addresses
- PC downloads

Which prerequisites must you fulfill to be able to print shop papers?

- First, use the customizing function **Define Shop Papers** to define which shop papers should be used in general. You refer to an output program, form routine, and form; these elements are where you define the layout and output control.

- In the customizing function **Define Shop Papers for Order Type**, you then define which shop paper you want to be printed for which order type.

- In the customizing function **User-Specific Print Control**, you finally define the printer on which the shop paper you choose should be printed for a particular user.

[+]

Recommendations for Printing

Use the customizing function **User-Specific Print Control** to activate the **Output immediately** option because, otherwise, the shop papers will be set only in the spool file, and you will have to trigger the printing separately from there.

In the same customizing function, you should also immediately print out the papers for the warehouse on the warehouse printer to ensure that the warehouse employees can schedule their pick tasks on time.

You have the following options when printing documents:

- You can trigger the order printing for an individual order while processing the order by choosing the function **More · Order · Print · Order** or by clicking the 🖶 button (see Figure 4.57).

Figure 4.57 Order: Print Popup

- For authorization reasons, you use a separate Transaction IW3D for printing individual orders.

- You can use the order list (Transaction IW38) to print several orders simultaneously by selecting the relevant orders and choosing the function **More · Order · Print Order**.

- If you want to send shop papers by fax instead of printing them, enter a recipient number in the relevant column.

- If you only want to print the changes to the order since the last print operation, select column **D (Delta print)**.

- If you want to send the shop papers by email, refer to SAP Notes 317851 and 513352.

The system sets the status of the order to PRT for the print operation.

> **Simplifying the Print Operation**   [+]
>
> If you find the dialog box for printing the orders a nuisance because you always want to print the predefined shop papers anyway, you can prevent the appearance of this box as follows: Within the order, choose **Extras · Settings · Default Values** to call the **Control** tab and activate the **Print without Dialog** option.

4.4.8   Paging

Another function of the order (and also the notification) is paging. This means that you can send short messages to one or more partners by using the ✉️button. These short messages can either be predefined standard texts or texts that you enter directly when you want to send a short message. You may also add your own texts to the predefined standard texts (see Figure 4.58).

Figure 4.58 Order: Paging

The following services are supported by paging:

- Pagers
- Fax
- Email
- SMS
- SAP mail

After the paging message has been sent, the status **PAGE** is set in the order (or in the message).

In order to use this function, the following requirements must be met:

- The components SAP Office and SAPconnect are active.
- In customizing, you have assigned a role *paging partner* to the order tape or notification type (customizing function **Define Partner Determination Procedure and Partner Function · Assign Partner Determination Procedure to Order** or **Assign Partner Functions to Notification Type**).

- The partner role paging partner is filled in the order (e.g., by transferring the contact person from the reference object).

- The communication data of the person concerned is maintained in the user master record (Transaction SU3 [Maintain User Profile] or SU01 [User Maintenance]; see Figure 4.59).

Figure 4.59 User Communication Data

With Paging You Can Contact Technicians Directly   [+]

With the paging function, you can quickly and easily send short messages to participants (e.g., the technician). The prerequisites for this are the definition of a paging partner in the partner role and the activation of the SAP components SAP Office and SAPconnect.

You have now completed all the preparatory work for implementing the order and can begin actually processing the order.

4.5   Processing

During the processing phase, you only need to enter the withdrawn materials in the system.

To enter material withdrawals in the system, the order must already have been released. You can make a material withdrawal either as a planned material withdrawal or as an unplanned material withdrawal.

A *planned material withdrawal* occurs when you have already performed material planning (Section 4.3) and have therefore created a reservation.

The standard transaction for a material withdrawal is Transaction MIGO (Goods Issue) (see Figure 4.60); enter a planned material withdrawal using the function **Goods Issue · Order**.

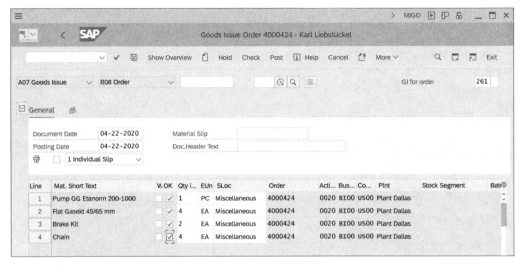

Figure 4.60 Goods Issue

However, since all required spare parts are rarely known in advance before an order is started in plant maintenance, the option of an *unplanned material withdrawal* is at least as important as a planned material withdrawal. You also perform an unplanned material withdrawal using Transaction MIGO but via the menu path **Goods Issue · Other · Movement Type 261**.

For activity-assigned orders, enter the order number and operation number as a posting rule (see Figure 4.61); for all other orders, enter only the order number.

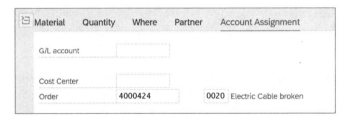

Figure 4.61 Unplanned Goods Issue Assigned to Order and Operation

Both the planned and unplanned goods movements are documented in the order. You can display the list of goods movements by choosing **Extras · Documents for Order · Goods Movements** (see Figure 4.62).

After processing the order, you must enter the accumulated data in SAP S/4HANA Asset Management.

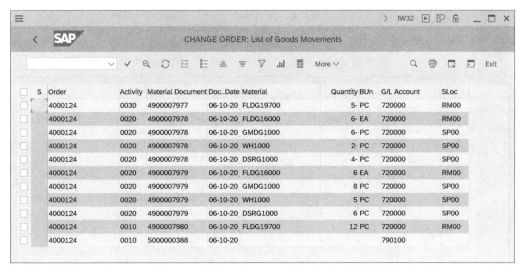

Figure 4.62 Order: List of Goods Movements

4.6   Completion

Now, enter the times that were required for processing the order (time completion confirmations) and then store the technical information such as the causes of damage or actions, for example (technical completion confirmation). After you enter this information, settle the order, which still must be technically and commercially completed. The execution of these tasks (time completion confirmation, technical completion information, technical completion and commercial completion with order settlement) will be introduced in the next sections.

4.6.1   Completion Confirmations

You perform time confirmations at the operation level in SAP S/4HANA Asset Management.

> **Simplifying Confirmation**
>
> If you find it too laborious or time-consuming to confirm each operation individually, create a final *completion confirmation* operation in the order. You can assign a control key only to this operation via the function **Confirmation provided**; you can assign a control key to all others that contain either the function **Confirmation not possible** or the function **Confirmation possible, but not necessary**.

Prerequisites to be met to ensure that you can enter time confirmations are as follows:

- You must release the orders to be confirmed.
- In customizing, use the function **Define Control Parameters for Confirmations** to define how you want to perform the time confirmations for each plant and order type. For example, you can define whether default values should appear or whether deviations should be allowed.

[!] **Taking Care with "Clear Open Reservations"**

Do not set the two indicators **Final confirmation** and **Clear Open Reservs** at the same time because, when you perform a final confirmation, the **Clear Open Reservs** option deletes the reservations that are not yet issued. The **Final confirmation** option automatically performs a final confirmation on the operation for a time confirmation that is greater than the planned time. If you do not now enter the material withdrawal promptly, but you do enter the confirmation without delay, the open reservations will be deleted, even though they are issued.

Different transactions are available for entering the actual times.

You can use the *individual time confirmation* (Transaction IW41, Figure 4.63) to enter exactly one completion confirmation for an operation.

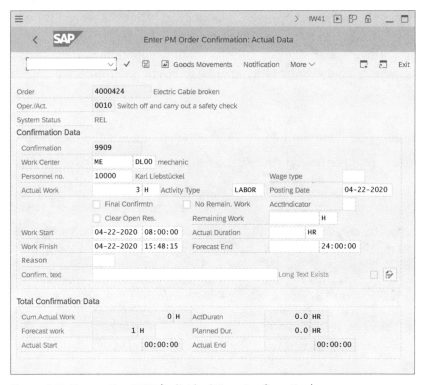

Figure 4.63 Transaction IW41 (Individual Time Confirmation)

If you want to enter other completion confirmations for the same operation or for a different operation of the same order, you can start this transaction several times in succession.

From an individual time confirmation, you can skip to entering other data (for example, material withdrawals or measurement documents).

You can use a *collective time confirmation* (see Figure 4.64) to confirm times for several operations and orders. Collective time confirmations are available with a preceding selection option (Transaction IW48) or without a preceding selection option (Transaction IW44).

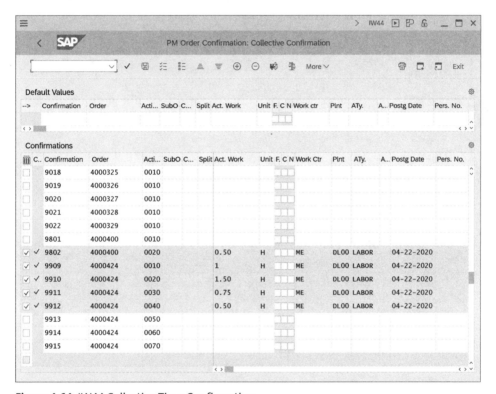

Figure 4.64 IW44 Collective Time Confirmation

Cross-Application Time Sheet (CATS) is an application you can use to enter several actual person-related times. This application is not only available in plant maintenance but is also available in other application areas such as human resources or production, for example.

As a prerequisite for using this function, you must define data entry profiles, which you can set via the customizing function **Set Up Data Entry Profiles**. In the data entry profiles, you define whether the actual times recorded need to be released and permitted separately, for how many periods the times can be recorded simultaneously, or whether totals rows should be displayed for each operation and day. The CATS process consists of the following steps (see Figure 4.65):

1. Record time data recording in the data entry sheet (Transaction CAT2, see Figure 4.66)
2. Optionally, release time data (Transaction CAT2 [Time Sheet], depends on the data entry profile)
3. Optionally, approve time data (Transaction CATS_APPR_LITE [Approve Working Times], depends on the data entry profile)
4. Transfer CATS data to the target application, in our case, to plant maintenance (Transaction CAT9 [CATS Transfer to Plant Maintenance]).

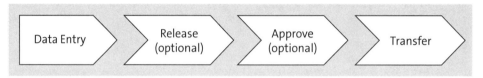

Figure 4.65 CATS Process

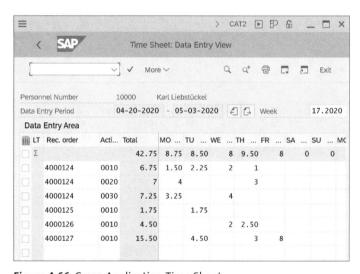

Figure 4.66 Cross-Application Time Sheet

You can use *overall completion confirmation* (Transaction IW42) not only to enter times for several operations of an order but also to enter material withdrawals, counter readings, causes of damage, measurement readings, and notification items (see Figure 4.67).

As a prerequisite for performing the overall completion confirmation, you must define data entry profiles using the customizing function **Set Screen Templates for the Completion Confirmation** and assign a data entry profile (Transaction IW42, **More · Extras · Settings**).

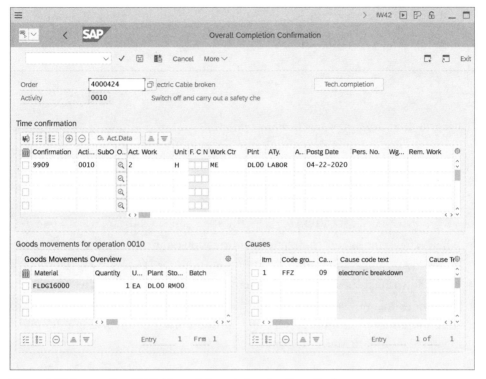

Figure 4.67 Transaction IW42 (Overall Completion Confirmation)

Advantage of Overall Completion Confirmation [+]

A particular advantage, compared to the other confirmation procedures, that has emerged in practice for the overall completion confirmation (Transaction IW42) is that, in addition to entering the actual data, you can also technically complete the order at the same time.

The recording of notification items and causes of damage was already the transition from the pure time confirmation to the technical completion confirmation.

4.6.2   Technical Completion Confirmations

You perform technical completion confirmations at the notification level and enter information such as the damage code, cause of damage, downtimes, actions, tasks, or system availability.

Figure 4.68 displays an overview of the options you can use to record a technical completion confirmation.

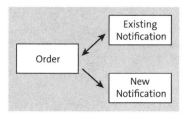

Figure 4.68 Technical Completion Confirmation

Specifically, depending on the specific use, the following will happen:

- If the order already contains a notification, for example, because it emerged from this notification, you can go directly from the order (Transaction IW32, `Notifctn    10000284    ✎` button) to the notification and enter the information there.
- When you use the overall completion confirmation (Transaction IW42), you can use or define a corresponding data entry profile and enter notification data there.
- You can also enter the information directly in the notification (Transaction IW22).
- If the order does not yet have a notification, you can create a new notification from the order, either at the header level using the **Notifctn** button or for each entry in the object list by clicking the ⬜ button.

4.6.3   Technical Completion

When you have processed the order, you have technically completed it, which has the following consequences:

- The status of the order is set to **TECO** (technically completed).
- Purchase requisitions that were not yet converted into purchase orders get the deletion indicator.
- You can still process purchase orders and enter goods receipts or invoice receipts.
- You can still enter time confirmations.
- Reservations that have not been issued are deleted.
- Open capacity loads are reduced, or capacities are released.

[+]

Completing Orders and Notifications Together

You can also complete notifications when you technically complete orders. Otherwise, you will have to complete the notifications separately.

Several options are available that you can use to technically complete orders:

- When you use the overall completion confirmation (Transaction IW42), you can technically complete the order and time confirmation at the same time from there by clicking the **Tech.completion** button.

- Otherwise, you can technically complete an individual order (Transaction IW32) by clicking the ☑ button.

- You can also technically complete several orders simultaneously from the list processing (Transaction IW38) by selecting the orders and then choosing **More** · **Order** · **Completion** · **Complete** technically or by clicking the ☑ button.

[+]

> **Simplifying Technical Completion**
>
> If you find the dialog box for the technical completion a nuisance because you want to complete the order anyway, without having to enter more data, you can suppress this as follows: Within the order, choose **Extras** · **Settings** · **Default Values** to call the **Control** tab and activate the **No Dialog Compl** option.

If you completed an order by mistake, you can also cancel the technical completion: Within the order, use Transaction IW32 and choose **More** · **Order** · **Functions** · **Complete** · **Cancel Technical Completion** in this case.

If business function LOG_EAM_CI_7 is enabled, you can use Transaction IW38 to cancel the technical completion for several orders at once. For this purpose, select the orders in the Transaction IW38 list and choose **More** · **Order** · **Complete** · **Cancel Technical Completion** in the context menu.

The order will thus be set to the exact status it had before the technical completion:

- Deletion indicators in the purchase requisition will be canceled.
- Capacity loads will be increased again.
- Reservations will become active again.
- The order will have the **Released** status.

If you had also completed notification(s) when you technically completed the order, these remain unaffected by the cancellation of the order completion: Although the notifications remain completed, you can set them separately to the **In Process** status again.

If the order is technically completed and all associated cost postings are entered in the order, you can also perform a business completion of the order.

4.6.4   Order Printing after Technical Completion

For a long time, in the SAP system, orders could not be printed after the technical completion. However, you may need to print individual order documents or the entire order after the technical completion of the order, for example, because you require a written order combination or because you want to have your documents complete.

Business function LOG_EAM_CI_7 is available for this purpose. In the customizing function **Define Printer**, enable the **Allow Print After Completion** function in **User-Specific Print Control**.

The actual print function then corresponds to the normal print function for released orders (Section 4.4.7).

4.6.5   Business Completion

Similar to the technical completion, business completion takes place by setting a status (**CLSD**, closed). When you have performed the business completion, no further costs can be posted to the order.

The following prerequisites must be met so that a business completion of an order can occur:

- The order must be technically completed (**TECO** status).
- The order is settled, and the actual cost balance is 0.
- The order no longer has an open purchase order.
- No further costs are otherwise expected to be posted to the order.

To perform the business completion, you have the following options:

- Completing an individual order within order processing (Transaction IW32) by clicking the **Complete (business)** button.
- Performing completions of several orders simultaneously from the list processing (Transaction IW38) by selecting the orders and choosing **More · Order · Complete · Complete Business Function**.

If you inadvertently performed a business completion for an order or you need to enter a subsequent debit (for example, an invoice), you can also cancel the business completion. Within the order, call (Transaction IW32) the function **More · Order · Functions · Complete · Cancel Business Completion** in this case. You can thus post to the order again, and you can enter the subsequent debit.

If business function LOG_EAM_CI_7 is enabled, you can use Transaction IW38 to cancel several orders at once. For this purpose, select the orders from the list in Transaction IW38 and choose **More · Order · Complete · Cancel Business Completion** in the context menu.

4.6.6   Document Flow

The document flow is an important tool which many users like to use. The document flow shows all documents that were created during notification and order processing (see Figure 4.69), including the following:

- Notifications
- Purchase requisitions
- Purchase orders
- Material withdrawals
- Confirmations
- Goods receipts
- Invoice receipts
- Service entry sheets

You can call the document flow at any time via the ▣ button. You can also use the field selection to define which fields you would like to display for which documents.

- To display a document in detail, double-click on the document.
- To enable this enhanced document flow, business function LOG_EAM_CI_6 must be activated.
- If you do not fulfill these prerequisites, a simplified document flow, without invoice receipts or field selection, is available.

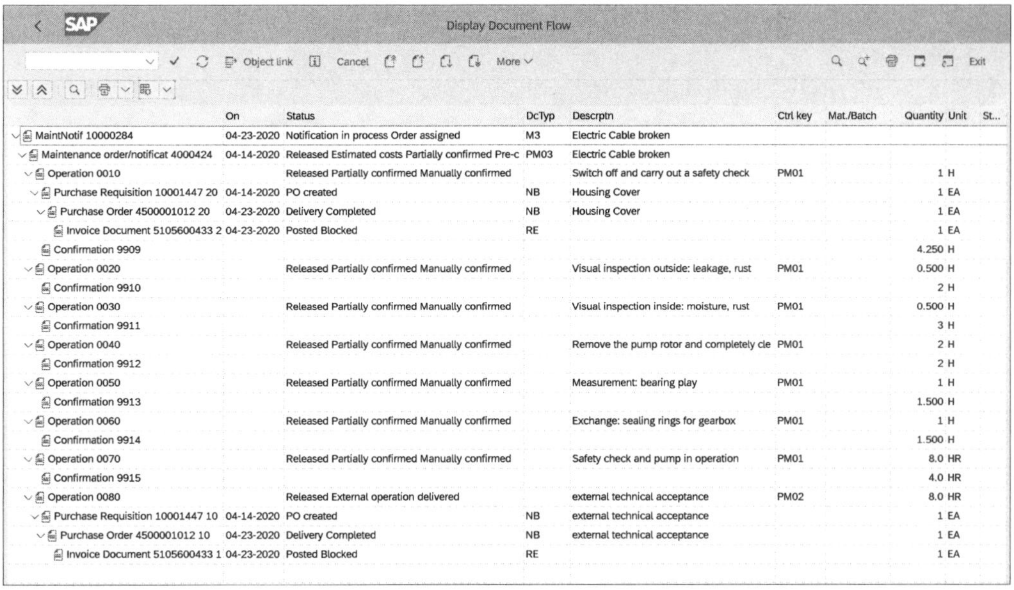

Figure 4.69 Order: Document Flow

4.6.7   Action Log

Another function that many users really like is the action log. You can use the action log to display all changes (see Figure 4.70) that you have made in the following objects:

- Order headers
- Statuses
- Operations
- Materials
- Production resources/tools

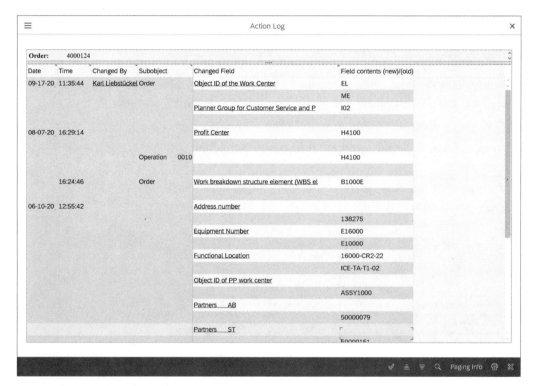

Figure 4.70 Order: Action Log

You can define the objects for which you want to generate change documents using the customizing function **Define Change Documents, Collective Purchase Requisitions MRP Relevance**. You call the action log via the menu within the order (**More · Extras · Documents for Order · Action log**).

This chapter explained the most important functions provided by SAP S/4HANA Asset Management for handling and processing the work order cycle.

4.7   Summary

SAP S/4HANA Asset Management provides a wide range of work order cycle functionalities. In this chapter, you learned about the most important functions of notifications and orders as well as how to use them. Nonetheless, before you map your work order cycle to SAP S/4HANA Asset Management, you should ask yourself some questions and answer them to the best of your current knowledge (e.g., which functions are necessary or if you should use notifications and/or orders).

In Section 4.2 you learned about the following:

- How to create a notification
- The structure and content of a notification
- How to use catalogs and catalog profiles
- How to assign documents and partners

In Section 4.3 you learned the following:

- Several ways to create an order
- The structure and content of an order
- How to create order operations or set up order hierarchies
- How to schedule an order
- How to assign components with or without electronic parts catalogs and how to assign PRTs
- How to assign documents and responsibilities
- How to use an object list
- How to cost an order and how to assign estimated costs

In Section 4.4, you learned the following:

- How to mass change orders and operations
- How to perform capacity planning and availability checks
- How to release and how to print an order

In Section 4.5, you learned how to withdraw materials from stock—with or without reservation.

In Section 4.6, you learned the following:

- How to perform order time confirmations with PM transactions and with CATS
- How to assign technical completion information to notifications
- How to complete an order—technical and business
- How to see document flows and action logs

Chapter 5
Preventive Maintenance

This chapter presents the range of possibilities of preventive plant main- tenance which SAP S/4HANA is offering you. You'll learn about different kinds of task lists. Various configuration levels of maintenance plans are shown, starting with a simple time-based single-cycle plan through a time-based or performance-based strategy plan up to condition-based maintenance.

The business process for preventive maintenance is characterized by the fact that you can plan required resources (work centers, materials, external companies, and so on) in advance in respect to content and scheduling. This type of business process is associated with the following scenarios:

- A pump undergoes a visual and functional inspection every 6 months, and the mechanical seal is changed every 12 months.
- The hydraulic oil must be changed regularly after every 1,000 operation hours (OPH) and the brake fluid after every 2,000 OPH on a forklift truck.
- The fire extinguisher in the building is refilled every 2 years.
- Test equipment is recalibrated every 120 days.

The preventive maintenance process thus differs from the work order cycle (Chapter 4) in terms of the ability to schedule it. This difference is due to the fact that only the content but not the date of a planned repair can be predetermined.

Preventive maintenance differs, in turn, from an immediate repair (see Chapter 6, Section 6.1) in terms of you being able to plan it in respect to content and scheduling. You can only respond to malfunctions in the course of an immediate repair, but you cannot plan them in advance.

This chapter will begin with a discussion of the basic principles of preventive maintenance in general and the SAP objects used in preventive maintenance. Next, it will cover the major aspects of preventive maintenance: task lists, time-based and performance-based maintenance plans, multiple-counter plans, inspections rounds, and condition-based maintenance.

5.1 Basic Principles of Preventive Maintenance

Preventive maintenance is always associated with effort only—both in its planning and execution. Nevertheless, you must or should perform preventive maintenance in your company for many reasons, as follows:

- **Legal requirements**
  Legislation relating to plant safety or industrial health and safety may stipulate that you must inspect or maintain your technical system regularly.

- **Quality assurance**
  The quality of a product largely depends on the condition of the production facility in which it is manufactured.

- **Reduction in frequency of malfunctions**
  One of the most important tasks in maintenance planning is to keep a production facility continuously available in the long term—and effective preventive maintenance ensures that a technical system does not break down and also reduces unnecessary costs that accrue due to repairs, replacing the system, or production downtimes.

- **Environmental protection requirements**
  Effective preventive maintenance can contribute to preventing system breakdowns that can lead to environmental impacts.

- **Recommendations of the manufacturer**
  The manufacturer of your technical system may recommend certain procedures for ensuring that the system always runs optimally.

- **Improved utilization control of capacities**
  The preventive maintenance ensures that you have a work list for utilizing your workshops more consistently (for example, if you have fewer breakdown repair tasks to process).

- **Decrease in maintenance costs**
  Whether you can decrease your maintenance costs through preventative maintenance is debatable and mainly depends on whether or not you have already reached the optimum intensity level of preventive maintenance.

The cost scheduling for preventive maintenance and repairs is inversely proportionate and specifically depends on the intensity level of the preventive maintenance (see Figure 5.1), as follows:

- The higher the intensity level of preventive maintenance, the higher the costs for preventive maintenance.

- The higher the intensity level of preventive maintenance, the lower the costs for repairs.

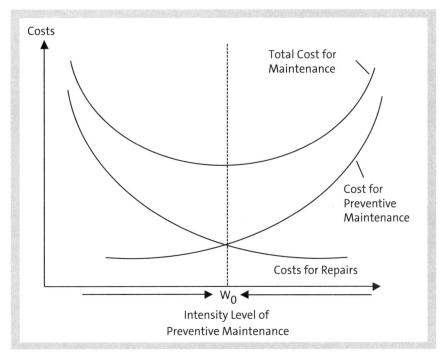

Figure 5.1 Plant Maintenance Costs

At an optimum intensity level, WO, the overall costs of plant maintenance are minimal. Follow-up costs that can be incurred because of inadequate preventive maintenance (for example, restarting costs) are not taken into account for this cost consideration, since they are only regarded as opportunity costs.

Three different types of preventive maintenance exist (see Figure 5.2), as follows:

- **Time-based maintenance**
  The preventive maintenance task is triggered after a certain period of time has expired (for example, every 6 months).

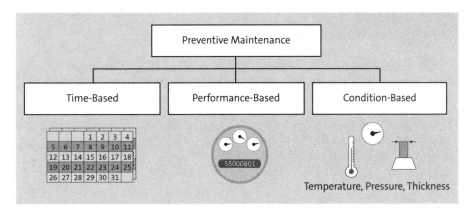

Figure 5.2 Types of Preventive Maintenance

- **Performance-based maintenance**
  The preventive maintenance task is triggered when a certain level of performance is reached (for example, every 10,000 miles).

- **Condition-based maintenance**
  The preventive maintenance task is triggered when a certain diagnostic value has not been reached or has been exceeded (for example, a pressure lower than 15 bars or temperature higher than 85°C).

5.2   Preventive Maintenance Objects

When performing preventive maintenance business processes, several objects are used in SAP S/4HANA Asset Management, whose significance and interrelationships are briefly explained in the following list (see Figure 5.3):

- **Maintenance strategy**
  A maintenance strategy contains the chronological sequence of maintenance activities (for example, maintenance packages every 3, 6, 12, or 24 months for time-based maintenance or every 1,000, 2,000, or 5,000 operation hours for performance-based maintenance). A maintenance strategy does not provide any details about the activity, object, or date and is only required for strategy-based maintenance plans (Section 5.4.2 and Section 5.5.2).

- **Maintenance task list**
  A maintenance task list describes activities (operations) and contains materials and deadlines (maintenance packages). Object-specific maintenance task lists include an equipment plan or a functional location plan, and neutral maintenance task lists include instructions. Strategy-based maintenance plans must contain a task list, while all other maintenance plans can optionally contain a task list.

- **Maintenance item**
  A maintenance item describes the activities to be performed, contains the reference object (or the object list), and has organizational data relevant for subsequent processing.

- **Maintenance plan**
  A maintenance plan contains one or more maintenance items and determines the maintenance dates as well as the maintenance call object (order, notification, and so on).

- **Deadline monitoring**
  Deadline monitoring (program RISTRA20H in SAP S/4HANA) runs automatically as a batch job and ensures that the maintenance call objects (for example, the orders) are automatically generated on the due date.

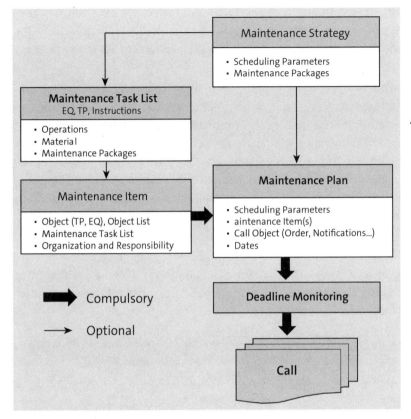

Figure 5.3 Interrelationships of Preventive Maintenance Objects

[+]

Preventive Maintenance in the Second Step of the Implementation

When reimplementing SAP S/4HANA Asset Management, you should think twice about whether you necessarily have to implement preventive maintenance in the first step, because preventive maintenance uses many special functions and requires a high level of acceptance among users.

SAP S/4HANA Asset Management provides you with maintenance plans that support preventive maintenance business processes. The following maintenance plan types can be selected (see Figure 5.4):

- **Single-cycle plans**
  You create single-cycle plans when you have to perform the same maintenance activities in full at regular intervals (time-based or performance-based). In this case, you can optionally include a task list.

- **Maintenance strategies and strategy plans**
  You create maintenance strategies and strategy plans when you have to perform maintenance activities that are based on each other or supersede each other—either

as a time-based strategy (for example, every 3, 6, or 12 months) or as a performance-based strategy (for example, every 10,000, 20,000, or 40,000 miles). In this case, you must include a maintenance task list, specifically, one that has the same strategy as the maintenance plan.

- **Multiple-counter plans**

  You create multiple-counter plans if determining the maintenance date is dependent on several influencing factors (for example, every 6 months, every 10,000 miles, or every 1,000 operation hours). Here, you can also optionally include a task list. With the simple multiple-counter plans, you only have one cycle (1,000 operating hours or 1 year); you can use the extended multiple-counter plan if you have successive cycles (1st cycle: every 2,000 operating hours or 1 year, 2nd cycle: every 4,000 operating hours or 2 years).

- **Inspection rounds plan**

  In the case of inspection rounds, you process not only a single object as with the other maintenance plan types, but you run through several objects and either carry out the same activities (simple inspection rounds plan) or different activities (extended inspection rounds plan) .

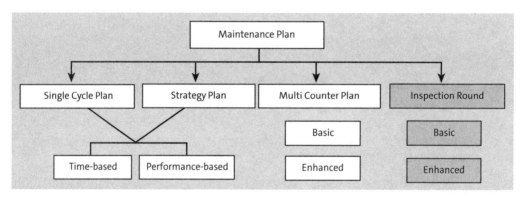

Figure 5.4 Maintenance Plan Types

You can use the customizing function **Set Maintenance Plan Categories** to define which of the following maintenance call objects should be called from the maintenance plan when due (see Figure 5.5):

- Select **Order** as the maintenance call object if you want to perform the specifications of the maintenance plan exactly as given, without further planning.

- Select **Notification** as the maintenance call object if you want to perform other detailed planning when due, for example, if you want to combine several notifications for an order based on the current capacity load utilization. In this case, several maintenance task lists are then copied into the respective order as an operation list.

- Select **Inspection Lot** as the maintenance call object if you want to perform a calibration inspection of test equipment. (For more information, refer to Chapter 6, Section 6.6).

- Select **Service entry sheet** as the maintenance call object if you have agreed on an outline agreement on regular services with an external company and you want the system to automatically generate, at regular intervals, the service entry sheets required for acceptance.

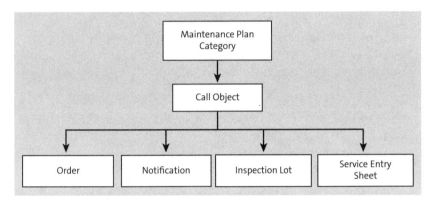

Figure 5.5 Maintenance Plan Categories and Call Object

Since the order maintenance call object represents the normal situation in preventive maintenance, this chapter will focus on this in the following descriptions but will also refer to the other maintenance call objects where appropriate.

5.3   Maintenance Task Lists

A maintenance task list essentially describes activities (operations) and contains materials that are required during processing of the activities.

Maintenance task lists are used not only in plant maintenance but also in the following areas in the SAP system:

- In discrete manufacturing as routings or reference operation sets
- In process manufacturing as a planning recipe
- In project processing as a standard network
- In quality management as an inspection plan

The following sections provide you with an overview of maintenance task lists before diving into the specifics of order and task lists, the action log, task list costing, and mass changes.

5.3.1   Basics of Maintenance Task Lists

In plant maintenance, maintenance task lists are primarily used for the following two purposes:

- **Preventive maintenance**
  In the area of preventive maintenance, in particular, maintenance task lists are widely used to map maintenance and inspection tasks, inspections, legal obligations, and so on.

- **Repairs**
  You can also use maintenance task lists in plant maintenance by predefining standard workflows for repair tasks or by defining a complete list of all possible maintenance tasks and then deciding, as the need arises, which of these tasks actually needs to be performed.

From a plant maintenance perspective, we can distinguish between three different types of maintenance task list:

- **Maintenance task list for equipment**
  You create a maintenance task list for equipment for exactly one piece of equipment (Transaction IA01 [Create Equipment Task List]) if you want to map specific tasks for the equipment. However, you can only use this maintenance task list in connection with this one piece of equipment.

- **Maintenance task list for functional location**
  You create a maintenance task list for a functional location for exactly one functional location (Transaction IA11 [Create Functional Location Task List]) if you want to map specific tasks for the functional location. Similarly, you can only use this task list in connection with this one functional location.

- **General maintenance task list**
  A general maintenance task list (Transaction IA05 [Create General Task List]) is not object specific and, as a result, is not assigned to any particular piece of equipment or functional location. However, you can indirectly make a general maintenance task list available for several pieces of equipment and/or functional locations. Here, you use the **Construction Type** field in the master record for the piece of equipment or functional location in the **Structuring** screen group. As a result, all pieces of equipment and functional locations for which a material number is entered in the **Construction Type** field ❶ can access general maintenance task lists for which the same material number is entered in turn in the **Assembly** field ❷ in the task list header (see Figure 5.6).

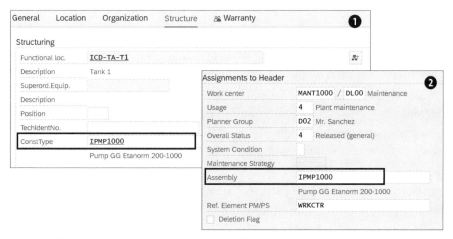

Figure 5.6 Technical Object and General Task List

> **Using General Maintenance Task Lists Whenever Possible**
>
> If you use maintenance task lists in plant maintenance, note the following:
>
> - Equipment and functional locations may have individual maintenance task lists or may access general maintenance task lists indirectly.
>
> - You should create general maintenance task lists if possible, which will save you time entering and maintaining data.
>
> - You should only create maintenance task lists for equipment or functional locations if you want to map tasks that are specific to a piece of equipment or functional location.

The numbers for equipment task lists and functional location task lists are assigned internally. When creating an equipment task list or a task list for a functional location, the system informs you of the number under which it saved the maintenance task list. The first maintenance task list you create for a specific piece of equipment or functional location is identified by a task list group number and a group counter. Subsequent task lists for the same piece of equipment are only identified by the sequential group counter within the group.

The numbers for general maintenance task lists can be assigned internally or externally.

> **Meaningful Numbers for General Maintenance Task Lists**
>
> When you create general maintenance task lists, you can use the task list number to indicate the objects for which the individual general maintenance task lists are suitable (for example, B. PUMP_MAN, FORK_MAN, MOT_REP). Using meaningful numbers will make selection easier later.

A task list is comprised of the following elements (see Figure 5.7):

- **Header data**
  Header data is information that is used to identify and manage the maintenance task list. This data is valid for the entire maintenance task list, for example, number, group counter, plant, main work center, and so on.

- **Operations**
  You can use operations to describe the work that you want to be performed when the maintenance task list is being implemented.

- **Material list**
  The material list contains spare parts that are required and consumed when implementing the task list.

- **Production resources/tools (PRTs)**
  PRTs (for example, tools, protective clothing, and hand pallet trucks) are also required for implementing the task list. However, unlike a material, they are not consumed.

- **Inspection characteristics**
  If inspections are to be conducted within an operation (for example, inspections of length, weight, and function), you can define these as inspection characteristics.

- **Maintenance packages**
  If the task list is used in a strategy maintenance plan, you use maintenance packages to control the frequency with which the maintenance work is performed—either on a time-dependent basis (for example, once every 3 months) or on a performance-dependent basis (for example, once every 1,200 operating hours).

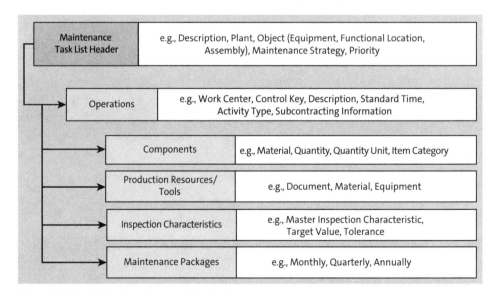

Figure 5.7 Task List: Structure and Content

An example of an operations list in a maintenance task list is provided in Figure 5.8.

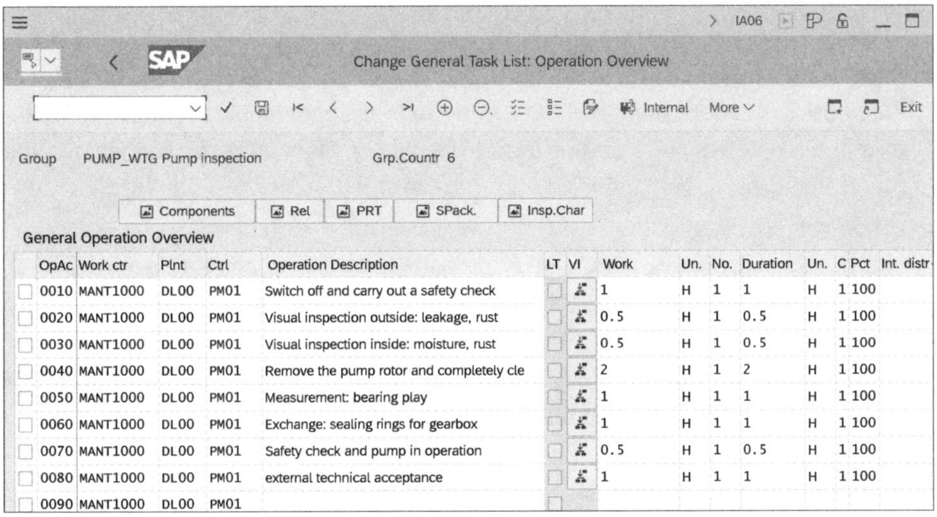

Figure 5.8 Task List: Operation Overview

You can assign components to a maintenance task list in one of the following ways:

- You assign material components from the bill of materials (BOM) of the maintenance object (equipment, functional location, or header assembly) that is assigned to the maintenance task list; in this case, the BOM matches the content of the structure list exactly.

- Alternatively, you assign stock materials that are not in the BOM of the maintenance object to the maintenance task list directly. This method is referred to as *free material assignment*. In this case, the materials are assigned by their material numbers. As a prerequisite for using free material assignment, you must specify a BOM usage (usually **Plant Maintenance Usage**) in customizing. In this case, use the customizing function **Define Default Setting for Free Material Assignment**. The SAP system thus creates an internal BOM in the case of a free assignment. This BOM cannot be edited by the application.

5.3.2   Order and Task List

The most common use of maintenance task lists will be discussed later in this chapter: the use of task lists and maintenance plans in preventive maintenance. However, you can also use maintenance task lists in connection with maintenance tasks by assigning a maintenance task list to an order directly. The following selection methods are available if you want to assign a maintenance task list within an order (Transaction IW31/32 [Create/Change Order], menu option **More · Extras · Task List Selection**):

- **Direct entry**
  If you know the task list group and group counter, you can use direct entry to select the maintenance task list.

- **General maintenance task lists**
  When using this selection procedure, you can select general maintenance task lists from a list. The selection criteria **Task list type** (A), **Plant**, and **Status** (released for order) are set by default. Individual criteria can still be added.

- **For object structure**
  This option displays all maintenance task lists that were created for the objects that are, in turn, sub-objects of the reference object.

- **For assembly**
  This selection procedure selects all maintenance task lists that have been created for the object entered in the **Assembly** field.

- **For reference object**
  This selection procedure is the simplest because it allows you to select maintenance task lists on the basis of the reference object. If an equipment with a construction type is specified as the reference object, all equipment task lists for the relevant equipment are displayed, as well as all general maintenance task lists with an assembly in the task list header that corresponds to the construction type of the equipment. The same applies for the functional location.

The system response to your selection of a maintenance task list depends on the personal settings you make under **More · Extras · Settings · Default Values** (see Figure 5.9).

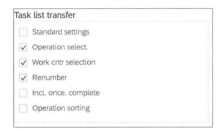

Figure 5.9 Order: Task List Settings

If you activate the **Operation select.** option, when the maintenance task list is transferred, a dialog box appears in which you can select specific operations. Selecting operations is useful, for example, if you do not require all of the operations in a maintenance task list for a specific scenario (see Figure 5.10).

If the **Operation select.** option is activated, you can also choose to execute operations multiple times in the dialog box (field **FCT** = factor), which may be necessary if, for example, you have added an object list to the relevant order.

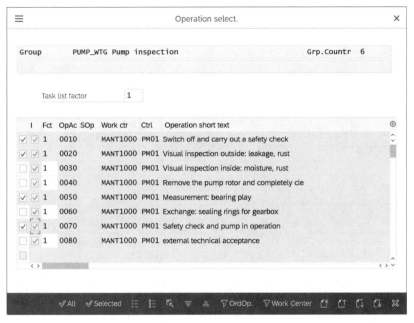

Figure 5.10 Order: Selecting Operations

Activating Operation Selection

If you select the **Operation select.** option in your personal settings, you not only have the option of selecting specific operations when a maintenance task list is transferred into an order; you can also execute individual operations multiple times using the execution factor (for example, if an object list exists).

If you activate the **Work cntr selection** option, you can replace the work centers of the maintenance task list with other work centers in the order (see Figure 5.11). You may need to choose work centers, for example, if the work centers you originally planned to use are already utilized to their maximum capacities.

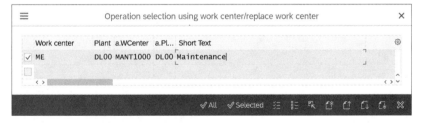

Figure 5.11 Order: Replacing Work Center

5.3.3   Action Log

Change documentation can now be used for maintenance task lists. To use this feature, choose **More · Extras · Action Log** in a maintenance task list to display the changes or start Transaction IA21 (Display Task List Change Documents) (see Figure 5.12), where you can display the changes across several maintenance task lists.

Grp.Count	Change to	Number	Operation short text	Valid From	Valid to	ChangeType	Changed On	Changed by
6	Task list header			04-10-2020	12-31-9999	Added	04-10-2020	LIEBSTUECKEL
	Operation	0010	Switch off and carry out a safety check	04-10-2020	12-31-9999	Added	04-10-2020	LIEBSTUECKEL
		0020	Visual inspection outside: leakage, rust	04-10-2020	12-31-9999	Added	04-10-2020	LIEBSTUECKEL
		0030	Visual inspection inside: moisture, rust	04-10-2020	12-31-9999	Added	04-10-2020	LIEBSTUECKEL
		0040	Remove the pump rotor and completely cle	04-10-2020	12-31-9999	Added	04-10-2020	LIEBSTUECKEL
		0050	Measurement: bearing play	04-10-2020	12-31-9999	Added	04-10-2020	LIEBSTUECKEL
		0060	Exchange: sealing rings for gearbox	04-10-2020	12-31-9999	Added	04-10-2020	LIEBSTUECKEL
		0070	Safety check and pump in operation	04-10-2020	12-31-9999	Added	04-10-2020	LIEBSTUECKEL
		0080	external technical acceptance	04-10-2020	12-31-9999	Added	04-10-2020	LIEBSTUECKEL
	Material Component IPMP1000 Pump GG Etanorm 200-1000			04-24-2020	12-31-9999	Added	04-24-2020	LIEBSTUECKEL

Figure 5.12 Task List: Action Log

The LOG_EAM_CI_3 business function must be activated in order for you to use the action log for maintenance task lists.

5.3.4   Task List Costing

Using Transaction IA16 (Task List Costing), you can also perform costings for maintenance task lists without having to create an order. The transaction thus answers the question as to what this maintenance task list would cost if executed. The costs are displayed (see Figure 5.13) separately by item type:

- **E**: Internal activity
- **F**: External service
- **M**: Material
- **G**: Overhead rates

Other potential item types such as a co-product or base planning object, however, are irrelevant for plant maintenance.

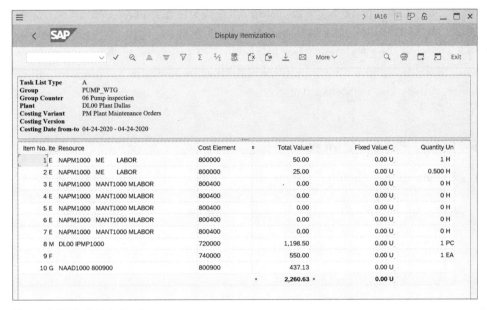

Figure 5.13 Task List: Costing

5.3.5 Mass Changes

You can use two transactions to make mass changes to maintenance task lists:

- Transaction CA87 to replace work centers (see Figure 5.14)
- Transaction CA77 to replace PRTs

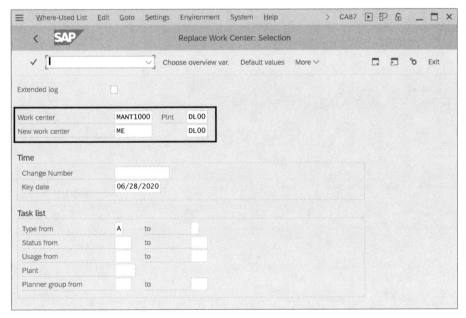

Figure 5.14 Task List: Mass Change

In both cases, after you execute the selection, the system displays an overview of the maintenance task lists or operations that have been found. From this overview, you can now select the maintenance task lists that are to be involved in the replacement.

Next, let's turn our attention to more elements that are essential to preventive mainte-nance, namely, the maintenance plan.

5.4   Time-Based Maintenance Plans

For time-based maintenance, the maintenance dates are calculated solely via the calen-dar (for example, every 6 months). Performance-based values (such as, for example, operation hours) have no effect. This section will cover both time-based single-cycle plans and time-based strategy plans.

5.4.1   Time-Based Single-Cycle Plan

You should create time-based single-cycle plans if you have to perform the same main-tenance activities in full at regular intervals. This section will first cover the initial steps of creating and scheduling a single-cycle plan. Because several influencing factors affect the calculation of the planned date, the next section explains in more detail the scheduling parameters. After that, this section walks through deadline monitoring, mass change, and cost displays. The section ends by looking at the scheduling overview and change documents.

Creating a Single-Cycle Plan

You can create the single-cycle plan via Transaction IP41 (see Figure 5.15). Here, you choose between internal and external number assignment.

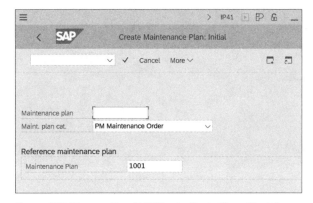

Figure 5.15 Transaction IP41 Single-Cycle Plan: Start Screen

If you want to copy maintenance plans, you must activate business function LOG_ EAM_CI_10. Then, there are two ways to copy maintenance plans:

- First, you can only copy maintenance plans which you have characterized as **Reference Maintenance Plan** (Transactions IP41/42/43) via the menu path **Create Maintenance Plan · Functions · Copy Template · Allow**).

- Second, with customizing function **Configure Special Functions for Maintenance Planning** you can activate the non-template-copying of maintenance plans to copy all maintenance plans.

Enable Non-Template-Based Copying

It's much easier to allow all maintenance plans as reference than to characterize maintenance plans manually for reference plans.

Specify the cycle where the maintenance is to take place directly in the maintenance plan, just like all other data required for a maintenance task (see Figure 5.16).

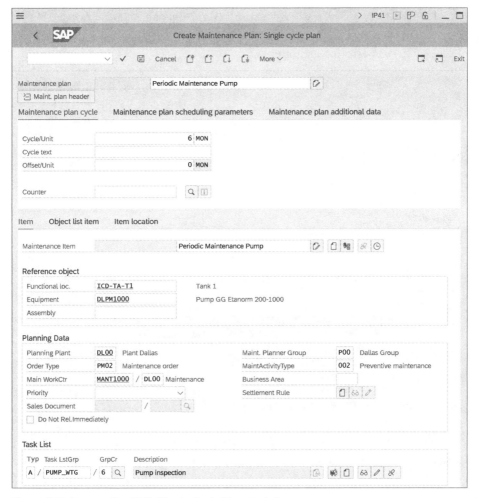

Figure 5.16 Transaction IP41: Single-Cycle Plan: Details

This data includes the following information:

- Short description (possibly with a long text)
- Reference object
- Order type and maintenance activity type that the subsequent orders are to receive
- Organizational responsibilities (planner group, work center)
- Maintenance task list if a maintenance task list is to be executed

[+]

Simplest Case: Time-Based Single-Cycle Plan

The time-based single-cycle plan involves the least amount of effort of all maintenance plan types in terms of entering and maintaining data, and experience has shown that this maintenance plan type is used the most. You should therefore also try to map as many of your maintenance activities as possible using this maintenance plan type.

Use Transaction IP10 or click the **Start** button to start the maintenance plan and create the first order. The system asks you for a **Start of cycle** date (see Figure 5.17), which is the date when you last performed maintenance.

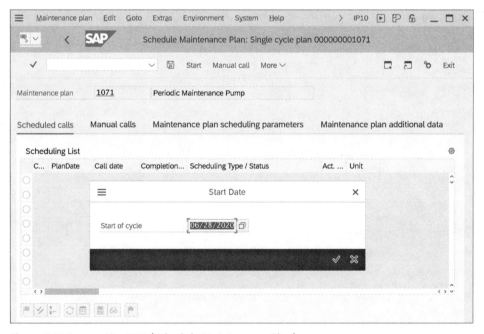

Figure 5.17 Transaction IP10 (Schedule Maintenance Plan)

The system calculates the first planned date based on the start of cycle and scheduling parameters and creates the first maintenance order when you save your data (see Figure 5.18).

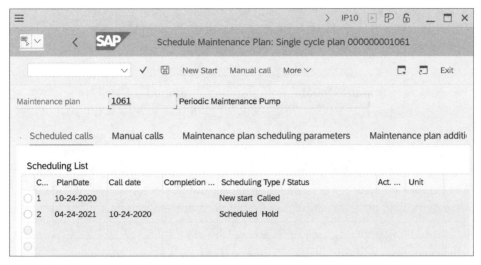

Figure 5.18 Maintenance Plan: Scheduled

Scheduling Parameters

You can also maintain the scheduling parameters for the single-cycle plan directly in the maintenance plan (see Figure 5.19).

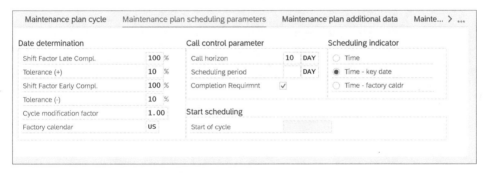

Figure 5.19 Maintenance Plan: Scheduling Parameter

You use the **Scheduling indicator** to define the basis for calculating the planned dates, as follows:

- **Time**
  The calculation basis for the month is always 30 days; all calendar days are counted. Example: cycle: 3 months, start of cycle April 1 results in June 30 as the planned date.

- **Time—factory calendar**
  The calculation basis for the month is always 30 days; only the factory calendar days are counted. Example: cycle: 3 months, factory calendar: Saturdays/Sundays/public holidays free, start of cycle April 1 results in a planned date around August 10 (depending on when the public holidays fall).

- **Time—key date**
  The calculation basis is the effective days of a month. Example: cycle: 3 months, start of cycle: April 1 results in July 1 as the planned date.

Scheduling Indicator: Key Date

Of the potential scheduling types, the key date time is the one most frequently used in practice.

You use the shift factor (SF) to control what percentage of the early completion date (**SF Early Completion** field) or late completion date (**SF Late Completion** field) is to be transferred to the next planned date. Take a look at the following examples of this scenario:

- Planned date: April 1; completion date: April 10; cycle: 3 months, key date scheduling; shift factor: late completion of 0% results in July 1 as the next planned date.

- Planned date: April 1; completion date: April 10; cycle: 3 months, key date scheduling; shift factor: late completion of 50% results in July 1 as the next planned date.

- Planned date: April 1; completion date: April 10; cycle: 3 months, key date scheduling; shift factor: late completion of 100% results in July 10 as the next planned date.

Shift Factors: 0% or 100%

Set the shift factors to either 0% or 100% for time-based maintenance plans, regardless of whether a single-cycle plan or strategy plan is used. In practice, other values are not normally important.

In reality, you may not be able to accept the calculated planned date but instead have to shift it by a few days, for example, if the planned date falls on a non-working day, if the utilization of workshops needs to be shifted slightly, or if production can only make the technical system available late for the maintenance order. Such small shifts will not normally affect the follow-up dates immediately. You can therefore use the tolerance to specify as of which deviation (expressed in percentages of the cycle) the shift factors should take effect. Take a look at the following examples of this scenario:

- Planned date: April 1; completion date: April 10; cycle: 3 months, key date scheduling; shift factor: late completion of 0%; tolerance: 10% results in July 1 as the next planned date.

- Planned date: April 1; completion date: April 5; cycle: 3 months, key date scheduling; shift factor: late completion of 100%; tolerance: 10% results in July 1 as the next planned date (tolerance = 10% of 90 days = 9 days not yet reached, shift factor does not take effect).

- Planned date: April 1; completion date: April 12; cycle: 3 months, key date scheduling; shift factor: late completion of 100%; tolerance: 10% results in July 12 as the next planned date (tolerance = 10% of 90 days = 9 days exceeded, shift factor takes effect).

Tolerance: ~10%

Only set a tolerance value if you have activated the shift factors (that is, greater than 0%).

If you set tolerances, note that values around 10% have proven themselves in practice.

Set the **Completion Requirement** parameter if you want the system to only generate subsequent orders once the previous order has been completed.

Deciding Completion Requirements Individually

Check whether or not you want to set the completion requirement in individual cases. Both cases occur regularly in practice.

You can define a scheduling period in the maintenance plan, with which you can create a preview of the pending maintenance dates. The scheduling period specifies the period of the preview in days, months, or years. If you want to have a preview for a maintenance plan for the entire year, for example, set the scheduling period to 365 days or 12 months.

Figure 5.20 shows a maintenance plan with a 6-month cycle, a start date of April 24, and a scheduling period of 2 years.

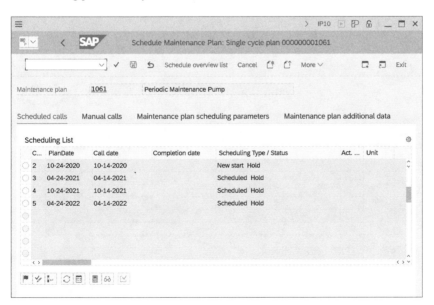

Figure 5.20 Maintenance Plan: Scheduling Period

[+]

Scheduling Period: 3–5 Next Plan Dates

In reality, a scheduling period to see the next 3–5 next plan dates is not rare. This period length allows a long-term preview of the pending maintenance plan dates.

You use the call horizon to specify in percentage or in days when an order should be created for a calculated maintenance plan date and, thus, how much time is to elapse between the two planned dates until the order is created in the system. The date as of which the order can then be created is known as the *maintenance call date*.

Take a look at the following example of this scenario: The maintenance cycle is 1 year; January 1 is specified as both the planned date and the completion date of the predecessor. The call horizon is as follows:

- **0%**
  The order can be created immediately if the predecessor order has been completed; the maintenance call date is thus January 1.

- **100%**
  The order can be called only when the next planned date is reached; the maintenance call date is thus January 1 of the following year.

- **75%**
  The order can be called if 75% of the time between January 1 of the previous year and January 1 of the following year has elapsed; the maintenance call date is thus October 2.

In the last two cases, the scheduling list of the maintenance plan has the **Hold** status (see Figure 5.21).

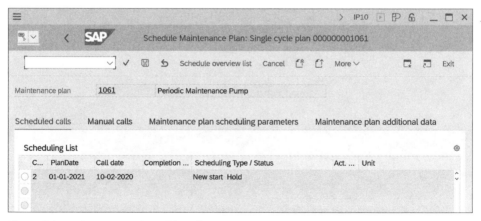

Figure 5.21 Maintenance Plan with Call Horizon

In practice, you can use the call horizon for dealing with time-based preventive maintenance in several ways.

You set the call horizon to 100% and then use the period for maintenance call objects in the deadline monitoring (Transaction IP30H or program RISTRA20H [Mass Schedule Maintenance Plans]) to control how much time before the maintenance call date the order is to be created by using the field **Timeframe**.

> **Calculation Formula for the Call Horizon**
>
> If you want to set a call horizon, you can use the following formula to calculate the initial phase in days, in percentages:
>
> $CH = (C - V) \times 100 \div C$
>
> - CH = call horizon in percentages
> - I = initial phase in days
> - C = cycle in days (for strategy plans, the smallest cycle)
>
> Always round off the result.

If you want the call horizon to control the maintenance call directly, proceed as follows:

- If your cycles are shorter than 1 year, set the call horizon to 0%. In this case, the subsequent orders can be created as of the date when the predecessor order was completed.

- If your cycles are longer than 1 year, set the call horizon to a high percentage value (greater than 80%) to ensure that the orders are not created too early and thus do not remain in the SAP system too long.

If this calculation of percentages appears too cumbersome or too complicated, you can now also specify in factory or calendar days the number of days before the planned date that the order should be called in the SAP system (see Figure 5.22).

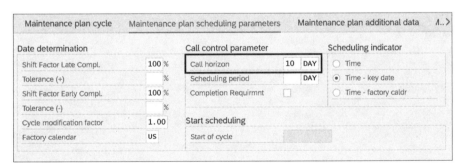

Figure 5.22 Maintenance Plan: Call Horizon in Days

In order for this function to be available, you must have activated the business function LOG_EAM_CI_6.

Deadline Monitoring and Mass Schedule Maintenance Plans

When you have started the maintenance plans, I advise that you do not monitor maintenance plans and create the subsequent orders manually; instead, let the system monitor the deadlines automatically. You can either start this in SAP S/4HANA online using Transaction IP30H or by scheduling an automatic batch job for the program RISTRA20H (Mass Schedule Maintenance Plans) (see Figure 5.23).

[+]   **Automate Deadline Monitoring**

Schedule a batch job for the RISTRA20H program. Since SAP S/4HANA is a very performant system, you can always run this job over all maintenance plans.

If you want to schedule several batch jobs (e.g., per plant), there are several selection criteria available to do so.

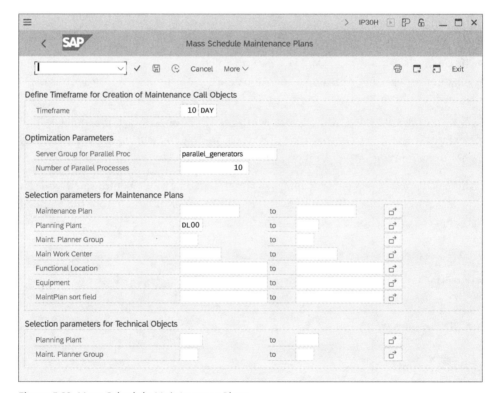

Figure 5.23 Mass Schedule Maintenance Plans

[+]   **Timeframe Not Too Short**

You use the timeframe to control how many days the order should be generated before the call date. Especially if you have set the call horizons to 100%, this value must be sufficiently large. Otherwise, the orders will be generated too late.

A scheduling log is automatically displayed after the scheduling (see Figure 5.24).

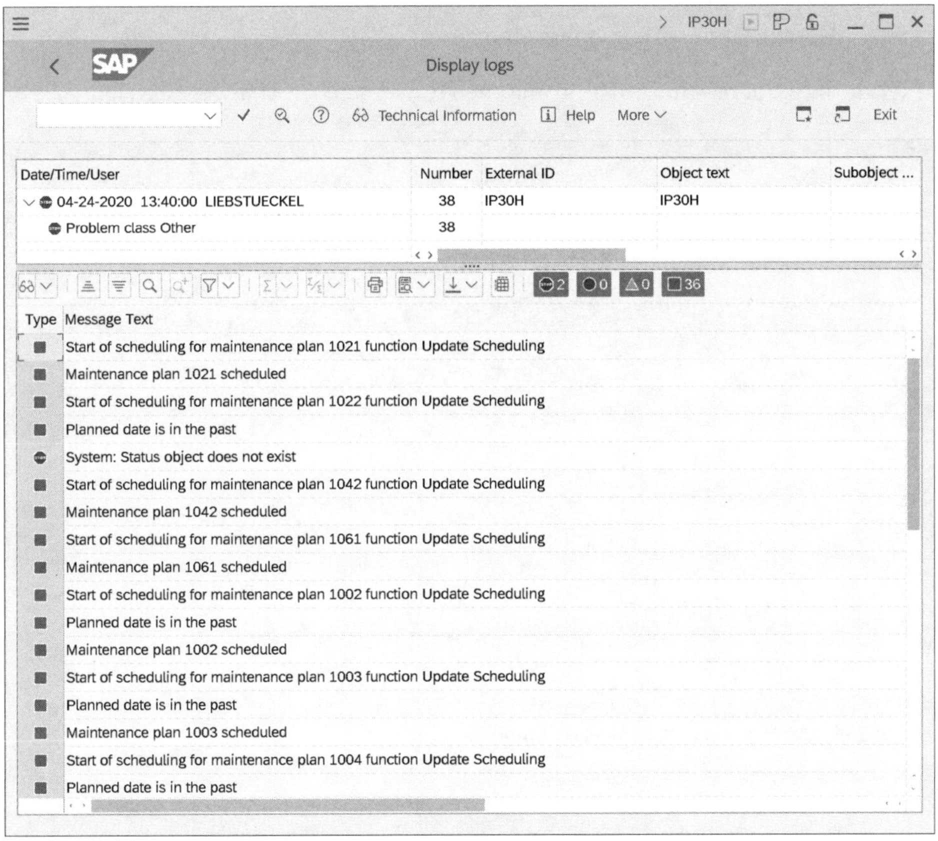

Figure 5.24 Mass Schedule Maintenance Plans: Log

Mass Change

As part of your daily business, you'll certainly encounter scenarios in which you need to assign the same information to several maintenance plans or maintenance items. This duplicated information is necessary, for example, in the following cases:

- You want to change the cycle for several maintenance plans at the same time.
- You want to provide an identical sort field for several maintenance plans because they are supposed to be scheduled simultaneously.
- You want to enter a new order type for several maintenance items.

In these or similar scenarios, proceed as follows:

1. Start Transaction IP15 for list change maintenance plans or Transaction IP17 for list change maintenance items and restrict the worklist (for example, by maintenance plan number or maintenance plant).

2. In the displayed list, select the maintenance plans or maintenance items you want to change simultaneously.

3. Select **More · Goto · Perform Mass Change**.

Enter the relevant new information and then implement the changes (see Figure 5.25).

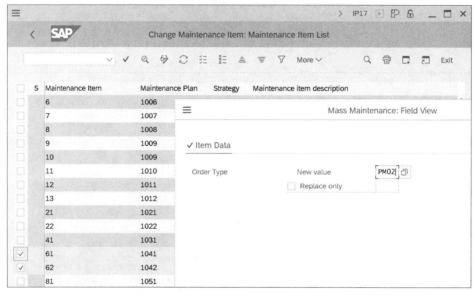

Figure 5.25 Maintenance Plan: Mass Change

To do so, business function LOG_EAM_CI_7 must be enabled, and the I_MASS authorization object must have been assigned to the MP authorization value.

Another possibility to change several maintenance plans or several maintenance items at the same time is Transaction MCH01 (Mass Changes for Maintenance Plans):

1. Start Transaction MCH01 and restrict the worklist (for example, by maintenance plan number or maintenance planning plant).

2. In the displayed list, select the maintenance plans or maintenance items you want to change simultaneously (see Figure 5.26).

3. Click the ![icon] button to determine the field(s) which you want to change. In Figure 5.26 the field order type on the maintenance item level is selected.

4. Enter the new value (e.g., order type PM02).

5. Click the ![icon] button to copy the new value to the rows.

6. At the end you save the new values.

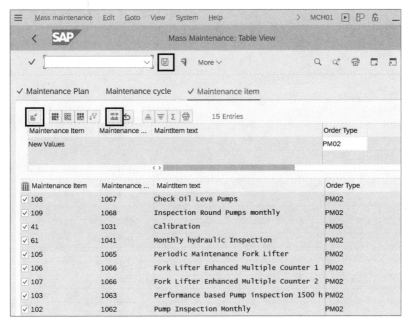

Figure 5.26 Transaction MCH01 (Mass Changes for Maintenance Plans)

Cost Display for Maintenance Plan

You can use the cost display for maintenance plan (Transaction IP31 [Maintenance Plan Costing]) to determine the expected costs of one or more maintenance plans for any period.

The following prerequisites must be fulfilled:

- You have scheduled the maintenance plans. The cost display for maintenance plan does not work if you have only created, but have not started, the maintenance plan.
- You have created orders from the maintenance plan. The cost display for maintenance plan does not work if you call notifications or service entry sheets.
- The maintenance plan must not have the **Inactive** or **Deletion flag** status.
- You must specify a maintenance task list in the maintenance plan and store data in the maintenance task list that is relevant for costing for the operations, for example, work center, activity type, standard time, and material. You have assigned prices to the activity type, and the materials were valuated.

The system determines the expected costs for the specified period as follows (see Figure 5.27):

- By calculating the existing calls (that is, orders)
- By simulating maintenance calls for the next period and determining expected costs

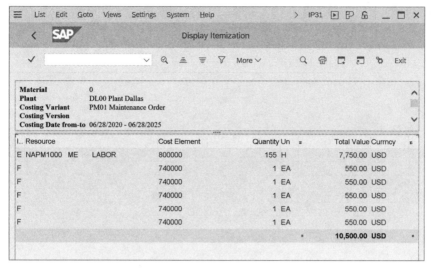

Figure 5.27 Maintenance Plan: Costing

Scheduling Overview

The following functions are available in the scheduling overview (see Figure 5.28), which you can reach via Transaction IP19 (Maintenance Scheduling Overview and Simulation):

- You can display when certain maintenance dates are to be expected for a particular reference object. The system displays the dates that have already been calculated and the dates simulated for the period you specified.

- You can shift maintenance dates.

- You can use the simulation function to edit the maintenance dates (e.g., release, shift, or fix).

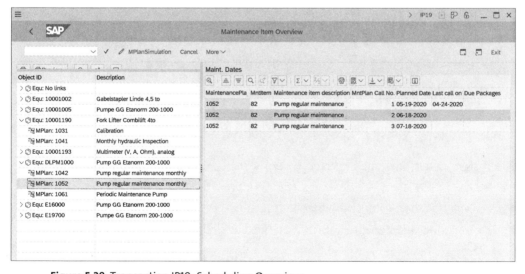

Figure 5.28 Transaction IP19: Scheduling Overview

Change Documents

As with many other objects in the SAP system, you can also display change documents for maintenance plans, maintenance items, and maintenance calls (see Figure 5.29). To do this, start the maintenance plan concerned and go to the transaction menu **More · Extras · Change Documents**.

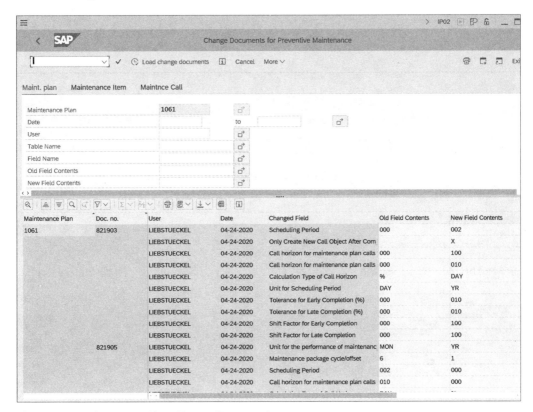

Figure 5.29 Maintenance Plan: Change Documents

5.4.2   Time-Based Strategy Plan

You create time-based strategy plans if you have to perform maintenance activities that are based on each other or supersede each other; for example, if you have a service manual from the manufacturer that contains activities with different deadlines, for example, every 3 months, every 6 months, every 12 months, and so on.

In this case, you must include a maintenance task list, specifically one that has the same strategy as the maintenance plan. You need a maintenance strategy and suitable maintenance task list to ensure that this type of business process will work.

Maintenance Strategy

You define maintenance strategies using Transaction IP11. A maintenance strategy contains the chronology of maintenance packages (see Figure 5.30).

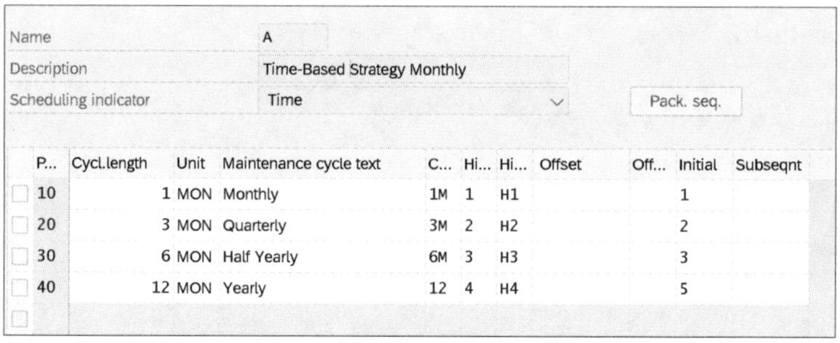

Name	A									
Description	Time-Based Strategy Monthly									
Scheduling indicator	Time			∨		Pack. seq.				

P...	Cycl.length		Unit	Maintenance cycle text	C...	Hi...	Hi...	Offset	Off...	Initial	Subseqnt
10	1		MON	Monthly	1M	1	H1			1	
20	3		MON	Quarterly	3M	2	H2			2	
30	6		MON	Half Yearly	6M	3	H3			3	
40	12		MON	Yearly	12	4	H4			5	

Figure 5.30 Transaction IP11 Maintenance Strategy

A maintenance strategy does not contain the following elements:

- Reference object
- Tasks
- Dates

The hierarchy indicators (the offset and the initial/subsequent phase) were described earlier in this section.

[+]

Subsequent Items

If you subsequently determine that you need additional packages, the procedure depends on the package numbers assigned so far:

If you have numbered your package numbers in steps of 1 (1, 2, 3...), always append these in the consecutive sequence. Otherwise, the maintenance plan will in the future fill your orders with incorrect operations from the maintenance task list.

Alternatively, you assign item numbers from the outset in increments of ten (10, 20, 30, and so on) to the individual maintenance packages. Using increments of ten enables you to add maintenance packages between the ten positions (10, 15, 20, 30, and so on). However, do not use existing item numbers.

Task List

To perform strategy-based preventive maintenance, you need a maintenance task list in addition to a maintenance strategy. Execute the following steps:

- Assign the same strategy to the maintenance task list at the header level that is to be included in the subsequent maintenance plan.
- Assign the maintenance packages to operations that are due (see Figure 5.31).

Op.	SOp	Operation Description	1M	3M	6M	12

Group   PUMP_WTG Pump inspection Etanorm monthly   Grp.Countr 7

Components   Rel   PRT   Insp.Char

Operat. Overview Maint. Packages

	Op.	SOp	Operation Description	1M	3M	6M	12
☐	0010		Switch off and carry out a safety check	✓	✓	✓	✓
☐	0020		Visual inspection outside: leakage, rust	✓	✓	✓	✓
☐	0030		Visual inspection inside: moisture, rust	☐	✓	✓	✓
☐	0040		Remove the pump rotor and completely cle	☐	☐	☐	✓
☐	0050		Measurement: bearing play	☐	☐	✓	✓
☐	0060		Exchange: sealing rings for gearbox	☐	☐	☐	✓
☐	0070		Safety check and pump in operation	✓	✓	✓	✓
☐	0080		external technical acceptance	☐	☐	☐	✓
☐							

Figure 5.31 Task List with Maintenance Packages

Strategy Plan

You can create the strategy plan in Transaction IP42. Choose between an internal and external number assignment. Rather than specifying the cycle where you want the maintenance tasks to take place, directly in the maintenance plan, you create the maintenance packages using the maintenance task list that is to be included (see Figure 5.32).

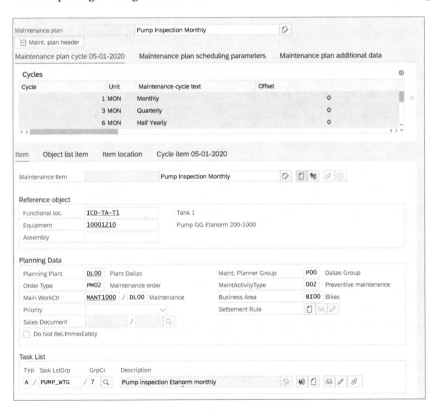

Figure 5.32 Transaction IP42: Strategy Plan

Scheduling Parameters

You already know about the majority of scheduling parameters for a strategy plan from the single-cycle plan.

The following values are suggested from the maintenance strategy that you can change in the strategy plan:

- Shift factors
- Tolerances
- Scheduling indicators
- Call horizons

You define the scheduling period and completion requirement individually for each strategy plan.

However, the strategy plan includes some scheduling parameters that either do not exist in the single-cycle plan or are not relevant there.

In the live system, you may discover that your maintenance intervals need to be adapted because maintenance is being performed either too often or too seldom. In this case, you can change the *cycle modification factor*. The default value is always set at 1.00. When you specify a cycle modification factor (values from 0.01 to 9.99), you can use it to extend or shorten the cycles specified in the maintenance strategy. A cycle modification factor greater than 1 extends the cycle, whereas a cycle modification factor less than 1 shortens it.

Cycle Modification Factor: Dynamic

You can use the cycle modification factor to extend or shorten the maintenance cycles individually for each strategy plan and thereby adjust the maintenance intensity, without having to change the maintenance strategy.

In principle, a cycle modification factor also exists in a single-cycle plan. However, this factor plays a minor role there because you could make a cycle adjustment directly by changing the cycle.

You maintain the hierarchy of the maintenance packages in the maintenance strategy (see Figure 5.30). The hierarchy determines which maintenance packages are executed if several maintenance packages are due at one time:

- **Same hierarchy number**
  If you want to execute the maintenance packages together for this date, the packages are given the same hierarchy number, for example, if an oil change is needed every 6 months and a filter change, every 12 months. SAP S/4HANA Asset Management then combines the maintenance packages into one order with several operations.

- **Different hierarchy numbers**
  If you only want to execute specific maintenance packages for this date, these packages must have a higher hierarchy number than the other packages. The SAP S/4HANA Asset Management thus always only selects the packages with the highest hierarchy number. If, for example, the spark plugs are cleaned every 6 months and changed every 12 months, it would not make any sense to first clean the spark plugs after 12 months and then change them: The package with the higher hierarchy (change spark plugs) thus replaces the package with the lower hierarchy (clean spark plugs).

Different Maintenance Package Hierarchies

You can achieve the most sophisticated control of maintenance activities when you assign different hierarchy numbers to all maintenance packages and then, if necessary, make a multiple assignment of maintenance packages in the maintenance task list. You would usually assign the hierarchy indicator in ascending order according to the term.

You assign the preliminary and follow-up buffers in the maintenance strategy at the level of the maintenance packages; they are always expressed in days. SAP S/4HANA Asset Management uses the preliminary and follow-up buffers to determine the basic start date and basic end date of the order based on the planned date.

Thus, for example, maintenance package 40 in Figure 5.30 with a lead float of 5 days, a follow-up float of 0 days, and a calculated planned date of May 15 results in the basic start date of May 10 and basic end date of May 15 in the order.

What is the business background? Maintenance activities take a certain amount of time, and long-term maintenance activities, in particular, cannot normally be completed in one day. You can therefore use the preliminary and follow-up buffers to specify a *from/to* time span from the outset.

Setting the Follow-Up Float to Zero

Always set at least one of the buffers to 0; otherwise, you will no longer be able to recognize the actual planned date by the basic dates of the order. We recommend that you always set the follow-up buffer to 0 because the required basic end date will then correspond to the planned maintenance date.

An offset ensures a one-off time shift. You assign offsets in the maintenance strategy at the maintenance package level; offsets are always expressed in the unit of the maintenance package. You use offsets in the following cases:

- The maintenance package is to be executed once only. In this case, only set the **Offset** in the maintenance package.

- The cyclical work is to start only after a certain time. In this case, set a **Cycle Duration** and an **Offset**.

Let's explain offsets using the following example. We received the following request from a former customer a while ago: Our company has a requirement that different operations be performed with a maintenance plan. Although these operations should have the same time interval, they are to be generated at a later point in time than the orders (see Table 5.1).

Interval Due	1Y	2Y	3Y	4Y	5Y	6Y
Operation1 3Y	•			•		
Operation2 3Y		•			•	
Operation3 3Y			•			•

Table 5.1 Operation Time Interval

In this case, we'll implement the customer's requirement using a maintenance strategy with three packages. All three packages include a cycle duration of 3 years. By setting an offset of 1 year in the second maintenance package and of 2 years in the third maintenance package, you achieve the required chronological sequence exactly (see Figure 5.33).

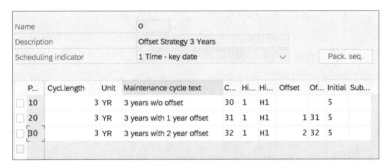

Figure 5.33 Transaction IP11: Maintenance Strategy with Offsets

[+]   **Offset for Offsetting Maintenance Packages**
By setting offsets, you achieve a chronological offsetting of maintenance packages.

Strategy Plan Scheduling

When you start a strategy plan, you must now decide whether this is a restart (for example, if a new machine is purchased) or a start in the current cycle (for example, an existing machine with maintenance dates already implemented):

- **Restart**

  You use Transaction IP10 (Schedule Maintenance Plan) (**Start** function) to start the maintenance plan and thus create the first order. The system asks you for a **Start of cycle** date (see Figure 5.34), which is the date when you put the reference object into operation or shortly after you put it into operation.

Figure 5.34 Start Function with Start Date

- **Start in cycle**

  However, if you already implemented maintenance dates for the reference object, you use the **Start in cycle** function in Transaction IP10. SAP S/4HANA Asset Management asks you not only for the **Completion date** (the date when you performed the last maintenance, see Figure 5.35), but also for an offset. Do not confuse this offset with the offset from the maintenance strategy, because this offset determines which maintenance package you executed last. Use the **Select package** function to call the table for selecting packages (see Figure 5.36) and set the **Start** offset there using the **Set start offset** function.

Figure 5.35 Start in Cycle Function with Completion Date

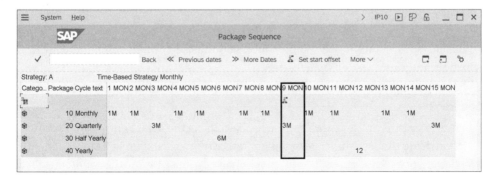

Figure 5.36 Start in Cycle with Start Offset

The system calculates the first planned date based on the start of cycle and scheduling parameters and creates the first maintenance order when you save your data.

In further procedures and all other functions, such as deadline monitoring, simulation, cost display for maintenance plan, and so on, the strategy plan does not differ from the single-cycle plan.

Time-Based Maintenance Plans: Little Administrative Effort
The system can calculate the planned dates as automatically as possible with the calendar for time-based maintenance plans—regardless of whether these are single-cycle plans or strategy plans. Ongoing effort is required for performance-based maintenance plans because counter readings are perpetually being entered. You should therefore stick to the time-based maintenance plans if possible.

We now come to the business processes of preventive maintenance where the calendar alone is no longer sufficient for calculating the maintenance dates, but rather where service indicators and counter readers are required. Thus, the business processes of the performance-based preventive maintenance are involved specifically here.

5.5   Performance-Based Maintenance Plans

For performance-based maintenance, the maintenance dates are calculated solely via performance-based values (such as operation hours, kilometers, or produced quantities). Calendar cycles (for example, a 6-month cycle), however, have no effect. This section will cover both performance-based single-cycle plans and performance-based strategy plans.

5.5.1   Performance-Based Single-Cycle Plan

A maintenance plan for a performance-based single-cycle plan has a maintenance cycle (for example, every 2,000 operation hours), and the maintenance dates are called based on counter readings. An order is always created whenever the counter reading has reached the cycle or is shortly before it.

To enable performance-based maintenance, you must first fulfill some prerequisites, which the following sections will discuss.

Counter

You must assign a counter to the reference object using the **Measuring points/counters** function. To do this, use the corresponding transactions (for example, Transaction IE02 for equipment or Transaction IL02 for functional locations). Define the counter itself as follows (see Figure 5.37):

- **Characteristic**
  The counter refers to a characteristic (for example, **OPH** here). You can maintain this characteristic using Transaction CTO4; note that in the **Characteristic** field the characteristic has the *numeric format* data type and the relevant unit (for example, h, mls, l).

- **Counter overflow reading**
  The counter overflow reading represents the first value that the counter can no longer display. If you had a 6-digit counter, for example, you would have to enter the value 1,000,000 in the **CntrOverReadg** field; the system needs this value for scheduling the maintenance plans.

- **Annual estimate**
  The annual estimate represents a value you estimated concerning the extent to which the reference object is used each year in relation to the counter. The system also needs this value for the scheduling.

- **Measurement reading transfer**
  If you have constructed a measuring point hierarchy, activate the **Measurement Reading Transfer** option and define the measuring point/counter from which the value is to be transferred.

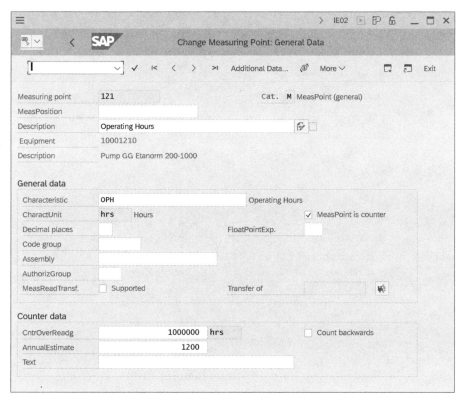

Figure 5.37 Counter for Technical Object

- **Decreasing counter reading**
  A continuously growing counter reading is without doubt the normal situation for performance-based maintenance. However, you may have situations (for example, for a decreasing tire diameter) where the counter reading continuously decreases and the maintenance is initiated when the counter reading goes below a limit. You can activate the **Count backwards** option in such cases. However, you must then set up an additional counter that counts forward and for which you activate a measurement reading transfer from the backward-counting counter. You refer the maintenance plan to the forward-counting counter.

Initial Counter Reading

You enter—and this is a must—an initial counter reading for the counter using Transaction IK11 (Create Measurement Document) (see Figure 5.38). This counter reading represents when the reference object was put into operation with a particular counter reading.

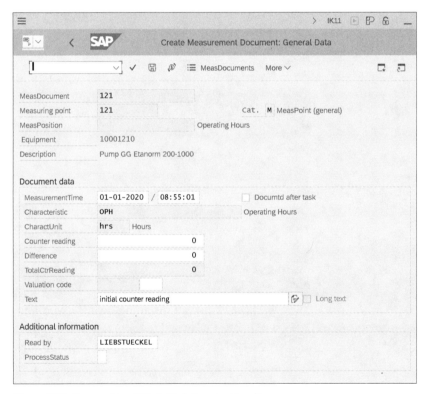

Figure 5.38 Transaction IK11: Initial Counter Reading

Like the time-based single-cycle plan, you create the performance-based single-cycle plan using Transaction IP41. You specify the counter and the cycle and where you want the maintenance to take place directly in the maintenance plan (see Figure 5.39). On the basis of the cycle unit, the system suggests the next step: If multiple counters with the same unit exist, a dialog box is displayed in which you can select the relevant counter. If only one counter with a suitable unit exists, this counter is entered directly by SAP S/4HANA Asset Management.

Cycle/Unit	1500 HR	
Cycle text	every 1500 operating hours	
Offset/Unit	0 HR	
Counter	121	🔍 ℹ Operating Hours

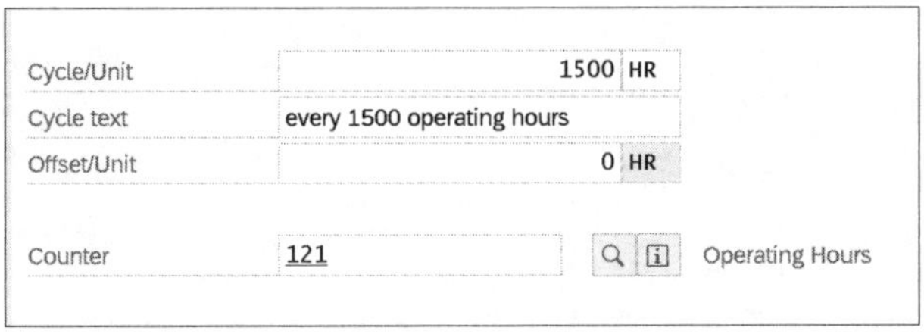

Figure 5.39 Transaction IP41: Single-Cycle Plan: Performance Based

You can use the scheduling parameters for a performance-based single-cycle plan as described in that section, but with one exception: The significance of the call horizon increases in performance-based maintenance.

[+]

Call Horizon Greater Than 90% or Less Than 5 Days

If you use a percentage value, set the call horizon to a high value (greater than 90%) for all performance-based maintenance plans or to a low value (<5 days) if you use days. Otherwise, SAP S/4HANA Asset Management would create the maintenance orders too early.

Scheduling

Let's now use a specific numerical example to demonstrate how performance-based maintenance is scheduled.

A piece of equipment is equipped with an operation-hour counter with an annual estimate of 2,500 operation hours (OPH) per year and contains a single-cycle plan with a maintenance cycle of 2,000 OPH and a call horizon of 95%. An initial counter reading was entered for March 1 with 0 OPH.

The geometric solution (see Figure 5.40) is as follows: If the equipment were utilized exactly as was estimated in the annual estimate, this would result in the counter being linear, and 2,500 OPH would be reached after 1 year. The intersection between the linear gradient and the maintenance cycle would now determine the maintenance date ❶.

The arithmetic solution is as follows:

03-01 (March 1) + 2,000 ÷ 2,500 × 365 days
= 03-01 (March 1) + 292 days
= 12-17 (December 17)

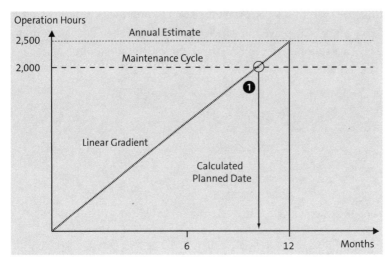

Figure 5.40 Initial Scheduling

A counter reading of 500 OPH is reached on April 1, which indicates that the equipment was used more extensively than was planned in the annual estimate.

[+]
Date Calculation for Each Entry of Counter Readings

Every time you enter a measurement document, the system reschedules the maintenance plan and determines a new maintenance date.

The geometric solution is as follows (see Figure 5.41): An equivalent to the annual estimate is drawn from the measurement document, and the intersection with the maintenance cycle determines the new maintenance date ❷.

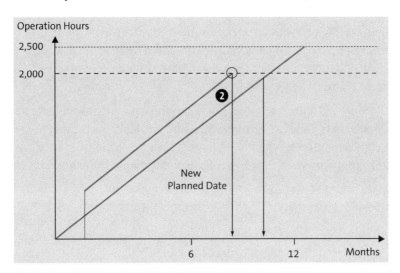

Figure 5.41 Scheduling Based on Counter Reading

The arithmetic solution is as follows:

04-01 (April 1) + (2,000 – 500) ÷ 2,500 × 365 days
= 04-01 (April 1) + 1,500 ÷ 2,500 × 365 days
= 04-01 (April 1) + 219 days
= 11-06 (November 6)

If you did not set a call horizon, the system would immediately create an order the moment you enter the first measurement document. Creating the order now is problematic because you are still far away from the maintenance cycle at the time of the first measurement document. As already recommended earlier in this section, you should therefore assign a high call horizon to the maintenance plan to ensure that the order is only created on time on the actual planned date. In our case, the call horizon was set to 95%, that is, 1,900 OPH.

The geometric solution in this case is as follows (see Figure 5.42): The intersection of the measurement document projection line with the line of the call horizon determines the maintenance call date ❸.

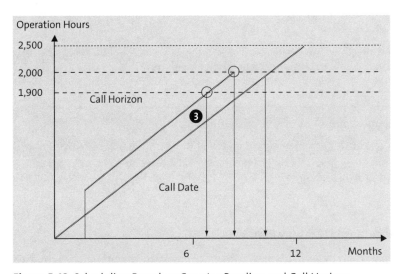

Figure 5.42 Scheduling Based on Counter Reading and Call Horizon

The arithmetic solution looks like this:

04-01 (April 1) + (1,900 – 500) ÷ 2,500 × 365 days
= 04-01 (April 1) + 1,400 ÷ 2,500 × 365 days
= 04-01 (April 1) + 204 days
= 10-22 (October 22)

Thus, in the specified combination, the planned date of November 6 would be calculated with a maintenance call date of October 22 in this situation.

Maintenance Calls with Orders

When is an order actually created? If you don't enter another measurement document, RISTRA20H deadline monitoring would create the maintenance call with an order the first time it runs on or after October 22.

However, this scenario is quite unrealistic. You should, in fact, continuously enter measurement documents for performance-based maintenance. The maintenance call is created with an order the moment you enter a measurement document that is above the call horizon (thus more than 1,900 OPH) and after the deadline monitoring runs for the first time.

Entering Counter Readings Regularly

To ensure that performance-based maintenance fulfills its purpose, enter counter readings regularly. Whether you do this daily, weekly, or in a different sequence will depend on each particular case.

Practical tip: You should plan for at least ten measurement documents between two maintenance sessions. If you perform, for example, maintenance after every 2,000 OPH, you should enter the counter reading at least at an interval of 200 OPH.

If you do not do this, performance-based maintenance will not fulfill its purpose and you should preferably switch to time-based maintenance.

Entering Counter Readings When Out of Operation

Even if you temporarily take the technical object out of operation, you must continue to enter counter readings. Even though the readings will always be the same, they will have a more current date each time.

5.5.2   Performance-Based Strategy Plan

You create time-based strategy plans if you have to perform maintenance activities that are based on each other or supersede each other; for example, if you have a service manual from the manufacturer that contains activities with different performance levels, for example, every 1,000 OH, every 2,000 OH, every 5,000 OH, and so on. In such cases, you must include a maintenance task list with the same strategy as the maintenance plan. You need a performance-based maintenance strategy and suitable maintenance task list to ensure that this type of business process will work. This section will discuss both of those topics, in addition to the strategy plan and scheduling.

Maintenance Strategy

You can also maintain performance-based strategies using Transaction IP11. The only differences compared to a time-based strategy are the scheduling indicator and unit (see Figure 5.43):

- You set the **Scheduling indicator** to 3 = activity.

- You use a service unit (operation hours, miles, number of pieces, tons, flow rates, and so on) as the unit.

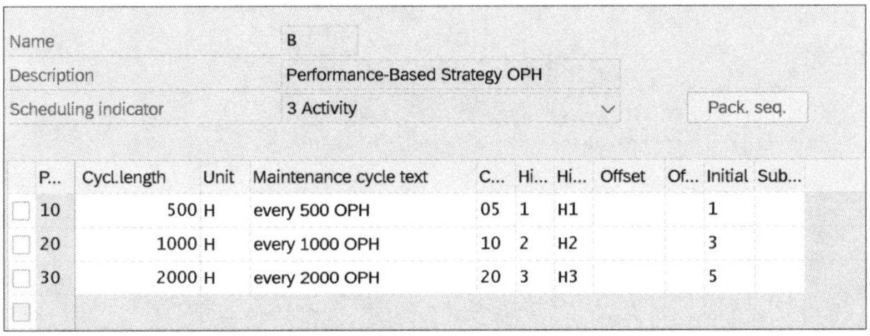

Name		B								
Description		Performance-Based Strategy OPH								
Scheduling indicator		3 Activity			⌄	Pack. seq.				

P...	Cycl.length	Unit	Maintenance cycle text	C...	Hi...	Hi...	Offset	Of...	Initial	Sub...
☐ 10	500	H	every 500 OPH	05	1	H1			1	
☐ 20	1000	H	every 1000 OPH	10	2	H2			3	
☐ 30	2000	H	every 2000 OPH	20	3	H3			5	
☐										

Figure 5.43 Transaction IP11: Performance Based Maintenance Strategy

All other control options (shift factors, call horizon, hierarchy, offset, and so on) correspond to the time-based maintenance strategy.

Task List

The only difference between the maintenance task list for a performance-based strategy plan and a maintenance task list for time-based strategy plans is that you assign a performance-based strategy to the maintenance task list header and performance-based maintenance packages to the operations.

Strategy Plan

Creating the strategy plan is practically a combination of the time-based strategy plan and performance-based single-cycle plan:

- You use Transaction IP42.
- You assign the reference object and a maintenance task list.
- SAP S/4HANA Asset Management proposes a counter, or you assign a counter manually.
- The maintenance packages are automatically entered from the used maintenance packages.

Figure 5.44 displays the result of a completed performance-based strategy plan.

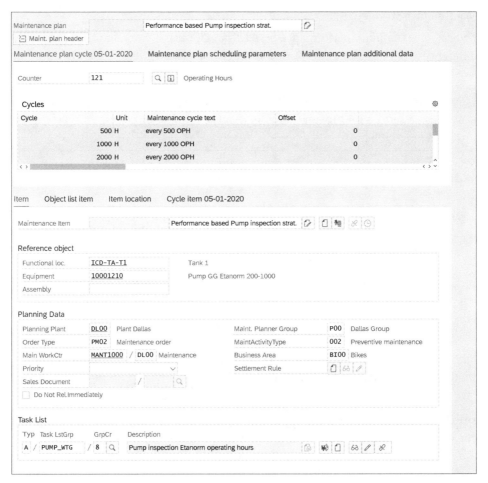

Figure 5.44 Transaction IP42: Performance-Based Strategy Plan

Scheduling

Starting the strategy plan is also a combination of the time-based strategy plan and performance-based single-cycle plan:

- Enter an initial counter reading for the reference object.

- Use Transaction IP10 (Schedule Maintenance Plan) with the **Start** function when you want to start a new maintenance cycle. In this case, you specify a start counter reading for when the cycle began (for example, 0 operation hours).

- Use Transaction IP10 (Schedule Maintenance Plan) with the **Start in cycle** function when you want to proceed in an existing maintenance cycle. In this case, you specify a completion counter reading in the **CountReading** field for when the last maintenance was performed and select the last executed package (see Figure 5.45).

Figure 5.45 Completion Counter Reading

The SAP system then calculates the next packages due, the next planned date, and the associated call date based on the maintenance strategy, current counter reading, annual estimate, completion counter reading, and start counter reading (see the relevant columns in Figure 5.46).

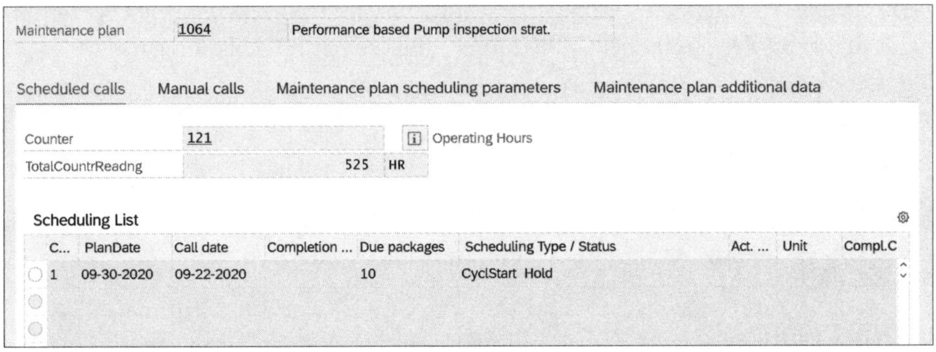

Maintenance plan	1064	Performance based Pump inspection strat.					

Scheduled calls	Manual calls	Maintenance plan scheduling parameters	Maintenance plan additional data

Counter	121		ⓘ Operating Hours
TotalCountrReadng		525 HR	

Scheduling List

C...	PlanDate	Call date	Completion ...	Due packages	Scheduling Type / Status	Act. ...	Unit	Compl.C
1	09-30-2020	09-22-2020		10	CyclStart Hold			

Figure 5.46 Performance-Based Strategy Plan: Started

The other procedures (such as processing orders, monitoring deadlines, and so on) and other functions (such as cost display for maintenance plan and scheduling overviews) are identical to the procedures and functions for all other maintenance plans.

5.6   Multiple-Counter Plans

For time-based and performance-based maintenance, the maintenance dates are calculated both via the calendar (for example, in a 6-month cycle) and on the basis of performance (for example, operation hours, kilometers, or produced quantities). This section will discuss both basic and enhanced multiple-counter plans.

5.6.1   Basic Multiple-Counter Plan

You can define maintenance cycles with different dimensions when using multiple-counter plans. Multiple-counter plans enable you to integrate performance and time dimensions into a maintenance plan, that is, every 1,000 operation hours, every 3,000 miles, every 12 months (see Figure 5.47).

Figure 5.47 Multiple Counters: Example

You can create cycle sets to reduce the effort of entering multiple-counter plans. Cycle sets are similar to maintenance strategies but are not a mandatory prerequisite for basic multiple-counter plans. The following sections discuss cycle sets, the key components of a multiple-counter plan, scheduling parameters, and scheduling itself.

Cycle Sets

You create cycle sets in Transaction IP11Z (Change Cycle Sets). Figure 5.48 shows the cycle set for the example above.

Name		FFZ				
Description		Fork Lifters				

P...	Cycl.length	Unit	Maintenance cycle text	C...	Offset	Of...
10	3000	MI	every 3000 miles	ML		
20	12	MON	every 12 months	MO		
30	2000	H	every 2000 operating hours	HR		

Figure 5.48 Transaction IP11Z: Cycle Set

Multiple-Counter Plan

If you now create a basic multiple-counter plan (Transaction IP43 [Create Multiple Counter Plan]), you can create the cycles directly in the maintenance plan itself or refer to an existing cycle set when you open it (see Figure 5.49). Due to the units specified in the cycle set, SAP S/4HANA Asset Management searches for suitable counters and suggests these for the relevant units. If the system does not suggest a counter, or if it suggests an incorrect one, you can also change these counters manually.

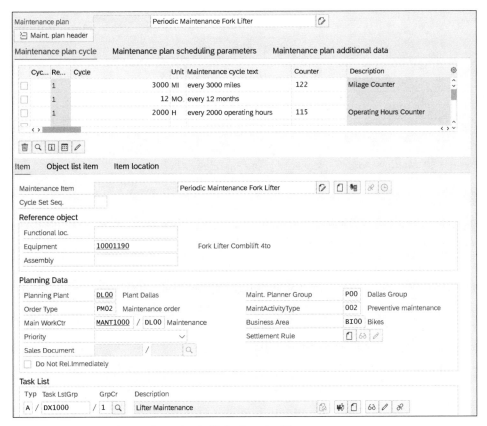

Figure 5.49 Transaction IP43: Basic Multiple-Counter Plan

Scheduling Parameters

You should already be familiar with most of the valid scheduling parameters in a multiple-counter plan. However, two new scheduling parameters have been added: the **operation type** parameter and the **lead float** parameter (see Figure 5.50):

- If you select the **OR - Link** radio button, an order will be created for the earliest planned date. The case that occurs first is crucial. This case is the standard case in performance-based maintenance with several dimensions.

- If you select the **AND - Link** radio button, an order will be created for the last planned date. The case that occurs last is crucial because this case is the exceptional case in performance-based maintenance with several dimensions.

- The **Lead float** specifies how many days before the planned date the basic start date of the order should be. The basic end date of the order is always created using the planned date.

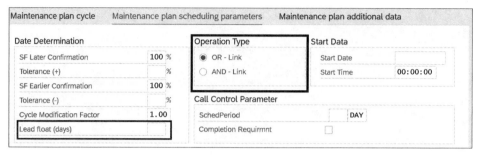

Figure 5.50 Multiple-Counter Plan: Scheduling Parameters

Scheduling

Starting the basic multiple-counter plan is a combination of a time-based single-cycle plan and a performance-based single-cycle plan:

- You have entered the initial counter readings in the reference object.

- You use Transaction IP10 with the **Start** function when you want to start a new maintenance cycle. In this case, you specify a start date when the cycle began.

- The SAP system then calculates the various planning data based on the current counter readings, relevant annual estimate, and start date.

- If you selected **OR - Link**, the system suggests the first planned date in the **PlanDate** field; if you selected **AND - Link**, it suggests the last planned date in the **PlanDate** field of the order (see Figure 5.51).

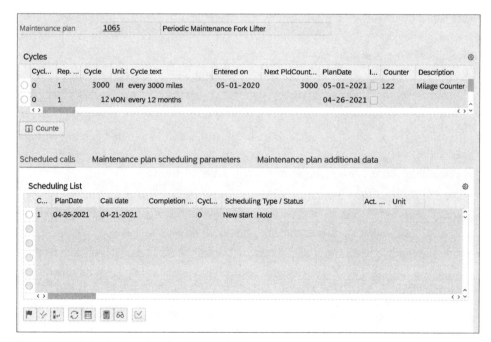

Figure 5.51 Multiple-Counter Plan: Scheduled

The other procedures (such as monitoring deadlines, processing orders, and so on) and other functions (such as cost display for maintenance plan and scheduling overviews) are identical to the procedures and functions for all other maintenance plans.

Note that you must not set a call horizon for multiple-counter plans. Instead, the SAP system sets a maintenance call date identical to the planned date, which results in the deadline monitoring generating the order.

5.6.2 Enhanced Multiple-Counter Plan

Unlike the basic multiple-counter plan, enhanced multiple-counter plans enable you to define several cycles that are based on each other, as the following examples show:

- Cycle 1 for small inspection (A): every 1,000 OPH or every 3,000 miles or every 12 months
- Cycle 2 for large inspection (B): every 3,000 OPH or every 9,000 miles or every 36 months

To put it another way, the enhanced multiple-counter plan is a combination of a performance-based strategy plan and a time-based strategy plan. The following sections will discuss the prerequisites for this type of plan, the plan itself, and scheduling.

Prerequisites

To enable an enhanced multiple-counter plan, you must fulfill the following prerequisites:

- In the customizing function **Set Special Functions for Maintenance Planning**, set the **Enhanced Multiple Counter Plan** option. Warning: Once you have activated the option, you cannot deactivate it.
- You must define cycle sets using Transaction IP11Z (see Figure 5.48). In the present example, one cycle set is sufficient. Why? First, the small inspection (maintenance position A) takes place at 2,000 operating hours/3,000 miles/12 months (whichever comes first) and at 4,000 operating hours/6,000 miles/24 months. The large inspection (maintenance position B) then takes place at 6,000 OPH/9,000 miles/36 months, i.e., after another 2,000 OPH/3,000 miles/12 months after the last small inspection. This corresponds to the existing cycles. So one cycle set is sufficient.
- You need two different maintenance task lists, one of which must be executed on the date when cycle set 1 is due and the other, on the date when cycle set 2 is due. Unlike the strategy maintenance plan, the maintenance task list header is not assigned the cycle set, and the operations are not assigned maintenance packages.

Figure 5.52 displays the basic structure and the effect for scheduling.

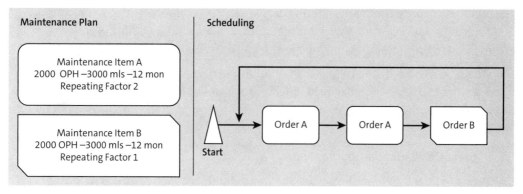

Figure 5.52 Multiple-Counter Plan: Sequence

Multiple-Counter Plan

Proceed as follows to define an enhanced multiple-counter plan (see Figure 5.53):

1. Create a multiple-counter plan using Transaction IP43 (Create Multiple Counter Plan).

2. Assign the required cycles 1 and 2 to the maintenance plan.

3. You then create two maintenance items. You assign cycle set sequence 1 to the first item and cycle set sequence 2 to the second item.

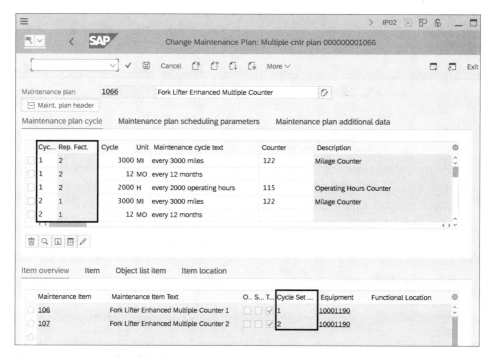

Figure 5.53 Transaction IP43: Enhanced Multiple-Counter Plan

4. Click the  button to change the repetition factors. Set the repetition factor to 2 for cycle 1 and the repetition factor to 1 for cycle 2. Thus, the first item is first performed twice, then the second item once, and then the first position twice again, and so on.

5. Due to the units specified there, SAP S/4HANA Asset Management searches for suitable counters and suggests these for the relevant units. If the system does not suggest a counter, or if it suggests an incorrect one, you can also change this manually.

6. The scheduling parameters (for example, AND/OR link) are identical to the scheduling parameters of the basic multiple-counter plan.

Scheduling

Starting the enhanced multiple-counter plan is a combination of the time-based strategy plan and performance-based strategy plan:

▪ You use Transaction IP10 (Schedule Maintenance Plan) with the **Start** function when you want to start a new maintenance cycle. In this case, you specify a start date when the cycle began.

▪ You use Transaction IP10 with the **Start in cycle** function when you want to proceed in an existing maintenance cycle. Here, you specify the **Cycle Set Sequence** and **Completion date**, for which the last maintenance was performed (see Figure 5.54).

Figure 5.54 Enhanced Multiple-Counter Plan: Start in Cycle

▪ The system then calculates the various planning data based on the current counter readings, relevant annual estimate, and start date.

▪ If you selected **OR - Link**, the system suggests the first planned date as the planned date; if you selected **AND - Link**, it suggests the last planned date as the planned date (**PlanDate**) of the order. The system also clearly shows which cycle set sequence is the next one due (see Figure 5.55).

The other procedures (monitoring deadlines, processing orders, and so on) and other functions (cost display for maintenance plan, scheduling overviews, and so on) are identical to the procedures and functions for all other maintenance plans.

You must activate the business function LOG_EAM_SHIFTFACTORS to enable multiple-counter plans in the displayed form.

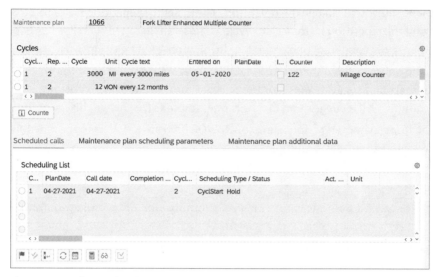

Figure 5.55 Enhanced Multiple-Counter Plan: Scheduled

5.7   Inspection Rounds

How do the functions for inspection rounds differ from those for maintenance planning described in the previous sections? Maintenance planning usually involves a single object for which a series of activities, some rather complex, is to be executed. The reverse is the case when it comes to inspection rounds. With an inspection round, you process a large number of objects, executing the same activities on each object. These activities are not usually overly complex and require the same tools, spare parts, and qualifications. Examples of such activities are as follows:

- Lubrication services
- Visual checks
- Counter readings
- Oil level checks
- Minor part replacements

You can map inspection rounds in the SAP system in two ways:

- Inspection rounds using an object list (basic inspection rounds)
- Inspection rounds using maintenance task list (enhanced inspection rounds)

5.7.1   Basic Inspection Rounds Using the Object List

If you always perform the same activities on the objects on the inspection round (for example, the lubrication condition of all objects must be checked and relubricated if necessary), use the following (see Figure 5.56):

- A single-cycle plan to store the organizational data (such as plant, order type, and so on) and to describe the content as maintenance plan text or maintenance plan item text
- An object list to define the technical objects that are to be inspected on the inspection round

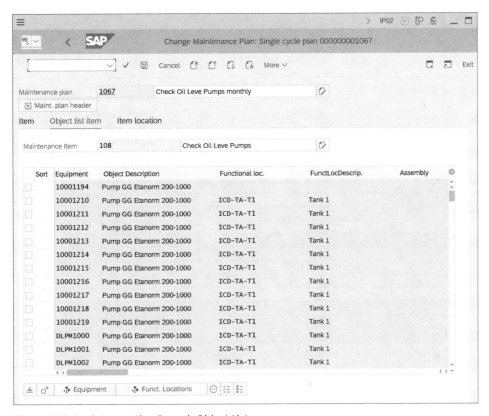

Figure 5.56 Basic Inspection Round: Object List

Order

When you start the maintenance plan, an order will be generated that usually contains an operation and an object list (see Figure 5.57).

Confirmation

To confirm the basic inspection round, using Transaction IW42 for the overall completion confirmation is best. You can first report the times there. Using the **More · Environment · Object List**, next navigate to the confirmation of the object list (see Figure 5.58) and select in the processing indicator column (**P**) the objects you have processed.

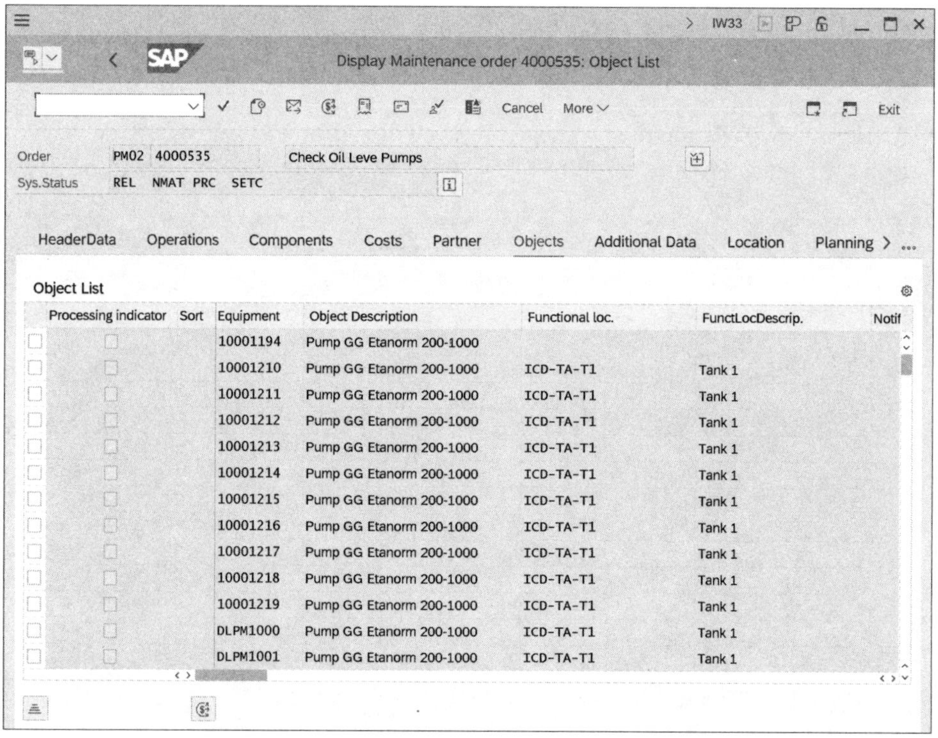

Figure 5.57 Basic Inspection Round: Order

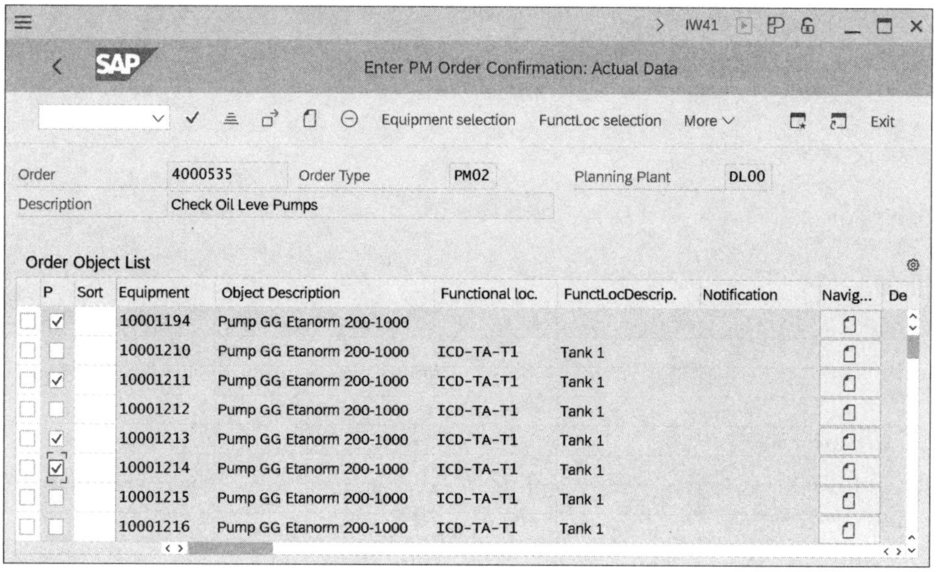

Figure 5.58 Basic Inspection Round: Confirmation

5.7.2   Enhanced Inspection Rounds Using the Maintenance Task List

You can use the enhanced inspection round via a maintenance task list if you perform different activities on the objects of the inspection round; these activities could include, for example:

- Object 1: check lubrication condition
- Object 2: record noise levels
- Object 3: read counter reading

> **Enhanced Inspection Rounds: Elements**
>
> You can map the enhanced planning and execution of inspection rounds in SAP S/4HANA Asset Management as follows:
>
> - Define the content of inspection rounds in maintenance task lists.
> - Define the frequency of inspection rounds in a maintenance plan.
> - Control the execution of inspection rounds using orders generated by the maintenance plan.
> - Document the confirmation of inspection rounds with the overall completion confirmation, which is the best way.

The following sections discuss how the task list, maintenance plan, orders, and confirmation work when used for enhanced inspection rounds. The section also discusses some prerequisites for using enhanced inspection rounds.

Task List

Maintenance tasks lists used for enhanced inspection rounds differ from other maintenance tasks lists in the following ways (see Figure 5.59):

- You use the sequence of operations to define the sequence of stations and the individual steps that make up the inspection round.
- You assign the technical object that is to be inspected to the operations (functional location, equipment, and, if necessary, an assembly).
- You can also assign any measuring points/counters, documents, lubricants, or test equipment you require for an operation to that operation.
- If the inspection round is to be executed on a regular basis (daily, weekly, or monthly), this frequency can be specified in a maintenance plan.
- You can execute the inspection round if certain events occur (for example, before/after a production start, before/after a shutdown). In this case, execute the maintenance task list using a manual order (Transaction IW31).

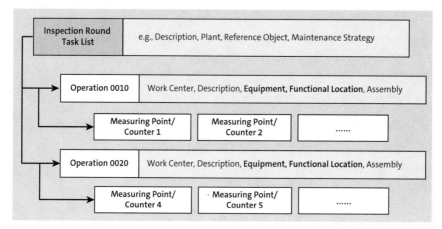

Figure 5.59 Enhanced Inspection Rounds: Maintenance Task List

Figure 5.60 shows a maintenance task list with various technical objects for which lubrication services are to be executed and counter readings taken.

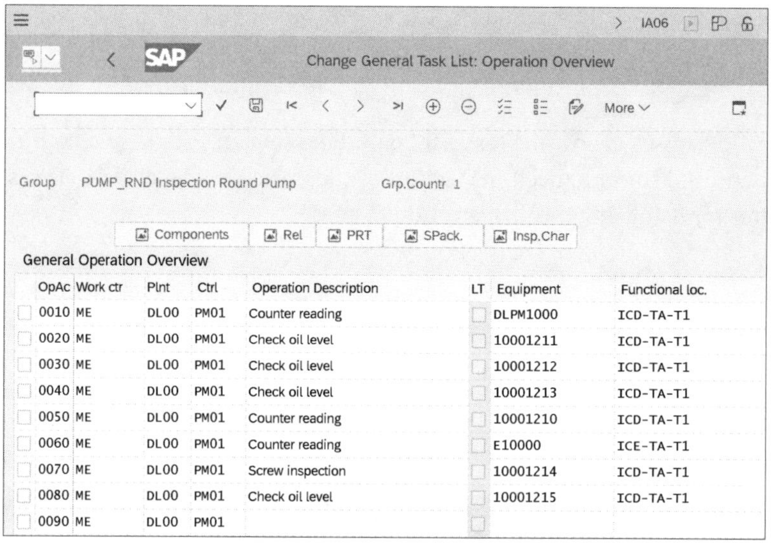

OpAc	Work ctr	Plnt	Ctrl	Operation Description	LT	Equipment	Functional loc.
0010	ME	DL00	PM01	Counter reading		DLPM1000	ICD–TA–T1
0020	ME	DL00	PM01	Check oil level		10001211	ICD–TA–T1
0030	ME	DL00	PM01	Check oil level		10001212	ICD–TA–T1
0040	ME	DL00	PM01	Check oil level		10001213	ICD–TA–T1
0050	ME	DL00	PM01	Counter reading		10001210	ICD–TA–T1
0060	ME	DL00	PM01	Counter reading		E10000	ICE–TA–T1
0070	ME	DL00	PM01	Screw inspection		10001214	ICD–TA–T1
0080	ME	DL00	PM01	Check oil level		10001215	ICD–TA–T1
0090	ME	DL00	PM01				

Group PUMP_RND Inspection Round Pump Grp.Countr 1

General Operation Overview

Figure 5.60 Enhanced Inspection Rounds: Maintenance Task List

You define the counters as PRTs for the operation (see Figure 5.61).

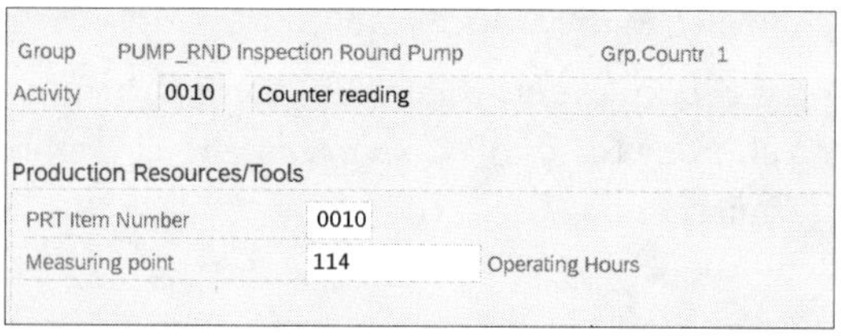

Group   PUMP_RND Inspection Round Pump   Grp.Countr 1

Activity   0010   Counter reading

Production Resources/Tools

PRT Item Number	0010	
Measuring point	114	Operating Hours

Figure 5.61 Enhanced Inspection Rounds: Counter

Enhanced Inspection Rounds: Which Maintenance Plan Category?

You can use a maintenance plan to define the frequency with which the inspection round task list is to be executed:

- You can use the time-based, single-cycle plan if you want the entire inspection round to be executed at defined intervals.

- You can use the time-based strategy plan if the inspection of individual stations takes place in different cycles.

- In contrast, performance-based maintenance plan categories are not relevant for inspection rounds because you'll want to inspect several objects with differing counter readings.

Maintenance Plan

Figure 5.62 shows a single-cycle plan that executes the inspection round task list created earlier on a monthly basis.

Figure 5.62 Enhanced Inspection Rounds: Maintenance Plan

Order

When you start the maintenance plan, the system generates an order that contains the technical objects (functional locations and equipment) and the measurement points as PRTs at the operation level (see Figure 5.63).

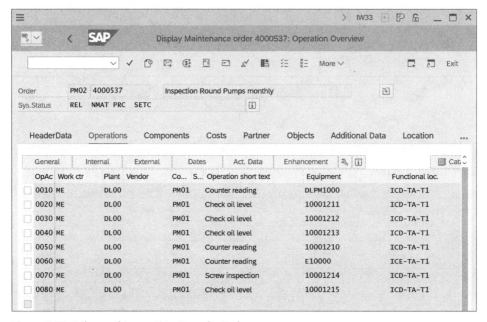

Figure 5.63 Enhanced Inspection Rounds: Order

In order for this to work, you must make the following setting: choose the customizing function **Define Notification and Order Integration** and deactivate the **Enhanced Object List for Assignment of Operations to Object List Entries** indicator.

Confirmation

To confirm the order for the inspection round, use Transaction IW42 (Overall Completion Confirmation), which allows you to record measurement/counter readings as well as confirm operations (see Figure 5.64). Please use the **mease. Points: Inspectn Planning** function key. Furthermore, you can directly create a new notification for technical confirmation for every operation to which an object is assigned from the overall completion confirmation.

As a prerequisite for confirmations, you must have defined data entry profiles using the customizing function **Set Screen Templates for the Completion Confirmation** and assigned a data entry profile (function **Extras • Settings** in Transaction IW42). When you define screen templates, you must activate the **Measurement/counter readings** screen area.

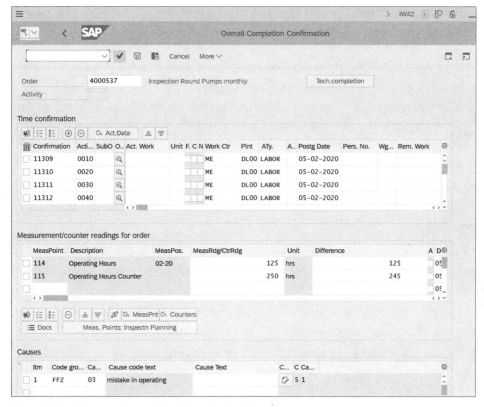

Figure 5.64 Enhanced Inspection Rounds: Confirmation

The LOG_EAM_CI_3 and LOG_EAM_CI_4 business functions must be activated so you can use inspection rounds completely.

> **Overall Completion Confirmation with Layout for Advanced Inspection Rounds**
>
> Define a screen layout for the overall completion confirmation of orders for advanced inspection rounds, which contains the operations and measuring points/counter readings and allows you to confirm all information relating to inspection rounds from a single screen template.

5.8   Condition-Based Maintenance

Condition-based maintenance is defined as a maintenance strategy for which a maintenance task is triggered by a difference in the actual condition of a technical system or part of a technical system compared to the target condition. The following definitions apply:

- *Counters* are the tools you can use in SAP S/4HANA Asset Management to represent the wear and tear of an object, consumption, or the reduction of an object's useful life, for example, an odometer, operation hours counter, numbers of pieces, or output in tons. Counters have a continuous (increasing or decreasing) counter reading.
- *Measuring points* in SAP S/4HANA Asset Management are used to indicate locations where the current condition of a technical system is described, for example, temperature, number of revolutions, pressure, level of contamination, and viscosity. You can specify target values and upper/lower limits on measuring points. Measuring readings have a discontinuous progression.

While we learned that counters are the basis for performance-based maintenance, measuring points and measurement readings form the basis for condition-based maintenance.

You must fulfill the following prerequisites for condition-based maintenance:

- You must first define the target conditions of the technical systems and parts of a technical system.
- You must monitor the technical system and parts of it regularly or permanently in terms of the target conditions.
- You are not required to define any maintenance plans.

While a maintenance task for time-based maintenance is triggered when a certain date is reached, and for performance-based maintenance when a specific counter reading is achieved, tasks for condition-based maintenance are triggered, for example, by the following events:

- The temperature has risen too high or fallen too low.
- The flow rate is too quick or too slow.
- The oil shows too high a level of pollution.
- The voltage has dropped too low or has built up too far.
- The viscosity of the lubricant is too high or too low.

Table 5.2 contains an overview of the differences between time-based, performance-based, and condition-based maintenance.

	Time-Based Maintenance	Performance-Based Maintenance	Condition-Based Maintenance
Basis	Calendar	Counters	Measuring point
Readings	N/A	Sporadic to regular	Regular to permanent

Table 5.2 Maintenance Strategies

	Time-Based Maintenance	Performance-Based Maintenance	Condition-Based Maintenance
Run chart	N/A	Continuous increase or decrease	Discontinuous
Maintenance plan	Yes	Yes	No
Task is triggered	When a date is reached	When a counter reading is reached	When target values have been exceeded or not reached

Table 5.2 Maintenance Strategies (Cont.)

How does condition-based maintenance work in the SAP system? Figure 5.65 shows an overview.

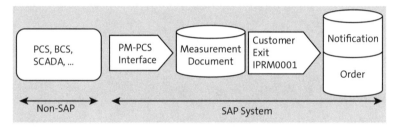

Figure 5.65 Condition Based Maintenance: Overview

You use an upstream system to obtain current data regularly or permanently about the condition of the technical system. Such systems can be:

- Process control systems
- Building control systems (BCS)
- SCADA (supervisory control and data acquisition) systems
- Electronic control stations
- Network monitoring systems
- Systems for plant data collection and machine data acquisition (PDC/MDA)
- Warehouse computers
- Systems for sound or vibration analyses
- Diagnostic systems
- Mobile data entry systems

For more information about the way these systems work and how data is transferred to SAP S/4HANA Asset Management, refer to Chapter 7, Section 7.3.

You can use the plant maintenance-production control system (PM-PCS) interface to transfer measurement readings from these upstream systems to SAP S/4HANA Asset

Management. The data is saved in measurement documents and can be further processed.

In customer exits, you define what the further processing should look like. Customer exit IMRC0001 is particularly important in this context because this customer exit can automatically trigger actions in SAP S/4HANA Asset Management if certain thresholds are exceeded (see Figure 5.66). You can define a target value and measurement range limits for each technical object, that is, a value range within which the measurement results must be.

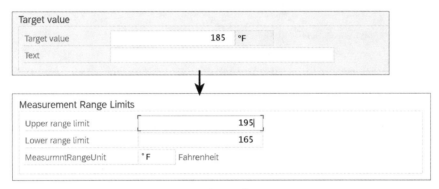

Figure 5.66 Measuring Point: Target Value and Ranges

You can use the customizing function **Define Measuring Point Categories** to specify that the SAP system must issue a warning or an error message if measurement ranges are exceeded or not reached. You can also define that a malfunction report is automatically triggered when a certain threshold is exceeded. Other tasks can be triggered through customer exits in the report (for example, orders can be created).

5.9   Summary

SAP S/4HANA Asset Management provides a wide range of functionality for preventive maintenance. In this chapter, you learned about the most important functions of maintenance task lists and maintenance plans as well as how to use them. Section 5.3 covered the following:

- The different types of task lists (equipment, functional location, and general task lists)
- The content of maintenance task lists (e.g., operations and components)
- How to create a task list
- How to assign a task list to an order
- How to perform additional functions (e.g., mass change or costing)

Section 5.4 through Section 5.7 covered maintenance plan-related topics, as follows:

- The different types of maintenance plans (single-cycle plans, strategy plans, multiple-counter plans, and inspection rounds)
- The fact that they are based on time or performance units
- The content of maintenance plans (e.g., items and task lists)
- How to create the different types of maintenance plans
- How to schedule maintenance plans
- The fact that you have to run deadline monitoring (Transaction IP30H) on a regular basis
- How the system determines plan and call dates based on the scheduling parameters
- How to perform additional functions (e.g., mass change or costing)

5

Chapter 6
Other Business Processes

In addition to the classic work order cycle (Chapter 4), there are a number of other business processes in which SAP S/4HANA Asset Management can support you, such as immediate repairs, external services, refurbishment, and various other processes. This chapter acquaints you with options as well as limitations; it also contains recommendations on how you can make the best use of the system.

In addition to the basic work order cycle, SAP S/4HANA Asset Management supports other business processes. These are based on the work order cycle's functionality and contain either additional functions or modifications in the order to be able to use the system for additional purposes. These are the following:

- Immediate repairs (performing maintenance tasks without planning)
- Shift notes and shift reports (documenting events during a shift)
- External assignment (using external companies for processing maintenance activities)
- Refurbishment (repairing spare parts or equipment from faulty to operational conditions)
- Subcontracting (external refurbishing at a contractor site)
- Test equipment calibration (regularly checking and calibrating test equipment)
- Follow-on order (creating a new order as a successor to an already processed order)
- Pool asset management (borrowing objects that are contained in a pool)
- Project-based maintenance (performing maintenance activities within a higher-level project)

6.1 Immediate Repairs

The business process for an immediate repair is characterized by the facts that immediate repairs are never known in advance and the necessary resources (work centers, materials, external companies, and so on) cannot be planned. You can and must react as quickly as possible to a business transaction such as a malfunction, for example. An immediate repair business process occurs, for example, in the following cases:

- A pump fails.
- A forklift truck breaks down in transit.
- An elevator in a building gets stuck.
- A closed valve cannot be opened.
- Measuring equipment, such as a scale, for example, displays nothing.
- A robotic arm no longer extends.

The process for an immediate repair thus differs from a classic work order cycle in terms of the ability to plan for it—you can only react to malfunctions but not plan them—and from preventive maintenance in terms of the prescribed schedule: maintenance and inspection tasks have regular cycles and, consequently, recurring deadlines.

Figure 6.1 shows how the process for an immediate repair could proceed. The five-step cycle of a plannable maintenance process is condensed into a three-step cycle for an immediate repair.

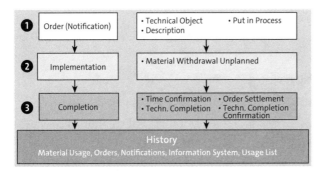

Figure 6.1 Immediate Repair

1. **Order creation**
   The starting point in the first step is the creation of an order in step ❶ (possibly with data about the notification) for damage or a malfunction. This order is not planned but is released immediately for processing, and shop papers that may be required are printed out.

2. **Processing**
   The processing phase in step ❷ involves the withdrawal of the spare parts from the warehouse and the actual processing of the order.

3. **Completion**
   After you complete the tasks, the required actual times are confirmed in the order completion in step ❸; technical completion confirmations about how the damage was processed and the status of the technical system are also entered here. In the final step, the order is settled by controlling.

There are various options for mapping the immediate repair in SAP S/4HANA Asset Management, which the following sections will discuss.

6.1.1 Creating Orders (with Notification) and Completion

For this business process, it's important to set up the repair order and print out the required shop papers as quickly as possible to enable the technician to start the repair work. The following sections will cover the order layout, notifications, and confirmation.

Simple Order Layout

An order with all the order data displayed is reflected in the layout of a fully detailed order type like the one shown in Figure 6.2. The order type consists of ten tabs with up to four subscreens on one tab, which can be too much detail and too confusing for quick ordering.

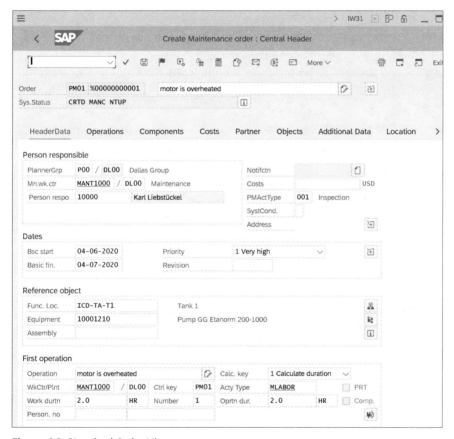

Figure 6.2 Standard Order View

Defining a Simple Order Layout

One of the most important functions in terms of an immediate repair involves defining a separate screen layout for each order type, one that is as basic as possible, preferably with only a single tab containing a few input fields. You achieve this via the customizing function **Simple Order View**.

You can use the **Define View Profiles** customizing function there to arrange the tabs according to your own requirements and the **Assign View Profiles to Order Types** customizing function to assign them to your order types.

Notification and Order Integration

You can also create a notification at the same time as setting up an order, provided that you activate the integrated entry of order and notification data for an order type in customizing. You do so via the customizing function **Define Notification and Order Integration**.

[!] **Entering Notification and Order Data in Only One Screen**

You can use the **Define Notification and Order Integration** customizing function to enable you to enter order and notification data on a screen.

A suitable reduced layout for an immediate repair could thus look like the one displayed in Figure 6.3. The tab with the order header data simultaneously contains notification data and the option to assign spare parts.

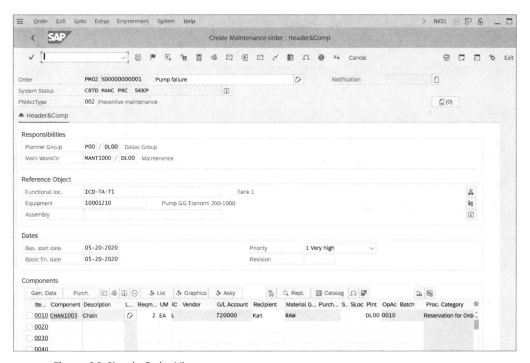

Figure 6.3 Simple Order View

You complete entering the order using the **Put in process** function (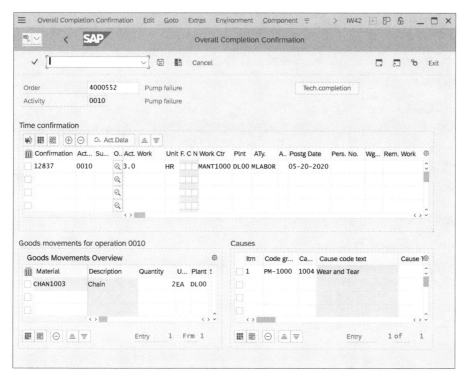 button) in order to immediately release the order and generate the shop papers.

Confirmation

I recommend that you use Transaction IW42 (Overall Completion Confirmation) for completing an order (Figure 6.4) for an immediate repair because not only can you enter the actual times here, but you can also enter the unplanned material withdrawals and technical data. You can also immediately complete the order and notification from there.

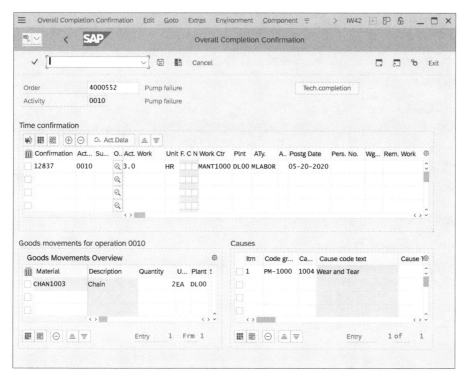

Figure 6.4 Overall Completion Confirmation

You must now also perform the functions for the order settlement and business completion.

At this point, you've completed the business process for an immediate repair, and the information has been entered into the SAP system in just two steps (order creation and completion), which does not require much time.

6.1.2   Special Case: After-Event Recording

The *after-event recording* business process is a modification of the *immediate repair* business process. After-event recording is characterized by the fact that, when you enter the order in the SAP system, the order processing has already taken place. This type of business process is associated with the following scenarios:

- A pump was put into operation again.
- A broken-down forklift truck was fixed.
- The backup of control elements was replaced in a process plant.
- A jammed sliding door in a building was made accessible.
- An unscheduled adjustment had to be made to test equipment.

The difference with the after-event recording process compared to an immediate repair process is that the repair work was already completed when you entered the order, and thus the work is only entered into the SAP system later on. Figure 6.5 shows the schematic diagram of after-event recording.

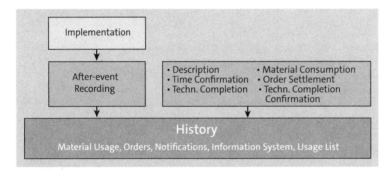

Figure 6.5 After-Event Recording

SAP provides two options for the after-event recording process:

- The **Confirm Unplanned Job** (only available in SAP Business Client)
- Transaction IW61 (Historical Order) (also available in SAP GUI)

Confirm Unplanned Job

The **Confirm Unplanned Job** function in SAP Business Client enables you to record an order including all actual data retroactively.

This function contains the following options (see Figure 6.6):

- **Create order**
  You create an order and enter order data such as the reference object, activity, execution date, and working times.
- **Enter goods movement**
  If a material has been consumed, you can also enter this information here.
- **Record measurement readings or counter readings**
  If the technical object has measuring points and/or counters, you can record measurement readings and/or counter readings.

- **Create malfunction data**

  You can also record notification data like malfunctions, damage codes, or cause codes.

- **Attach document**

  If a document is created when processing an order (for example, an image or measurement log), you can attach the document to the order confirmation.

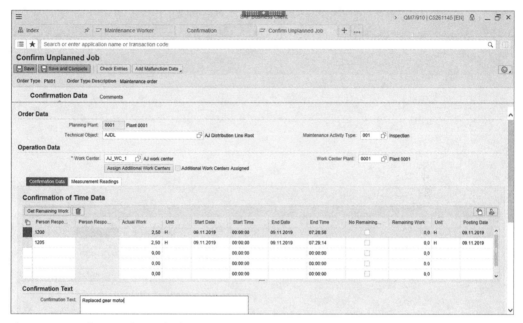

Figure 6.6 Confirm Unplanned Job

When saving, the following technical steps occur in the background:

- An order is created with or without a notification and is released.
- A confirmation is recorded for the actual times entered, and the order receives a final confirmation.
- If necessary, a material withdrawal is posted to the order.
- If necessary, counter readings and/or measurement readings are stored.
- If necessary, the document is attached.
- The order is technically complete.

You still have to perform a business completion and order settlement.

To use unscheduled tasks comprehensively, you must activate the business functions LOG_EAM_SIMP, LOG_EAM_SIMPLICITY, and LOG_EAM_SIMPLICITY_2.

Historical Order

Another option to document work that has already been performed is using the so-called *historical order*. Historical orders are usually automatically generated during the reorganization of technically completed orders. Extracts, such as costs or operations, are stored as historical orders, but all other data is deleted.

You can also directly record a historical order using Transaction IW61 (Create Historical Order) and thus update the history of a technical object.

The historical order then contains the same critical information as a normal order (see Figure 6.7):

- Reference objects
- Operations
- Object list
- Partners
- Components

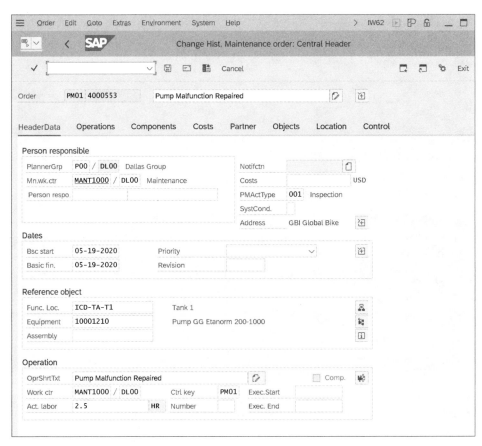

Figure 6.7 Historical Order: Header

However, this information is interpreted as actual data and not as planned data. As a result, you record actual work (not planned work) and actual costs directly in the order (not estimated costs; see Figure 6.8).

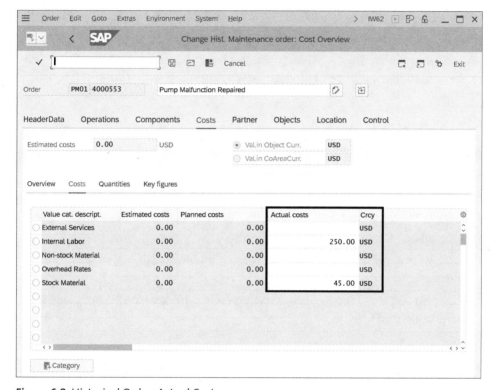

Figure 6.8 Historical Order: Actual Costs

All data is imported to the history of the reference object and can be evaluated—including all costs—through the logistics information system (see Chapter 8, Section 8.2.3). *But* (and this is the major disadvantage of this approach) the costs are not booked in other SAP applications, such as cost accounting and materials management. As a result, the performing cost center may not be credited, and the asset cost center may not be debited. How can you solve this?

> **Cost Accounting for Historical Orders**
>
> For historical orders, you can create a separate order type for manually recorded historical orders.
>
> Develop a batch program that selects these orders and perform cost accounting between two cost centers (performing cost center of the work center and receiving cost center of the technical object) in the same way as Transaction KB21N (Enter Direct Activity Allocation).

6.2   Shift Notes and Shift Reports

You can use shift notes and reports to document events that occur during a shift. In a shift note, you enter information about an event, such as comments, times, or objects.

A shift report is a PDF generated at the end of a shift by the person responsible for the shift. It is comprised of the shift notes that have been recorded and other documents, such as confirmations, material issues, counter readings, and so on. A digital signature can be used to sign a shift report, if necessary.

6.2.1   Shift Notes

Shift notes can, for example, contain the following information:

- General notes (for example, shift interruptions, power outages)
- Breakdown documentation (for example, a turning machine breakdown from/to)
- Suggestions for improvement (for example, "Reduce machine speed by 10% because...")
- Notes on employees (e.g., "Mr. Huber finished one hour early because...")
- Notes on material usage (for example, "Casing should be clamped with a maximum pressure of 10 bar")
- Comments on the use of tools (for example, "Hand brace 9700 is not suitable for material T-B400)

You create shift notes using the following transactions:

- Transaction ISHN1 (Create Maintenance Shift Note) if you want to start by creating a reference to a technical object (functional location, equipment)
- Transaction SHN1 (Create Work Center Shift Note) if you want to start by creating a reference to a work center (see Figure 6.9)

You enter information about the work center, the date and time (from/to), and text in a shift note.

You can also assign a **Category** to the shift note. The category indicates whether the shift note is a general note, a malfunction notification, a note on employees, or similar. You can define the categories in customizing and select them using the $\boxed{\text{F4}}$ help.

In customizing, you can also specify the reference objects to which you want your shift notes to refer. The following reference objects can be selected:

- Equipment
- Functional locations
- Materials
- Production orders
- Process orders

- Maintenance notifications
- Quality notifications
- Other objects

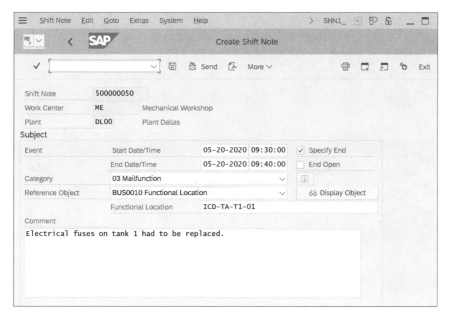

Figure 6.9 Transaction SHN1: Create Shift Note

Shift notes also offer the following functions:

- If you click the **Send** button, you can send the shift note to a recipient by email.
- You can send alerts automatically; alerts are notifications such as SMS or emails that are triggered when a particular event occurs. Thus, you can specify, for example, that the production manager is to receive an SMS with a notification and the material number if a shift note of the material category is triggered.
- If you click the ⤴ button, you can output the shift note as a PDF form.
- The **Display Object** button displays the shift note's reference object (for example, the production order or the equipment).
- The ⬚∨ object service allows you to attach documents to the shift note.
- If you want to display or change shift notes, you can conduct a full-text search in fuzzy mode in the F4 help.
- You can display a list of shift notes in Transaction SHN4 (List Shift Notes) or Transaction ISHN4 (List Maintenance Shift Notes).
- You can use Transaction SHN5 (Shift Note Cockpit) to display a shift note monitor with which you can monitor several work centers simultaneously (see Figure 6.10).

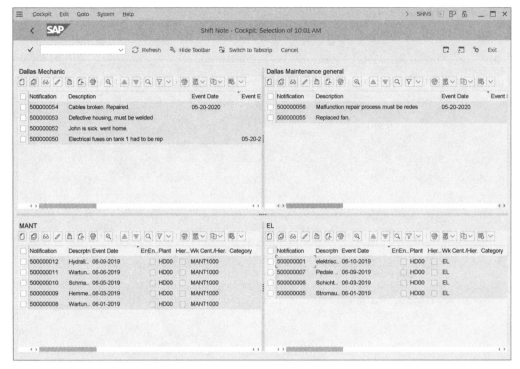

Figure 6.10 Transaction SHN5 (Shift Note Cockpit)

To use shift notes, you must ensure that certain prerequisites are met in relation to the customizing settings for the work center and technical object (functional location, equipment).

You must first perform the following steps in customizing:

- Create a new notification type (for example, SN). To this end, choose the customizing function **Define Notification Types**.

- Assign a separate screen layout to the notification type using the customizing function **Define Screen Templates**. As a minimum, assign the value **130 Shift Note** in the **Screen Area** field.

- Make specific settings for the shift note notification type using the customizing function **Make settings for shift note type**, where you can assign the category and reference objects, among other things.

In each work center and in each technical object (functional location, equipment) in the **General Data** screen group, you must also enter the shift note type in the **Note Type** field and the shift report type in the **Report Type** field (see Figure 6.11).

Figure 6.11 Work Center or Technical Object

6.2.2   Shift Reports

A shift report is a PDF document generated at the end of a shift by the person responsible for the shift and is intended to facilitate the handover to the next shift. A shift report may include the following elements:

- Shift notes
- Production activities
- Confirmations
- Goods movements
- Maintenance notifications
- Quality notifications
- Maintenance orders
- Measurement documents
- Graphical analyses

You create shift reports using the following transactions:

- Transaction ISHR1 (Create Maintenance Shift Report) if you want to start by creating a reference to a technical object (functional location, equipment)
- Transaction SHR1 (Create Shift Report General) if you want to start by creating a reference to a work center (see Figure 6.12)

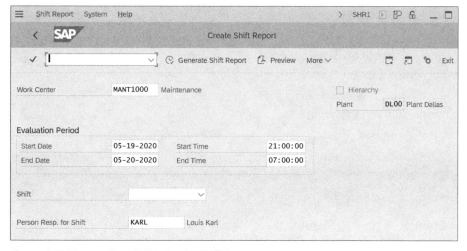

Figure 6.12 Transaction SHR1: Create Shift Report

A specific shift report is generated on the basis of the selection criteria entered and the layout settings you defined in customizing (see Figure 6.13).

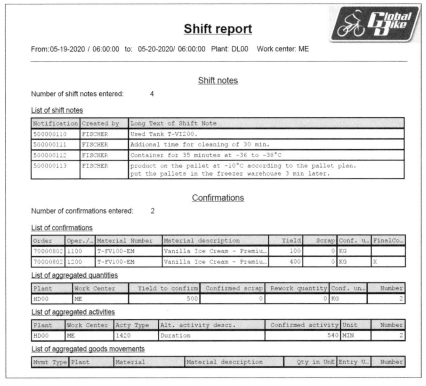

Figure 6.13 Shift Report: Result

Shift reports also offer the following functions:

- To use a digital signature, check the shift report and then sign it by using the menu function **Shift Report · Signing**.

- If you want to delete a shift report, use the menu function **Shift Report · Discard**. The status report is then assigned the status **Discarded**. You can then create a new shift report for the relevant shift.

- You can click the **Send** button to send a shift report. The SAP S/4HANA system then sends the shift report as a link.

- To print a shift report, open the PDF document and click the 🖶 button.

- You can create a list of shift reports that have already been generated in Transaction SHR4 (List Shift Reports) or Transaction ISHR4 (List Shift Maintenance Reports).

- You can run a full-text search in a list of generated shift reports.

To use shift notes, you must ensure that certain prerequisites are met in relation to the customizing settings for the work center and technical object (functional location, equipment).

You must perform the following steps in Customizing:

- Create a shift report type (for example, SR) via the customizing function **Define Shift Report Types**. Here, you can specify, for example, whether the sequence of shift reports is to be continuous (with no gaps), whether you want to use a signature, or whether you want to send the shift reports by email. You also need to assign a layout to the shift report.

- The layout is defined by a form. SAP delivers the COCF_SR_PDF_LAYOUT form for shift reports as standard. If you require a separate form, you can define one in Transaction SFP.

- If you require an electronic signature, you can configure this using the customizing functions **Define Authorization Groups for Signature in Shift Report**, **Define Individual Signatures**, and **Define Signature Strategies**.

In addition, you are required to enter the shift report type in each work center and each technical object (functional location, equipment).

The business functions LOG_PP_SRN_CONF and LOG_PP_SRN_02 must be activated in order for you to use shift notes and shift reports.

[+]

Clear and Concise Shift Reports

Shift reports provide a clear and concise overview of all events occurring during a shift. Their layouts can be adapted flexibly to suit your needs.

6.3   External Assignment

External assignment means that external companies are used or orders are assigned externally for processing pending maintenance activities. This section will first walk you through the basic principles of external assignment and then cover an external process as a single purchase order, with external work centers and with service specifications.

6.3.1   Basic Principles of External Assignment

External assignment is extremely important in plant maintenance, considerably more so than in production, for example. A non-representative short survey of SAP user companies in the German-speaking SAP user group showed that, on average, approximately half of their maintenance costs result from external processing. Some companies do not have their own maintenance workshops, using instead, coordination points (for example, work scheduling or planners), which are responsible for planning, monitoring, and approving external processing. Let's now look at why you would use external assignment and how to initiate it.

Reasons for External Assignment

Why has there always been external assignment in plant maintenance, and why is this trend increasing even further in the course of national and international division of labor and globalization? The main reasons for external assignments are the following:

- **Lack of qualifications**
  A company cannot employ separate technicians who are qualified for every type of work that arises in plant maintenance; instead, work is often awarded specifically to external companies who specialize in a particular field (for example, elevator service, air conditioning, electronic controls, robot maintenance, and so on).

- **Lack of capacity**
  External companies can support internal maintenance departments in covering peak capacity times (for example, for revisions, shutdowns, work required at year-end, and so on).

- **Possibly lower costs by using external companies**
  The argument as to whether external companies are really more economical than your own workshops is often only one-sided when you compare an allocation record X of your own manual workers to a lower allocation record Y of the external company.

  For a cost comparison, you must not only use the primary costs (invoice amount) of the external assignment, but you must also take into account the secondary costs associated with the external assignment, such as internal administration and control effort (for example, order planning, purchase order, acceptance of services performed, invoice verification, and so on). You must also consider that an internal award "only" concerns costs, whereas an external award involves expenditure and payment.

- **Outsourcing**
  During restructuring, departments are often outsourced, and independent companies are established. A department that is often affected by such outsourcing is plant maintenance, which is established as "Maintenance GmbH" in such cases. Although colleagues still sit across the hall from each other, they now work for a different company. Since a separate company code has to be set up in the SAP system for this company, this external assignment exists only in purely technical terms.

Initiating the External Assignment

You use a control key to initiate external processing. You can use different control keys (see Figure 6.14), depending on how you want the assignment and processing to occur.

The specification of the control key in this case controls the type of external assignment:

- If you have configured a *work center for an external company* and you want to execute external processing using an internal order in the same way as you do for your own work centers (see Chapter 2, Section 2.2), initiate this type of external processing using a **control key** (PM01 or similar). This **control key** should have the **Ext. processing** option set to **Internally processed operation** and the **Service** indicator not set.

- If you want to execute external processing using a *purchase requisition* and a single standard purchase order, initiate this type of external processing using a control key (PM02 or similar) for which the **Ext. processing** option is set to **Externally processed operation** and the **Service** indicator is not set.

- If you want to execute external processing using *service specifications* and a subsequent service entry sheet (Section 6.3.4), initiate this type of external processing using a **control key** (PM03 or similar) for which the **Ext. processing** option is set to **Externally processed operation** and the **Service** indicator is set.

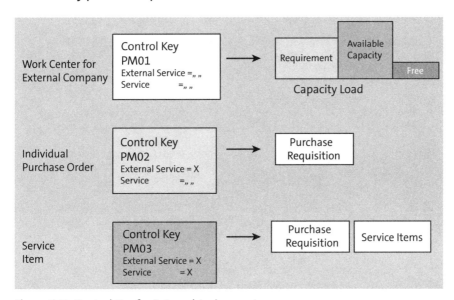

Figure 6.14 Control Key for External Assignment

6.3.2 External Processing as a Single Purchase Order

If you want to assign external services as a single purchase order, the procedure is generally the following (see Figure 6.15):

1. When you plan external processing in an order, a purchase requisition is automatically triggered in the background.

2. The purchasing department (or materials requirement planning [MRP] controllers in plant maintenance) converts the purchase requisition into a purchase order.

3. After the external company has rendered the services, enter them in the system. However, you do not confirm external processing in the same way as normal time

confirmations. Instead, you enter a service confirmation as a goods receipt for the purchase order. If the goods receipt is valued (an option available for the service item in the purchase order), actual costs are posted to the order at this point in time.

4. The invoice receipt concludes this process. If the invoice amount differs from the amount on the purchase order, a correction automatically takes place, and the order shows the net costs of the invoice.

Let's now look at these steps in more detail.

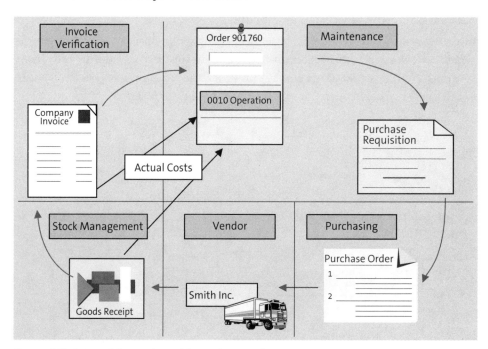

Figure 6.15 External Processing with Purchase Order

Create Order

You plan the external service at the level of an order operation. You cannot assign an external company using notifications or order header data.

[+] **Separate Order Types for External Assignments**

A separate order type is often set up for external processing, which has several advantages: You can specifically set default values (for example, ensure that the PM02 control key [external processing] is always used for the PM02 order type). You can also search for and summarize data more selectively in lists and reports.

To process the external assignment further, you need control and organizational information in the purchase requisition and purchase order (see Figure 6.16), such as the following:

- Material groups
- Cost elements
- Purchasing groups
- Purchasing organizations
- Ship-to parties
- Unloading points

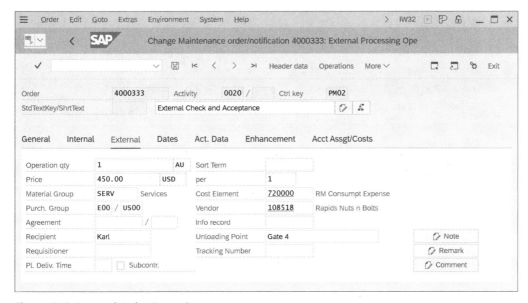

Figure 6.16 External Order Operation

Since the information required by purchasing must remain as consistent as possible, you should use the option to store default values to ensure that these do not always have to be entered again in each order.

The operation overview previously included only a selection of fields predefined by SAP. Several purchasing data items were sorely missed. If you activate business function LOG_EAM_CI_5, you can maintain all purchasing data in the operation overview (for example, vendor, material group, goods recipient, unloading point, or purchasing group) as well as on the detail screen.

Another new feature is part of the business function LOG_EAM_CI_8: If you activate it, you can display the supplier's name, material group text, and general ledger account short text—both in the overview and on the detail screen.

Previously, you could only add a single long text for the external operation, which then was transferred to the purchase requisition as item text. The business function LOG_ EAM_CI_12 brings in another innovation here: If you activate it, up to four texts are available. This is flexible, so that you can use several customizing functions to define the type of text for purchase requisitions:

- Which types of text you want to use
- Which text type of the non-stock item should be copied to which text type of the purchase requisition
- Which labelling texts should appear on the function keys.

Figure 6.16 shows possible text types (e.g., note, remark, comment), which you can then call up individually by clicking a button.

The business function LOG_EAM_CI_9_ORD_OPER_COMP brings another innovation. With this business function, you can copy operations and sub-operations using the function key 🗐 at the operation list when processing maintenance orders in the corresponding transactions and in the simple order view.

Default Values

You can store the default values using the customizing function **Create Default Values for External Procurement** in order to then assign them to the order type for each plant in the **External Profile** field using the Customizing function **Default Values for Maintenance Task List Data and Profile Assignments**. The same applies for external material: The assignment here is made using the **Material Profile** field.

However, you can also store the default values based on users by calling **Extras · Settings · Default Values** within an order and storing the data on the **External processing** tab (see Figure 6.17). The same applies for external material, but in this case, you would fill out the **Ext. procurement** tab.

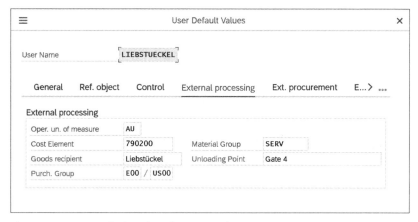

Figure 6.17 User Default Values for External Processing

If both default values and user-based default values are stored in customizing, the user-based default values have priority.

Purchase Requisition

A purchase requisition is automatically generated in the background on the basis of the external processing operation. You can display the number of the purchase requisition on the **Actual Data** tab and also go directly to the purchase requisition from there. The information from the order has been transferred identically to the purchase requisition (see Figure 6.18).

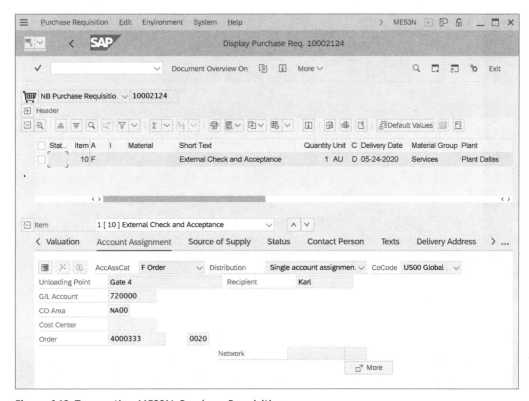

Figure 6.18 Transaction ME23N: Purchase Requisition

Purchase Order

Depending on the organizational responsibility, the purchase requisition is converted to a purchase order either by purchasing or by the technical department itself. When specifying an outline agreement number, you can also execute a maintenance call from an outline agreement in the same way.

The purchase requisition is automatically assigned to the order, and this assignment cannot be changed.

Goods Receipt

You do not confirm external services like internal services; instead, you enter a goods receipt (Transaction MIGO, [Goods Receipt for Purchase Order]). If you ordered a general service unit (SU) as a unit, you can only confirm or not confirm the service. If you triggered the purchase order on an hourly basis, you can accept the effective hours, which can be more or fewer hours than ordered (see Figure 6.19).

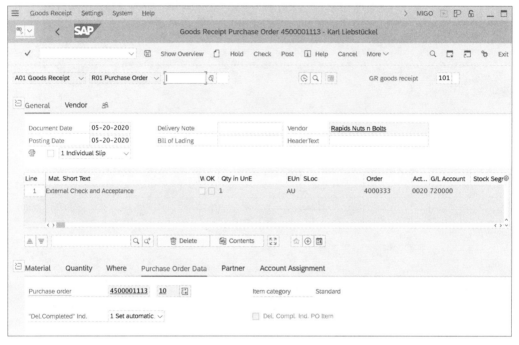

Figure 6.19 Transaction MIGO: Goods Receipt

To ensure that the goods receipt can be entered, you must release the order but must not yet perform a business completion for it.

If you set the **Goods receipt valuated** indicator in the purchase order, the purchase order value is debited on the order at this point, and the offsetting entry is made on a clearing account.

Invoice

When the invoice is received (see Figure 6.20, Transaction MIRO [Enter Incoming Invoice]), the value is automatically cleared again on the clearing account. Any differences between the purchase order value and the invoice value are subsequently debited or credited.

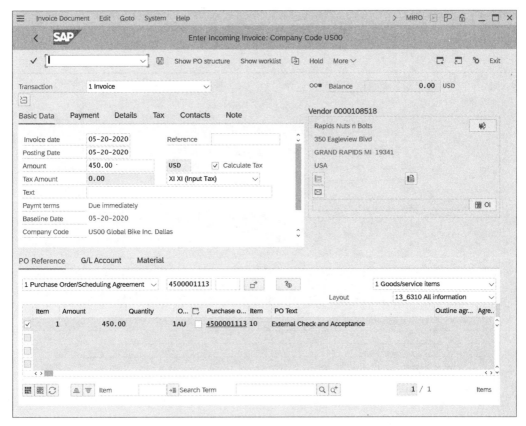

Figure 6.20 Transaction MIRO: Invoice

6.3.3 External Services with External Work Centers

Many companies work with service companies permanently or for smaller tasks. These external companies provide staff and perhaps even have their own offices on the premises. They work "on call" and process many tasks in the course of a day, week, or month in this way.

Do you also work with such companies? If you were now to commission these companies according to this model, you would have the following cycle for each individual task: order → purchase requisition → purchase order → goods receipt → invoice receipt. This level of administrative effort can no longer be justified.

So what can you do to reduce the administrative effort? The following section will describe a model for external services with work centers, which is now being used in many companies and which may also help you to work with these external companies without a high level of administrative effort.

Prerequisites

To use this model, you must fulfill the necessary prerequisites. Figure 6.21 provides an overview of this case.

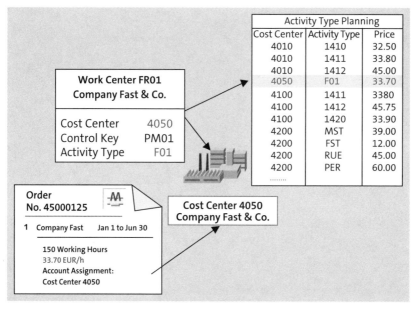

Figure 6.21 External Work Center: Prerequisites

The prerequisites are as follows:

- **Cost center**
  You must have a cost center where the external services will be cleared. You have three options in terms of the cost center: You can use your own maintenance cost center, you can set up a new cost center (for all external companies in total), or you can set up several new cost centers, one for each external company.

- **Standard purchase order**
  You must set up a standard purchase order which is assigned to a cost center, has a runtime (month, quarter, year), and contains the hourly rate of the external company. You can also open purchase orders with several items—for example, if you have agreed on different allocation records with the external company (for example, technicians, assistants, trainees).

- **Activity planning**
  In Transaction KP26, you must perform activity type planning where you store prices for the periods, cost centers, and activity types.

- **Work center**
  You must set up a work center for each external company. On the **Costing** tab, you assign a cost center, the *internal processing* activity type, and the formula key for the internal processing (for example, SAPOO8) to this work center.

External-Like Internal Work Centers

The settings for this work center do not differ from your own work center settings. Therefore, if you enter a control key on the **Default Values** tab, for example, the control key will be used for internal processing (for example, PM01).

6

Order Processing

The processing of maintenance tasks that you perform with this work center barely differs from the processing that is described in Chapter 4 for processing with internal work centers.

- You can set up your orders with the external work center as the performing work center. Whether you also enter it as the main work center does not matter.
- You can print the shop papers.
- You can confirm the orders using the same transactions that you also use for the internal orders (Transactions IW41, IW42, IW44, and IW48).
- You can settle these orders exactly like internal orders, which would credit the cost center entered in the work center and debit the asset cost center.

Shop Papers for External Work Centers

To differentiate shop papers on a purely visual basis, shop papers for external companies should look different from internal shop papers. After the order is completed, you should sign the shop papers and give copies to the external company.

Invoice

Some special features arise in relation to invoicing (see Figure 6.22):

- You receive an invoice periodically (for example, monthly), rather than for each individual service.
- The invoice total contains the value of all services performed since the last invoice was issued.

Checking Invoicing

Where invoicing is concerned, you should make sure that the list of executed orders is also specified on the invoice as additional information. You may also perhaps ask the external company to attach copies of the shop papers. Otherwise, you will not be able to verify the orders the issued invoice references.

- Due to the account assignment of the purchase order, the invoice amount is debited to the external company cost center (not to the individual orders).

- The external company cost center must clear in the medium term; in other words, the total credits via orders and the total debits via invoices must be equally high. If they are not, you can simultaneously use the cost center as a controlling instrument that shows that the external company invoiced amounts for services other than those that were rendered.

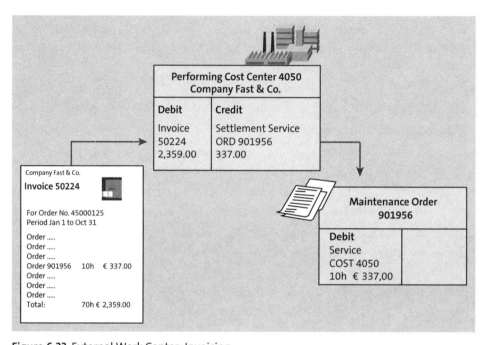

Figure 6.22 External Work Center: Invoicing

The savings relating to the administrative cost, compared to the processing with individual purchase orders illustrated in Section 6.3.2, are obvious:

- You have no purchase requisitions.

- You have only one purchase order rather than a number of purchase orders.

- You have a confirmation, rather than a goods receipt.

- You have only one invoice per period, not an invoice for each purchase order.

[+]

Reducing Administrative Effort with Work Centers for External Companies

Compared to individual purchase orders, you can save a considerable portion of the administrative cost with external companies with which you regularly work by processing with external work centers.

6.3.4 External Processing with Service Specifications

The *external services with service specifications* business process differs from the *external services with individual purchase order* business process in that the services to be rendered by the external company do not occur inclusively through a verbal description in the short and long text of the purchase order item, but rather, the services are specifically rendered individually using a services specification. This gives rise to the following differences in the process flow (see Figure 6.23):

- You perform the planning in the order using a service specification.

- You can store limits for planned and unplanned services in the order planning.

- You enter a service entry sheet, rather than a goods receipt. This entry can also be carried out by the vendor.

- Unlike the goods receipt, the service entry sheet enables you to add unplanned items.

- You must release the services entered using an acceptance of services performed (dual-control principle) to ensure that an invoice can be issued.

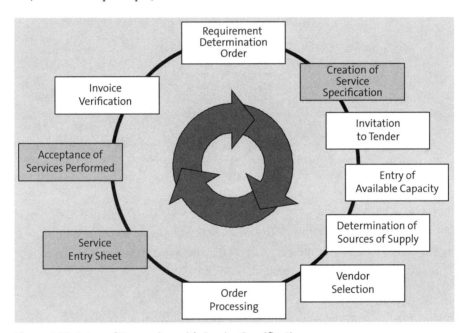

Figure 6.23 External Processing with Service Specifications

You can use the following options to plan the services to be assigned externally within the order:

- You can plan the services manually, that is, without using any default values.

- You can plan the services using service master records. In this case, you use Transaction AC03 (Create Service Master Record).

- You can plan the services using service specifications from other documents (such as an outline agreement, purchase order, order, and so on).

- You can plan the services using model service specifications (see Figure 6.24). You can store service lines and an outline in a model service specification. You can also specify a purchasing organization, vendor, and contract as default values. You maintain model service specifications via Transactions ML10 through ML12.

- You can define prices and conditions of service master records either inclusively (Transaction ML45), for vendors without a plant (Transaction ML39), or for vendors with a plant (Transaction ML33). Defined prices and conditions are included as default values in the order service specification and can be changed there.

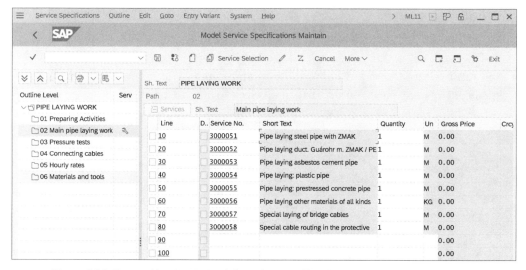

Figure 6.24 Transaction ML10: Model Service Specifications

The general data of the external operation is no different from that of an external service as an individual purchase order.

In addition, you can enter the following specific data for external services management if you navigate, by clicking the 🖾 button, from the original display to the full screen (see Figure 6.25):

- You can enter service lines with or without a service number, price, cost element, quantity, and so on.

- You can enter limits. The overall limit represents the upper limit for unplanned additional services. The expected value must thus be less than or equal to the overall limit and is entered in the standard costing and in the purchase order commitment.

The values of the individual services are shown as the total for the complete service specification.

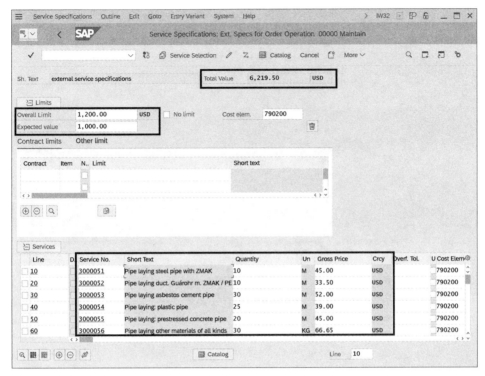

Figure 6.25 Order with Service Specifications

Purchase Requisition

A purchase requisition is automatically generated in the background on the basis of the external processing operation. You can display the number of the purchase requisition on the **Actual Data** tab and also go directly to the purchase requisition from there. The service specification of the order is transferred identically to the purchase requisition.

Purchase Order

Depending on the organizational responsibility, purchasing or the technical department itself converts the purchase requisition into a purchase order; the purchase order adopts the service specification from the purchase requisition in this case. The purchase order is then transferred to the service company.

Service Entry Sheet

If you have ordered external services on the basis of a service specification, you enter the rendering of the services not with a goods receipt but rather with an entry of services performed, using service entry sheets (see Figure 6.26). You use Transaction ML81N (Create Service Entry Sheet).

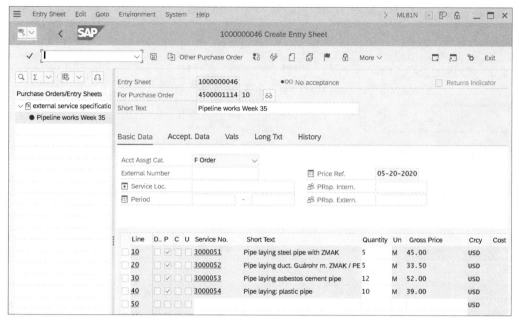

Figure 6.26 Transaction ML81N: Service Entry Sheet

You have to be careful to differentiate between the entry of services performed and the acceptance of services performed in the SAP system. These two functions can (if the authorizations exist) be performed by the same person. However, you could also distribute responsibility to several people using the dual-control principle.

[+]   Entry by External Persons, Acceptance by Internal Persons

In practice, the service entry is often performed on the Internet by the service provider, and the service is accepted by the people responsible in your own company.

Invoice

The accepted service entry sheet represents the basis for the invoice verification. The order is debited with actual costs at the time of acceptance. A goods receipt document is generated when the service entry sheet is accepted.

6.4   Refurbishment

The refurbishment business process is characterized by spare parts being held as reserves in the warehouse (for example, for ensuring system availability). Different statuses exist for spare parts (for example, new, operational, faulty). Faulty parts are refurbished by your own staff or external staff to restore them to operational status.

As a prerequisite, you must manage repairable spares with different accounting values in the warehouse. When you refurbish a repairable spare, it has a higher value than it would have had in a faulty status. The repairable spares are either managed as material only or as individual units only (using material serial numbers).

> **Multiple Prices for the Same Material**
>
> With the refurbishment process, you can ensure that the refurbished material or individual unit subsequently has a higher value than it had before.

You process the management of spare parts by processing refurbishment orders as follows (see Figure 6.27):

❶ Procuring spare parts
You store spare parts for certain critical and high-value components that are used in a technical system so you can replace the components immediately if a breakdown occurs.

❷ Withdrawing functional spare parts and returning faulty spare parts
If a material (single unit) managed as a spare part in a technical system is faulty, you replace it with a functional spare part. To do this, you remove the faulty spare part from the technical system and return it to the warehouse, whereas you withdraw a functional spare part from the warehouse and install it in the technical system.

❸ Creating and releasing a refurbishment order
As soon as the number of faulty repairable parts has reached a certain amount in the warehouse, you create a refurbishment order. You schedule all required operations, materials, tools, and so on for the refurbishment.

❹ Withdrawing parts from the warehouse
The employees responsible for the refurbishment withdraw the faulty spare parts from the warehouse, including all other materials scheduled in the order that they need for the refurbishment.

❺ Refurbishing
You perform the refurbishment. You can post confirmations for internal services, goods receipts, or service entries for external material or external services.

❻ Returning parts to warehouse
You return the refurbished spare parts to the warehouse per goods receipt. In the case of repairable spares that cannot be refurbished, you cancel the reservation and post a scrapping.

❼ Scrapping
If faulty spare parts can no longer be refurbished, you scrap them. Do not forget to also post a goods issue for this situation.

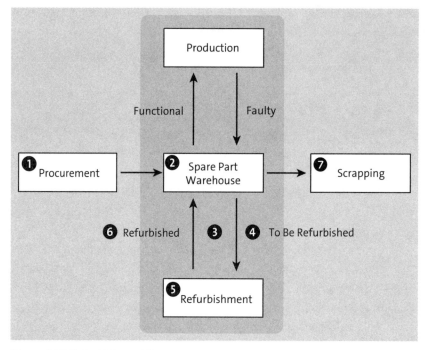

Figure 6.27 Refurbishment Process

Notification of Refurbishment

In order to document the history of a technical object in full, we recommend that you enter a notification for a faulty spare part, which serves as a request for refurbishment.

The following sections will walk you through refurbishment, from the prerequisites to the final costs.

6.4.1   Prerequisites

To enable you to initiate and process the business process for refurbishing spare parts, you must first fulfill some prerequisites.

You need your own order type. In customizing, you set this up for the refurbishment process using **Indicate Order Types for Refurbishment Processing**. You implement this setting at client level so that it applies to all plants.

Separate Notification Type

If you want to request refurbishment services using a notification, we advise, for various reasons (such as selection or screen control), that you define a separate notification type.

[+]

> **Separate Order Type**
>
> You need a separate order type for the refurbishment business process. However, you cannot use an order type that you selected for the refurbishment for "normal" maintenance processes. You can define your own notification type, but you are not required to do so.

For the spare parts, you need a material master that has a split valuation. You create the basis for a split valuation in customizing using the function **Configure Split Valuation** to define a valuation category C (status) and several valuation types, such as **C1** (as new), **C2** (refurbished), and **C3** (to be refurbished).

[+]

> **Ideal Number of Valuation Types**
>
> You should use two or three valuation types for the refurbishment; fewer valuation types would not make any sense, and more valuation types would no longer be manageable.

You can perform the refurbishment process at either the material level or the serial number level (that is, equipment). If you want a separation with serial numbers, the material master must have a serial number profile that enables you to store and remove equipment in the warehouse.

To use the material master of the spare part for the refurbishment, you must define the valuation category (for example, C for status) in the accounting data at the plant level and then create several valuation types for the valuation category (see Figure 6.28).

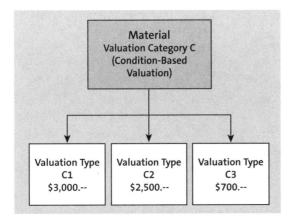

Figure 6.28 Material Master: Valuation Category and Valuation Type

Figure 6.29 shows the accounting data of a material master for which the valuation category C was set in the **Accounting** view and a price was defined for the valuation type C2.

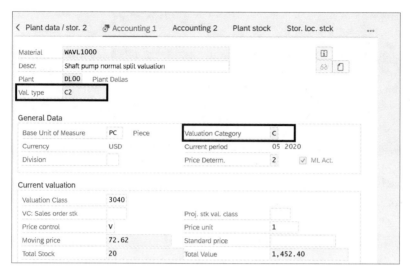

Figure 6.29 Material Master with Valuation Category and Valuation Type

Each valuation type is shown separately in the stock overview (see Figure 6.30).

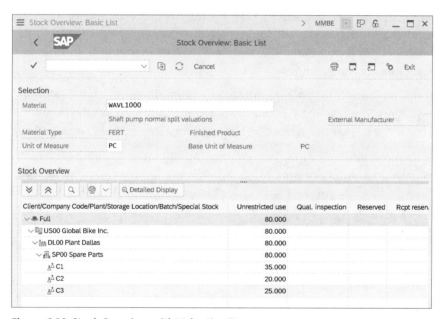

Figure 6.30 Stock Overview with Valuation Types

6.4.2   Refurbishment Notification

Figure 6.31 shows a notification that can be used to request a refurbishment process. The notification has its own notification type (here, M4) and, as an object type, has been assigned a material number, serial number, and equipment number. Refurbishment notifications are an option, not a must.

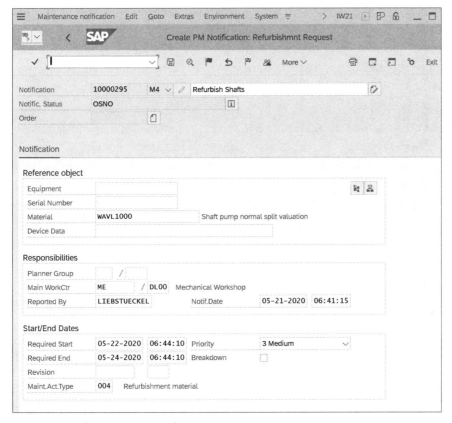

Figure 6.31 Refurbishment Notification

You now have several options for ensuring the assignment of notifications and refurbishment orders:

- You generate a refurbishment order from a notification.
- You generate a refurbishment order and assign the relevant notification to it later.
- You can merge several notifications for a refurbishment using the object list.

The LOG_EAM_ROTSUB, LOG_EAM_ROTSUB_2, and LOG_MM_SERNO business functions must be activated so that you can use a notification for a refurbishment order.

6.4.3   Material Requirements Planning

You can now also generate refurbishment orders in material requirements planning, see the results in the stock/requirements list, and convert them into a refurbishment order.

The business logic behind this function is that whenever the quantity of functional parts drops below the reorder point but non-functional parts are in stock, material requirements planning should automatically generate planned orders. Previously, you could only convert planned orders into purchase requisitions for purchasing, production orders in discrete manufacturing, or process orders in process manufacturing. Now, however, you can also convert the automatically generated planned orders into refurbishment orders to ensure that you always have the required quantity of operational parts.

In order to convert planned orders into refurbishment orders, you must first assign a **Spare Part Class Code** on the **Basic Data 2** screen in the material master and define the code as either a repairable spare with a component maintenance model (CMM, code 2) or as a repairable spare without a component maintenance model (CMM, code 6) (see Figure 6.32). In order for these fields to appear, you must assign subscreen 2000 in the configuration of the material master from the program SAPLADRT21.

Figure 6.32 Material Master with Spare Part Class Code

After MRP has run (Transaction MD01 [MRP Run] or MD02 [Single Level Single Item Planning]), you will see the generated planned orders in the stock/requirements list (Transaction MD04). Confirm this action by clicking the **–> Refurbishment Order** button (see Figure 6.33).

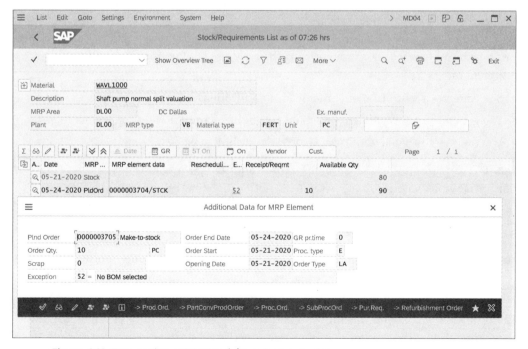

Figure 6.33 Transaction MD04 Stock/Requirements List

On the next screen, you can enter additional details for the refurbishment order—in particular, information about the valuation types (see Figure 6.34).

Refurbishment Integrated in Material Requirements Planning

Refurbishment has now been integrated into material requirements planning, which means that you can generate a refurbishment order from a planned order.

The LOG_EAM_ROTSUB, LOG_EAM_ROTSUB_2, and LOG_MM_SERNO business functions must be activated in order for you to convert a planned order into a refurbishment order.

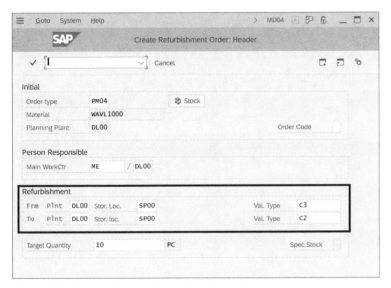

Figure 6.34 Refurbishment Order from Stock/Requirements List

6.4.4   Refurbishment Order

Setting up a refurbishment order differs from setting up a "standard" maintenance order in the following ways (see Figure 6.35):

- You use the specific Transaction IW81 (Create Refurbishment Order).
- You use a specific order type (for example, PM04).
- You always specify a **From material number**.
- You can also specify a **To material number** if a new material number should result from the refurbishment process.
- If you want individualized refurbishment processing, you add the objects of the serial numbers to the material number.
- You cannot specify a reference object; in other words, you cannot specify a functional location or equipment.

- The system generates a MAT settlement rule with the material number as the receiving object.
- You always specify an amount, which can be greater than 1.
- You always specify a **From plant** from which the material should be withdrawn, the storage location, and the valuation type.
- The SAP system automatically creates a reservation for the goods issue.
- You always specify a **To plant** to which the material should be returned, as well as the storage location and the valuation type.
- The SAP system automatically creates a reservation for the goods receipt.

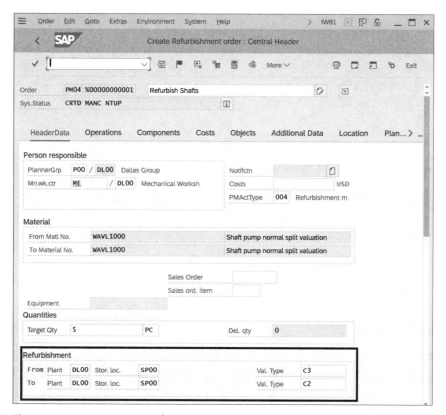

Figure 6.35 Transaction IW81 (Create Refurbishment Order)

The refurbishment order does not differ from a normal maintenance order in other functions (operations, material planning, cost estimation, and so on). You can perform all planning operations as they are described in Chapter 4, Section 4.3.

6.4.5   Goods Issue

When you created the refurbishment order, a reservation for the withdrawal of materials to be refurbished was automatically created. You can then book this out using

Transaction MIGO (Goods Issue) (movement type 261) with reference to the order. Note that the withdrawal occurs from the special stock **Valuation Type** (here, C3) (see Figure 6.36).

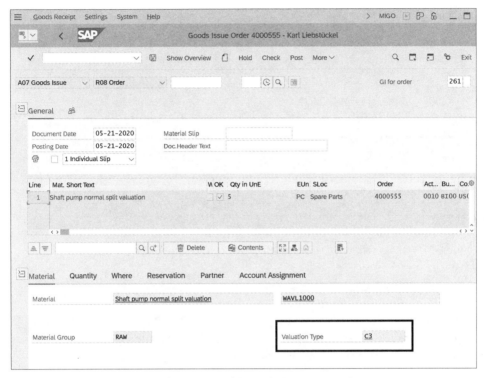

Figure 6.36 Transaction MIGO (Goods Issue) for Refurbishment Order

If you have set up the refurbishment order for individualized processing, also specify the serial numbers to be withdrawn for the material withdrawal.

6.4.6   Goods Receipt

When you created the refurbishment order, a reservation for the goods receipt of materials to be refurbished was automatically created. You can then book a goods receipt by using standard Transaction MIGO (movement type 101) with reference to the refurbishment order or with the special refurbishment Transaction IW8W including any potential change of material. Note that the booking in is performed in the special stock **Valuation Type** (here, **C2**) (see Figure 6.37).

If you have set up the refurbishment order for individualized processing, also specify the serial numbers to be placed in storage for the goods receipt.

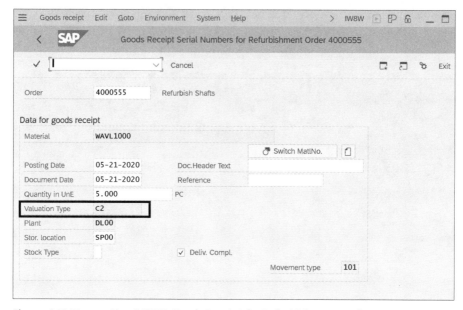

Figure 6.37 Transaction IW8W: Goods Receipt for Refurbishment Order

6.4.7   Costing

After you have entered the goods issues, time confirmations, and goods receipts and after you have settled the order, the cost situation of the refurbishment order is now represented as follows (see Figure 6.38):

- Cost element 720000 represents the debiting of the order that has occurred due to the goods issue of the parts to be refurbished.

- Cost element 720000 represents the debiting of the order that has occurred due to the goods issue of other materials that were additionally required for the refurbishment as well.

- Cost element 800000 represents the debiting of the order that has occurred due to the time confirmations.

- Cost element 741600 (credit to warehouse) represents the crediting of the order that occurred due to the goods receipt of the refurbished parts. The moving average price of the material was initially adjusted with the goods receipt. Since the value of a refurbished part is higher than the value of a faulty part, the moving average price also increases with the goods receipt.

- Cost element 741600 (credit from settlement) represents the value of the order settlement. The values are normally settled on the stock assets or, to be more specific, on the material number and thus change the moving average price of the material again. In our case, the refurbishment costs were lower than the value that was credited to the **C2** movement type by the goods receipt; thus, the moving average price decreases again.

```
|Order: Actual/Plan/Varance            Date:  05-21-2020 08:50:52
|--------------------------------------------------------------------
|Order/Group             4000556      Refurbish Shafts
|Reporting period         1 - 12 2020
--------------------------------------------------------------------
```

Kosten	Actual	Plan	Var (abs)	Var (%)	Actual Amount
720000 RM Consumpt Expense	200,00	75,00	125,00	166,67	5 EA
800000 Labor	600,00	500,00	100,00	20,00	12 H
* H,S	800,00	575,00	225,00	39,13	✖
741600 Production Settlement	436,90-		436,90-		
* Credit from settlement	436,90-		436,90-		
741600 Production Settlement	363,10-	363,10-			
* Credit to warehouse	363,10-	363,10-			
**					

Figure 6.38 Refurbishment Order Cost Elements

The cost burden through goods issues and labor hours as well as the cost relief through the goods receipt are also shown in the cost overview (see Figure 6.39).

Overview	Costs	Quantities	Key figures		
Group/Dscrptn		Est. costs	Plan costs	Act. costs	Currency
⌄ ⌐ Costs		0.00	575.00	800.00	USD
⌐ Internal Labor		0.00	500.00	600.00	USD
⌐ Stock Material		0.00	75.00	200.00	USD
⌄ ⌐ Goods Receipt		0.00	0.00	363.10-	USD
⌐ Miscellaneous		0.00	0.00	363.10-	USD

Figure 6.39 Refurbishment Order Cost Overview

Settling Refurbishment Orders Promptly

Settle the order as quickly as possible after the goods receipt that you used to post the final delivery. If the refurbished material was already withdrawn from the warehouse before the settlement, the costs can only be allocated to an allocation cost center, not to the material.

6.5 Subcontracting

The *subcontracting* business process, also known as subcontracting for MRO (maintenance, repair, and overhaul) processes, describes the process used when having a spare part or a piece of equipment (that is, a material serial number) repaired by a service provider. As a result, in contrast to the processes used for external processing (Section 6.3), the object to be repaired or maintained is sent to the service provider, processed, and then returned in a subcontracting business process.

Subcontracting = Refurbishment + External Service

Since the subcontracting operation may also be associated with refurbishment, this business process can be viewed as the link between the external service and refurbishment processes.

The LOG_EAM_ROTSUB and LOG_EAM_ROTSUB2 business functions must be activated to use subcontracting as follows.

The subcontracting process is comprised of the following steps (see Figure 6.40):

❶ You have a faulty part that requires maintenance or repair and is to be processed by a service provider. You therefore create a maintenance order with a subcontracting operation.

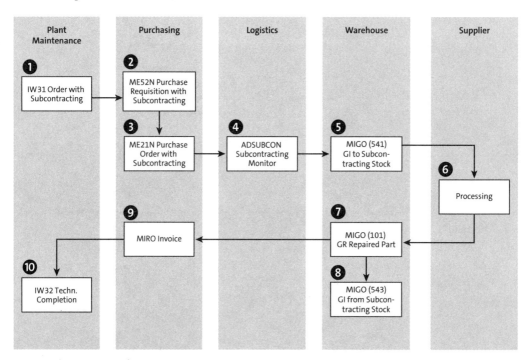

Figure 6.40 Subcontracting Process

❷ The SAP system then uses the maintenance order to generate a purchase requisition for the external repair or maintenance service, with a subcontracting item (item category L) and the material serial number or material number only.

❸ You convert the purchase requisition into a purchase order for the external repair or maintenance service. The purchase order item is indicated as a subcontracting item

(item category L) and is assigned the part that is to be returned following repair (material serial number or material number only).

❹ You send the part to be repaired to the subcontractor using an outbound delivery.

❺ The parts provided are managed as stock provided to vendor (subcontracting stock). The provision represents a transfer posting from unrestricted-use stock to stock provided to vendor (subcontracting stock).

❻ The subcontractor repairs, modifies, replaces, or exchanges the faulty part and returns the serviceable part.

❼ You create a goods receipt posting for the part delivered, which refers to the subcontracting item in the purchase order.

❽ A goods issue is posted from the subcontracting stock for the components.

❾ You receive an invoice for the service provided by the subcontractor.

❿ You complete the maintenance order.

Let's now look at these steps in more detail.

6.5.1 Subcontracting Order

You create a maintenance order using Transaction IW31 (Create Order). Note the following differences between this order and a "standard" maintenance order.

You set up an external processing operation in which you select the **Subcontr.** (subcontracting) indicator (see Figure 6.41).

Figure 6.41 Subcontracting: External Operation

In addition, you schedule the material number of the serial number for the operation and select the material provision indicator **S** (refurbishment material) for the material item, as shown in Figure 6.42. When you set this indicator, the same material number is expected both at goods issue to the vendor and at goods receipt from this vendor.

Figure 6.42 Subcontracting: Refurbishment Material

[!]
Do Not Forget Indicator

When creating the subcontracting order, ensure that the **Subcontr.** indicator is set on the **External** tab (external processing operation) and that the value **S** is selected in the **Mat. Prov. Ind.** (material provided indicator) field for the material components.

6.5.2   Purchase Requisition

A purchase requisition is automatically generated in the background when you save the order. This purchase requisition differs from a "standard" purchase requisition in the following ways (see Figure 6.43):

- The purchase requisition item contains the material components instead of the external service.
- The item has item category L (subcontracting).
- If the item contains a serial number that belongs to the material number, you can check it via the [icon] button.

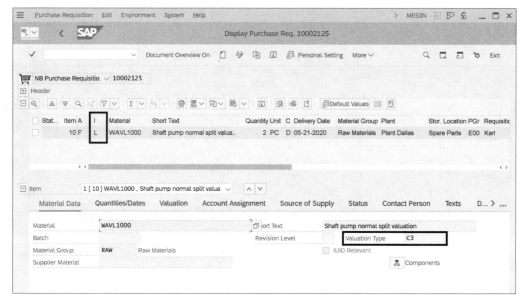

Figure 6.43 Subcontracting: Purchase Requisition

6.5.3   Subcontracting Monitor

You can execute steps ❸, ❹, ❺, ❼, and ❽ in the subcontracting monitor (Transaction ADSUBCON, see Figure 6.44). You can use the monitor to create an overview of all subcontracting items or to perform targeted searches for specific documents (for example, by vendor or material number).

> **[+]** **Subcontracting Monitor**
>
> The subcontracting monitor not only provides an overview of the current status of the subcontracting processes but also supports you in executing them.

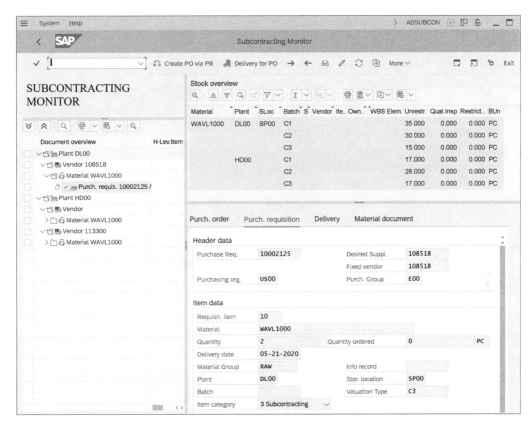

Figure 6.44 Transaction ADSUBCON: Subcontracting Monitor

Your next steps are then as follows:

- You then convert the purchase requisition into a purchase order using the function **Create PO Via PR**. The purchase order also contains a material item with item category L (subcontracting) and, if necessary, the serial number of the equipment.
- You can then create an outbound delivery for the purchase order for the component using the **Delivery for PO** button.

- You provide the component via the function **Post Goods Issue for Purchase Order** or by clicking the → button. This function executes a transfer posting from your own stock to the subcontracting stock. If necessary, the reference to the serial number of the equipment is retained here also. The stock overview shows the defective part provided to the subcontractor in the *stock provided to vendor* special stock and shows the functional part you expect to be returned in the on-order stock (see Figure 6.45).

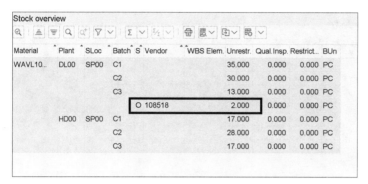

Figure 6.45 Subcontracting: Stock Overview

- You can also enter the goods receipt of the functional part in the subcontracting monitor with the function **Post Goods Receipt for Purchase Order** or by clicking the ← button. This function simultaneously triggers two functions in the background:
  - The goods receipt of the functional part is executed.
  - The goods issue of the defective part from the *stock provided to vendor* special stock is triggered, and this special stock is canceled.

If the material references the serial number, and therefore to the equipment, it is preserved in both postings. If the purchase order is then completed, the subcontracting monitor will no longer display the reference.

6.5.4   Serial Numbers

For the process to work with serial numbers, you must fulfill the following prerequisites:

- You have to activate business function LOG_MM_SERNO.
- You must assign a serial number profile to the material master on the **General Plant Data/Storage 2** tab.
- You must also assign a serial number profile to the document types of the purchase order and the purchase requisition in the customizing settings for purchasing.

You maintain serial number profiles using the Customizing function **Define Serial Number Profiles**. There, you must assign, in particular, PRSL (serial numbers in purchase requisitions) and POSL (serial numbers in purchase orders) to the MMSL serialization procedures (maintain goods receipt and issue document).

On the items details screen, you can then click the ⛏ button on the **Material Data** tab in the purchase requisition or the **Delivery Schedule** tab in the purchase order to maintain the serial numbers (see Figure 6.46).

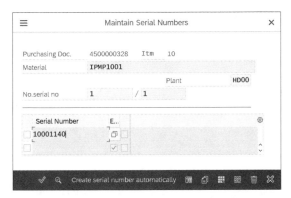

Figure 6.46 Purchase Order with Serial Number

The scenario described in this section is known as *recursive repair*, which is undoubtedly the subcontracting scenario encountered most frequently in practice. Table 6.1 provides an overview of all scenarios, explaining what the individual scenarios involve and indicating how each scenario affects the material provision indicator in the order or the subcontracting type in the purchasing documents.

Scenario	Definition	Material Provision Indicator in Order	Subcontracting Type in Purchase Order
Recursive repair	Same physical part, same material number A, same serial number 1	Material A with S (refurbishment to subcontractor)	1 (refurbishment; material number unchanged)
Unit exchange	Different physical part, same material number A, different serial number 2	Material A with S (refurbishment to subcontractor)	1 (refurbishment; material number unchanged)
Modification	Same physical part, different material number B, same serial number 1	Two materials: Material A with S (refurbishment to subcontractor) Material B with S (refurbishment from subcontractor)	2 (refurbishment; material number changed)

Table 6.1 Scenarios in Subcontracting

Scenario	Definition	Material Provision Indicator in Order	Subcontracting Type in Purchase Order
Replacement	Different physical part, different material number B, different serial number 2	Two materials: Material A with S (refurbishment to subcontractor) Material B with S (refurbishment from subcontractor)	3 (replacement)

Table 6.1 Scenarios in Subcontracting (Cont.)

6.6   Test Equipment Calibration

In many companies, test equipment such as scales, gauges, calipers, or similar is used for quality inspections in the intermediate and final checking of products and for checking equipment. To ensure that specified performance criteria are always met, the test equipment being used must be regularly checked and calibrated. You can use the functions of test equipment management to perform the following actions:

- Manage equipment
- Plan and schedule inspections
- Execute orders and inspection lots for processing calibration inspections on equipment

Figure 6.47 provides an overview of the objects and process of test equipment calibration, as follows:

- An inspection plan is created for the test equipment (normally a general task list).
- The master inspection characteristics describe the properties that must be measured (for example, visual inspections and linear measurements).
- The inspection plan is incorporated into a maintenance plan.
- The maintenance plan generates an order and an inspection lot.
- Both the processes in inspection lot management (results recording, error recording, usage decision) and the processes of order management (time confirmation, technical confirmation) run for each test.

Let's now look at each of the objects and processes in detail.

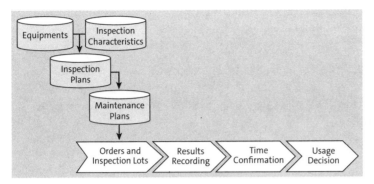

Figure 6.47 Test Equipment Calibration Process

6.6.1   Equipment

You can manage the test equipment itself as equipment master records (see Figure 6.48). Test equipment has its own tab on which the specific data relating to the production resources/tools is to be maintained. The task list usage is important here so that the relevant test equipment can be used in maintenance-specific task lists.

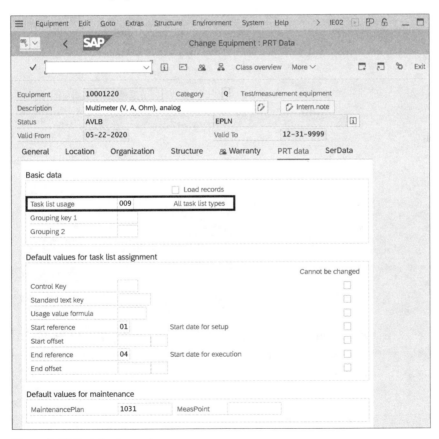

Figure 6.48 Test Equipment

Separate Equipment Category for Test Equipment

You need a separate equipment category for test equipment. In this case, use the customizing function **Maintain Equipment Category** to create an equipment category that is referred to as a **Production Resource/Tool Reference Category**. In the customizing function **Define Additional Business Views for Equipment Categories**, you must also activate the **PRT flag** option.

6.6.2   Inspection Characteristics

If inspection characteristics are often required, you can record them as master records and then use them in inspection plans. Master inspection characteristics are managed by means of Transactions QS21 through QS23 (see Figure 6.49).

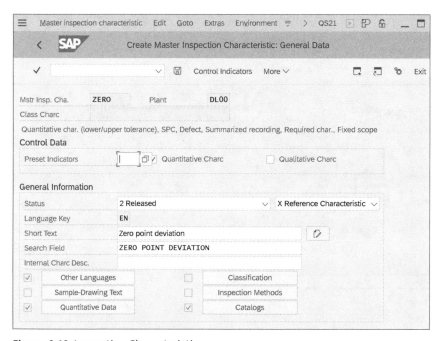

Figure 6.49 Inspection Characteristic

6.6.3   Task List

In a maintenance task list, you describe the inspections to be subsequently carried out. You can create this either as a general task list (Transaction IA05, see Figure 6.50) or as an equipment task list (Transaction IA01).

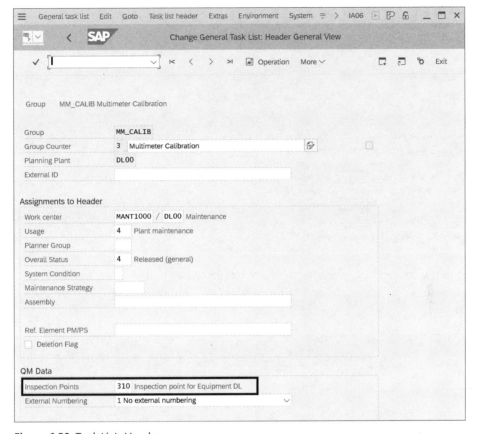

Figure 6.50 Task List: Header

Inspection Point for the Inspection Plan

To use your maintenance task list at a later stage as an inspection plan for equipment, you must define an **Inspection point** for equipment in customizing using the function **Define Inspection Points** and then assign it to the header data of the maintenance task list.

The inspection plan must now contain at least one operation that is indicated as requiring inspection, even if this operation is merely used as an anchor for the actual inspections (see Figure 6.51). You can do this by using a control key provided for this purpose (here, QM01).

Separate Control Key for Inspection Operations

You can use the customizing function **Define Control Key for Inspection Operation** to define a control key for which the **Inspection Characteristic Expected** indicator is activated.

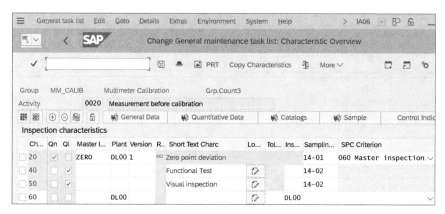

Figure 6.51 Task List: Operations

Due to the control key, you can now click the **Insp.Char** button to assign inspection characteristics in which the actual inspections are contained, including (see Figure 6.52):

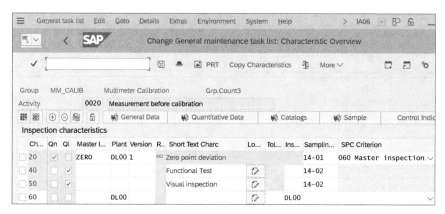

Figure 6.52 Task List: Inspection Characteristics

- Description
- Identification as qualitative (**Ql** indicator) or quantitative (**Qn** indicator)
- For quantitative inspection characteristics, select the unit of measurement and the inspection specifications (target value, upper limits, lower limits) via the **Quantitative Data** button (see Figure 6.53)
- Sampling procedures are created using Transaction QDV1. You need one sampling procedure for quantitative characteristics (14-01 in Figure 6.54) and one sampling procedure for qualitative characteristics (14-02 in Figure 6.54). On a detail screen, you assign the sample size = 1. You can have a look at the sampling procedure on the task list using the **Sample** button.

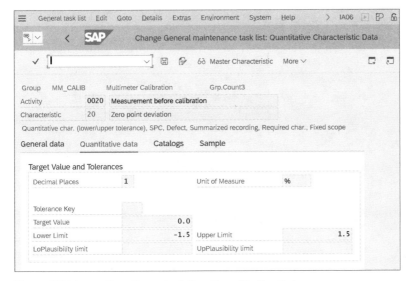

Figure 6.53 Inspection Characteristics: Quantitative Data

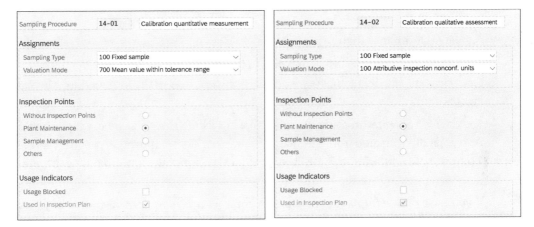

Figure 6.54 Inspection Characteristics: Sampling Procedures

You also create the relevant control indicators for each inspection characteristic by clicking the **Control Indicators** button (see Figure 6.55). The control indicators contain the following information:

- Whether upper and lower limits should be measured for a quantitative characteristic
- How the results confirmation is to be performed (for example, summarily, that is, only entering one number, or with individual entry, that is, the measurement of each individual item, and so on)
- Whether a mandatory or an optional characteristic is involved
- Whether the sample size is unrestricted or fixed
- Whether result documentation is required

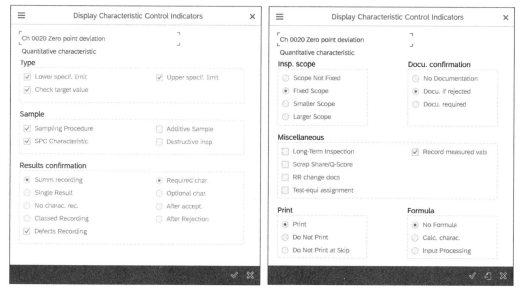

Figure 6.55 Inspection Characteristics: Control Indicators

6.6.4   Maintenance Plan

Now, you can include the inspection plan in a maintenance plan (for example, as a single cycle plan) and define the frequency of the inspections in the form of the cycle (see Figure 6.56).

The details you enter in the maintenance plan include the order type, which should receive an order created from this maintenance plan. For this purpose, you must create a separate order type (here, PMO5) because you can cannot use any order type that you have already set up for normal maintenance or repair work.

If you have now set up a maintenance plan for your test equipment in this way, not only will an order be created, but an inspection lot will be also, when a maintenance call occurs. In quality management, the inspection lot corresponds to an order and is a request to perform a quality inspection on a certain quantity of a material, in this case, on test equipment.

[!]
> **Separate Order Type for Test Equipment Management**
>
> To ensure that you can map the business process for calibrating test equipment in the SAP system, you need a separate order type.
>
> In addition to the usual basic settings, you can assign an inspection type (corresponds to an order type in quality management) to this order type using the customizing function **Assign Inspection Types to Maintenance and Service Order Types**.

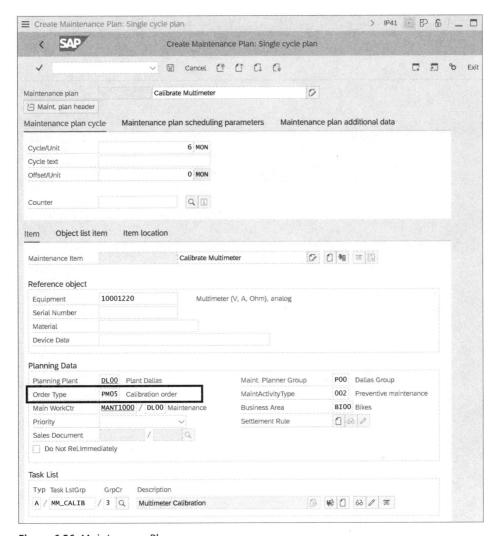

Figure 6.56 Maintenance Plan

6.6.5 Order and Inspection Lot

The calibration order created only differs from "normal" maintenance orders in two areas (see Figure 6.57):

- The calibration order has the status **ILAS** (inspection lot assigned), and thus, you can select according to this status, for example.

- The calibration order contains the additional ⊗ button in its header. This enables you to go directly to the display of the inspection lot with usage decision (see Figure 6.58).

Figure 6.57 Calibration Order

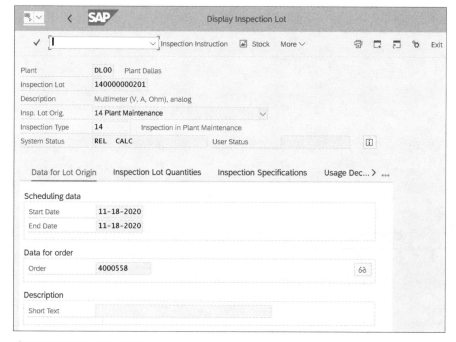

Figure 6.58 Inspection Lot

6.6.6   Results Recording

You can now either enter the recorded results in Transaction QE17 for a single inspection lot (see Figure 6.59) or enter all results in Transaction QE51N for several inspection lots. If the entered results are within the tolerance limits or if they are qualified as being good, the system performs a positive valuation (✓).

If the entered results are not within the tolerance limits or if they are qualified as being bad, the system performs a negative valuation (⊗).

When you save the recorded results, you can also immediately specify the required time for the inspection (see Figure 6.60).

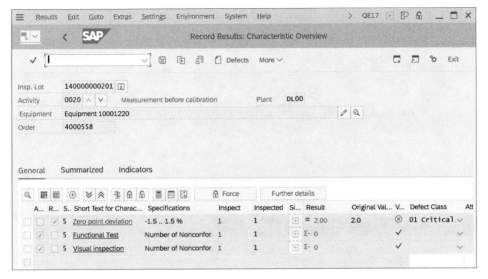

Figure 6.59 Results Recording

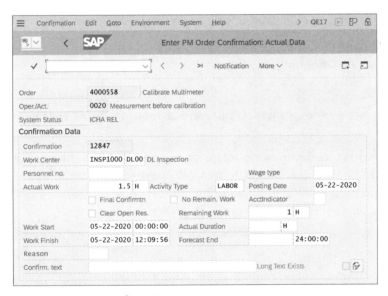

Figure 6.60 Time Confirmation

6.6.7   Usage Decision

When you save the recorded results, you can also make a usage decision at the same time. Alternatively, however, you can also use the special Transaction QA11 (Record Usage Decision) for this purpose. Figure 6.61 shows the window for the usage decision.

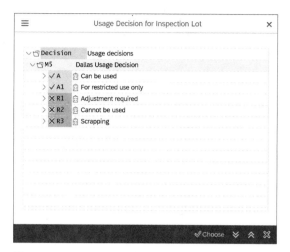

Figure 6.61 Usage Decision

6.6.8   Follow-Up Actions

You can have follow-up actions automatically triggered with the usage decision:

- Indicating equipment as no longer ready for use
- Technical completion of the order
- Changing the cycle modification factor in the maintenance plan

You can define follow-up action using the customizing function **Define Follow-up Action**.

As an example, if you have set the follow-up action for locking the equipment, you will be asked when you make the usage decision to accept the suggestion for the lock or to change it manually (see Figure 6.62). You can also change the cycle modification factor for the maintenance plan in the same window.

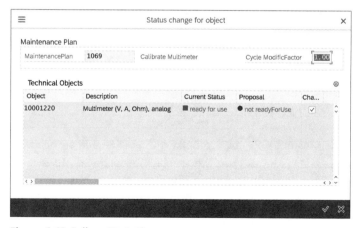

Figure 6.62 Follow-Up Actions

The **NPRT** status (PRT not ready for use) is thus set in the equipment master, thereby locking the equipment from further use (see Figure 6.63). However, you can use a maintenance task, for example, to set the equipment to an operational status again and reset the status again. Or you can release equipment manually using the **Release PRT** button.

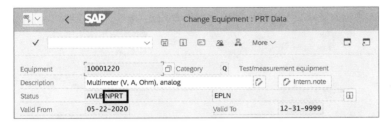

Figure 6.63 Equipment Status

The maintenance plan will create the next order with an inspection lot on the next due date.

6.7 Follow-On Order

Often in real life, you may want to create a new order as a successor to an already processed order (see Figure 6.64).

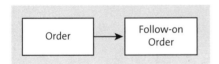

Figure 6.64 Follow-On Order

This may be the case in the following situations:

- If a problem is solved and the plant is up and running again but needs to be repaired
- If defects were detected during an inspection round and which need to be eliminated
- If you performed a calibration after which the equipment was locked and repair and recalibration are required to make the equipment available again

The majority of the users would create a suborder for an order in these cases. However, the disadvantage with using suborders is that the technical completion of this suborder would depend on both orders.

You can create follow-on orders if business function LOG_EAM_CI_7 is enabled. Various options are available for this purpose.

6.7.1   Direct Creating

When creating an order (Transaction IW31), you can select the **Create Follow-On Order** indicator and define the order for which you want to create a follow-up order (see Figure 6.65). With this approach, you can specify which data you want to copy (operations, materials, documents, etc.).

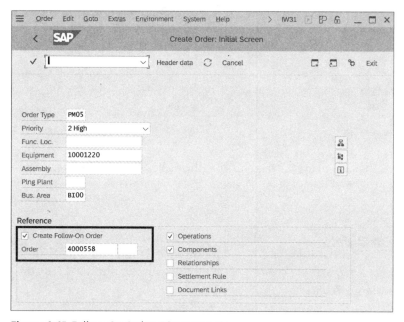

Figure 6.65 Follow-On Order: Direct Creating

6.7.2   Indirect Creating

You can also create follow-on orders for processed or confirmed orders in an indirect way. For this purpose, the new **Create Follow-On Order** button is available for order processing in the operations list (Transactions IW32/33) and confirmation (Transaction IW41) (see Figure 6.66).

To create a follow-on order, the system navigates to Transaction IW31 for the creation of orders. The system selects the **Follow-On Order** checkbox and copies the order number and operation number of the predecessor order.

You can display predecessor and follow-on orders for an order or a confirmation in the document flow. In the document flow, select the order or confirmation and click the **Follow-On Orders** button. The system maps the relationship between the predecessor and follow-up order as a hierarchical list (see Figure 6.67). If you have created follow-on orders for several order operations, the system displays all follow-on orders that have been created for the selected order or for related operations.

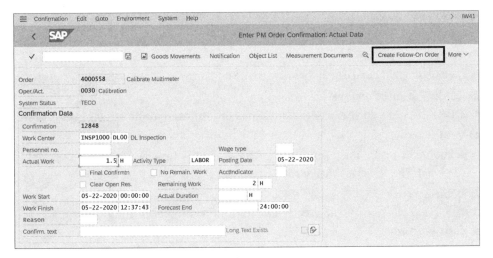

Figure 6.66 Follow-On Order: Indirect Creating

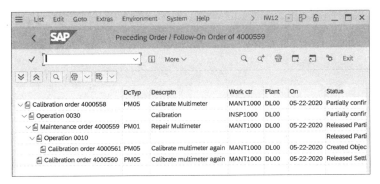

Figure 6.67 Preceding and Follow-On Order

6.8   Pool Asset Management

You can use pool asset management to manage objects that are contained in a pool, from which objects can be borrowed for a certain time. Examples of such objects include:

- Fleet objects
- IT equipment (notebooks, projectors, and so on)
- Cell phones
- Tools
- Other objects

These objects are returned to the pool after they have been borrowed, and the cost unit (for example, cost center) is charged for the service. Figure 6.68 shows the complete pool asset management process, using the example of a pool of fleet objects. Pool asset management works in the same way for other types of pools. Here, pool asset management is comprised of the following steps:

❶ Request

An employee enters a demand for a vehicle in the system.

❷ Vehicle scheduling

A vehicle scheduler assigns a vehicle to the demand.

❸ Confirmation of reservation

The employee receives an automatic email to confirm that the vehicle is reserved.

❹ Vehicle issue

A kilometer reading is taken for the vehicle and the time at which it is required is recorded. The vehicle is then issued to the employee.

❺ Vehicle return

The employee returns the vehicle and another kilometer reading is taken and the date is recorded.

❻ Cost allocation

The costs of the employee's use of the vehicle are calculated and are allocated to the account assignment object.

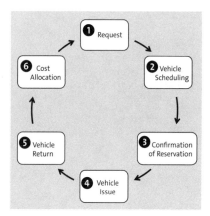

Figure 6.68 Pool Asset Management Process

Let's now look at each of these steps in more detail.

6.8.1   Request

As with any other maintenance notification, you use Transaction IW21 to create a requirement notification for a pool asset (see Figure 6.69).

[+]

Separate Notification Types for Pool Asset Management

We recommend using a separate notification type for pool asset management requirement notifications so that they have a layout that is specific to pool asset management. You can maintain this notification type using the customizing function **Screen Layout for Extended View**. Assign the notification type **10\ TAB23 Pool Asset Management**.

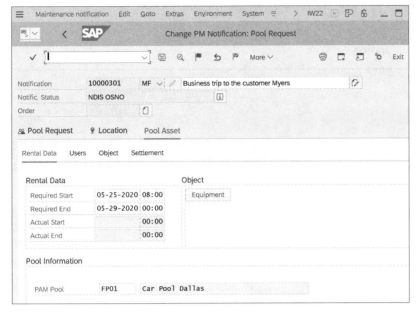

Figure 6.69 Pool Asset Management: Request

In addition to the trip data, you can specify the following information:

- Information about the persons (requester, driver, and so on)
- Information about account assignment (cost center, internal order)
- Information about the vehicle equipment (see Figure 6.70), where you can freely define the equipment characteristics using the class system

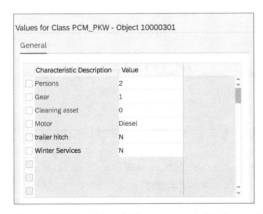

Figure 6.70 Pool Asset Management: Equipment features

6.8.2   Scheduling via Planning Board

Requirement notifications are sent to the planning board for pool asset management (Transaction PAMO3). Here, the vehicle scheduler can use drag-and-drop requirements to vehicles (see Figure 6.71). The various colors used for the vehicles have the following meanings:

- Yellow: Outstanding demand
- Red: Reserved (the pool asset has been assigned)
- Green: Issued
- Gray: Returned
- Blue: Settled

All assets belonging to the pool asset management pool selected on the initial screen of the planning board are displayed here.

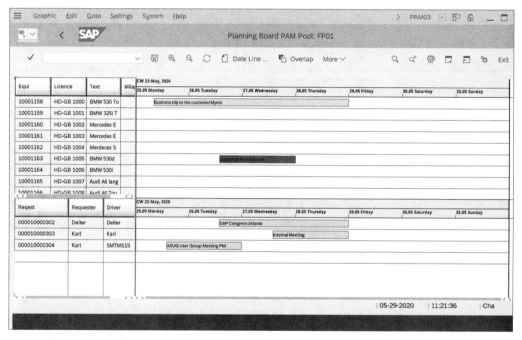

Figure 6.71 Pool Asset Management: Planning Board

[!] **Functions of the Planning Board**

In addition to providing an overview of the current situation with regard to reservations, the planning board for pool asset management also helps you execute the business transactions **Reserve**, **Issue**, **Return**, and **Settle** the assets.

To reserve a vehicle, double-click on one of the schedule bars. A dialog box is then displayed, in which you can make the reservation by clicking the **Reserve** button (see Figure 6.72).

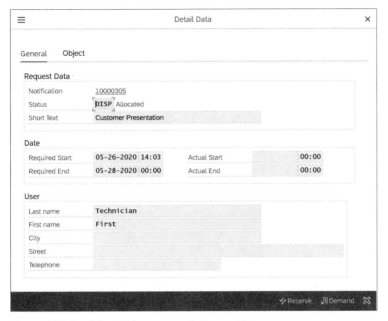

Figure 6.72 Pool Asset Management: Reservation

6.8.3   Confirmation

Once the reservation is created, an email is automatically sent to the employee who requested the vehicle to confirm that it has been reserved (see Figure 6.73).

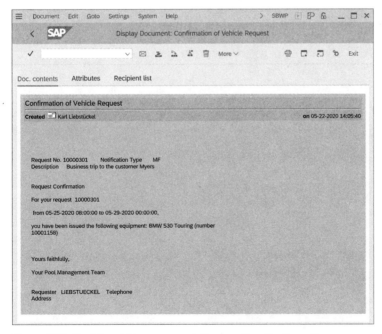

Figure 6.73 Pool Asset Management: Reservation Confirmation

6.8.4   Issue

If you double-click on the bar that indicates a reserved asset and then click the **Issue** button, the vehicle is shown in the dialog box, with the current counter reading and the date recorded (see Figure 6.74).

Figure 6.74 Pool Asset Management: Issue

6.8.5   Return

Similarly, you can double-click on the relevant bar and, in the dialog box that opens, click the **Return** button to enter the return of the vehicle, together with the current data (date of return, current counter reading) in the planning board (see Figure 6.75).

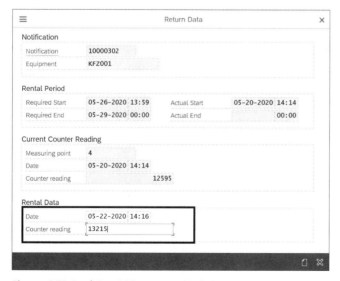

Figure 6.75 Pool Asset Management: Return

6.8.6 Settlement

Based on the current data (number of days, number of miles driven, free miles), the costs are settled to the cost center or to a settlement order. To execute the settlement function, click again on the relevant bar and click the **Settle** button. The system now displays the settlement information, for example, how many days or how many miles are settled.

6.8.7 Prerequisites

To use the *pool asset management* business process, you must ensure that certain prerequisites are met:

- First, you must use the customizing function **Basic Settings for Pool Asset Management** to implement basic settings (for example, a confirmation text or the class for requirement notifications).

- You must maintain the categories of your vehicles by using the **Define Pool Categories** function (for example, small car, medium-class car, station wagon, delivery vehicle, and so on).

- You must use the **Define Service Types for Pool Categories** function to maintain the service types that are required for settlement for each pool category (for example, daily flat rates, prices per mile, free miles).

- You must maintain the allocation rates themselves via Transaction KP26.

- You must create one pool asset management pool using Transaction PAM01 or Transaction PAM02. A pool asset management pool is merely a functional location incorporating a list of equipment (see Figure 6.76).

- The LOG_EAM_PAM business function must be activated in order to use pool asset management.

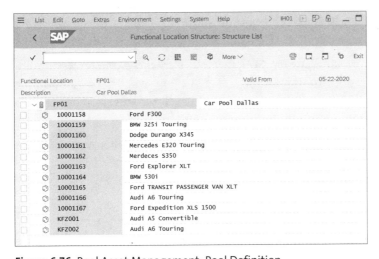

Figure 6.76 Pool Asset Management: Pool Definition

6.9   Project-Based Maintenance

One of the following two situations occurs in most companies:

- Individual maintenance tasks accumulate within the framework of a higher-level project. For example, this situation occurs for new construction of technical systems or relocations.

- The maintenance task itself reaches such a scale that it can be referred to as a project. This situation occurs, for example, when maintaining aircraft, during shutdowns in refineries, or for the revision of power plants.

You can use two tools in SAP S/4HANA for project-based maintenance:

- **Project system**
  With the project system (PS), you can plan both project types.

- **Maintenance Event Builder**
  With the Maintenance Event Builder, you can plan small to medium-sized projects of the latter project type. The former project type cannot be mapped in this manner.

6.9.1   Project System

When you use the project system (PS) for project-based maintenance, you perform the higher-level planning in PS and the order planning in SAP S/4HANA Asset Management. This section will walk you through PS objects, manual and automatic assignment of order to PS objects, and various integration functions.

Project System Objects

A project is a one-off task, limited in duration and function, for solving a complex plan involving various user departments. Projects can be used to control and check this task in relation to dates, resources, capacities, costs, revenues, and funds. A project is divided into different phases for this purpose (as shown in Figure 6.77). You can create projects using Transaction CJ06 (Create Project Definition) or CJ20N (Project Builder).

You use work breakdown structure (WBS) elements as elements of the project system to define the planning, organization, and structure of a project and to break down the project into individual, hierarchically arranged, multilevel structural elements. In this way, you describe detailed tasks.

WBS elements have functions such as time scheduling, budget allocation, progress analysis, and so on. You can create WBS elements using Transaction CJ11 (Create WBS Element) or CJ20N (Project Builder).

You use a network to plan the workflow of your processes and arrange the elements in a chronological sequence. In project processing, you use networks as the initial basis for planning, controlling, and monitoring dates, costs, and resources. You have similar functions available in networks for planning materials, machines, and people as you do in planning maintenance orders. You can maintain networks using Transaction CN21 (Create Network) or CJ2ON (Project Builder).

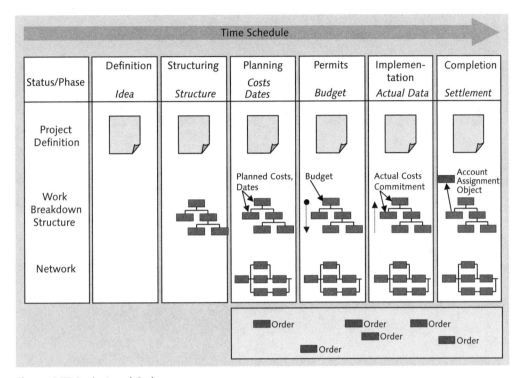

Figure 6.77 Project and Orders

Manual Assignment

You can now assign your orders to PS objects manually or automatically. When you manually assign your orders, you link them either to WBS elements or projects.

You assign individual orders to a WBS element on the **Additional Data** tab using Transaction IW32 (Change Order) (see Figure 6.78). Use this option if the maintenance area has taken over individual orders within a project and a network had not been created for the activity.

WBS Element	P/9000		Development of Ultralight Bike
Project Definition	P/9000		Development of Ultralight Bike (I)
Subnetwrk of/Oprtn.	4000000	/ 0010	General concept

Figure 6.78 Assign Order to WBS Element

You can assign individual orders to a network on the **Additional Data** tab using Transaction IW32 (Change Order). In this way, you transfer WBS elements, profit centers, and other information into the order (see Figure 6.79). You can use this option if the maintenance area has taken over individual orders within a project and a network exists for the activity.

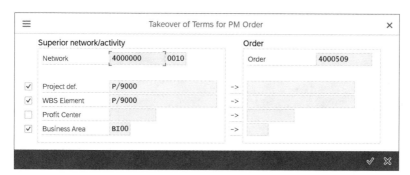

Figure 6.79 Takeover of Terms for Order

To assign a maintenance order to a network, you must establish an assignment between the network type and the order type using the customizing function of the project system **Define Parameters for Subnetworks**.

Automatic Assignment

To automatically assign orders to WBS elements, use Transaction ADPMPS (Order Assignment to Project). The idea behind this process is that extensive maintenance tasks in the maintenance area are repeated at regular intervals. You can use this automatic assignment option to avoid having to manually assign orders to WBS elements every time.

You must fulfill three prerequisites for this purpose:

- **Define field values for the reference element**
  You must maintain the fields that will subsequently create the cross-connection, using the customizing function **Define Field Values for PM/PS Reference Element**.

- **Assign the reference element to a maintenance task list or maintenance item**
  You must assign the PM/PS reference element to a maintenance task list (see Figure 6.80) or maintenance item. When you create a maintenance item with a maintenance task list, the reference element is automatically transferred to the maintenance item (see Figure 6.82, later in this section).

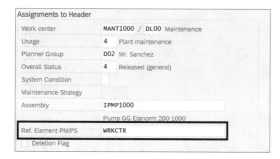

Figure 6.80 PM/PS Reference Element in Task List Header

■ **Assign the reference element to standard objects or operational objects**
You must assign the **PM/PS** reference element to either standard objects (standard WBS, standard network) or operational objects (WBS element, network; see Figure 6.81).

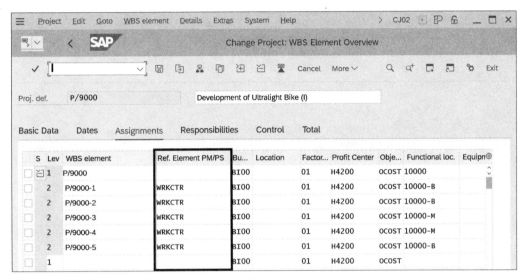

Figure 6.81 PM/PS Reference Element in WBS Element

When you create a project relating to a standard project or a network or WBS relating to a standard network or a standard WBS, the field values are transferred from the referenced object for the reference element (see Figure 6.82).

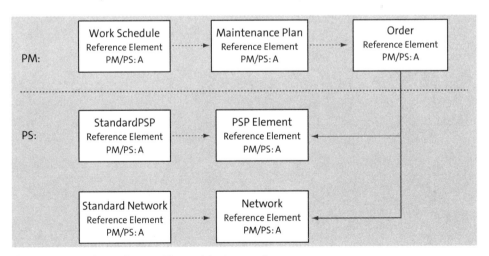

Figure 6.82 PM/PS Reference Element Assignment

To make a semi-automatic assignment, perform the following steps in Transaction ADPMPS (Order Assignment to Project) (see Figure 6.83):

1. First, select the orders to be assigned.

2. Then, select the WBS elements to be assigned.

3. In the left-hand area of the screen, select the orders to be assigned.

4. In the right-hand area of the screen, select the WBS element to which you want to assign orders.

5. Start the assignment manually in the foreground by clicking the **Assign manually** function.

Now, to make an automatic assignment, perform the following steps in Transaction ADPMPS:

1. First, select the orders to be assigned.

2. Then, select the WBS elements to be assigned.

3. In the left-hand area of the orders, select the **Reference Element PM/PS** column.

4. Also select the **Reference Element PM/PS** column in the right-hand area of the projects.

5. To start the automatic assignment in the foreground, click the **Assign Automatic** function.

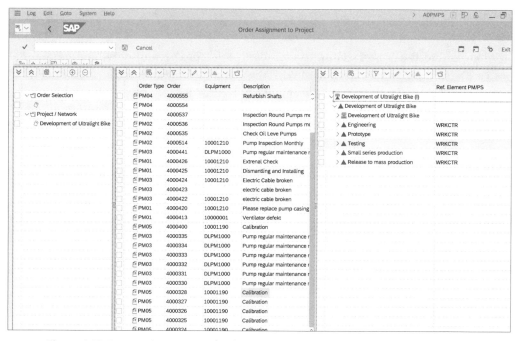

Figure 6.83 Transaction ADPMPS (Order Assignment to Project)

Integration Functions

Which functions now become available by assigning orders to PS objects?

- You can combine the order dates with the project dates, that is, a shift in the project will automatically result in a shift in the order.

- You can use active availability control to check whether sufficient budget is still available for performing the task. For more information, refer to Chapter 8, Section 8.3.4.

- You can valuate the projects including all assigned orders together in the SAP project system.

The following points summarize project-based maintenance based on PS:

- You can use the operational objects of the project system (WBS elements, networks) in connection with orders to plan and control bigger maintenance projects.

- You can also assign individual orders to WBS elements or networks if plant maintenance carries out work within a different project.

- You make the assignment either individually or using Transaction ADPMPS.

- The assignment makes available integration functions such as budget availability control, commitment to deadlines, and so on.

External Project Tools

To plan and process maintenance projects, you can also use the interface for shutdown planning with external project systems. This interface connects SAP S/4HANA to external project systems (for example, Primavera P3 or MS Project).

[+]

6.9.2   Maintenance Event Builder

The Maintenance Event Builder was initially a component of the SAP for Aerospace and Defense industry solution and was made available for all user companies later on. You can use the Maintenance Event Builder to plan smaller maintenance projects in the form of individual *work packages*. You start the Maintenance Event Builder using Transaction WPS1. The Maintenance Event Builder is technically a workbench that supports you when you perform the following tasks:

- Check the work list of notifications (backlog)
- Bundle the notifications into revisions
- Create orders from notifications
- Assign the tasks

- Display the different information such as open work requirements, due dates, orders, and so on
- Check the availability of resources

You can then process the work packages in up to five steps (see Figure 6.84), as discussed in the following sections.

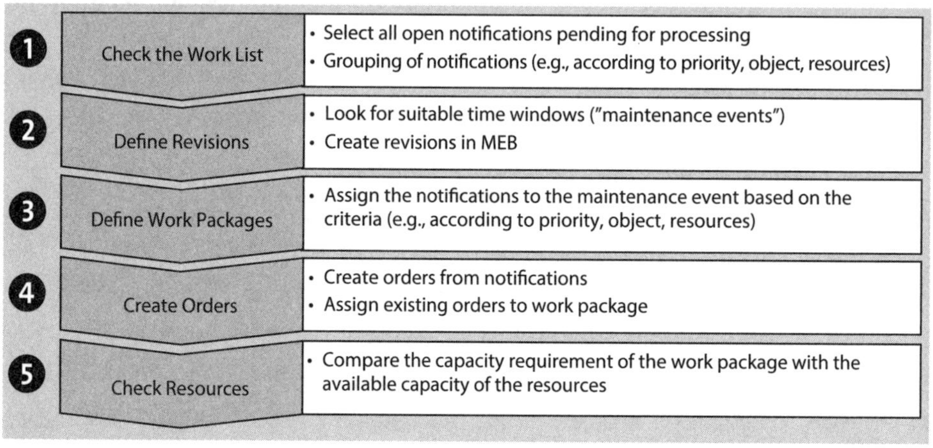

Figure 6.84 Maintenance Event Builder: Overview

Check Work List

The Maintenance Event Builder enables you to select the pending notifications and group them according to different criteria such as priority, reference object, and work center responsible (step ❶ in Figure 6.84). The notifications may, but do not have to, be already assigned to a revision at this point.

Define Revision

Together with those responsible for the technical system from production (for example, the operations engineer, production supervisor, person responsible for work scheduling), you need to look for suitable time slots (maintenance events) when the technical system can be released for maintenance tasks. You create revisions for these time slots in the Maintenance Event Builder in the **Revision Work Area** section by clicking the ⬚ button (step ❷ in Figure 6.84). Revisions have start and end dates and status management (for example, created, released, assignments exist, and so on), as shown in Figure 6.85.

You can display different views in the Maintenance Event Builder workbench: Figure 6.86 shows the notification view in the upper part of the list and the revision view in the lower part of the list. Other views can be, for example, the work center view, order view, or object view.

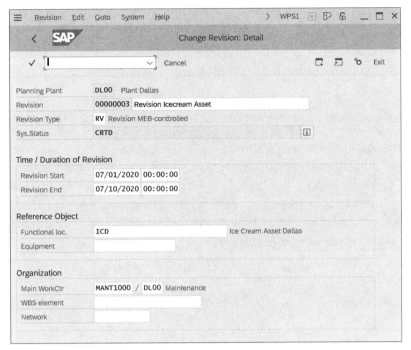

Figure 6.85 Maintenance Event Builder: Revision

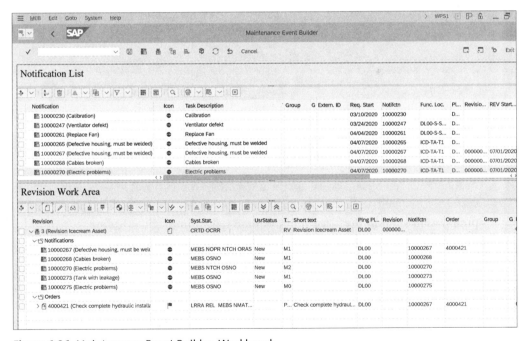

Figure 6.86 Maintenance Event Builder: Workbench

Define Work Packages

Now, you create work packages by assigning, from the work list, the notifications to be processed to a revision using drag and drop (step ❸ in Figure 6.84). At this point, you could then create simulation orders to check the capacity load, for example.

Create Orders

You then create the orders (step ❹ in Figure 6.84). If an assigned notification already has an order, this order is also assigned to the work package. For all other cases, the Maintenance Event Builder enables you to create orders all at once from all notifications assigned to a work package by clicking the ⊕ button (see Figure 6.87). These orders receive an **MEBS** status to enable you to differentiate them from the other orders. When you remove a notification from a work package again, the automatically created orders receive a deletion flag (status **DLFL**).

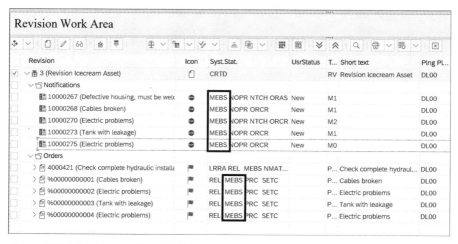

Figure 6.87 Maintenance Event Builder: Create Orders

Check Resources

At this point, you could also assign the orders to the operational objects of the project system (WBS elements, networks) by clicking the ⛏ button, which is useful, for example, if you have budget restrictions or want to synchronize dates.

The resource view of the Maintenance Event Builder gives you a quick overview of the capacity situation of the work centers involved: Are the work centers already working to full capacity in the period of a work package, or is there still free capacity available for other orders (step ❺ in Figure 6.84)?

The LOG_EAM_POM and LOG_EAM_POM_2 business functions must be activated in order for you to use the Maintenance Event Builder.

What is so special about the Maintenance Event Builder?

- The Maintenance Event Builder enables you to plan smaller maintenance projects (maintenance events).

- You can use the Maintenance Event Builder to perform the majority of required planning steps from a single transaction.

- In agreement with the system operators and on the basis of the planning in the Maintenance Event Builder, you can, to some extent, ensure that the maintenance tasks will be performed and prevent the system from having to be shut down several times.

- You can link the orders created from the Maintenance Event Builder to WBS elements and networks.

6.10 Summary

Based on the work order cycle, SAP S/4HANA Asset Management offers, beside the standard work order cycle, a wide range of additional business processes. In this chapter you were made familiar with these business processes as well as how to use them.

For the immediate repair process, you have several possibilities:

- You can perform a shortened work order cycle: create an order and a notification in one step; after the task is completed, perform an overall confirmation and technical completion.

- For an after-event recording you can use SAP Business Client for confirming an unplanned job, or you can create an historical order.

You can use shift notes and shift reports to document events which are taking place during a shift.

There are several reasons to assign an order to an external supplier, such as lack of qualification or insufficient capacities. You have several possibilities for an external assignment:

- You can assign external services as a single purchase order

- You can assign external services to a supplier as an external work center

- You can assign external services using service specifications

The refurbishment business process is characterized by spare parts being held as reserves in the warehouse with different statuses (for example, new, operational, faulty). Faulty parts are refurbished by your own staff or external staff to restore them to operational status.

The subcontracting business process describes the process when you have a faulty spare part or a piece of equipment repaired by a service provider. The object is sent to the service provider, processed, and then returned as an operational spare part.

In many companies, test equipment is used for quality inspections for checking products and for checking equipment. The test equipment must be regularly checked and calibrated. Orders and inspection lots are offered for processing calibration inspections on equipment.

If necessary, you can create a follow-on order as a successor to an already processed order directly or indirectly.

You can use pool asset management to manage objects that are contained in a pool from which objects can be borrowed for a certain time. It supports all steps within the rental process: requesting, scheduling, reservation confirmation, issue, return, and settlement.

For project-oriented maintenance tasks, you can use either the project system in SAP S/4HANA for all kinds of projects or the Maintenance Event Builder to plan small to medium-sized projects.

Chapter 7

Integrating Applications from Other Departments

*Plant maintenance is constantly exchanging data with other depart-
ments in the company. The SAP system reflects that situation in the
broad and deep integration of plant maintenance with applications
used by other departments. This chapter illustrates the integration of
SAP S/4HANA Asset Management with other applications within the
SAP S/4HANA system, with other SAP systems, and with non-SAP systems.*

Plant maintenance is a service area of your company and thus works closely together
with the other departments of the company in handling your business processes.
These business processes do not stop at departmental boundaries or system boundaries. To provide the required services, a permanent exchange of information must exist
between the applications and systems that other departments use. Information must
flow in both directions—between plant maintenance and other departments in your
company.

Several questions must be answered when you want to integrate the applications of
other departments with SAP S/4HANA Asset Management:

- Which departments may potentially require an exchange of information with plant
  maintenance?
- How are these departments involved in the business processes of plant maintenance?
- What information must be exchanged?
- In which direction does the information flow? Does the information flow from plant
  maintenance to another department, does plant maintenance require information
  from other departments, or must information be exchanged mutually?
- Which systems are used to exchange information? Does it involve integration
  within SAP S/4HANA, or is data required from another SAP system or from a non-
  SAP system?

Appendix B, Section B.3, contains a table that provides a detailed, but not exhaustive,
overview of the interrelationships of SAP S/4HANA Asset Management with the different departments.

Highly Diverse Integration

The varied experiences of numerous customer projects have shown that business processes are too different and the system landscapes in use too complex to be able to create a list of all points of contact and systems involved.

Nevertheless, the table in Section B.3 gives you some idea of the differentiated and complex interaction of plant maintenance with other departments.

This chapter will discuss in detail the implementation of integration of SAP S/4HANA Asset Management:

- Integration of SAP S/4HANA Asset Management within SAP S/4HANA
- Integration of SAP S/4HANA Asset Management with other SAP systems
- Integration of SAP S/4HANA Asset Management with non-SAP systems

7.1   Integration within SAP S/4HANA

SAP S/4HANA is a highly integrated system. Just like the pieces of a puzzle, the individual parts of SAP S/4HANA fit together exactly to create a whole (see Figure 7.1).

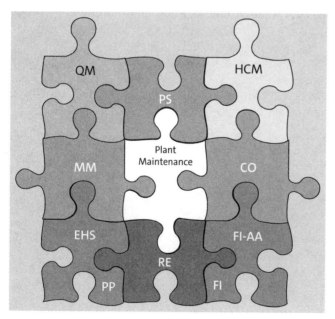

Figure 7.1 Integration within SAP S/4HANA

This section discusses the most important integration points of SAP S/4HANA Asset Management within SAP S/4HANA. The chapter also shows what this integration looks like and how it can be organized.

[!]

Focus on: Controlling and Materials Management

First things first: Integrating SAP S/4HANA Asset Management with controlling and materials management is most important for plant maintenance.

Let's start with one of the most important aspects: the integration of SAP S/4HANA Asset Management with materials management.

7

7.1.1   Materials Management

In previous chapters, we presented the following points of contact of SAP S/4HANA Asset Management and materials management with SAP S/4HANA, but let's summarize them briefly now:

- **Reservations**
  Chapter 4, Section 4.3, illustrates how a reservation is automatically triggered when you plan a stock material or component with item type L in your order.

- **Purchase requisitions from non-stock material**
  The same section showed how a purchase requisition is automatically generated when you schedule a non-stock material or component with item type N in your order.

- **Purchase requisitions from external services as individual purchase orders**
  Chapter 6, Section 6.3.2, explained how a purchase requisition is automatically generated when an external service is scheduled as an individual order in your order if you use a control key (for example, PM02) with the appropriate properties.

- **Purchase requisitions from external services with service specifications**
  Chapter 6, Section 6.3.4, showed how a purchase requisition is automatically generated when you schedule an external service with service specifications and you use a control key (for example, PM03) with the appropriate properties and then schedule the required services.

- **Availability check**
  Chapter 4, Section 4.4.5, explained how you can perform a dynamic availability check for your scheduled stock materials. This check enables you to determine whether or not your order is feasible on the scheduled date.

[+]

Unique Differentiator: Availability Check

A dynamic availability check is a unique feature of an integrated system like SAP S/4HANA that differentiates SAP S/4HANA Asset Management from non-SAP plant maintenance systems. This check requires information about the existence of material requirements planning (MRP) elements for the scheduled material, such as, for example, the following:

- Scheduled issues from reservations (also reservation for non-maintenance orders like production orders and reservations for cost centers)
- Scheduled issues from sales requirements
- Scheduled issues from secondary requirements
- Scheduled receipts from purchase orders
- Scheduled receipts from purchase requisitions
- Scheduled receipts from planned orders
- Scheduled receipts from production orders
- Scheduled receipts from shipping notifications

A dynamic availability check involves information from inventory management, purchasing, production, sales, project management, and other areas that require the same material. Only an integrated system can provide such a function.

Standalone CMMS (computerized maintenance management systems) like DIVA, Maximo, or other systems may have interfaces to SAP S/4HANA, but only batch interfaces are involved here, which are simply capable of sending information in a delayed one-way manner (for example, transferring a reservation to SAP S/4HANA).

- **Actual costs from acceptance of services performed**
  Chapter 6, Section 6.3.4, showed that actual costs are stated on the order when accepting services performed via service entry sheets.

- **Actual costs from goods receipts for external services**
  Chapter 6, Section 6.3.2, showed that when entering the goods receipt for a purchase order for external services, the actual costs are stated on the order when the **Goods Receipt Valuated** flag is set with the purchase order.

- **Actual costs from incoming invoices for external services**
  In Chapter 6, Section 6.3.2, you learned that when entering the incoming invoice for a purchase order, the goods receipt/invoice receipt (GR/IR) clearing account is reversed again, and the order is then debited with the actual costs invoiced.

- **Goods receipts and invoice receipts for external material**
  Here, the same applies as in the previous point.

- **Actual costs from material withdrawals**
  Chapter 4, Section 4.5, showed how you can withdraw planned and unplanned materials for an order. These withdrawals trigger related actual costs in the relevant order.

- **Inventory management of equipment**
  Chapter 3, Section 3.3, showed how you can use material serial numbers to manage inventory for equipment and the required preconditions in the equipment and material master data.

- **Refurbishment of spare parts**
  Chapter 6, Section 6.4, explained how you can use the refurbishment process to

repair faulty spare parts. We covered withdrawing faulty spare parts, returning operational spare parts, and managing separate inventories.

- **Subcontracting**
  Chapter 6, Section 6.5, showed how you can use the subcontracting process to repair faulty spare parts with the help of service providers and illustrated, among other things, the shipping of faulty spare parts and the goods receipt of operational spare parts.

[+]

Materials Management Transactions Are Only the Second-Best Solution

You can also use purchasing documents (purchase requisitions, purchase orders) with materials management transactions (for example, Transaction ME51N [Create Purchase Requisition] or Transaction ME21N [Create Purchase Order]) and assign them to the order. However, the costs that arise are initially visible as actual costs in the orders. With this approach, you avoid any required budget checks. Thus, you should always create purchase documents from orders.

Let's now discuss some more aspects of the integration of SAP S/4HANA Asset Management with SAP S/4HANA materials management. Let's start with the central element of logistics: the material master.

Material Master

Users have often asked whether SAP S/4HANA Asset Management has its own spare parts management or if SAP S/4HANA Asset Management uses the same parts as materials management. The answer is "yes and no." Material masters managed in SAP S/4HANA are used by all areas in logistics: inventory management, purchasing, production, sales, project management, and even plant management. Individual spare parts management is usually desired because of the internal organization of a company. The control of the material master is in the hands of the warehouse or the purchasing department, for example.

[+]

Separate Material Type for Spare Parts

To work with spare parts management, create a separate material type, for example, SPAR (spare parts) or MESP (machine equipment and spare parts), in customizing and transfer responsibility for the material master of this material type to plant maintenance.

Creating a separate material type provides, among other things, the following benefits:

- You can assign separate authorizations.
- You can use a specific number range.
- You can define your own screen layout.

- You can define the field selection.
- You can activate special stock and consumption accounts.
- You can define your own quantity and value update.
- You can select according to your own material type.

Figure 7.2 shows how a separate material type is represented in the SAP system.

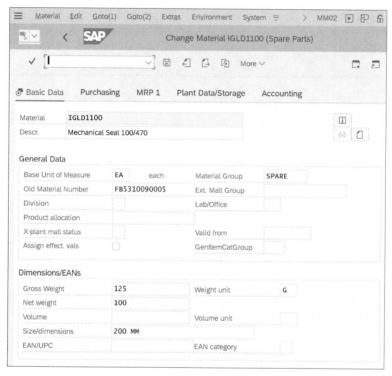

Figure 7.2 Material Master for Spare Part

Material Requirements Planning

The most common procedure for material requirements planning (MRP) of spare parts is reorder point planning (see Figure 7.3).

The basis of reorder point planning is the comparison of available stock and the defined receipts with the reorder point. If the available stock is smaller than the reorder point, procurement is triggered.

The level of the reorder point is based on the expected average material requirements during the replenishment lead time as well as the safety stock. Accordingly, the following values must be considered when defining the reorder point:

- Safety stock
- Previous use and expected future requirements
- Replenishment lead time

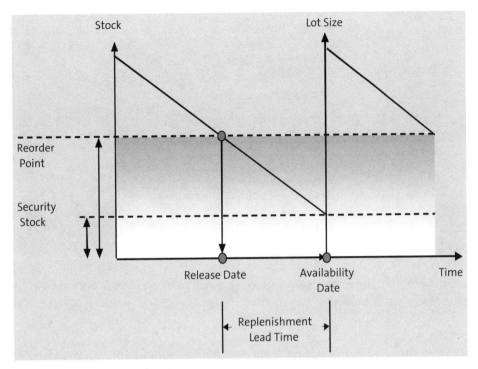

Figure 7.3 Reorder Point Planning

The safety stock covers unplanned material use during the replenishment lead time and additional requirements during delivery delays.

The standard version of SAP S/4HANA contains MRP type VB (manual reorder point planning) for this purpose. A disadvantage of using this MRP type, however, is that it performs only a comparison of the actual warehouse stock and reorder point. As a result, the SAP system triggers replenishment only if you issue a material and its stock falls below the reorder point. However, nothing happens if the stock falls below the reorder point because of a reservation in the future, as no procurement transaction is triggered, which may result in not enough stock when you want to remove the part from the warehouse.

Separate MRP Type for Maintenance

Create your own MRP type, for example, V1 (manual reorder point planning with regard to external requirements), and assign it to the material type *spare parts*. This MRP type ensures that MRP considers your reservations from maintenance orders and triggers procurement transactions on time.

You maintain MRP types using the customizing function **Define MRP types** (see Figure 7.4). Set **Include ext. reqmts** to 2 (external requirements within the replenishment lead time) and activate the **PM/ntwork Reserv.** setting.

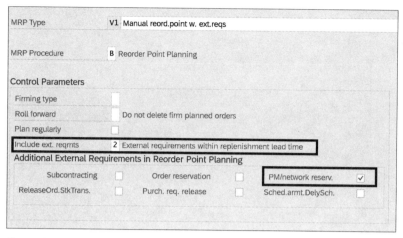

Figure 7.4 MRP Type

Then, perform the assignment per plant in the material master in the **MRP procedure** screen group (see Figure 7.5).

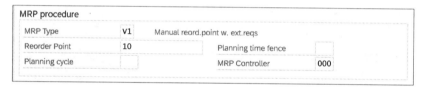

Figure 7.5 Material Master with MRP Procedure

Handling Unit Management

A *handling unit* is a physical unit of packaging and the material contained on or in it. A handling unit has a unique identification number that can be called with the data on the handling unit. The packaging material consists of loading equipment (pallets, wire baskets, crates, trucks, and so on) and the packaging itself (cartons, wrap, and so on) (see Figure 7.6). Handling units can be nested, which means that you can build a new handling unit from several handing units as often as desired.

Handling unit management looks at handling units rather than individual materials. The common unit for the flow of materials and information is the handling unit. A business process for a handing unit implies related business transactions in the background for the materials and packaging contained in the handling unit. A business transaction thus replaces individual entry of multiple material movements.

You can manage serial numbers in handling units or assign a serial number to a handling unit. When you create handling units, you can specify materials with serial numbers in the items of the handling unit (see Figure 7.7).

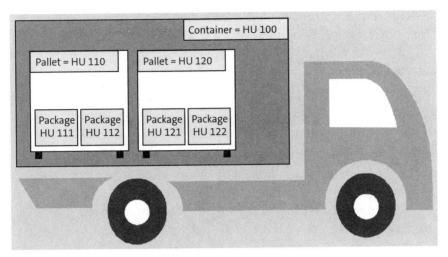

Figure 7.6 Handling Units

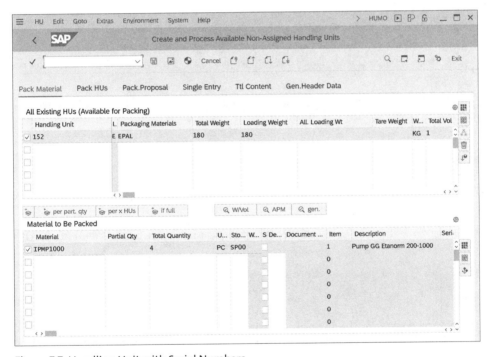

Figure 7.7 Handling Unit with Serial Numbers

At any given time, a serial number can be found in a maximum of one handling unit. When you assign a serial number to a handling unit, the system sets the status to HUAS in the master record. The serial number can then be processed only in business processes with handling units.

To enable serial numbers in handling units, you must use the function **Define Serial Number Profiles** to create a serial number profile to which you assign the serialization procedure HUSL in customizing. You must enter the serial number profile in the material master record of the serial number.

When you post a goods issue of a handling unit, the serial numbers of the handling unit are copied to the material document, and the SAP system resets the system status of the serial numbers to **HUAS** in the master record. In the serial number history, you can see the handling unit used to post the goods issue.

When you post the goods receipt of a handling unit to a storage location that requires a handling unit, the serial numbers of the handling unit are also copied to the material document. The SAP system sets the system status of the serial numbers to HUAS in the master record. In the serial number history, you can see the handling unit used to post the goods receipt.

[+]

Managing Serial Numbers on Handling Units

You can manage serial numbers on handling units and assign a serial number to a handling unit. A business transaction with handling units (for example, goods issues and goods receipts) therefore replaces individual entry of several material movements.

Now, let's look at another integration aspect within logistics: the integration with production planning and control.

7.1.2   Production Planning and Control

The integration of SAP S/4HANA Asset Management with production planning and control in SAP S/4HANA involves four elements:

- You can use the master data of technical objects to create a cross-reference to the work center as a production planning resource.
- You can make scheduled maintenance orders in the production planning board visible.
- You can use production orders to create your own spare parts.
- You can make the maintenance work center aware of specific procedures or suborders in the context of production orders.

Work Center

In the master data of a technical object—whether a functional location or equipment—you will find the **Work center** field in the **Location data** field group (see Figure 7.8).

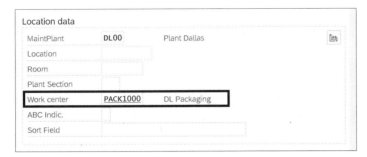

Figure 7.8 Functional Location: Work Center

This work center is often confused with the work center responsible for maintenance activities. However, this confusion is incorrect because you use the **Main WorkCtr** field in the **Responsibilities** field group for this purpose. In contrast, the **Work center** field is intended as a cross-reference and answers the question as to which production planning work center, thus which capacity resource on the part of production, corresponds to this functional location or equipment.

Not All Work Centers Are Created Equal

By assigning a technical object to the work center, you create a cross-connection to production planning. The main work center is the workshop responsible for maintenance activities. A 1:n relationship exists here: Several technical objects can be assigned to a production planning work center.

No Automatic Calculation of Available Capacity

The number of individual capacities of the production planning work center, which represent an essential factor in determining the capacity that production planning can offer, is not calculated by the number of assigned technical objects.

Pure assignment of a technical object to a work center is initially only a cross-reference that does not create any reservations, capacity loads, and so on when a maintenance order for the related technical object is pending.

Maintenance Orders in the Production Planning Board

If you want maintenance tasks to influence production planning, however, you must first fulfill the following prerequisites:

- Assign the technical object to a work center (see Figure 7.8).
- Use the function **Create System Conditions or Operating Conditions** in customizing to define an operating condition for which the **Reservation by PM** option is activated.

If you want to make your SAP S/4HANA Asset Management order visible in production planning, enter an appropriate value in the **SystCond.** field of the order header as shown in Figure 7.9.

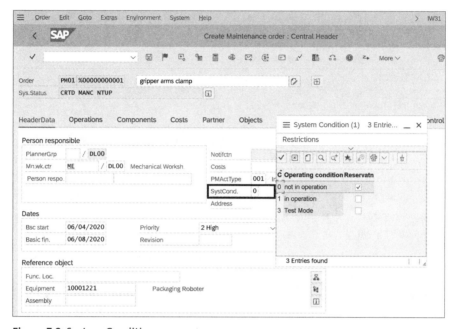

Figure 7.9 System Condition

The upper part of the production planning board (Transaction CM21 [Capacity Leveling]) now displays the maintenance orders scheduled for this resource by plant maintenance, including the production orders of the resource (see Figure 7.10). However, you will see only the maintenance orders that require machine downtime, that is, those for which the system condition indicator is set to **Reservation**. The production planning board does not display maintenance orders that can be performed during production and for which you have not set the system condition indicator.

> **Showing Maintenance Orders in the Production Planning Table**
>
> Showing maintenance orders in the production planning board serves only as an indication to production that plant maintenance has scheduled an order on the date. No automatic load or block of the production resource occurs. If the date cannot be met from the production perspective, manual communication must occur between production and plant maintenance.

However, the production scheduler cannot change the maintenance order from the production planning board. The scheduler cannot reschedule it, for example, if production cannot release the resource on that date for maintenance tasks.

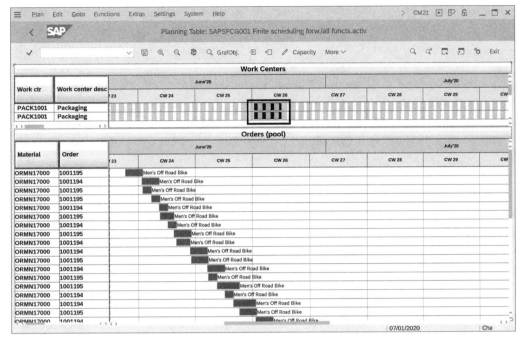

Figure 7.10 Transaction CM21: Production Planning Table

In-House Production of Spare Parts

A maintenance order requires spare parts that can or should not be procured externally. Instead, these parts could be manufactured in-house by the plant maintenance or production department.

You create a production order (Transaction CO01 [Production Order Create]) for the spare part. In addition to the general transaction and material planning information, you enter the maintenance order as the settlement rule (see Figure 7.11).

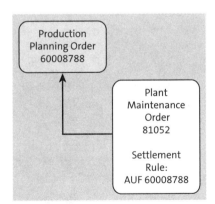

Figure 7.11 Production Order Settles to Maintenance Order

[+]

Assigning a Production Order to a Maintenance Order

When you manufacture your own spare parts, you create a production order. The costs generated by the production order are visible in the maintenance order. The costs are settled to the maintenance order and are indicated in the history of the technical object.

After the spare part is finished, you settle the production order to the maintenance order (Transaction KO88 [Actual Settlement Order]).

Maintenance Services for Production

More or less the opposite situation occurs when plant maintenance performs services as part of production orders, such as retooling procedures, rebuilding, and so on.

You schedule the maintenance order and enter the production order as the settlement rule (see Figure 7.12).

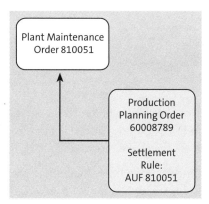

Figure 7.12 Maintenance Order Settles to Production Order

[!]

Assigning Maintenance Order to a Production Order

When plant maintenance performs services in the context of production, you create a maintenance order that you then settle to a production order. After the maintenance order is settled, the costs incurred in plant maintenance are visible in the production order and become part of follow-up calculations for the product.

[!]

Always Settle Suborders First

Make sure that the subordinate order is always settled and closed first from an organizational and technical perspective.

Having encountered in-house production of spare parts in the course of several projects, let's digress briefly to discuss how we resolved this scenario, which involves answering the question about which order type you should use in the SAP system if spare parts are to be produced for stock.

7.1.3 Digression: In-House Production of Spare Parts for Stock

To implement the in-house production of spare parts in stock, you can choose from two completely different approaches:

- Via a production order
- Via a refurbishment order

Let's explore these two options next.

Spare Part Production Using a Production Order

The spare part production process using production orders is as follows:

- **Material master**
  A material master is required (for example, the material type SPAR), which must have the follow special features: moving average price, MRP type PD to plan the spare part automatically, and the procurement type E or X so that the part can be produced by a production order.

- **Material BOM**
  A material bill of material (BOM) is required (Transaction CS01 [Create Material BOM]), which contains the components that are required for the production of the spare part and which has the special feature of usage 1 (production).

- **Routing**
  A routing is required (Transaction CA01 [Create Routing] or CS11 [Create Reference Operation Set]), which contains the steps for the production of the spare part and which has the following special features: the number of the routing equals the material number and usage 1 (production).

- **Production order**
  A production order must be set up (Transaction CO01 [Production Order Create]). The order type can be, for example, PP01. Only the end date must be filled out manually in the order header; all other data is set automatically (see Figure 7.13).

- **Automatic routing explosion**
  The operations are generated using an automatic routing explosion.

- **Automatic BOM explosion**
  The component list is generated using an automatic BOM explosion. The required quantities are automatically calculated on the basis of the lot size of the order.

- **Goods issue**

  The goods issue is performed as usual via Transaction MIGO.

- **Confirmation**

  The confirmation is performed using a production transaction, for example, Transaction CO1F (Progress Confirmation) or Transaction CO15 (Confirmation of the Order).

- **Goods receipt**

  The goods receipt of the produced spare part is performed using Transaction MIGO (Goods Receipt).

- **Order settlement**

  The order settlement of the refurbishment order is the material. A new moving average price ensues for the spare part after the order settlement (Transaction KO88 [Actual Settlement Order]).

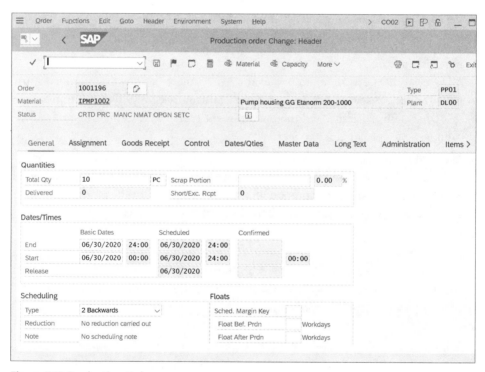

Figure 7.13 Production Order

Spare Part Production Using a Refurbishment Order

The spare part production process using refurbishment orders is as follows:

- **Material master without split valuation**

  A material master is required (for example, the material type SPAR) that has the special feature of moving average price. You do not require any split valuation here as with normal materials to be refurbished.

- **Material BOM**
  A material BOM is required (Transaction CS01 [Create Material BOM]), which contains the components that are required for the production of the spare part. A material BOM has one special feature: usage 4 (maintenance).

- **General maintenance task list**
  A general maintenance task list is required (Transaction IA06 [Create General Task List]), which contains the steps for the production of the spare part. A general maintenance task list has the following special features: internal or external number assignment, usage 4 (maintenance), and the assembly number will equal the material number of the spare part.

- **Refurbishment order**
  A refurbishment order is set up (Transaction IW81 [Create Refurbishment Order]), for example, with the order type PM04. You do not enter any **From** or **To** valuation type as with normal refurbishment orders (see Figure 7.14). The system now displays a window with a warning message because the refurbishment order was originally developed for a different purpose.

- **Data in the order header**
  All data in the order header must be filled out manually.

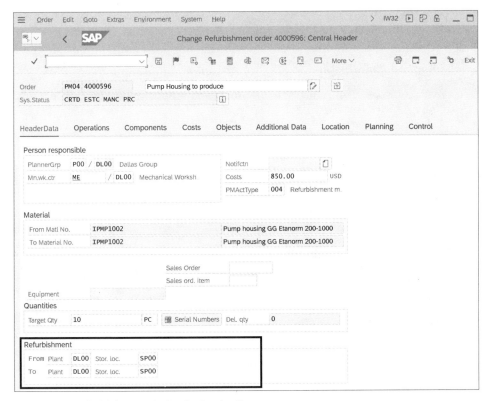

Figure 7.14 Refurbishment Order for Production

- **Manual selection of general maintenance task list**
  The operations must be generated via a manual selection of the general maintenance task list. You can control the quantity of the spare part to be produced via the
  execution factor.

- **No automatic BOM explosion**
  The BOM is not exploded automatically, but the BOM must be exploded manually,
  and the components must be manually selected. The execution factor ensures that
  the correct quantities are reserved. An automatic reservation is also created for the
  spare part to be produced, which is necessary from the production perspective.

- **Goods issue**
  The unnecessary reservation is also displayed for the material withdrawal (Transaction MIGO [Goods Issue]) but may not be withdrawn.

- **Confirmation**
  The confirmation is performed using a maintenance transaction (for example,
  Transaction IW42 [Overall Confirmation]).

- **Goods receipt**
  The goods receipt of the produced spare part is also performed using a maintenance
  transaction (Transaction IW8W [Goods Receipt for Refurbishment Orders]).

- **Order settlement**
  The order settlement of the refurbishment order is the material. A new moving aver-
  age price ensues for the spare part after the order settlement (Transaction KO88
  [Actual Settlement Order]).

A summary comparison of refurbishment orders and production orders can be found
in Table 7.1.

	Refurbishment Order	Production Order
Bill of materials (BOM)	Maintenance BOM	Production BOM
Task list	General maintenance task list with manual assignment of material number	Routing with direct reference to material number
MRP	Possible with automatic generation of planned orders	Possible with automatic generation of planned orders
Order	Maintenance transaction	Production transaction
Routing explosion	Manual assignment of general maintenance task list with dialog boxes	Automatic

Table 7.1 Comparison of Refurbishment and Production Order

	Refurbishment Order	Production Order
Bill of materials (BOM) explosion	Manual selection of components, unnecessary reservation	Automatic
Confirmation	Maintenance Transaction IW41 and others	Maintenance Transaction CO11 and others
Goods receipt	Maintenance Transaction IW8W total	Transaction MIGO
Settlement	In stock	In stock

Table 7.1 Comparison of Refurbishment and Production Order (Cont.)

So, what are the advantages of using production orders versus replenishment orders? You will find the answer in the following two boxes.

Advantages of Using Production Orders

The production order has a functional advantage over the refurbishment order. You have to accept a few functional restrictions in the refurbishment order.

Advantages of Using Refurbishment Orders

If you are working with the refurbishment order, you do not need to implement production planning. Furthermore, you can remain in your usual interface when processing the business processes and do not need to change interfaces for your daily work.

For this reason, many companies have opted to use refurbishment orders.

7.1.4   Quality Management

In terms of quality management, the following integration aspects are important:

- You can manage the test and measurement equipment used in quality management as equipment master records.
- The inspections performed with this test and measurement equipment are entered in a maintenance task list, either as a general maintenance task list or as an equipment task list.
- A maintenance plan for the equipment takes care of controlling the inspection dates for you.
- To perform the inspection, the maintenance plan generates both a maintenance order and a quality management inspection lot that are uniquely assigned to each other.

- In the context of inspection lot processing, results recording, and the usage decision, the maintenance plan ensures that the equipment is set to the correct status (blocked or available).

Chapter 6, Section 6.6, described the business process and the required prerequisites (in customizing, for example) in detail, so we won't discuss them any further here.

The last topic for integrating into SAP S/4HANA logistics is the interaction with the SAP application for environment, health, and safety, which will be discussed next.

7.1.5 Environment, Health, and Safety

The SAP Environment, Health, and Safety Management (SAP EHS Management) solution has the following main functions:

- **Product safety**
  Product safety contains functions that are required for hazardous substance management in the company, even in a company that produces hazardous substances.

- **Hazardous substance management**
  Hazardous substance management contains functions that are required for hazardous substance management in the company.

- **Dangerous goods management**
  With dangerous goods management, dangerous goods master records can be managed, dangerous goods checks can be performed, and dangerous goods papers can be created.

- **Waste management**
  You can use waste management to develop waste disposal processes, which create reports necessary for transport and disposal, and distribute the resulting costs by usage within the company.

- **Occupational health**
  With occupational health, health surveillance protocols can be planned and performed in your company, and occupational health questionnaires can be created and managed.

- **Occupational health and safety**
  With the occupational health and safety functions, health and safety in the company can be organized and loads that arise can be managed. In addition, events with or without personal injury can be handled and reports such as operating instructions and accident notifications can be created.

Unfortunately, several functional areas have been swapped out of the SAP S/4HANA core system to the effect that these areas are no longer available to be called up via transactions. The functional areas concerned are occupational healthcare, waste management, and hazardous substance management.

As far as the integration to SAP S/4HANA Asset Management is concerned, business function /EAMPLM/LOG_EAM_WS (Worker Safety) is available, with which plant maintenance tasks and the SAP EHS Management tools can be integrated. These functions are intended to assist you in creating a safe work environment; the most important tools are the safety measure list and the safety plan.

Using a *safety measure list* (see Figure 7.15), you can classify standard objects as safety measures, for example, documents, permits, maintenance task lists, and production resources/tools (PRTs). Thus, you can create a list of safety-relevant objects from all available objects. By assigning these safety-relevant objects in maintenance orders and maintenance task lists, you can provide safety information during the planning and performance of maintenance tasks that are critical to safety.

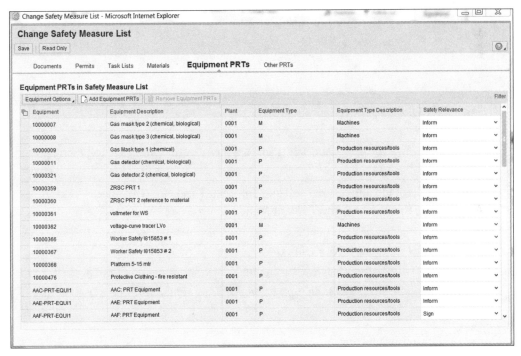

Figure 7.15 Safety Measure List

With a *safety plan* (see Figure 7.16), you support safety aspects in plant maintenance planning and implementation. By using a safety plan, the person responsible for maintenance planning can ensure that all safety measures that are necessary to reduce identified risks are assigned in maintenance orders and maintenance task lists. All information contained in the safety plan can be issued as part of the shop papers.

Thus, the maintenance workers responsible for the implementation of maintenance are informed of the safety risks and can ensure that they take all necessary safety measures into account.

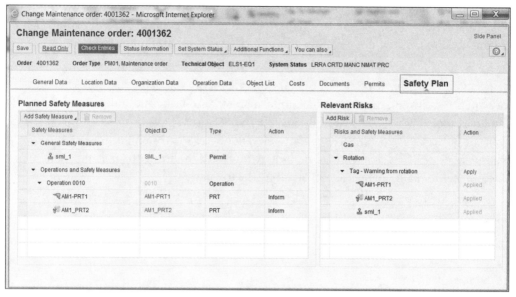

Figure 7.16 Safety Plan

To enable safety measures and safety plans, you must first fulfill the following prerequisites:

- You have made all required settings for health and safety using the customizing function **Health and Safety in Plant Maintenance**.

- You have activated the business functions /EAMPLM/LOG_EAM_WS, LOG_EAM_SIMPLICITY_2, and /PLMU/WEB_UI.

- You use SAP Business Client with the PFCG roles *Maintenance Worker* (SAP_COCK-PIT_EAMS_MAINT_WORKER2) and *General EAM Functions* (SAP_COCKPIT_EAMS_GENERIC_FUNC2).

7.1.6   Financial Accounting

This section will discuss another important aspect of integration, the connection between financial accounting and plant maintenance.

> **[!]**
>
> **General Ledger Accounts as the Basis of all Business Processes**
>
> Integrating SAP S/4HANA Asset Management with financial accounting is fundamental, as the general ledger accounts, on which all business processes in SAP S/4HANA are based, are maintained in financial accounting.

For example, if you take another look at the cost report for a maintenance order (see Figure 7.17), you'll see general ledger accounts based on the following business transactions:

Cost Element	Cost Element (Text)	Σ	Total Plan Costs Σ	Total Actual Costs Σ	Plan/actual variance	P/A var(%)	Currency
740000	Auxiliary and operating materials		450.00	450.00	0.00		USD
720000	Raw Material Consumption Expense		1,278.86	100.45	1,178.41-	92.15-	USD
720000	Raw Material Consumption Expense		40.00	0.00	40.00-	100.00-	USD
720000	Raw Material Consumption Expense		140.00	0.00	140.00-	100.00-	USD
700000	External Labor		690.00	690.00	0.00		USD
800000	Internal Labor		1,075.00	912.50	162.50-	15.12-	USD
Debit		▪	**3,673.86** ▪	**2,152.95** ▪	**1,520.91-**		**USD**
740000	Auxiliary and operating materials		0.00	450.00-	450.00-		USD
800000	Internal Labor		0.00	712.50-	712.50-		USD
720000	Raw Material Consumption Expense		0.00	100.45-	100.45-		USD
800000	Internal Labor		0.00	200.00-	200.00-		USD
700000	External Labor		0.00	690.00-	690.00-		USD
Settlement		▪	**0.00** ▪	**2,152.95-** ▪	**2,152.95-**		**USD**
		▪ ▪	**3,673.86** ▪ ▪	**0.00** ▪ ▪	**3,673.86-**		**USD**

Figure 7.17 Cost Element Report

- Consumption of spare parts
- External procurement of spare parts
- External procurement of services
- Internal labor
- Settlement
- For a refurbishment order, postings to the stock assets can be added to these rows.

Chapter 6, Section 6.3.2, covered invoice receipts related to external services, which refer to a purchase order. But what happens when there's no order? What happens if your vendor delivered something "as required" and now sends an invoice?

You use the general function for invoice entry (Transaction FB60 [Enter Vendor Invoice] or Transaction F-43 [Enter Vendor Invoice General]) and assign the amount to the order (see Figure 7.18).

> **[+]**
>
> **Invoices without Purchase Orders**
>
> You can also post an invoice that does not relate to a purchase order. You would assign the invoice to the SAP S/4HANA Asset Management order; the costs are available in the history.

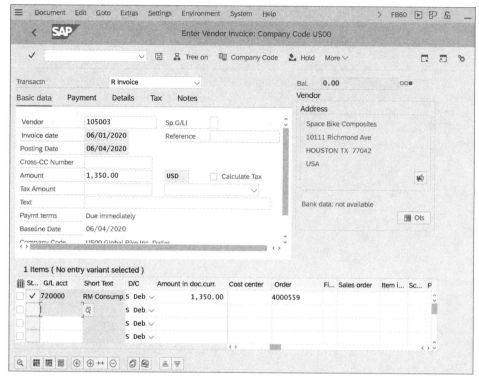

Figure 7.18 Transaction FB60: Vendor Invoice.

7.1.7   Asset Accounting

SAP S/4HANA Asset Management has the following integration points with asset accounting:

- You can assign an asset master record to your technical objects.
- You can automatically generate equipment when you create asset master records.
- You can automatically change equipment master records when you change asset master records.
- You can automatically generate asset master records when you create equipment master records.
- You can automatically change asset master records when you change equipment master records.
- You can activate your maintenance services and settle them to an *asset under construction*.

You can have your equipment and/or your functional location refer to an asset number in the **Account assignment** screen group (see Figure 7.19).

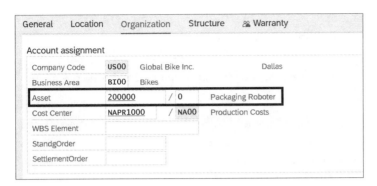

Figure 7.19 Asset Master in Technical Object

The reference involves a 1:n link, which means that you can assign several technical objects to a single asset number, but you cannot assign one technical object to several asset numbers.

When you display the asset master record, you can navigate from there to the assigned technical objects (Transaction AS03 [Display Asset Master], **More · Environment · Equipment** and **Environment · Functional Locations**).

Synchronizing Equipment and Assets

Many users are unaware of the option to match equipment master records and asset master records to each other. However, this option can be a useful timesaver.

> [!]
> **Synchronizing Assets and Equipment**
>
> SAP S/4HANA offers you a synchronization mechanism that you can use to generate equipment when you create asset master records, and vice versa. The synchronization mechanism also works for the change mode.

For example, when you change the cost center of an asset, you can set the system to change the cost center of the equipment automatically in the background.

> [!]
> **Not Possible to Synchronize Assets and Functional Locations**
>
> The standard delivery of SAP S/HANA does not include a synchronization mechanism to match assets and functional locations.

To enable synchronization, you must fulfill the following prerequisites.

In customizing, choose the menu path **Financial Accounting · Asset Accounting · Master Data · Automatic Creation of Equipment Master Records · Specify Conditions for Synchronization of Master Data** to define the direction of synchronization based on the asset class and equipment type (i.e., asset → equipment and/or equipment → asset).

- You can use the same function to define whether synchronization should occur immediately or a workflow should be triggered or both.

- In customizing, choose the menu path **Automatic Creation of Equipment Master Records · Assign Master Data Fields of Assets and Equipment** to define the fields to be synchronized.

If you then create an asset (Transaction AS01 [Create Asset]) and have defined in customizing that an equipment master is to be generated immediately, the equipment number will be displayed directly in the asset master record (see Figure 7.20). You can click the **Create** button to generate additional equipment that can also be assigned to this asset.

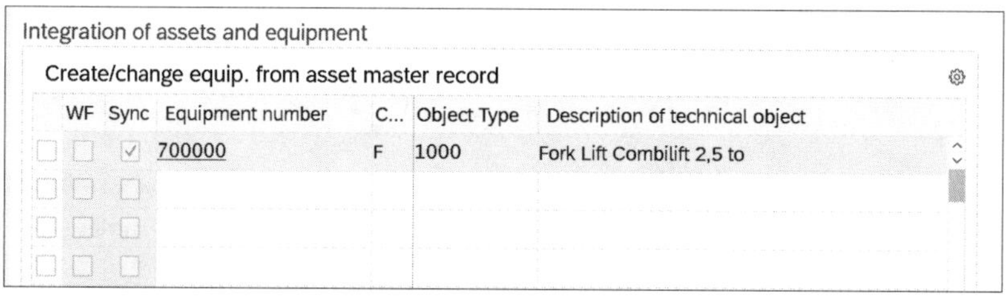

Integration of assets and equipment

Create/change equip. from asset master record

WF	Sync	Equipment number	C...	Object Type	Description of technical object
☐	☐ ✓	700000	F	1000	Fork Lift Combilift 2,5 to
☐	☐ ☐				
☐	☐ ☐				
☐	☐ ☐				

Figure 7.20 Integration of Assets and Equipment

Activating Maintenance Services

Certain services in maintenance departments require activation or can be activated. Especially when value-added orders are involved, for example, cases of modernization, rebuilding, installing additional components, and so on, these tasks should not be settled to the cost center and thus posted to the expenses. In such case, the values should be activated.

You create an order and enter "FXA" (i.e., asset) as the account assignment category in the settlement rule and enter the asset number as the account assignment object. When the order is completed, you settle it with Transaction KO88.

The values generated in plant maintenance are assigned to the asset master record as an **Acquisition internal settlement to assets under construction**, the procurement value is increased, and the settlement amounts are adjusted (see Figure 7.21).

[!]

Required Consultation with Asset Accounting

Consult closely with asset accounting, especially with regard to the activation of internal activities.

We've now come to a wide-ranging and deep integration, which along with the integration with materials management, is the most important integration: the integration of plant maintenance with controlling.

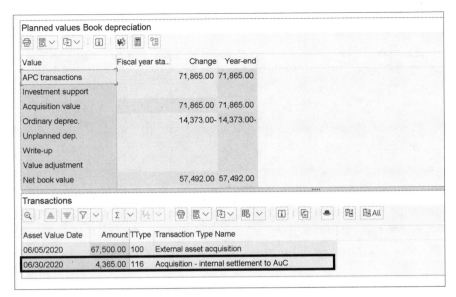

Figure 7.21 Asset Values

7.1.8 Controlling

The following factors influence the integration of plant maintenance with controlling:

- To enable integration between SAP S/4HANA Asset Management and controlling in SAP S/4HANA Finance, make sure that all required cost elements are available in the chart of accounts.
- Assign a cost center (as a receiving cost center) to the functional locations and/or equipment as a possible cost object.
- Assign a cost center (as a performing cost center) to the work center.
- Define the activity types and, based on those, the allocation rates (prices) of plant maintenance.
- In controlling customizing, define how you want to cost your orders.
- Define a settlement rule in the order and settle the order.
- You determine the overhead rates for your orders (if necessary).
- You can use the tools of controlling (for example, cost center reports or order reports) to analyze your maintenance activities.

Cost Elements

Information is always exchanged between plant maintenance and controlling using cost elements.

[+]

Completing Cost Elements

When you implement SAP S/4HANA Asset Management, make sure that you have all the required cost elements for costing and settling orders. You may have to supplement the existing chart of accounts.

The following cost elements are required to cost and settle SAP S/4HANA Asset Management orders:

- Cost elements for the consumption of spare parts (cost element category 1 = primary costs)

- Cost elements for the external procurement of spare parts (cost element category 1 = primary costs)

- Cost elements for the external procurement of services (cost element category 1 = primary costs)

- Cost elements for the entry of time confirmations (cost element category 43 = internal activity allocation)

- Cost elements for the overhead rates (cost element category 41 = overhead rates)

- Cost elements for the order settlement (cost element category 21 = internal settlement)

Cost Centers

To ensure that internal activity allocation (IAA) can charge maintenance services to the asset cost centers, you must perform the following activities:

- Assign a cost center as a performing cost center to the work centers of plant maintenance.

- Assign a cost center to the functional locations and/or equipment as the receiving cost center.

[!]

Cost Centers in Technical Objects

In 90% of cases, maintenance services are settled to the asset cost center. Thus, you should assign a cost center to your technical objects so that they can be transferred automatically to the order as a settlement rule.

Activity Types and Prices

You need an activity type for the producing cost center. An activity type is a unit within a controlling area that classifies the services of a cost center and that you can use to differentiate the charge rates of the cost center. You define activity types with Transaction KL01 (Create Activity Type).

If each maintenance cost center only has one charge rate, one activity type is sufficient. If you have differentiated cost rates for each maintenance cost center, however, you'll need more activity types. What are the likely reasons for differentiated charging rates? You can differentiate maintenance services, for example, according to the following criteria:

- **Urgency**
  Rush orders, normal orders, worklist

- **Time of occurrence**
  Normal shift, night shift, weekend

- **Qualification**
  Foreman, technician, extra hours, trainees

- **Type of activity**
  Normal hours, hazardous bonus, dirty work bonus

- **Type of tools used**
  Work with special machines, use of trucks, and so on

Activity types can be used to differentiate the charge rates of plant maintenance. Thus, you can avoid differentiating by urgency, for example, by having the contracting entities give every order a priority of 1.

You set the charge rates once a year for each cost center and activity type with Transaction KP26 (Change Activity Type/Price Planning) (see Figure 7.22).

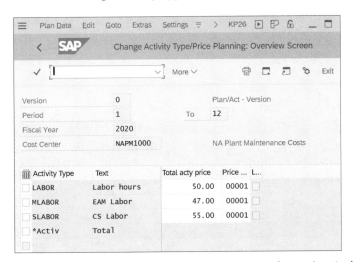

Figure 7.22 Transaction KP26 (Change Activity Type/Price Planning)

Costing

You can control costing (planned, actual) via the customizing function **Costing Data for Maintenance and Service Orders**. The tables involved here build on each other. Thus, you should proceed in the following sequence (see Figure 7.23):

1. **Maintain the costing sheet**

   First, use the customizing function **Maintain Costing Sheet** (step ❶) to define which cost elements should be used as the **Basis** for the costing, how high the percentage or absolute overhead rate should be, and which cost center serves as the credit for the relevant amounts.

2. **Define valuation variant and define costing type**

   Use the customizing function **Define Valuation Variant** (step ❷) to define how the material valuation should occur (usually valuation according to price control in the material master), how the activity types are to be valuated (normally the planned price of the period), and which costing sheet (step ❸) should be used.

3. **Maintain costing variants**

   Use the customizing function **Maintain Costing Variants** (step ❹) to combine the **Costing Type** and the **Valuation Variant**.

4. **Assign costing parameters and results analysis keys**

   Use the customizing function **Assign costing parameter and results analysis key** (step ❺) to define for each plant and type of order the costing variant that should be used in the preliminary costing and final costing (which are normally identical).

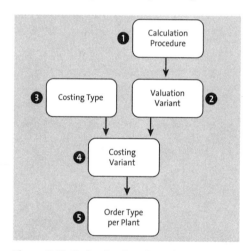

Figure 7.23 Order Costing Overview

Preliminary costing of an order occurs automatically when you save or when you click on the 🖩 button during order processing. The actual costing of an order also occurs automatically when you perform cost postings (material withdrawals, confirmations, and so on).

Allocation of Overhead Costs

When you cost an order, overhead rates are calculated automatically within the standard cost estimate and are assigned to the planned costs if they have been defined in the costing sheet.

Calculating overhead rates does not occur automatically during actual costing. Overhead costs are not automatically surcharged to the actual costs (goods movements, time confirmations, invoices, and so on).

Overhead costs are calculated and surcharged to actual costs in the following manner:

- Final costing of an order using Transaction KGI2 (Actual Overhead Calculation: Individual Processing)
- Final costing of a group of orders using Transaction KGI4 (Actual Overhead Calculation: Collective Processing)

No Automatic Determination of Overhead Rates in the Actual Costing [!]

As overhead rates are automatically charged in preliminary costing but not in final costing, you must recost the orders. For safety's sake, schedule a batch job in background processing to perform final costing at short intervals.

Order Settlement

What does order settlement mean? During processing of the order, the entry activities trigger actual costs on the order. As the order cannot be a permanent cost object, even as an internal order, the costs must be settled periodically (for example, once a week) or after completion (for example, when technically completed) to the actual target account assignment and re-debited (see Figure 7.24).

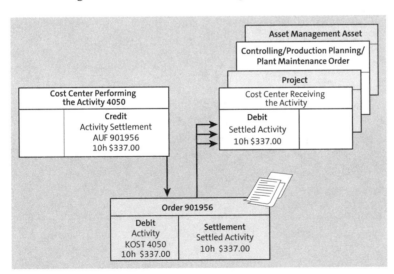

Figure 7.24 Order Settlement

During the order settlement, the debit cost elements are transformed into settlement cost elements, and the costs are redirected to the target account assignment via the settlement cost elements.

The following prerequisites must be met so that you can settle an order:

- You have maintained a settlement profile using the customizing function **Maintain Settlement Profile**. You have set the permitted receivers there.

- You have also assigned a settlement profile to the order type in customizing by choosing **Configure Order Types**.

- You have used the customizing function **Settlement Rule: Define Time and Creation of the Distribution Rule** to define order release or technical completion as the time for creating the settlement rule for the order type.

[+]

Time for Creating the Settlement Rule

The best time to select as the time for creating the settlement rule is the order release. Otherwise, you cannot settle the order if it lasts longer than the cycle of your periodic order settlement.

- The order has a settlement rule, which you can verify via the status **SETC** (settlement rule created).

- If you work with overhead rates in actual costing, you have determined the actual cost surcharges either with Transaction KGI2 (Actual Overhead Calculation: Individual Processing) for an individual order or with Transaction KGI4 (Actual Overhead Calculation: Collective Processing) for a group of orders.

Who are the possible *receivers*? In most cases, the cost center serves as the receiver of order settlement in plant maintenance. However, you can also settle your orders to asset numbers, work breakdown structure (WBS) elements, or another order.

[+]

Default Account Assignment CTR

In 90% of cases, the cost center of the technical object is the target account assignment of the maintenance orders. In customizing, enter default object type **CTR** (cost center) for the settlement profile. Then, the cost center of the reference object will be automatically transferred to the order as the account assignment; you do not have to maintain it manually.

What does the settlement rule look like in the order? Figure 7.25 shows a typical settlement rule for maintenance orders. The order is settled 100% to an asset cost center.

If you have a settlement rule created automatically, the SAP system generates two entries for the settlement type:

- **PER (periodic settlement)**
  For monthly settlement, the system considers only the costs that arise in the specified period.

- **FUL (full settlement)**
  Here, the system considers all the costs that arise up to the time of settlement.

When PER settlement rules are present, they are applied ahead of FUL settlement.

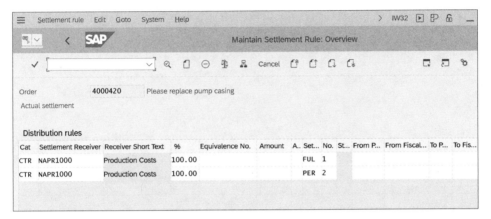

Figure 7.25 Settlement Rule

[+]

Period Accruals in the Order Settlement

You also have the option to use period accruals (from period and to period) to settle costs over time to different target account assignments.

[!]

Do Not Forget the FUL Settlement Rule

Make sure that a **FUL** settlement rule is present in your order as the settlement rule. Otherwise, not all costs might be settled to the target account assignment.

Amount Settlement

You also have the option to settle a fixed amount. You need this option, for example, when you have agreed on a fixed price with the contracting entity. In such a case, enter a settlement rule as is indicated in Figure 7.26:

- **Amount**
  You create a settlement rule with the amount. As a result, the relevant amount is settled to the specified settlement rule (for example, asset cost center).

- **Amount rule category**
  Do not forget to specify the amount rule category in the **ARulCat** column. Set the amount rule category to 1 if you want the amount to be settled once. Leave the amount rule category empty if the amount is to be settled in each period.

- **Percentage rate settlement**

  You can create one or more percentage rate settlements. As a result, the effective actual costs are settled to this account assignment rule (usually the maintenance cost center).

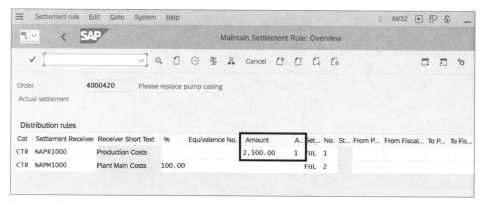

Figure 7.26 Order Settlement by Amount

To perform a settlement by amount, select the **Settlement Amount** option (customizing function **Maintain Settlement Profile**).

[+] **Settlement at a Fixed Price**

You can also settle your orders at a fixed price. You simply activate settlement by amount in the settlement rule. Then, enter the first settlement rule with the amount for target account assignment and a second settlement rule with 100% assigned to the performing cost center.

At this point, you have two options to settle orders:

- You can use Transaction KO88 (Individual Settlement) and settle an individual order.

- You can use Transaction KO8G (Collective Settlement)—a batch program is the best approach—and settle all orders that can be settled at the end of a period (month-end, for example) with the actual costs that have arisen during that time.

How can you tell if an order has been settled? What is the result of order settlement?

Settlement re-debits all debits of the order to the target account assignment; thus, the report on individual costs will be zero (0) in the overall total of actual costs (see Figure 7.27).

Cost Element	Cost Element (Text)	Σ	Total Plan Costs Σ	Total Actual Costs Σ	Plan/actual variance	P/A var(%) Currency
740000	Auxiliary and operating materials		450.00	450.00	0.00	USD
720000	Raw Material Consumption Expense		1,278.86	100.45	1,178.41-	92.15- USD
720000	Raw Material Consumption Expense		40.00	0.00	40.00-	100.00- USD
720000	Raw Material Consumption Expense		140.00	0.00	140.00-	100.00- USD
700000	External Labor		690.00	690.00	0.00	USD
800000	Internal Labor		1,075.00	912.50	162.50-	15.12- USD
Debit		**▪**	**3,673.86** ▪	**2,152.95** ▪	**1,520.91-**	**USD**
740000	Auxiliary and operating materials		0.00	450.00-	450.00-	USD
800000	Internal Labor		0.00	712.50-	712.50-	USD
720000	Raw Material Consumption Expense		0.00	100.45-	100.45-	USD
800000	Internal Labor		0.00	200.00-	200.00-	USD
700000	External Labor		0.00	690.00-	690.00-	USD
Settlement		**▪**	**0.00** ▪	**2,152.95-** ▪	**2,152.95-**	**USD**
		▪ ▪	**3,673.86** ▪ ▪	**0.00** ▪ ▪	**3,673.86-**	**USD**

Figure 7.27 Settled Order

Controlling Information System

You can see the total of services and costs incurred by the order in cost center reports, such as the report created with Transaction S_ALR_87013611 (Cost Centers: Actual/Plan Deviation).

Figure 7.28 illustrates a typical result for a performing cost center: The cost center is credited with the cost elements of internal activity allocation (**800000** in this example).

Cost Elements		Actual	Plan	Dev (abs)
720000	RM Consumpt Expense	9.000,00	12.000,00	3.000,00
790100	External Services	10.845,89	15.000,00	4.154,11
* Debit		19.845,89	27.000,00	7.154,11
800000	Internal Labor	33.400,01-	50.000,00-	16.599,99-
800100	Assessed Costs			
800400	EAM Cost Allocation	4.623,78-	5.000,00-	376,22-
* A,H,L		38.023,79-	55.000,00-	16.976,21-
**		18.177,90-	28.000,00-	9.822,10-

Figure 7.28 Cost Center Report: Performing Cost Center

Figure 7.29, however, shows a typical receiving cost center: The cost center is debited with the cost elements of order settlement (here, for example, **800000** and so on).

Cost Elements		Actual	Plan	Dev (abs)
720000	RM Consumpt Expense	29.675,00	35.000,00	5.325,00-
740000	Aufw H&B	1.000,00	12.000,00	11.000,00-
790100	ext. Services		27.500,00	27.500,00-
790200	Non-stock material		42.800,00	42.800,00-
800000	internal Labor	208.010,00		208.010,00
800200	settl. CO order	134.983,91	65.900,00	69.083,91
800400	EAM Cost Allocation	540,00		540,00
800500	settl. PM order	45.750,00	56.400,00	10.650,00-
816099	Engineering Services	2.000,00	4.000,00	2.000,00-
818757	Cleaning Services	2.000,00	4.000,00	2.000,00-
* Debit		423.958,91	247.600,00	176.358,91
800000	internal Labor	529.225,70-	500.000,00-	29.225,70-
* A,H,L		529.225,70-	500.000,00-	29.225,70-
**		105.266,79-	252.400,00-	147.133,21

Figure 7.29 Cost Center Report: Receiving Cost Center

7.1.9   Real Estate Management

Flexible Real Estate Management (RE-FX) with SAP S/4HANA offer functions that you need when managing real estate, for example:

- Managing various types of real estate objects: business entities, properties, buildings, rental units, rental spaces, and rental rooms
- Managing real estate contracts: renting to and from contracts, service contracts, and maintenance contracts
- Area management: size and equipment
- Business processes related to real estate: new construction, order processing, and activity allocations

Real Estate Objects and Functional Locations

At every level in the *utilization view*, you can assign a functional location to a real estate object:

- To a business unit if it involves real estate holdings that are related to each other (in an industrial park, for example).
- To a building if it involves an object that creates the basis for renting space (apartments, warehouses, and businesses). A building is a component of a business unit.
- To a rental object, such as an area pool, rental space, and rental unit.

Figure 7.30 illustrates the assignment of a functional location to a real estate object from the perspective of the object—a building, in this case (Transaction REBDBU [Building Display]).

> **Creating Functional Locations Automatically**
>
> You can use the customizing function **Flexible Real Estate Management (RE-FX) • General Settings for Master Data and Contracts • Assignment of Objects from Other Components • PM Integration • PM Integration: Define Settings Per Object Type** to define per company code and type of object whether a functional location should be generated automatically when you create a real estate object.

You can also display the assignment from the perspective of the functional location (Transaction IL03 [Display Functional Location]): All functional locations that are assigned to a real estate object have a **Real Estate** tab, where the assignment is automatically entered (see Figure 7.31).

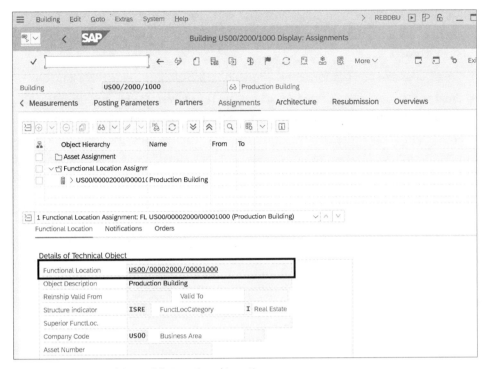

Figure 7.30 RE-FX: Object with Functional Location

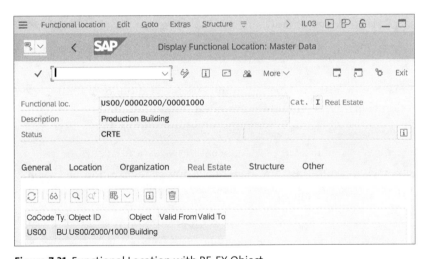

Figure 7.31 Functional Location with RE-FX Object

In the architectural view, you can also manually assign a functional location to a real estate object. In customizing, you can also use **Flexible Real Estate Management (RE-FX) · Master Data · Architectural View · PM Integration · Define Settings per Architectural Object Type** to define whether or not a functional location is automatically created for the architectural object type (area, building, property, and so on).

Subsequent Processes

If you have assigned the real estate object and functional location, you can initiate the following processes:

- Create or assign notifications for the functional location from the real estate object.

- Create orders for the functional location from the real estate object or from Transaction IW31 (Create Order) and assign them to the real estate object.

- Settlement of the order can occur on a real estate object such as a rental unit, a settlement unit, or a usage object. The costs are then stated for each real estate object and can be used later on in service charge settlement (see Figure 7.32). To this end, use Transaction REISCOLIBD (Real Estate Objects Actual Line Items).

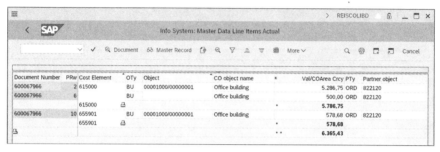

Figure 7.32 RE-FX Object: Settled Costs

7.1.10   Human Capital Management

SAP Human Capital Management for SAP S/4HANA offers functions related to human resources:

- Personnel management (recruitment, remuneration, vacation, organization, personnel development, retirement provisions, and so on)

- Payroll accounting (gross, net, reduced hours workers, pensions, and so on)

- Time management (schedules, time entry, incentive wages, and so on)

- Event management (events, speakers, room management, registration, and so on)

- Continuing education and training

SAP Human Capital Management for SAP S/4HANA and SAP S/4HANA Asset Management are always actively integrated when you assign a personnel number to objects or business processes of plant maintenance.

Work Centers and Personnel Numbers

The assignment of persons to work centers is the starting point for the use of persons in the business processes of plant maintenance. You can assign a person as shown in Figure 7.33, either directly or indirectly using positions. You link the two using transactions for maintaining work centers (Transactions IR01 and IR02 [Maintain Maintenance

Work Center]) or via SAP Human Capital Management for SAP S/4HANA transactions (e.g., Transaction PA30 [Maintain Personal Number]).

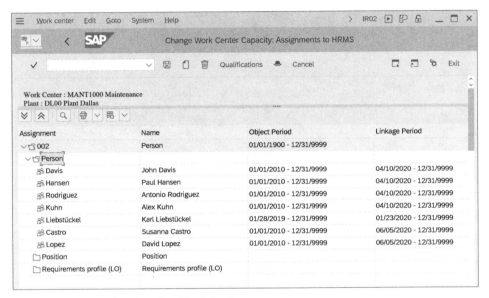

Figure 7.33 Personal Assigned to Work Center

Technical Objects and Personnel Numbers

Your firm may want to store named contact persons in the master data records of technical objects, for example, the addressee in the event of further questions.

[!]

Assigning Persons in the Technical Object Using the Partner Determination Procedure

You can always assign equipment and functional locations to a person if you have assigned a partner determination procedure, which includes a partner role that refers to partner type PE (HR master record), to the equipment type, or to the functional location type.

See Chapter 3, Section 3.11.7, for details about defining and assigning partners.

Figure 7.34 shows, for example, the assignment of equipment to two partner roles of type PE.

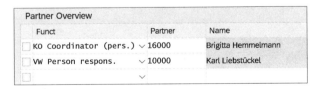

Figure 7.34 Technical Object and Personnel

Notifications and Personnel Numbers

When you want to assign a contact person by name to a notification, the procedure is similar to that for master data records.

> **[!]**
>
> **Assigning Persons in Notifications Using the Partner Determination Procedure**
>
> You can always assign persons to a notification if you have assigned a partner determination procedure, which has partner roles that refer in turn to partner type PE (personnel master data), to the notification type. If the same partner role is present in the type of the technical object, the relevant person is transferred to the notification.

Orders and Personnel Numbers

Chapter 4, Section 4.3.5, showed how you can assign a personnel number to several levels of an order.

You can name a responsible person in the order header. This person is usually from the responsible work center and serves as the central contact person during performance of the order, for example, the person who would answer any questions that arise (see Figure 7.35).

Figure 7.35 Order Header: Responsible Person

You can also assign an operation to the person who should perform it, usually a person from the work center (see Figure 7.36).

Figure 7.36 Order Operation: Executing Person

You can also assign several persons to an operation if it involves several technicians. Enter the number of persons involved and then indicate the persons for the requirements specifications (see Figure 7.37).

	Spl	Dispat...	Person	Work	W...	Normal...	D...	Date	Time	Suit.
Components		Reqmnts Assignment			Relationships					
Capacity cat.		002			Person					
☐	1	☐	Davis	2.0	HR	2.0	HR	06/05/2020	09:07	100.00
☐	2	☐	Hansen	3.0	HR	3.0	HR	06/05/2020	09:07	100.00
☐	3	☐	Rodriguez	1.0	HR	1.0	HR	06/05/2020	09:07	100.00
☐	4	☐			HR		HR	06/05/2020	09:07	0.00

Figure 7.37 Order Operation: Several Executing Persons

Confirmation and Personnel Numbers

In all confirmation transactions, you have the option to enter a personnel number along with the confirmation. During confirmation with the maintenance Transactions IW41 (Single Confirmation), IW42 (Overall Confirmation), IW44 (Collective Confirmation), and IW48 (Collective Confirmation with Selection), you can optionally enter a personnel number, but during confirmation via the CATS (Cross-Application Time Sheet) application via Transaction CAT2 (Time Sheet Data Entry), you must specify a personnel number.

[!]

Laws When Using Confirmations with Personnel Numbers

When you execute confirmations with personnel numbers, please consider local and national laws. In Germany, for example, you can only do this if you have given your employee representatives a written company agreement in which, among other things, you state that the information will not be used to evaluate employee performance.

How can you reasonably work with confirmations at the level of the personnel number? You can check to see if all the attendance time was settled to orders. Figure 7.38 shows an example of this.

[!]

Ensuring Confirmations Are Complete

Based on person-related times, you can evaluate if the relevant person entered the time spent on the orders or if, for example, confirmations were forgotten. If you do not enter all attendance times in orders, the allocation record of the workshops tends to increase in the next period.

A similar evaluation exists in time management using time leveling (Transaction PW61, see Figure 7.39). Time leveling shows the planned attendance times and the time accounted to orders.

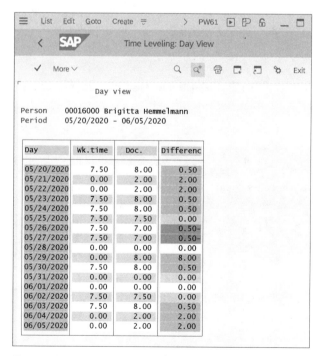

S	Confir...	Order	Op...	Postg Da...	Pers.No.	Name of employee	Func. Loc.	Equipment	Act. wo...	Un.	WkAct	AcType (plan)	WkCtrAct
	4240	4000154	0010	07/31/20...	16000	Brigitta Hemmelmann			8.0	HR		MLABOR	ME
	4241	4000154	0020	08/01/20...					5.0	HR		MLABOR	ME
	4242	4000154	0030	08/02/20...					3.0	HR		MLABOR	ME
	4247	4000154	0080	08/05/20...					5.0	HR		MLABOR	ME
	4248	4000154	0090	08/05/20...					4.0	HR		MLABOR	ME
	4249	4000154	0100	08/06/20...					4.0	HR		MLABOR	ME
	5201	4000165	0010	08/06/20...			ICE-TA-T1-02	TEQP0000	3.0	HR		MLABOR	ME
	8732	4000255	0010	09/23/20...			ICE-M2	E16000	5.0	HR		LABOR1	ME
	8891	4000286	0010	12/09/20...			ICE-FR		4	H		LABOR1	ME
					16000				4	H			
									37.0	HR			
	4243	4000154	0040	07/31/20...	10000	Karl Liebstückel			6.0	HR		MLABOR	ME
	4244	4000154	0050	08/01/20...					2.0	HR		MLABOR	ME
	4245	4000154	0060	08/02/20...					4.0	HR		MLABOR	ME
	4246	4000154	0070	08/02/20...					3.0	HR		MLABOR	ME
	8326	4000200	0010	08/05/20...			ICE-TA-T1-02	TEQP0014	2.5	HR		MLABOR	ME
	8701	4000240	0010	08/05/20...				E10001	4.0	HR		MLABOR	ME
	8717	4000243	0010	08/06/20...				10001002	5.0	HR		MLABOR	ME
	8719	4000245	0010	08/06/20...			ICE-TA-T1-02	E10000	3.0	HR		LABOR1	ME
	9909	4000424	0010	04/22/20...			ICD-TA-T1	10001210	3	H		LABOR	ME
					10000				3	H			
									29.5	HR			
									7	H			
									66.5	HR			

Figure 7.38 Transaction IW47: Confirmation List with Personal Number

Day view

Person   00016000 Brigitta Hemmelmann
Period   05/20/2020 – 06/05/2020

Day	Wk.time	Doc.	Differenc
05/20/2020	7.50	8.00	0.50
05/21/2020	0.00	2.00	2.00
05/22/2020	0.00	2.00	2.00
05/23/2020	7.50	8.00	0.50
05/24/2020	7.50	8.00	0.50
05/25/2020	7.50	7.50	0.00
05/26/2020	7.50	7.00	0.50–
05/27/2020	7.50	7.00	0.50–
05/28/2020	0.00	0.00	0.00
05/29/2020	0.00	8.00	8.00
05/30/2020	7.50	8.00	0.50
05/31/2020	0.00	0.00	0.00
06/01/2020	0.00	0.00	0.00
06/02/2020	7.50	7.50	0.00
06/03/2020	7.50	8.00	0.50
06/04/2020	0.00	2.00	2.00
06/05/2020	0.00	2.00	2.00

Figure 7.39 Transaction PW61 (Time Levelling)

7.1.11 Service and Sales

If you have distinctive customer service, we recommend that you implement customer service with SAP S/4HANA, which is a sister functional area to SAP S/4HANA Asset Management that has functions and business processes oriented to customer service (see Figure 7.40). In particular, customer service offers the following capabilities:

- Structuring and maintaining service objects using functional locations, equipment, and installations
- Warranty management with warranty claim processing
- Managing service contracts and service-level agreements
- Creating offers for service offerings
- Returns processing
- Advance shipment of spare parts
- Operating customer interaction centers
- Service processing with service notification, service orders, and sales orders
- Maintaining a solution database
- Invoicing of services provided
- Monitoring notifications with reaction times and availability times
- Connecting service objects and business partners

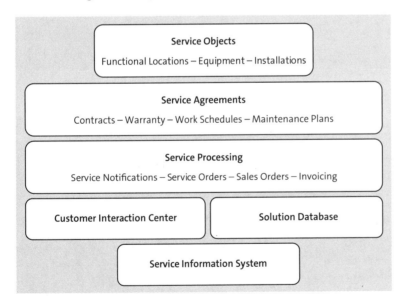

Figure 7.40 SAP S/4HANA Customer Service: Overview

Even if you do not have distinctive customer service requirements, but simply provide services in the context of sales orders at irregular intervals, you can also benefit from integration with sales. For example, the following services could be involved:

- A technician can undertake an assembly at a customer site.
- A customer can return a device that is then repaired in the workshop.
- A technician can repair a machine at a customer site.
- A technician can brief an employee at a customer site as part of the sales order.

To map these business processes in your system without having to implement a complete customer service system, you must fulfill the following prerequisites:

- You have a regular sales order.
- You create a maintenance order when one of the cases previously noted occurs.
- You can assign the maintenance order to a sales order item (see Figure 7.41). As a requirement, the sales order must be entered as a **Valid Receiver** in the settlement profile.
- You perform the maintenance order as normal.
- You settle the maintenance order to the sales order.

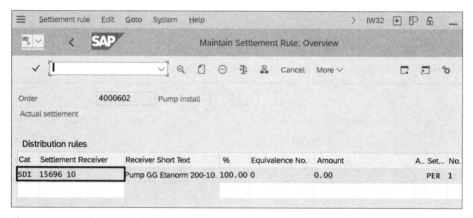

Figure 7.41 Settlement Rule Customer Order

The sales order states the settled costs (see Figure 7.42); you can invoice these and reduce the profit expected from the sales order.

[+]

Assigned Maintenance Orders versus Customer Service Orders

If you have distinctive customer service requirements, we recommend that you implement customer service with SAP S/4HANA. If you perform services related to sales at irregular intervals, you could benefit from customer service's integration with sales and settle the maintenance order to the sales order.

Sales Document/Item 15696/ 10		
Material	IPMP1000 Pump GG Etanorm 200-1000	
Plant	DL00 Plant Dallas	
Actual Quantity	1 PC Piece	

Cost Element	Σ	Total Plan Costs Σ	Total Actual Costs	Currency
650100		2,900.00-	2,900.00-	USD
650100	▪	2,900.00- ▪	2,900.00-	USD
741000		0.00	1,198.50	USD
741000	▪	0.00 ▪	1,198.50	USD
800200		0.00	200.00	USD
		0.00	110.00	USD
		0.00	299.63	USD
800200	▪	0.00 ▪	609.63	USD
800500		0.00	1,198.50	USD
800500	▪	0.00 ▪	1,198.50	USD
Debit	▪ ▪	2,900.00- ▪ ▪	106.63	USD
	▪ ▪ ▪	2,900.00- ▪ ▪ ▪	106.63	USD

Figure 7.42 Cost Analysis Customer Order

Customer Service Discontinued in 2027

In 2012, SAP announced the termination of maintenance service for SAP ERP by the end of 2025; however, since then, that date has been postponed to December 31, 2027 for standard contracts (with the option of extending to 2030 with non-standard contracts). This also is true for customer service with SAP S/4HANA, which has the same deadlines. In 2018, SAP announced SAP C/4HANA as the new customer relationship management solution (SAP C/4HANA has since been renamed SAP Customer Experience, with customer service being a part of it). Still, there are many uncertainties regarding which functionalities SAP Customer Experience will be offering for technical-oriented customer service or even if certain functions in SAP S/4HANA will be maintained over extended periods of time. Keeping track of SAP announcements as well as those of large user associations like ASUG or DSAG is advisable.

These integrations should be the most important ones to link plant maintenance to other departments that use SAP S/4HANA functionality. However, as SAP offers other systems beyond the SAP S/4HANA environment, which other departments may use and which affect plant maintenance, the next section will focus on integrating with other SAP systems.

7.2   Integration with Other SAP Systems

In addition to the integration points described in the previous sections within SAP S/4HANA, functions of SAP Master Data Governance (SAP MDG), SAP NetWeaver

Master Data Management (SAP NetWeaver MDM), and SAP Supplier Relationship Management (SAP SRM) are used essentially in plant maintenance.

7.2.1 SAP NetWeaver Master Data Management

Because master data forms the basis for business processes in most enterprises, data quality plays a major role. Master data provides information that is used in business processes, other data (e.g., transaction data), evaluations, and administrative and MRP-based applications. Consequently, the *quality of the master data* directly influences processes, stock levels, revenues, costs, and reporting and thus directly influences the success of the enterprise. Therefore, accurate and consistent master data must be considered an essential success factor.

To reduce errors and problems and to keep the resulting consequences and costs to a minimum, more and more enterprises accept proper *master data management* as a critical instrument for corporate governance. Master data management is an enterprise-wide task which is comprised of several components. On the one hand, *strategic* decisions must be made, such as the development of a master data strategy or the creation of a profitability analysis. In addition, *organizational* decisions must be made: Processes need to be defined; roles and responsibilities must be determined. Finally, *system-technical* decisions must also be made that deal with the IT components to be used, especially choosing the appropriate software to support the master data management.

Many companies use not only an integrated system like SAP S/4HANA, but possibly many other systems that handle business processes and manage master data (e.g., SAP Customer Relationship Management [SAP CRM] or SAP SRM systems). As a result, master data will be distributed across various systems, applications, and tables, which leads, almost by necessity, to inconsistencies and conflicts.

These potential problems can be illustrated by the following example: A spare part is purchased from various suppliers in different plants. Each supplier uses a different part number, and each plant uses its own material number for the spare part in its system. The spare part is never scheduled in common, and its availability is never made known to the other plants, which inevitably leads to increased inventory. Using SAP NetWeaver MDM, you can identify duplicates as well as consolidate, synchronize, distribute, and centrally manage master data objects from various IT systems.

SAP NetWeaver MDM attempts to achieve these goals at various levels (see Figure 7.43):

- **Master data consolidation**
  Master data consolidation (step ❶) identifies identical master data from various systems, compares the master data objects centrally in SAP NetWeaver MDM, and supplies decentralized systems with mapping information. Data is loaded into SAP NetWeaver MDM and consolidated there. Any required corrections occur in the decentralized systems, which can be SAP or non-SAP systems.

- **Master data harmonization**

  With master data harmonization (step ❷), data is also maintained in decentralized SAP and non-SAP systems and is loaded into SAP NetWeaver MDM and harmonized there. In this case, the master data is distributed to SAP and non-SAP systems, where it is updated or re-created.

- **Central master data maintenance**

  With central master data maintenance (step ❸), the master data is centrally maintained and stored on the SAP NetWeaver MDM server. Distribution mechanisms are used to distribute the data to the SAP and non-SAP systems to be addressed. The difference between this approach and master data harmonization is that the data is maintained in SAP NetWeaver MDM and distributed from there, rather than being loaded and consolidated from the decentralized systems.

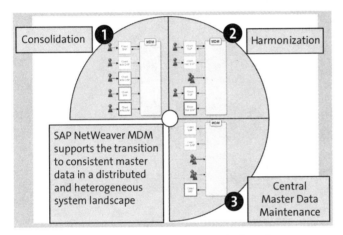

Figure 7.43 SAP Master Data Management: Overview

Which objects that are relevant from a plant maintenance perspective can be processed by SAP NetWeaver MDM? The most important objects include the following:

- Materials
- BOMs
- Vendors
- Personnel

Other master data objects (such as retail materials or customers) do not play any role from a plant maintenance perspective.

7.2.2 SAP Master Data Governance

SAP Master Data Governance is the newer and in the future exclusive software, which is supposed to support you in ensuring the quality of your master data. You can use it in two different scenarios (see Figure 7.44):

- As a standalone system that distributes the master data to the operational systems (as a so-called *master data hub*).

- As an integrated component within the SAP S/4HANA system. The master data remains within the SAP S/4HANA system or can be distributed across operational systems.

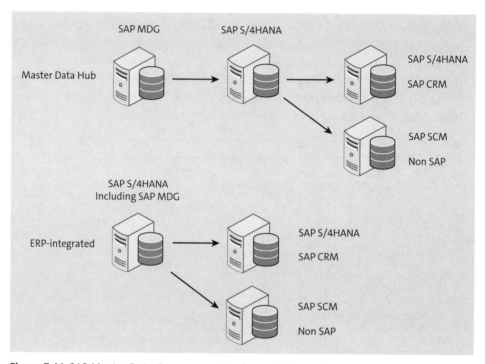

Figure 7.44 SAP Master Data Governance: Deployment Scenarios

The most important functions of SAP Master Data Governance include the following:

- **Centralized master data management**
  You can manage master data centrally in the SAP Master Data Governance system. You can request changes to existing master data or the creation of new master data via change requests. A workflow that supports additional functions such as approval or forwarding is not possible here.

- **Replication of master data**
  The data replication framework enables you to replicate your master data to the individual target systems. You can use filters to define which data should be sent to which target systems.

- **Loading of master data**
  You can load data of upstream systems to the SAP Master Data Governance system to evaluate the data there.

- **Consolidation of master data**
  You can consolidate master data from different sources and identify possible duplicates.

Currently, SAP Master Data Governance supports the following data objects:

- Financial data
- Material master data
- Vendor master data
- Customer master data
- Business partners
- Equipment
- Functional locations
- Bills of materials

Figure 7.45 illustrates a simplified master data maintenance process with SAP Master Data Governance, as follows:

❶ In a separate area (staging area), the master data is centrally recorded. Because the data is not immediately released or used but needs to be approved first, you create a *change request* for this purpose. A change request is the central component of the master data maintenance with SAP Master Data Governance. You can only maintain, that is, create or change, master data objects using change requests. Usually, each master data process has a separate change request in enterprises. For example, the create material process may be started via a change request, and the change material or create vendor process may be assigned separate change requests. Figure 7.46 shows an example of a change request for an existing material master record. Here, you maintain information such as validity period, reason for change, or priority.

❷ In this optional second step, you can validate the data—for example, by using external services, performing address cleansing, or searching for duplicates.

❸ In case of the dual-control principle, an approver must now release the master record for further usage. If a third control instance is added, a reviewer and an approver are responsible for this task. Only when finally approved is the data transferred to the *active area* and stored there. To process the change request according to your requirements, a workflow is assigned to every change request. This assigned workflow enables you, for example, to assign approval steps with validation checks to a change request.

❹ In the fourth step, the master data is distributed across the connected SAP systems and non-SAP systems.

❺ In both SAP systems and non-SAP systems, you can then adapt the data and add local data.

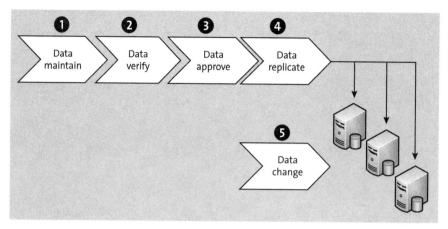

Figure 7.45 SAP Master Data Governance: Process

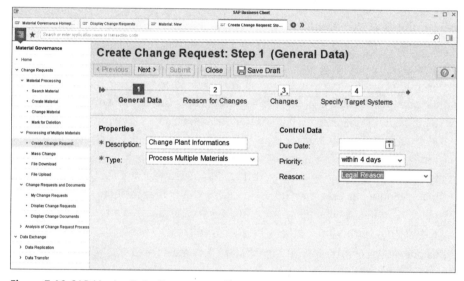

Figure 7.46 SAP Master Data Governance: Change Request

Further Reading

For further information please refer to the appropriate literature, e.g., Kalwachwala et al., *SAP Master Data Governance*, (SAP PRESS, 2nd edition, 2019), available at *http://www.sap-press.com/4883*.

7.2.3 SAP Supplier Relationship Management

SAP Supplier Relationship Management is an alternative purchasing system from SAP that can be used instead of or parallel to the purchasing component in SAP S/4HANA. SAP Supplier Relationship Management includes the following functions:

- **Self-service procurement**
  Employees can use this function to make purchasing easier and to create and manage their own order processes to accelerate procurement transactions.

- **Service procurement**
  This function is used for the procurement of services.

- **Plan-driven procurement**
  Plan-driven procurement is used to cover requirements that are reported from other systems.

- **Spend analysis**
  This function is used to analyze procurement expenses in the company.

- **Strategic sourcing**
  Strategic sourcing is used to manage sources of supply.

- **Catalog content management**
  Catalog content management is used to manage sales catalogs.

- **Contract management**
  This function is used to manage contracts and delivery schedules.

From a plant maintenance perspective, *plan-driven procurement* is the most interesting component because it deals with the procurement of material and service requirements that originate in external planning systems. For plant maintenance in particular, SAP Supplier Relationship Management supports a scenario for *plan-driven procurement with plant maintenance*.

Two variations of the scenario exist:

- Classic scenario (see Figure 7.47)
- Enhanced classic scenario (see Figure 7.48)

In the classic scenario, SAP S/4HANA generates a purchase requisition and sends it as an external requirement to SAP Supplier Relationship Management via an open XML interface.

SAP Supplier Relationship Management executes sourcing for the required product. Purchasing agents can use functions to create contracts for the requirements or trigger bid invitations.

SAP Supplier Relationship Management generates one or more purchase orders that it transfers to SAP S/4HANA for subsequent processing of the purchase order.

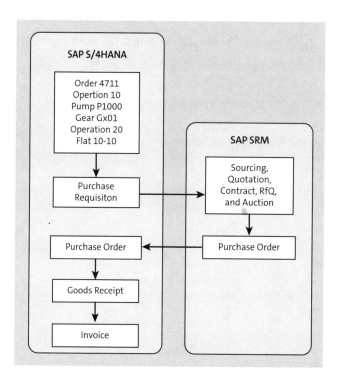

Figure 7.47 SAP SRM Integration: Classic Scenario

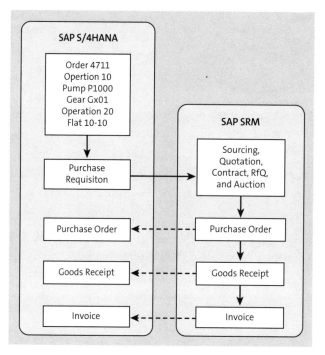

Figure 7.48 SAP SRM Integration: Enhanced Classic Scenario

In the enhanced classic scenario, the subsequent processing occurs in SAP Supplier Relationship Management, but the documents arising from goods receipts and invoice receipts are still stored in SAP S/4HANA.

[!]

Setting Classic or Enhanced Scenario?

When you decide whether to use the classic scenario or the enhanced classic scenario to process materials in SAP S/4HANA, use the customizing function **Integration with other SAP Components** • **Supplier Relationship Management** • **Plan Driven Procurement** • **Maintain Profile for External Procurement** or **Control External Procurement**. This function will help you direct the procurement process to a system other than the SAP S/4HANA system, depending on the product group and purchasing group of the material.

These are likely to be the most important of the SAP systems that are used by other departments and interact with SAP S/4HANA Asset Management.

When you implement SAP S/4HANA Asset Management, however, you may have to deal with other systems used by other departments and with which you must exchange data. Such cases are the subject of the next section.

7.3 Integration with Non-SAP Systems

Implementing SAP S/4HANA Asset Management often leads to situations in which existing non-SAP systems (for example, from the area of plant data collection, construction, and building services) must be coupled with SAP S/4HANA Asset Management. These non-SAP systems can be different general categories of systems, such as the following:

- **Operations monitoring systems**
  Process control systems, network monitoring systems, building control systems, and diagnostic systems

- **Operations information systems**
  CAD systems, GIS systems, and network information systems

- **Systems for entry of services performed**
  Systems for measurement acquisition

7.3.1 Operations Monitoring Systems

Operations monitoring systems monitor, control, regulate, and optimize operations events online and nearly in real time. Depending on the industry and purpose, the following systems are used:

- **Process control systems**

  Process control systems are used in process industries like chemicals, pharmaceuticals, and food. They help monitor, control, regulate, and optimize a technical process. Examples include refrigeration in a plant that produces ice cream and the throughput speed of a unit that dries powder.

- **Manufacturing execution systems**

  Manufacturing execution systems (MES) are used in discrete manufacturing and differ from production planning systems in SAP S/4HANA because an MES is directly connected to automated production in real time. As a result, MES enable control of production in real time, including controlling electronic control stations and traditional data entry such as production data collection (PDC), machine data acquisition (MDA), and personnel data entry (PDE).

- **Building control systems**

  Building control systems are used in building management and monitor, regulate, and optimize a technical process within a building, such as air conditioning or ventilation.

- **Network monitoring systems**

  Network monitoring systems are used in the energy industry and by major energy consumers. These systems help monitor, control, regulate, and optimize the production and distribution of electricity. Another form of network monitoring system is used in telecommunications to monitor, control, and optimize telecommunications networks.

- **Diagnostic assemblies**

  In addition to the complete systems just mentioned, diagnostic assemblies exist for individual units like robots, flexible manufacturing cells, vehicles, and elevators. The assemblies can recognize, diagnose, and register errors automatically. Examples include the lack of hydraulic pressure in an elevator, a slowing down of the rotational speed of a robot, and the lack of pressure in a vehicle's brake system.

Operations monitoring systems provide a variety of data related to a process, building, assembly, or infrastructure. You have two ways of transmitting the information from your operations monitoring systems to an SAP system:

- **RFC connection**

  With the first option, a direct remote function call (RFC) connection links the operations monitoring system and the SAP system (see Figure 7.49).

- **SCADA systems**

  An indirect connection is established using SCADA (supervisory control and data acquisition) systems, which perform a filtering function. SCADA systems filter out data relevant to maintenance and thereby protect the SAP system from being flooded with data. SCADA systems also establish communications between one or more process control systems and the SAP system (see Figure 7.50).

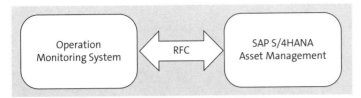

Figure 7.49 Direct Connection to SAP S/4HANA

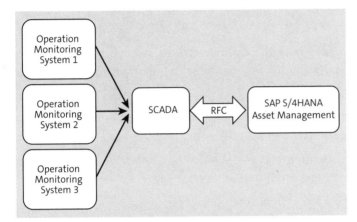

Figure 7.50 Indirect Connection to SAP S/4HANA

The plant maintenance-production control system (PM-PCS) interface is a basic element of SAP S/4HANA Asset Management for recording data from external systems. This data not only includes not only data from operations monitoring systems but also data captured with mobile devices (laptops and barcode readers). Using this interface, you can transfer measurements and counter readings from upstream systems to the SAP system.

How can you use the PM-PCS interface with SAP S/4HANA Asset Management?

- **Performance-based maintenance planning**
  The PM-PCS interface supports performance-based maintenance planning, where the next maintenance date is recalculated based on transferred counter readings (see Chapter 5, Section 5.5 and Section 5.6).

- **Condition-based maintenance**
  The PM-PCS interface enables you to work with condition-based maintenance, where malfunction messages are issued based on transferred measurements (see Chapter 5, Section 5.8).

- **Documentation**
  The measurement documents that are created form the basis for documentation of the actual situation for reports on asset security, work safety, and environmental protection (see Chapter 3, Section 3.11.4).

- **Consumption billing**
  The measurement documents then can be used as the basis for consumption billing when managing real estate (Section 7.1.9).

[!]

> **Data Transfer with the PM-PCS Interface**
>
> The PM-PCS interface is a flexible instrument for transferring measurements and counter readings from upstream systems to SAP S/4HANA Asset Management and processing them further there.

In addition to systems that intervene directly in operations, systems that support the construction and building of operating facilities are also important to plant maintenance.

7.3.2   Operations Information Systems

Essentially, operations information systems involve CAD systems (computer-aided design) and GIS systems (geographical information systems).

CAD systems are used, for example, in the following areas:

- In asset construction as diagrams for piping and instrumentation (P&I diagrams, see Figure 7.51 [Aucotec AG, see *https://www.aucotec.com*])
- In facility management as building plans, room specifications, and surface usage
- In construction for developing complex devices (industrial robots and airplanes, for example)

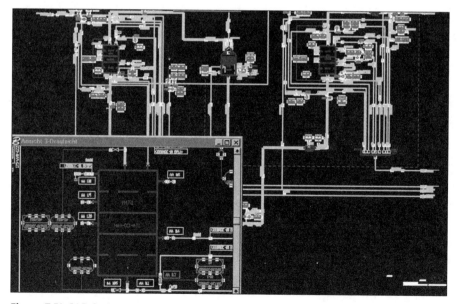

Figure 7.51 CAD System

Common CAD systems like AutoCAD, MicroStation, and CATIA have certified interfaces to the SAP system.

GIS systems exist in different forms: as country information systems, land information systems, environmental information systems, and other systems. From a plant maintenance perspective and concerning your connection to SAP systems, the most important GIS systems are network information systems (NIS). The NIS is an instrument for capturing, managing, analyzing, and presenting data on operating resources from network topology. Utilities and waste disposal companies work with these kinds of GIS. The primary use is for geometric and graphic documentation of connections (see Figure 7.52 [see *https://www.mettenmeier.de/en/products-and-solutions/small-world-gis/*]).

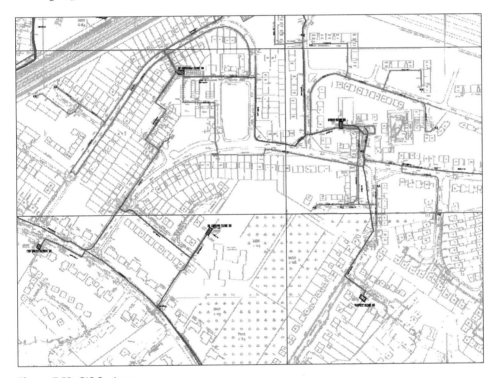

Figure 7.52 GIS System

Familiar GIS manufacturers like GE Smallworld, Bentley, Intergraph, ESRI, and others have SAP-certified GIS interfaces.

What do these CAD and GIS interfaces do? The functional scope varies from manufacturer to manufacturer, but here are some of the available options:

- Create, change, search, and display equipment
- Create, change, search, and display functional locations
- Create, change, search, and display materials

- Create, change, search, and display BOMs
- Synchronize classification data
- Create, change, search, and display a notification or order and visualize the status of the notification/order

The interfaces can use different approaches to technical implementation:

- You are working in your CAD or GIS application, and you want to see the data in the SAP system for a graphical object you have selected in the CAD or GIS system. You start a query on the SAP application server and see the result in an SAP window and in the CAD or GIS application.
- You see the result in a CAD or GIS window.
- You are working in your SAP system and want to see the CAD or GIS drawings for a highlighted technical object (equipment or functional location). You start a query on the SAP application server, and the CAD or GIS application loads the drawing.
- You can use the business connector, the GIS business connector, or SAP Process Integration (PI) for technical realization.

[+] **Extreme Differences in Functional Scopes**

Because the functional scope of your CAD or GIS system and technical realization can vary quite considerably, ask the manufacturer for more detailed information.

7.3.3   Service Specifications and Entry of Services Performed

When you deal with business processes on the basis of service specifications with vendors (see Chapter 6, Section 6.3.4), you have two ways of exchanging data with your vendors.

Exchanging Data over Interfaces

SAP offers interfaces that you can use to transfer data to your vendors or to receive data from vendors and record it in the SAP system. You can also use the interfaces to import predefined, standard service specifications to storage devices in the SAP system.

You can exchange the following data with the service providers (see Figure 7.53):

- Requests for quotations and quotations
- Service master data
- Contracts and purchase orders
- Service entry sheets

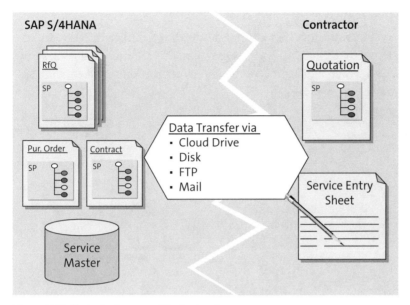

Figure 7.53 Data Exchange with Contractors

The following media are available for exchanging data:

- Cloud drives
- File Transfer Protocol (FTP)
- SAP Mail and Internet email
- Storage media such as CDs or USB drives

Exchanging data with contractors enables you to simplify and accelerate the business processes for entry of services performed. Data is exchanged via the following steps:

1. You send contractors the service specifications as purchase orders, contracts, or service master records (for example, by email).
2. After the services are performed, the vendor creates a service entry sheet and sends it to you, for example, by FTP or via a cloud drive.
3. You record the service entry sheet in the SAP system.
4. You then perform a formal acceptance of the services.

[!]

No Expenses for Entry of Services Performed

If you use data exchange with contractors, the greatest advantage is that you incur no expenses for entering the services performed.

Entry of Services Performed via the Internet

If you connect to your contractors via web application, they can fill in the service entry sheets and transfer them to your SAP S/4HANA system. This requires your contractors being equipped with a web application or an SAP Fiori app connected to your SAP S/4HANA system (see Figure 7.54).

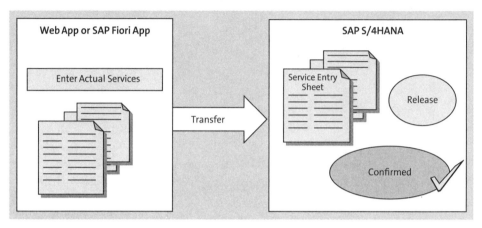

Figure 7.54 Web Connection to SAP S/4HANA

The data entered on the intranet/Internet is transferred to SAP S/4HANA via the BAPI ENTRY SHEET.CREATE.

7.4   Summary

In this chapter, integration with SAP S/4HANA was discussed, as well as integration with other SAP systems and with non-SAP systems. Integration within SAP S/4HANA includes the following functionality:

- Materials management concerning reservations, purchase requisitions, goods receipts, goods issues, refurbishment of spare parts, and subcontracting
- Production planning and control, such as a planning board
- Quality management using the calibration process for test and measurement equipment
- SAP Environment, Health, and Safety Management creating safety measure lists and safety plans
- Financial accounting, such as vendor invoices
- Asset accounting with respect to connecting technical objects to the asset master
- Controlling concerning cost centers, costing, overhead costs, and settlement
- Real estate in regard to connecting technical objects to real estate objects

- SAP Human Capital Management for SAP S/4HANA in terms of assigning personnel numbers to technical objects, notifications, orders, operations, and confirmations
- Sales and service, using maintenance technicians for customer services

Integration with other SAP systems was discussed for the following solutions:

- SAP NetWeaver Master Data Management for checking materials and vendors
- SAP Master Data Governance for checking materials, vendors, equipment and functional locations
- SAP Supplier Relationship Management for the purchasing process as a classic scenario or as an enhanced classic scenario

For non-SAP systems, integration was discussed in terms of the following:

- Operation monitoring systems (e.g., PCS or MES) to transfer usage information
- Operating information systems (e.g., CAD or GIS) to exchange master data
- Service specification systems to exchange purchasing and specification data

Chapter 8
Plant Maintenance Controlling

Controlling can be understood in several different senses. Operational controlling is used to control current business processes, whereas analytical controlling is intended to support tactical and strategic decision making. This chapter looks first at the active control of plant maintenance tasks and then also considers the options and limits of the tools SAP provides for reporting.

Controlling should be understood as a generic concept, containing elements of guiding, influencing, managing, checking, and regulating, depending on which application or task has to be mastered. Given this definition, the term *plant maintenance controlling* refers to the instruments for guiding and checking plant maintenance processes.

This chapter begins by discussing what, exactly, plant maintenance controlling involves. The next section covers the tools for obtaining information about your plant maintenance system. Finally, the chapter concludes with information on the SAP tools available for budgeting.

8.1 What Plant Maintenance Controlling Involves

Depending on the time period and scope involved, different levels of plant maintenance controlling may occur (see Figure 8.1):

- **Operational controlling (level ❸)**
  Operational plant maintenance controlling is a short-term approach and is thus focused on daily business (for example, third-party outsourcing of plant maintenance contracts, damage analysis of machines, utilization of workshops).

- **Tactical controlling (level ❷)**
  Tactical controlling has a medium-term focus and relates to business processes (for example, change of business processes, negotiations, and preparing contracts with service companies).

- **Strategic controlling (level ❶)**
  The long-term goals are the subject of strategic controlling and are used to ensure the survival of the company (for example, outsourcing the service department, attracting new markets).

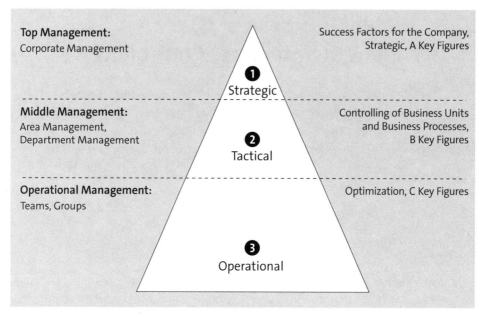

Figure 8.1 Controlling Levels

You know the term *controlling* from the commercial sector, where controlling is a central organizational unit with a critical business function. In the technical area, controlling is not usually established in its own organizational unit but has a central corporate function. Table 8.1 outlines a few major differences between commercial controlling and technical controlling.

Commercial Controlling	Technical Controlling
Oriented toward commercial organizational structures (for example, company code, controlling area, cost centers, profit centers)	Oriented toward technical organizational structures (for example, machines, work centers, tools, materials)
Evaluates commercial posting objects (for example, general ledger accounts and cost elements)	Evaluates technical processing objects (for example, orders, damage notifications, and purchase orders)
Determines cost values/key figures only	Determines technical and cost values/key figures

Table 8.1 Comparison of Commercial and Technical Controlling

Commercial controlling is oriented toward commercial organizational structures; accordingly, the focus of commercial controlling is on organizational units like company codes, controlling areas, cost centers, and profit centers. On the other hand, *technical controlling* is oriented toward the technical conditions and evaluates units like machines, systems, materials, and work centers.

In *commercial controlling*, commercial posting objects like general ledger accounts and cost elements are evaluated, while *technical controlling* focuses on technical processing objects like notifications, orders, confirmations, purchase orders, goods movements, or deliveries.

Finally, only costs, expenses, revenue, income, and other business key figures are calculated in the context of *commercial controlling*, whereas cost figures and technical figures are the focus of *technical controlling*. Figure 8.2 shows an overview of the plant maintenance controlling tasks.

Provide Data Basis for Decision-Making ...
- Operational Decisions (e.g. external or internal order processing)
- Tactical Decisions (e.g. Changing Business Processes)
- Strategic Decisions (e.g. Defining the PM Strategy)

... regarding View Levels ...
- Measure-Based Controlling (e.g. per Order)
- Object-Based Controlling (e.g. per Functional Location)
- Period-Based Controlling (e.g. per Month)

... at Different Aggregation Levels ...

  Lists → Reports → Key Figures

... at Different Intervals ...

  Daily → Weekly → Monthly → Annually

... using Different Media
- Paper
- IT Applications (SAP S/4HANA, SAP Business Warehouse, SAP Lumira Discovery ...)
- Mail, Workflow
- Mobile Apps, SAP Fiori Apps

Figure 8.2 Controlling Levels

You can distinguish between the following topics depending on the view level of plant maintenance controlling:

- **Measure-based controlling**
  Here, the focus is on either a single measure (for example, recalculating an order) or a group of measures (for example, analyzing a revision).

- **Object-based controlling**
  The focus here is on a technical object (for example, the ranking list of equipment by actual costs or damage analysis of functional locations).

- **Period-based controlling**
  Here, the focus is on analyses over a certain time period (for example, use of replacement parts per month or planned costs per week).

The information calculated and provided in the context of plant maintenance controlling is at different aggregation levels:

- **Lists**
  For example, lists of open notifications, of pending maintenance plan orders, and of blocked equipment

- **Reports**
  For example, the total plant maintenance costs per functional location and the number of malfunction reports per month

- **Key figures**
  For example, the relation between planned and actual costs, mean time between failures (MTBF), and average time per order

Depending on your needs, information must be available and/or provided in different cycles.

- Daily (a list of open malfunction reports)
- Weekly (a weekly schedule of maintenance plan orders)
- Monthly (total costs incurred)
- Annually (a comparison of budget with actual costs)

Depending on the role of an employee in the company and his technical possibilities, information must be available or distributed in different media:

- **Paper**
  If access to online data is not desired, not possible, or not necessary, the information must be provided as a printout.

- **SAP systems**
  The information can be called online in SAP S/4HANA or SAP Business Warehouse (SAP BW) or also via SAP Fiori launchpad or SAP Lumira, discovery edition, if needed promptly and if direct access should be possible.

- **Email or workflow**
  The information is sent via email or using a workflow if information is desired online but the SAP system is not accessible.

- **Mobile devices**
  External sales technicians must be able to access the desired information via mobile devices, for example.

The following questions are thus the focus of the following two sections, respectively:

- What tools does SAP offer you for obtaining information, and how do you use them?
- What tools does SAP offer you for budgeting, and how do you use them?

8.2   SAP Tools for Obtaining Information

The tools listed in this section do not affect business processes and their mapping in the SAP system. Their task is, rather, to provide you with the necessary information so that you can make organizational decisions on that basis—every day, you'll have plenty of decisions to make, which refer in turn to different time horizons:

- **Operational decisions**
  In operational plant maintenance controlling, for example, decisions are made about the composition of a weekly schedule, the external assignment of an order, or tasks for capacity leveling.

- **Tactical decisions**
  In tactical plant maintenance controlling, for example, decisions are made about tasks as warranties expire, about scrapping a machine, about tasks to avoid errors, about the conclusion of service agreements, and about decisions for or against a particular type of machine.

- **Strategic decisions**
  In the course of operational plant maintenance controlling, for example, decisions are made about the outsourcing or reintegration of a task area or about structural changes.

> **An IT System Does Not Make Any Decisions**   [!]
>
> You need to make the right decisions yourself, but the IT system can provide you with the necessary information.

As tools for obtaining information, the following sections introduce you to the options and limits of SAP List Viewer, QuickViewer, logistics information system (LIS), SAP Business Warehouse, and SAP Lumira, discovery edition.

8.2.1   SAP List Viewer

SAP List Viewer does not present information to you as a rigid list, allowing you instead to adapt lists flexibly to meet your own information requirements. All SAP S/4HANA Asset Management lists are available with SAP List Viewer technology. The following lists are available:

- List of *functional locations* (Transactions IL05, IL06, and IH06)
- List of *reference functional locations* (Transactions IL15 and IH07)
- List of *equipment* (Transactions IE05 and IH08)
- List of *vehicles* (Transactions IE36 and IE37)

- List of *object links and object network* (Transactions IN15, IN16, IN18, and IN19)
- List of *measurement documents* (Transactions IK17 and IK18)
- List of *material serial numbers* (Transaction IQ08)
- List of *materials* (Transaction IH09)
- List of *measuring points* (Transactions IK07 and IK08)
- List of *reference measuring points* (Transactions IK07 and IK08)
- List of *notifications* (Transactions IW28 and IW29)
- List of *tasks* (Transactions IW66 and IW67)
- List of *actions* (Transactions IW64 and IW65)
- List of *notification items* (Transactions IW68 and IW69)
- List of *orders* (Transactions IW38 and IW39)
- List of *order operations* (Transactions IW37 and IW49)
- Combined order/operation list (Transactions IW37N and IW49N)
- List of *components* (Transactions IW3K and IW3L)
- List of *permits* (Transactions IPM2 and IPM3)
- List of *confirmations* (Transaction IW47)
- List of *goods movements* (Transaction IW3M)
- List of *maintenance plans* (Transactions IP15 and IP16)
- List of *maintenance items* (Transactions IP17 and IP18)
- List of *counter readings* (Transaction IP24)
- List of *maintenance task Lists* (Transactions IA08 and IA09)
- List of *maintenance task lists and operations* (Transaction IA30)
- List of *shift notes* (Transaction SHN4 or Transaction ISHN4)
- List of *shift reports* (Transaction SHR4 or Transaction ISHR4)

When you use SAP List Viewer, processing always takes place in the following sequence: selection ❶ → basic list ❷ → further processing ❸ (see Figure 8.3).

This section introduces SAP List Viewer using an example of an order list (Transaction IW38). However, the information provided in this section can be applied to any of the available lists.

Selection

When you call up a list, you see a selection screen containing all selection options, which extend over two to four pages, depending on the list and the screen resolution. Experience shows that the options listed on the second or subsequent pages are rarely needed. Therefore, the first step should be to create a selection variant.

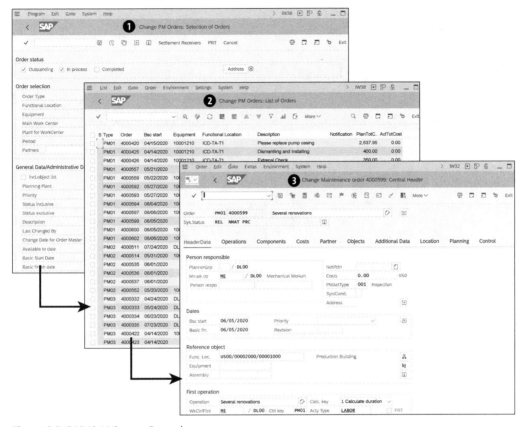

Figure 8.3 SAP List Viewer: Procedure

[+]

Creating a Selection Variant

I recommend that you create a selection variant which contains one page of selection conditions at most. All selection variants that you create in the future should also follow this basic rule.

You create a selection variant by saving the selection screen by first clicking the 🖫 button and then making active and purposeful use of the checkboxes in the **Hide field** column on the following screen (see Figure 8.4).

Since list variants can significantly contribute to increasing usability and user acceptance (for more details, see Chapter 10), be sure to create other selection variants.

You can call up for your list variants by clicking the 🗇 button, which is found on the initial screen of every list. You can also display a list of selection variants in this manner and select the desired variant. Since, however, this list can become quite extensive over time, here is the next practical tip for you.

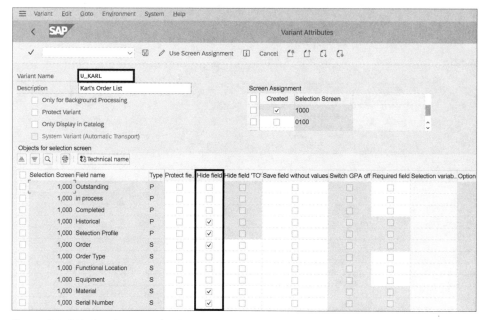

Figure 8.4 SAP List Viewer: Selection Variant

[+]

Default Variant U_USERNAME

The selection variant that you use most often should be named U_ followed by your SAP user name (see Figure 8.4). This selection variant is then automatically displayed when you call up the list.

For each selection field, you can use the following selection options:

- **Single value**
  You can search for a single value (for example, order type PM01) or multiple single values (for example, order types PM01, PM05, and PM10).

- **Interval**
  You can search for an interval (for example, order types PM01–PM05) or multiple intervals.

- **Wildcard search**
  You can do a wildcard search (for example, order type PM* selects all order types that start with PM).

- **Exclusion of elements**
  You can exclude values and intervals (for example, not order types PM03 and PM05–PM08).

- **Clipboard**
  You can paste in search values from the Windows clipboard.

A particularly useful capability is that you can define selection variables for dynamic date calculation, where, depending on the current date, the from/to date selection is dynamically calculated based on the selection option chosen (see Figure 8.5).

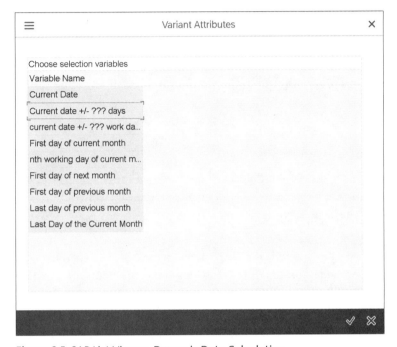

Figure 8.5 SAP List Viewer: Dynamic Date Calculation

Let's explore the following example scenario: On September 1, you set the list with the selection *Start date equals current date 180 days and +60 days*. Thus, on September 1, you would be selecting the dates from March 4 to October 31.

Dynamic Date Calculation

You can use **dynamic date calculation** selection variables to determine the selection date of the list dynamically.

Activating Monitors If Possible

Some lists (but not all) allow you to activate a monitor. Depending on the parameter selected (for example, basic date), the list entries are then red, yellow, or green (for example, red for overdue orders, yellow if the start date has been reached but the finish date has not been reached yet, and green for future orders).

You activate the monitor by making a selection in the field **Reference Field for Monitor** (see Figure 8.6).

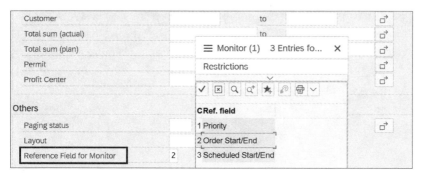

Figure 8.6 SAP List Viewer: Monitor

List Display

If you now start the list, you'll see an initial basic list created on the basis of the selections and settings you made (see Figure 8.7).You now have the following options for adjusting the layout of the list to fit your own requirements:

- **Showing and hiding fields**
  You can show additional fields or hide the visible fields; almost all fields of the object to be evaluated are available. For functional locations and equipment, you can also show fields from their classifications.

- **Sorting**
  You can sort by a single criterion (for example, by date) or by several criteria (for example, by cost center and then, within the cost center, by date).

- **Calculating totals**
  For value and quantity fields (for example, actual costs), you can calculate totals and display subtotals (for example, for each order type).

- **Showing counters**
  The LOG_EAM_CI7 business function offers a new function, one that had been requested by users for a rather long time: If it is enabled, you can select the **Counter** field. The heading then displays the total number of list entries, and you can form subtotals for the counter, for example, if you want to know how many orders are listed for which order type (see the **Counter** column in Figure 8.7).

- **Changing column width**
  You can optimize the column width.

- **Searching**
  You can search, within a list, for a certain term (for example, "leaks"), which can be especially useful for large lists.

- **Filtering**
  You can filter a displayed list (for example, display only entries with system status **Rel**).

- **Performing ABC analysis**
  You can perform an ABC analysis based on a key figure (for example, an ABC analysis of orders relative to actual costs).

- **Generating graphical representations**
  You can generate a graphical representation (for example, a bar chart with the number of orders for each order type).

- **Using display variants**
  You can save your settings as a display variant.

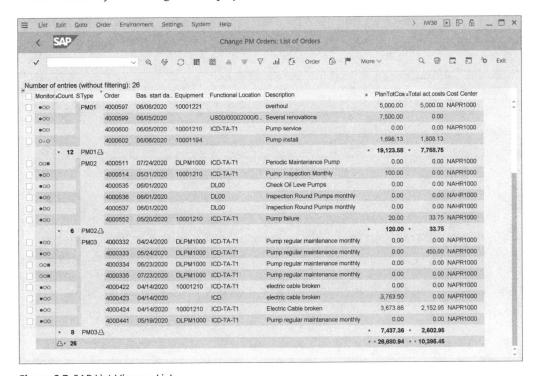

Figure 8.7 SAP List Viewer: List

[+]

Presetting for Display Variant

You should mark the most frequently used display variant as a presetting.

Further Processing

If you now have the list in the form you want, the following options are available to you for further processing:

- **Details**
  You can select a certain line and call the database object (for example, a certain order so that you change the date in that order).

- **Mass processing**
  You can select several lines and perform the same function for all of the lines selected (for example, print all orders selected or technical complete all orders).
- **Mass change**
  In conjunction with list processing, the **Mass change** function can be used for requests and notifications that can change, in a single step, practically any field in all of the objects selected (e.g., to assign new dates or a new responsible work center).
- **Send**
  You send the list via SAP mail.

[+]
No Email Button?

If you cannot find a button for sending a list (for example, ✉), use the function **More • List • Save • Office**.

- **Download**
  You can save the list in any current Microsoft Office format and process it further there (for example, download the order list to Excel in order to display it there using pivot functions).

[+]
Schedule Lists as a Periodic Job

You can also schedule lists as a periodic job, which then runs automatically at regular intervals and performs certain follow-up functions (for example, an email containing the maintenance plan orders for the coming week can be sent to the production managers).

Limitations

The lists in SAP List Viewer are predefined in SAP S/4HANA Asset Management for certain database objects. As a result, SAP List Viewer has some limits: on one hand, in cases where you require information or fields not defined in SAP List Viewer. A *material* list, for instance is available, but SAP List Viewer cannot show the storage bin where each material is stored.

·On the other hand, displaying information or fields for different database objects in a single list is not possible. Thus, notification information (for example, damage codes) and order information cannot be displayed together in a single-level list.

SAP provides one tool that is both easy to use and offers greater flexibility: Quick-Viewer.

8.2.2   QuickViewer

QuickViewer (Transaction SQVI or menu path **More · System · Services · Quick Viewer**) starts where SAP List Viewer reaches its limits and provides options for exceeding those limits:

- QuickViewer allows you to display any database field in a list. Thus, you can, for example, create a list of materials with their storage bins.
- You can use QuickViewer to link database tables. For instance, you could show notification and order information together in a single list.
- QuickViewer enables you to answer ad hoc questions that cannot be answered using SAP List Viewer, for example, what equipment lacks a maintenance plan or which functional location can access which general maintenance task list via the construction type.

Let's look at QuickViewer based on a specific example: One of my customers wanted to know how many actual work hours were being spent on which damage code and in which work center. This requirement could not be met using the techniques of SAP List Viewer because information was needed from notifications, from orders, and from confirmations. The creation of a QuickView helped in this case.

Database Sources

When you create a new QuickView, you are asked for the names of the database tables. The determination of the relevant database tables is the most difficult part of creating a QuickView; to search by the desired table, you have several options:

- You can navigate via the application hierarchy (press F4 help in the field **Table · SAP Applications**) and work through the hierarchy to the desired database table.
- You can navigate via the information system (press F4 help in the field **Table · Info System**) of the QuickViewer and search for a keyword (see Figure 8.8).

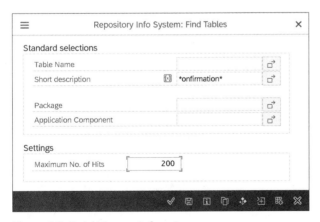

Figure 8.8 QuickViewer: Infosystem

> **[!]** **Keyword Search in the Information System**
>
> The keyword search in the information system of the QuickViewer is *case-sensitive*, that is, distinguishing between uppercase and lowercase letters. Thus, if you are looking for the table of time confirmations in plant maintenance and aren't sure of the name of the table in the short text, searching for "*onfirmation*" is the best solution.

- The simplest and safest way to go seems to be to call the original transaction (for example, Transaction IW41 for time confirmations) and use the F4 help • **Technical Info** (see Figure 8.9).

Figure 8.9 QuickViewer: Technical Field Information

In our specific example, the tables **QMEL** (notification), **QMFE** (notification items), **AFRU** (order confirmations), and **CRHD** (work center) would be relevant. These tables are now linked via a table join (see Figure 8.10).

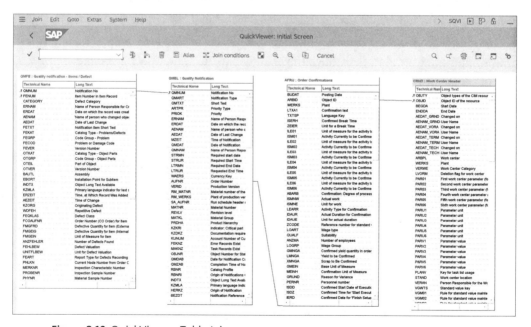

Figure 8.10 QuickViewer: Table Join

Surface and Results

The QuickViewer surface provides you with various options for list layout and list processing (see Figure 8.11):

- **Selecting fields**

  You can select lists by any fields (for example, by damage code or period of time).

  You have the same options as for SAP List Viewer (single, multiple, range selections, exclusion).

- **Displaying fields**

  You can display any fields (for example, damage code, notification number, order number, work center, date, actual time).

- **Calculating totals**

  You can calculate totals for value and quantity fields (for example, actual time).

- **Sorting and forming subtotals**

  You can sort and form subtotals based on one or more criteria (for example, damage code and work center) and then display individual lines or the totals lines only.

- **Using output formats**

  You have various output options (for example, output as SAP List Viewer or download to an Office format).

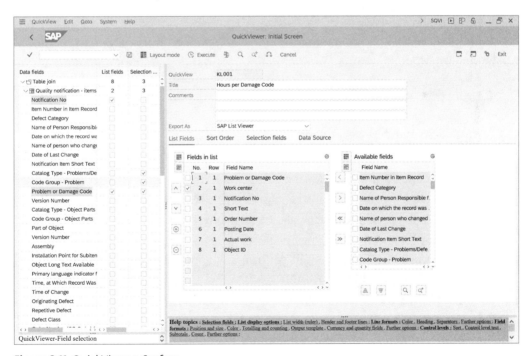

Figure 8.11 QuickViewer: Surface

- **Creating graphical representations**
  You can format the results as a graphic.
- **Sending the list**
  You can send the list as an SAP mail or as an email.

Figure 8.12 shows possible QuickViewer results.

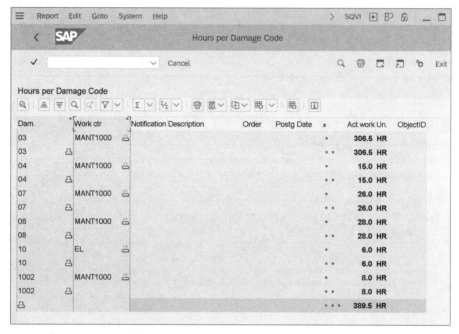

Figure 8.12 SAP QuickViewer: Result

Limitations and their Negotiation

However, QuickViewer also has its limits, as already indicated:

- You cannot use the operational database object from the list of QuickViewer; thus, you cannot view the individual confirmation directly in our example.
- QuickViewer itself is user-dependent, that is, only the user who created a QuickView can execute it.
- Using QuickViewer, you cannot perform any arithmetic operations, for example, calculating totals, differences, or ratios.
- QuickViewer cannot be connected to the correction and transport system. As a result, you cannot create a QuickView in a development system and then transport it to your production system after successful testing.

These restrictions should not mean that the QuickViewer is unsuitable in principle for you. Various ways to overcome these limits include the following:

- **ABAP program**
  QuickViewer generates an ABAP program in the background. If you want to insert authorization checks, mathematical calculations, or other functions, you can do it directly in this program. Similarly, the ABAP program can be transported to another system. The ABAP program generated has a name similar to the following: AQTGSYS-TQV000033QKL001=======. The AQ is fixed, as is SYSTQV; TG is a code for the client, and 000033 stands for the thirty-third user to create a QuickView in this system and client. QKL001 is the name the user gave the QuickView, and ====== are fill characters.

- **Calling by different users**
  To make a QuickView accessible to multiple users, convert the QuickView to an SAP query by starting Transaction SQ01 (Create Query) and call up the function **Query · Convert Quick View** (see Figure 8.13).

Figure 8.13 Convert QuickView to Query

- **Transporting to the production system**
  Both the queries and the generated programs are connected to the correction and transport system and can thus be transported to the production system using Transaction SE10 (Transport Organizer).

- **Transaction**
  In addition, you can create a transaction with an additional authorization check for SAP Query or QuickViewer via Transaction SE93 (Maintain Transaction), which is also connected to the correction and transport system.

Now let's look at another tool provided by SAP S/4HANA for obtaining and presenting information: the logistics information system (LIS).

8.2.3   Logistics Information System

The logistics information system (LIS) is used for logistics applications in SAP S/4HANA and has specific variant names like the purchase information system, inventory control, and so on. In plant maintenance, the PMIS (plant maintenance information system) is used. All logistics information systems have the same structure (see Figure 8.14).

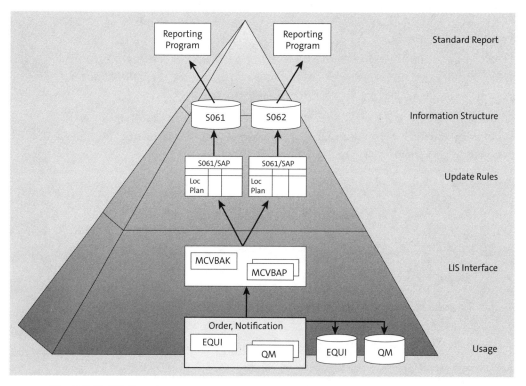

Figure 8.14 LIS: Overview

In the LIS, information structures are filled on the basis of update rules using transfer programs. These information structures are standalone databases, separate from the operational databases. The LIS makes the transition from an OLTP to an OLAP system easy. An online transaction processing system (OLTP) is a system in which business processes like work order cycle are handled. An Online analytical processing system (OLAP) is a system in which only evaluations and analyses are carried out.

[!]   **The LIS as an OLAP System**

By nature, the logistics information system is an OLAP system. As a result, reports from the LIS are significantly more efficient and faster than reports from operational databases.

The LIS is supplied with information via the LIS interface.

> **Synchronous or Asynchronous?** [!]
>
> Using the customizing function **Logistics Information System (LIS) · Logistics Data Warehouse · Updating · Updating Control · Activate Update · Plant Maintenance**, you can control whether an information structure should be supplied synchronously (that is, in parallel with posting to the operational database) or asynchronously.

The following sections will discuss the relevant topics regarding the LIS: information structures, standard reports available in the PMIS, flexible reports, and the early warning system, SAP EarlyWatch.

Information Structure

Information structures are the focus of the LIS. An information structure consists of the following three elements (see Figure 8.15):

- **Key figure**
  A key figure is the value to be aggregated (for example, the number of orders, actual costs, breakdown duration, or number of notifications)

- **Characteristic**
  A characteristic is a value used to aggregate data (for example, per plant, piece of equipment, order type, or cost center)

- **Period**
  A period specifies the rhythm of aggregation (normally monthly, but daily or weekly periods are also conceivable, for example)

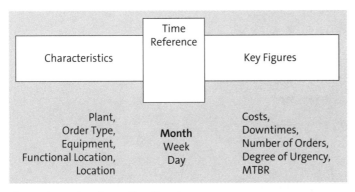

Figure 8.15 LIS: Information Structure

Let's visualize these three components of an information structure through the virtual multidimensional information cube shown in Figure 8.16, as follows:

- Drawer ❶ contains the key figure *number of orders for equipment 1,000 of order type PM01 in the month of January.*

- Drawer ❷ contains the key figure *number of orders for equipment 1,000 of order type PM02 in the month of January.*
- Drawer ❸ contains the key figure *number of orders for equipment 1,000 of order type PM01 in the month of February.*
- Drawer ❹ contains the key figure *number of orders for equipment 1,001 of order type PM01 in the month of January.*

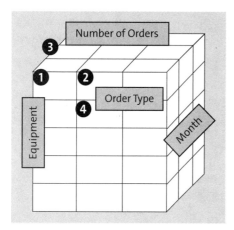

Figure 8.16 LIS: Multidimensional Information Cube

Standard Reports of the PMIS

Standard reports are provided by SAP. SAP provides the following standard reports and transaction codes for plant maintenance:

- Transaction MCI1 (Object Class Report)
- Transaction MCI2 (Manufacturer Report)
- Transaction MCI3 (Location Report)
- Transaction MCI4 (Planning Group Report)
- Transaction MCI5 (Damage Report)
- Transaction MCI6 (Object Statistics)
- Transaction MCI7 (Failure Analysis)
- Transaction MCI8 (Cost Analysis)
- Transaction MCIZ (Vehicle Consumption Report)

You can find more details in Appendix B, Section B.4, which provides a list indicating which standard report is based on which information structure and which characteristics and key figures are in each information structure.

Next, let's walk through the workings and various options of PMIS, based on an example cost analysis (information structure S115, Transaction MCI8).

The list in Figure 8.17 shows you the estimated, planned, and actual costs for each order type for a selected time period.

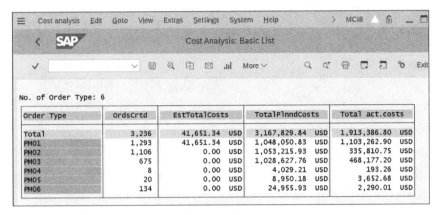

Figure 8.17 LIS: Transaction MCI8: Cost Analyses

The displayed basic list can be changed online (that is, without starting any other report and without restarting the present report) using the following functions:

- **Selecting key figures**
  You can display other key figures from a predefined list of figures (for example, completed orders).

- **Switching drilldown**
  You can switch drilldown, that is, show the list according to a different characteristic (for example, not by order type, but by equipment).

- **Sorting**
  You can sort the list according to any key figure (for example, sort equipment by actual costs in descending order to obtain a hit list).

- **Inserting comparison values**
  You can compare the values in the list against comparison values (for example, from the previous year) and calculate percentage deviations.

- **Displaying as a time series**
  You can show the list as a tabular time series (for example, to see how many orders were made in each month).

- **Using statistical functions**
  You can use the list to calculate statistical functions like ABC analyses, correlations, or segmentations. Figure 8.18 shows a cumulative curve based on an ABC analysis.

- **Drilldown by new characteristics**
  You can drill down by a different characteristic (for example, from the total value for each order type, you can display which equipment is affected).

- **Further list processing**
  You can print, save as an Office file (e.g., csv or txt), or email the list.

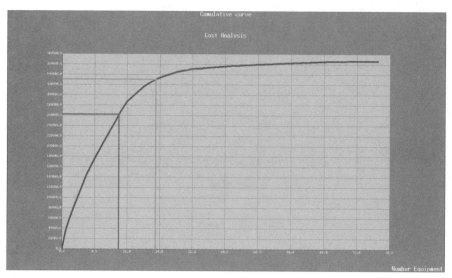

Figure 8.18 LIS: ABC Analysis

However, the standard reports in the LIS have their limits:

- **Unappealing layout**
  The presentation of results does not have an up-to-date layout. (For example, SAP List Viewer is not used here.)

- **Rigid information structures**
  The information structures are rigid and cannot be changed.

- **Deficits in technical reports**
  The PMIS plant maintenance information system has weaknesses in terms of technical reports.

- **No calling of operational database objects**
  You cannot call the operational database objects from the total values. Thus, if you have found an unusual cost value, you cannot directly display the order that led to it.

- **No cross-application key figures**
  The key figures do not apply to all applications. For instance, you cannot calculate a key figure like *maintenance rates* because the actual costs come from SAP S/4HANA Asset Management and the replacement value comes from asset accounting in SAP S/4HANA Finance.

- **No arithmetic operations**
  You cannot perform any arithmetic operations in the LIS, for example, calculating totals, differences, or ratios.

Flexible Reports

You can avoid the restriction preventing arithmetic operations if you define flexible reports. With flexible reports, you define your own evaluation structure either on the basis of an operational database table (for example, orders) or on the basis of an information structure (for example, cost analysis) (see Figure 8.19).

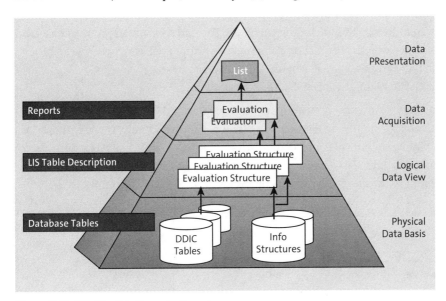

Figure 8.19 LIS: Flexible Reports Overview

Based on this report structure, you can define reports, within which, in turn, you can define your own key figures. For example, you can define the key figure *average order costs* as the ratio of two predefined key figures: *actual costs* and *number of orders*.

Defining Your Own Reports

Using flexible reports, you can evaluate any DDIC tables and information structures, thus allowing you to define your own key figures and calculate them.

Figure 8.20 shows you an example, output as an Excel table.

Characteristics	Total act.costs	Orders created	average
** PM01..PM08	1.913.386,84 USD	3.236	591,28
* PM01	1.103.262,91 USD	1.293	853,26
* PM02	335.810,74 USD	1.106	303,63
* PM03	468.177,23 USD	675	693,60
* PM04	193,26 USD	8	24,16
* PM05	3.652,69 USD	20	182,63
12/1998	91,75 USD	1	91,75
03/2004		1	
06/2006		1	
04/2013	735,73 USD	4	183,93
05/2013	2.825,21 USD	13	217,32
* PM06	2.290,01 USD	134	17,09

Figure 8.20 LIS: Flexible Analysis

Early Warning System

The early warning system, SAP EarlyWatch, is integrated into the LIS. The LIS provides the data that is analyzed by SAP EarlyWatch. SAP EarlyWatch can be used in any information system in logistics, including the PMIS. The early warning system is based on the information structures—information that can be updated in structures can be analyzed with SAP EarlyWatch. You can use SAP EarlyWatch both to display defined alarm situations and to highlight specific data in a population.

You can use the early warning system interactively in standard reports or run it periodically in the background (see Figure 8.21). When used interactively, the warning situations are highlighted in color in the reports or are filtered, which allows you to detect alarm situations at an early stage. In periodic analysis, a list of exception data is automatically sent to the desired recipients by fax, by email, or via a workflow.

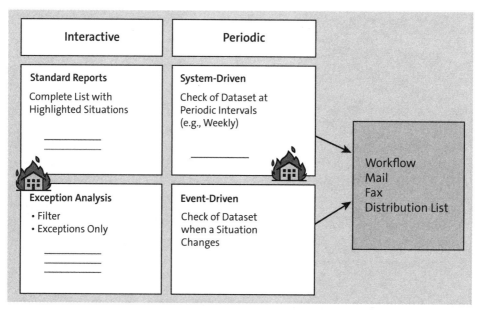

Figure 8.21 LIS: SAP EarlyWatch System Overview

[+]

Proactive Instead of Reactive

Using the early warning system, you can turn the PMIS—if used correctly—into a proactive system. The early warning system allows searches for exception situations, thus helping to detect and correct threatening errors early.

Perhaps, you'd like to be notified by email if the actual costs per month for a piece of equipment exceed a threshold of 10,000 USD. To this end, you would use Transaction MC=E to create an *exception*, which contains the characteristics *equipment* and *month* and includes the key figure total actual costs. Next, you would define a threshold value of 10,000 USD and set subsequent processing as an email notification, which you schedule as a daily job using Transaction MC=N. Figure 8.22 shows the result.

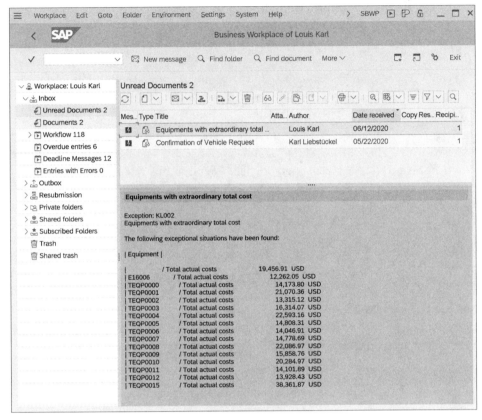

Figure 8.22 LIS: Mail with Exception Notification

The LIS provides a whole series of—frequently underestimated—possibilities but also has some serious disadvantages. The main disadvantages of the PMIS are its inflexibility and the fact that SAP is no longer developing it. A more detailed list of strengths and weaknesses can be found in Section 8.2.4 comparing the LIS and SAP Business Warehouse in a comparative view. SAP has built SAP Business Warehouse as a strategic system for the entire analytical area.

8.2.4   SAP Business Warehouse and SAP BW/4HANA

In the first sections of this chapter, you learned about some tools that you can use to provide maintenance-specific information. Why do we need SAP Business Warehouse (SAP BW) or SAP BW/4HANA as another technical platform for information provision? Several reasons include the following:

- Reporting with SAP BW or SAP BW/4HANA relieves SAP S/4HANA.
- Standardized reporting tools for company-wide data are available in SAP BW and SAP BW/4HANA.
- SAP BW and SAP BW/4HANA work closely with Microsoft Excel.
- You can evaluate across applications in SAP BW.
- SAP BW and SAP BW/4HANA are *the* strategic analysis products from SAP.

You will discover further advantages of SAP BW and SAP BW/4HANA compared to the SAP S/4HANA reporting tools in the course of this section. However, SAP BW and SAP BW/4HANA are supposed to supplement the SAP S/4HANA world, rather than replace it. Many basic ideas and concepts from the LIS have been incorporated in SAP BW and SAP BW/4HANA. In contrast to the LIS, however, SAP BW and SAP BW/4HANA allow reporting on data not just from operational ERP applications, but also from other business applications. Moreover, data can be extracted from external sources like databases, online services, and the Internet and analyzed. The following description refers to SAP BW, but the same applies to SAP BW/4HANA.

Concept and Basic Terms

The components and basic terms of SAP BW can be seen in Figure 8.23.

SAP BW provides a wide variety of extraction, transformation, and loading (ETL) functionality, which supports data transfers at the application and file level. ETL allows you to load data from practically any source. Source systems can be:

- SAP systems (also other SAP BW systems)
- Flat files in which the metadata is maintained manually and the data is sent to SAP BW via a data interface
- Database management systems from which the data can be loaded without using an external extraction program but via DB Connect from a database supported by SAP
- External systems in which the data transfer works through BAPIs

The *persistent staging area* is the physical input buffer for data from the source systems in SAP BW. The transferred data remains unchanged and is initially stored in the source system.

A *DataStore* object (DSO) is a data store in which the data is stored at the document level. DSOs are generally used for cleansing and consolidating data inventories, since data inventories often originate from different source systems.

The *Data Warehousing Workbench* is the work environment for the administrator. Using the functions of the Data Warehousing Workbench, SAP BW can be configured, controlled, and administrated.

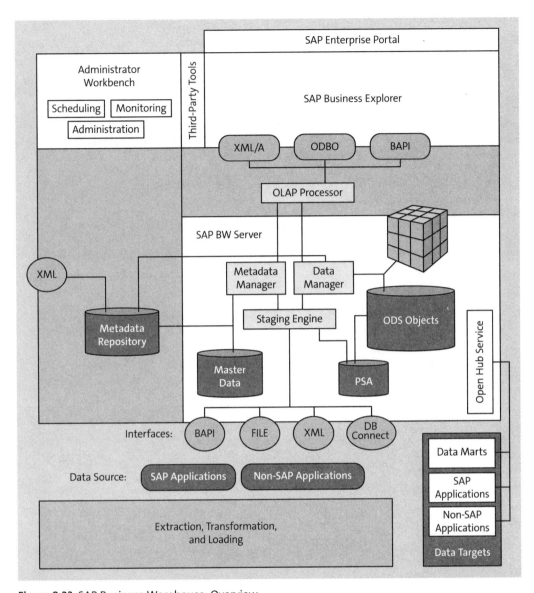

Figure 8.23 SAP Business Warehouse: Overview

The central data containers on which reports and analyses are based in SAP BW are called *InfoCubes*. For example, in plant maintenance, the following InfoCubes may be defined:

- Orders
- Notifications
- Measurement results
- Equipment and functional locations

463

Like the LIS, SAP BW works with *key figures* and *characteristics*. Typical key figures in plant maintenance are, for example, the number of orders, the number of breakdowns, MTBF (mean time between failures), and the actual costs. Typical characteristics in plant maintenance are, for example, cost centers, order types, equipment, and planner groups.

SAP *Business Explorer* (SAP BEx) is the component of SAP BW that provides reporting and analysis tools, for example, to define queries. SAP BEx enables access to the information in SAP BW in different ways:

- Using SAP Enterprise Portal (for example, via an iView)
- Using the intranet or Internet (web application design)
- Using mobile devices such as smartphones or tablets

In the interest of time, we can't go into the details of data procurement, modeling, and evaluation in SAP BW.

Business Content

Under the term *business content*, SAP BW provides preconfigured objects that can support your departments with predefined solutions.

Business content includes the following objects:

- **Extractors**
  Extractors are part of the SAP system and determine the range of data to be supplied to SAP BW.
- **InfoObjects**
  InfoObjects are comprised of characteristics and key figures.
- **InfoCubes**
  Key figures and characteristics are stored in the InfoCubes.
- **Queries**
  Queries generate reports and views of the InfoCube.
- **Web templates**
  The analyzed data for web applications is provided in web templates.
- **Roles**
  The exact reports needed by the user for his or her work are provided using roles.

For an overview of what goes into business content, Table 8.2 provides a list of important InfoCubes with their characteristics and key figures from the business content in SAP S/4HANA Asset Management.

InfoCube	Examples of Characteristics	Examples of Key Figures
Equipment installation in functional locations	• Equipment • Functional location	• Duration of installation • Number of installations
Notifications	• Material • Plant • Functional location • Equipment	• Number of notifications • Number of notifications, on time • Number of measures • Processing time • Downtime • Number of downtimes
Notifications with linear asset management data	• Starting point • End point	• Number of notifications • Number of notifications on time • Number of measures • Processing time • Downtime • Number of downtimes
Notification items	• Plant • Functional location • Equipment • Damage code • Object parts	• Frequency • Total
Notification causes	• Equipment • Functional location • Assembly	• Number of causes
Orders	• Order type • Equipment • Functional location • Maintenance activity type • Planner group • Plant	• Processing time • Number of orders • Completed orders • Planned orders • Unplanned orders
Order costs	• Order • Partner object • Cost element • Controlling area	• Amount • Quantity • Currency

Table 8.2 Examples of InfoCubes with Key Figures and Characteristics

InfoCube	Examples of Characteristics	Examples of Key Figures
Order operations	■ Order type ■ Equipment ■ Functional location ■ Maintenance activity type ■ Planner group ■ Work center ■ Plant	■ Planned work ■ Actual work ■ Unit
Order scheduling	■ Order type ■ Calendar year ■ Equipment ■ Functional location	■ Planned work ■ Actual work ■ Number of orders completed on time ■ Processing time
Measurement results	■ Equipment ■ Functional location ■ Assembly	■ Counter reading ■ Measurement reading
Vehicle consumption data	■ Vehicle ■ Calendar year	■ Distance traveled ■ Fuel volume ■ Actual costs

Table 8.2 Examples of InfoCubes with Key Figures and Characteristics (Cont.)

Additional InfoCubes include:

■ Notification actions

■ Notification measures

■ Notification response time

■ Notification items with linear asset management data

■ Notification costs with linear asset management data

■ Orders with commitment line item

■ Backlog/stock shortfalls

■ Degree of completion of order operations

■ Reworking of orders and notifications

■ Maintenance task list simulated costs

■ Maintenance plan simulated costs

■ Work centers, available capacities and capacity requirements

■ Budgeting data

[!]

Using InfoCubes as Templates for Your Own Content

SAP delivers InfoCubes with the most important key figures and characteristics as business content. You can also create your own InfoCubes.

Based on the InfoCubes included in the business content, the following queries are also delivered:

- Equipment installation and removal
- Notification report
- Damage report
- Cause report
- Measure report
- Action report
- Failure report
- Object errors
- Orders
- Order operations
- Planned/actual cost deviation
- MTTR (mean time to repair)
- MTBR (mean time between repair)
- Pending work
- Overdue work
- Planned maintenance work
- Schedule fulfillment
- Measurement results
- Vehicle costs per kilometer
- System availability
- Stock shortfall
- Capacity load utilization
- Degree of completion
- Rework
- Budget proposal
- Budget comparison
- Budgetary control
- Equipment failure

[!]

Using Queries as Templates for Your Own Content

SAP delivers current queries as business content. However, you can also create your own queries.

Other business content is provided:

- For roles (for example, plant maintenance technician)
- For web templates (for example, special queries)
- For DataSources (for example, hierarchy and functional locations)

If you start a query, SAP BW creates a basic list for you (see Figure 8.24). You can change the displayed basic list using the following functions without starting any other report and without restarting the present report:

- **Adding other key figures**
  You can display other key figures from a predefined list of key figures (for example, number of notifications).

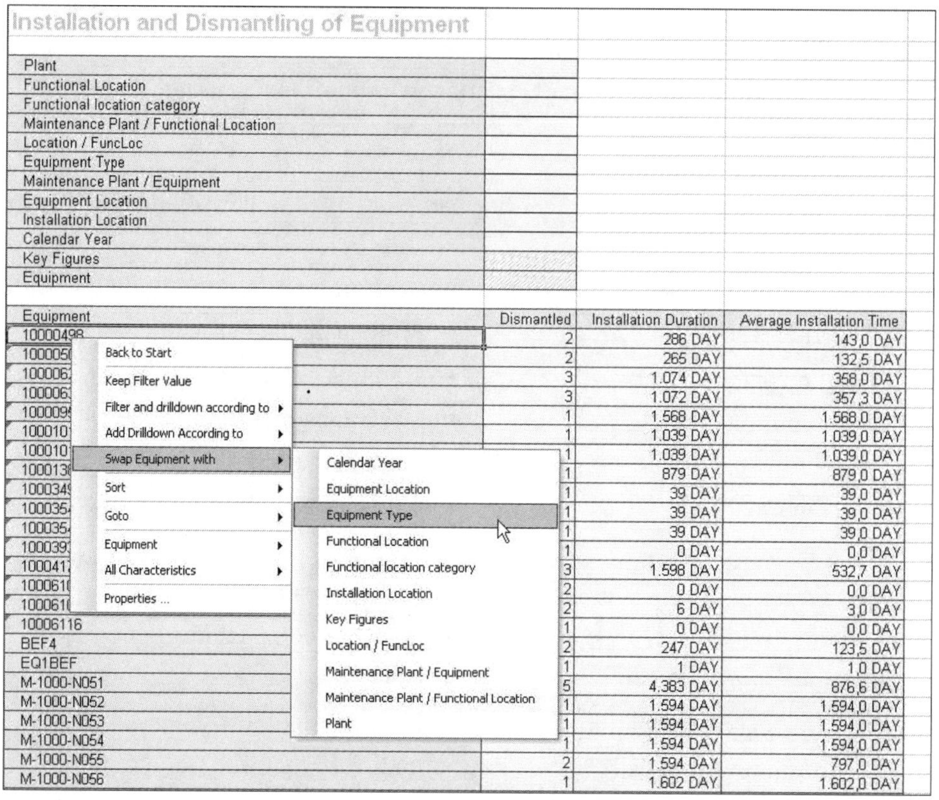

Figure 8.24 SAP Business Warehouse: Table Example

- **Switching views**
  You can switch views, that is, show the list according to a different characteristic (for example, not by functional location, but by work center).

- **Sorting**
  You can sort the list according to any key figure (for example, sort equipment by number of malfunctions in descending order to obtain a hit list).

- **Including comparison values**
  You can compare the values in the list against comparison values (for example, from the previous year) and calculate percentage deviations.

- **Displaying graphical time series**
  You can show the list as a graphical time series (for example, to see how many malfunctions or orders have accrued in which month, see Figure 8.25).

- **Creating statistics**
  You can use the list to calculate statistical functions like ABC analyses, correlations, or segmentations.

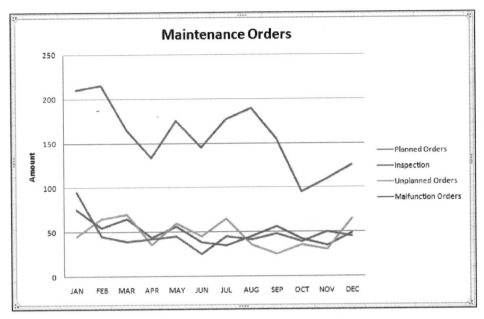

Figure 8.25 Time Series

- **Performing drilldown**
  You can use the drilldown technique to view by a different characteristic (for example, from the total value for each functional location, you can display which equipment is affected).

- **GEO data**
  Using extended navigation options (geographical drilldown), regional relationships can be highlighted (for example, the information for an energy provider as to the states or cities in which malfunctions are occurring). Figure 8.26 shows an example of this kind of SAP BEx map.

- **Access to SAP S/4HANA Asset Management data**
  Using a RemoteCube, you can access original data in SAP S/4HANA Asset Management from SAP BW.

- **Exceptions**
  By defining exceptions, you can use SAP BW as an early warning system.

- **Various display options**
  You can present the data based on MS Excel with the SAP BEx Analyzer, on the web in SAP BEx web applications, or on mobile devices using SAP BEx mobile intelligence.

- **Alert Monitor/Ticker**
  On the web, you have other functions available, for example, the alert monitor or the ticker.

Figure 8.26 SAP Business Warehouse: Geo Data Analyses Example

While extensive, we have not listed all the options that SAP BW has to offer. To list all the possibilities would go beyond the scope of this book.

Now, you may ask yourself whether you should use SAP BW or the LIS. We will help you answer that question next by directly comparing the two tools.

Comparison of the LIS and SAP Business Warehouse

What are the differences and similarities between the LIS and SAP Business Warehouse?

- The LIS is integrated into SAP S/4HANA, while SAP BW needs a separate system, which you have to administer.
- As mentioned in the documentation and in flyers, you can also import data from an external system into the LIS, but we have never done this in practice. On the other hand, importing and aggregating data from different systems is a necessity in SAP BW as a company-wide business intelligence product.
- Both solutions are in the SAP price list and are available without any additional licensing fees.
- The introduction and use of the PMIS is generally a decision made by a specific department. Thus, the use of the PMIS can be designed and defined within a normal SAP S/4HANA Asset Management implementation project.

- On the other hand, introduction and use of SAP BW is an enterprise-wide decision. An overall design must be created, ranging from system operations to be used by all the business departments involved.

- The LIS and thus the PMIS are no longer being developed, but SAP BW is the strategic product from SAP for the entire analysis area.

- The PMIS uses the normal SAP GUI interface. Most reports are tabular and character-oriented. On the other hand, in SAP BW, you either work with an Excel interface or in a web environment, or you access data with a mobile device. SAP BW also uses many graphical elements (speedometer, curves, columns, maps, and so on).

- Even though the application possibilities are often somewhat underestimated, the functional scope of the PMIS is, in fact, quite limited, while the features of SAP BW seem entirely limitless.

- The PMIS is rigid in its structure. While the PMIS provides certain standard reports, it is difficult to expand its capabilities. For instance, key figures can only be calculated if their data refers to objects in SAP Enterprise Asset Management (SAP EAM).

- SAP BW not only provides broadly defined business content that is continually being further developed, but it is also flexible and extensible with respect to your own reporting needs. Thus, you can determine key figures across applications.

- From the aggregated results from the PMIS (for example, number of orders), you cannot call functions to get more details. On the other hand, you can call a list of details directly from SAP BW.

Table 8.3 shows a clear comparison of the LIS and SAP BW.

LIS	SAP BW
(+) Integrated into SAP S/4HANA	(–) Separate system, separate installation
(–) Data from SAP S/4HANA only	(+) Import of data from external sources
(+) Project at departmental level	(–) Company-wide project
(–) Not being further developed	(+) Strategic business intelligence product from SAP
(–) SAP GUI interface	(+) Excel, web, mobile interface
(–) Restricted functionality	(+) Broad, deep functionality
(–) Rigid structure	(+) Very flexible (for example, cross-application reports)
(–) No navigation to original document	(+) Drilldown capabilities
(+) Free of charge	(+) Included in the SAP S/4HANA license

Table 8.3 Comparison of the the LIS and SAP BW

8.2.5   SAP Lumira, Discovery Edition

SAP Lumira, discovery edition, is an application with which you can visualize data and create presentations of results. You can import, edit, and format data and enrich with it with formulas to obtain new data. You can create visualizations to graphically format the data. You can use the visualizations for your own purposes (e.g., for presentations or for decision making processes) or share them with colleagues and the public.

SAP Lumira, discovery edition, is installed locally and can use local or remote data from one or more data sources. Diagrams created by you are automatically stored and can be printed or shared as email attachments.

The process of creating and editing evaluations in SAP Lumira, discovery edition, is always the same (see Figure 8.27):

- Importing the data as data sets
- Preparing and enriching the data for visualization
- Visualizing the data as diagrams or presentations
- Presenting the data with texts and forms as PDF

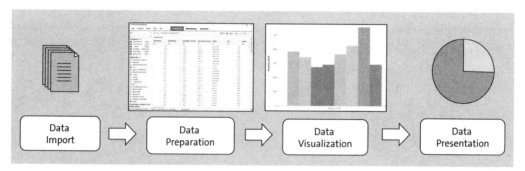

Figure 8.27 SAP Lumira: Overview

Let's explain the process and options of SAP Lumira, discovery edition, using an example from plant maintenance: The cost analysis from the LIS (Section 8.2.3) is supposed to be visualized with several graphics, enriched with further key figures, and published as a presentation.

Data Import

For this purpose, call Transaction MCI8 (Cost Analysis) in SAP S/4HANA Asset Management. Select all key figures and export them as an *.xls* file and save them locally via the menu path **Cost analysis · Export · Transfer to XXL** (see Figure 8.28).

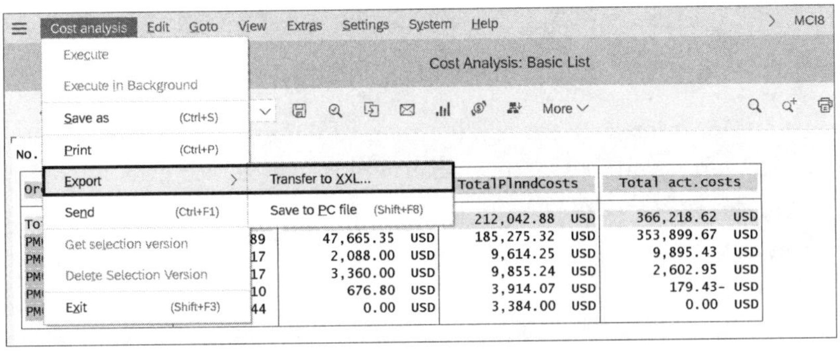

							TotalPlnndCosts	Total act.costs
			212,042.88	USD	366,218.62	USD
	89	47,665.35	USD	185,275.32	USD	353,899.67	USD
	17	2,088.00	USD	9,614.25	USD	9,895.43	USD
	17	3,360.00	USD	9,855.24	USD	2,602.95	USD
	10	676.80	USD	3,914.07	USD	179.43-	USD
	44	0.00	USD	3,384.00	USD	0.00	USD

Figure 8.28 LIS: Export to XXL

SAP Lumira, discovery edition, provides several options for importing the data that you want to analyze (see Figure 8.29):

- **Microsoft Excel**
  You can load Microsoft Excel tables as data sets. For our case study, we selected this function and specified the local storage location of the file.

- **Text file**
  The same applies to text files. You can import *.csv*, *.txt*, *.log*, *.prn*, and *.tsv* files.

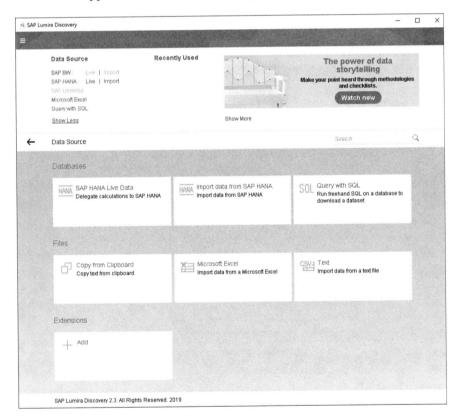

Figure 8.29 SAP Lumira: Import Sources

- **SAP HANA**

  You can download analytic views from an SAP HANA instance and edit them locally. An *analytic view* is a cluster of linked database tables. You can also establish a connection to an SAP HANA instance and edit the analytic views online, that is, you can use SAP Lumira as a frontend tool for the visualization of SAP HANA data.

- **SAP BusinessObjects universe (as extension)**

  You can import data from SAP BusinessObjects universe files. Universe files have *.uns* or *.unx* file formats.

- **SQL query**

  You can create a new data set by manually specifying the SQL coding for a target data source. Among others, Apache, Amazon, Salesforce, or SAP S/4HANA systems can be used as sources here.

- **SAP BW data acquisition (as extension)**

  You can import data from SAP BW data sources. Organizations that generate big data usually store the data in SAP BW InfoCubes.

Data Preparation

Before you visualize data, you may have to take preparatory measures. During the import, SAP Lumira, discovery edition, automatically assigned the data to key figures and dimensions (see Figure 8.30).

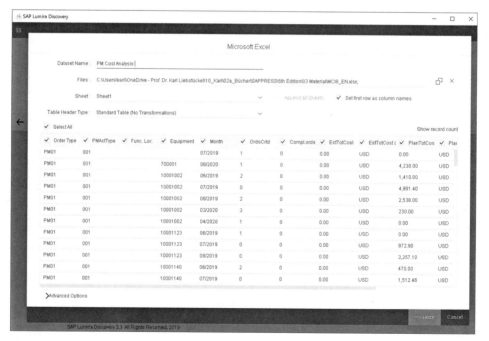

Figure 8.30 SAP Lumira: Data Preparation

Among others, the following preparatory measures could be required:

- You can add a *calculated key figure* to an existing key figure. In our case study, we add the new DIFF key figure, which is supposed to indicate the difference between planned costs and actual costs.

- You can change the *aggregation type* for a key figure. For example, you could change a **Total** to **Average** or **Maximum**.

- If SAP Lumira, discovery edition, does not recognize a *dimension* as a key figure automatically; you could change the dimension into a key figure.

- You could link individual dimensions to *geodata* if you want to perform geographical evaluations at a later stage.

- You could set a fixed *filter* if you only want to evaluate specific data (e.g., only data from 2020 or only orders with the PM01 order type).

Data Visualization

When you finish preparing the data, you go to the board for the visualization of the data (see Figure 8.31), where you'll see the following:

❶ Chart selection

❷ Measures

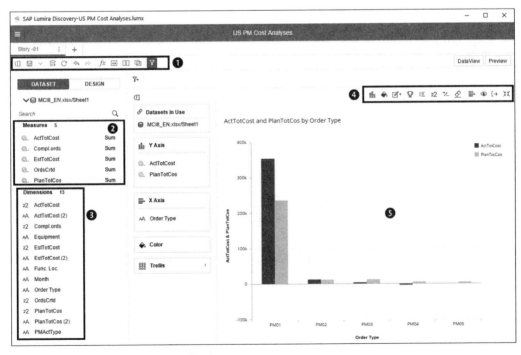

Figure 8.31 SAP Lumira: Data Visualization

❸ Dimensions

❹ Functions

❺ Current chart

This board provides many options for creating the desired graphic, as follows:

- **Chart types**
  First, you select the chart you want to use for the visualization. All common and known chart types are available, including bar charts, column diagrams, line diagrams, pie charts, and tables. Some lesser-known chart types are available for your visualizations: For example, you could use the color intensity of a heat map or various sizes of fields to highlight critical information.

- **Key figures**
  Next, select one or more key figures via drag and drop that you want to visualize.

- **Dimensions**
  Select one or several dimensions via drag and drop.

- **Filter**
  Using the toolbar, you can set filters which include or exclude specific selections. For example, you may want to exclude specific order types or limit the evaluation to specific functional locations.

- **Sorting by dimensions**
  You can also sort by dimensions, for example, by equipment number.

- **Ranking by key figures**
  You can create a ranking by key figures, for example, the top 10 most expensive type of equipment based on actual costs.

- **Chart overview**
  You can also create various charts, which are displayed in the overview of the created charts.

Data Presentation

On the **Design** tab, you can create presentations with one or more pages for your charts. In this tab, you can insert the graphics and enrich them with explanatory text, images, icons, or forms (see Figure 8.32).

Using the [→ button, you can export your presentation to a PDF file.

The following section introduces important plant maintenance controlling techniques that enable budgeting.

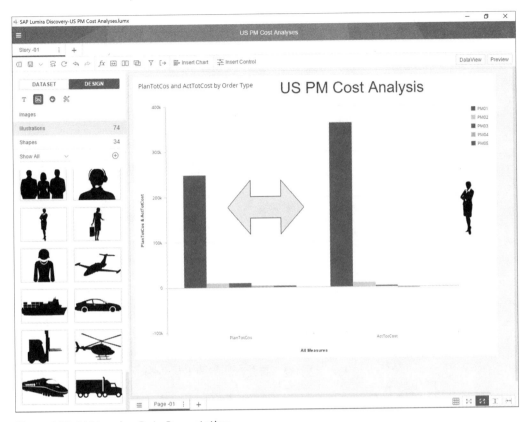

Figure 8.32 SAP Lumira: Data Presentation

8.3   SAP Tools for Budgeting

Depending on which functions and applications are active in your company, you have various options for managing budgets for your plant maintenance tasks: order budgeting, cost center budgeting, budgeting for investment management, budgeting in the project system, and maintenance cost budgeting.

8.3.1   Order Budgeting

The simplest, but at the same time most limited, type of budgeting is order budgeting, with which you can assign a budget to a single order. An order budget is assigned with Transaction KO22, either as a total budget or distributed over several years (see Figure 8.33).

For each actual posting (for example, time confirmations, goods issue), the system checks whether the order budget is sufficient. Depending on the settings in the budget profile, a warning or error message is issued.

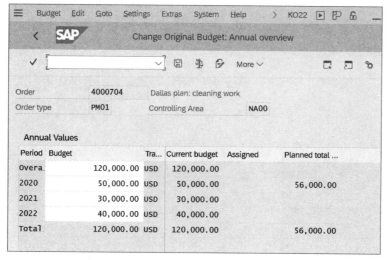

Figure 8.33 Transaction KO22 Order Budgeting

> **Preventing Budget Overruns with Active Availability Control**
> The activation of the availability control prevents the order budget from being overrun by actual posts. The planned costs have no effect on the order budget; that is, while planning the order, the order budget is not checked.

Order budgeting supports you in controlling for an individual order. From my perspective, therefore, the following areas of applications are possible:

- Larger plant maintenance tasks (like moves or renovations)
- Standing orders or long-term orders

Budgeting for all plant maintenance activity would mean that you would have to assign an order budget to each and every order, which is too time-consuming and not normally done.

The prerequisite for an order budget is that you must assign a budget profile to the order type using the customizing function **Configure Order Types**. The budget profile itself and the control of checks on availability (availability control) are set up using the controlling customizing function **Maintain Budget Profiles** and **Determine Tolerance Limits for availability control**.

The settings shown in Figure 8.34 would have the following effects in controlling area NAOO with budget profile PM:

- When 90% of the order budget is exceeded, a warning message would be issued.
- When 100% is exceeded, an email would also be sent to the responsible parties.

- When 105% of the order budget is exceeded, an error message would be issued, which means that the budget could be exceeded by 5% at most.

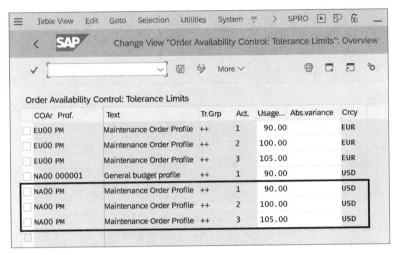

Figure 8.34 Budget Profile for Availability Control

[!]

Order Budgeting: Simple, but Limited, Resource

In all, order budgeting is a simple, but still limited, instrument for budgeting. The budget check for orders can only be activated when the order is not assigned to a budgeting work breakdown structure (WBS) element or investment management program.

8.3.2   Cost Center Budgeting

[!]

Cost Center Budgeting Is Actually Cost Center Planning

A quick note right at the start: Cost center budgeting does not involve budgets with the option of active availability control. Rather, this process is cost center planning with the assignment of planned values; a check as to whether the budget has been exceeded or observed is done via reporting tools.

Planned values can be created for activity types (Transaction KP26 [Change Activity Type/Price Planning]), cost elements (Transaction KP06 [Change Cost Element/Activity Input Planning]), and statistical key figures (Transaction KP46 [Change Statistical Key Figure Planning]). *Cost center budgets* offer the option of distributing a budget at the cost center level, with no restrictions to certain cost or activity types (Transaction KPZ2 [Change Budget Planning]).

Figure 8.35 shows the planning for a receiving cost center at the cost element level and displays the cost elements with which the cost center is debited by settling plant maintenance orders.

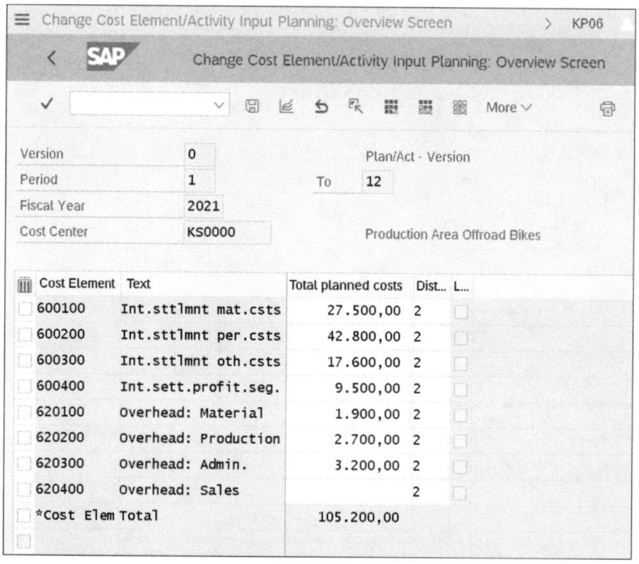

Cost Element	Text	Total planned costs	Dist...	L...
600100	Int.sttlmnt mat.csts	27.500,00	2	
600200	Int.sttlmnt per.csts	42.800,00	2	
600300	Int.sttlmnt oth.csts	17.600,00	2	
600400	Int.sett.profit.seg.	9.500,00	2	
620100	Overhead: Material	1.900,00	2	
620200	Overhead: Production	2.700,00	2	
620300	Overhead: Admin.	3.200,00	2	
620400	Overhead: Sales		2	
*Cost Elem Total		105.200,00		

Figure 8.35 Transaction KP06 Cost Center Planning

Monitoring for adherence to this planned data is done in the context of normal reporting at the cost center level. Figure 8.36 (Transaction S_ALR_87013611 [Cost Centers: Actual/Plan/Variance]) shows a section from such a cost center report, particularly listing how cost centers have been debited by order settlement from plant maintenance.

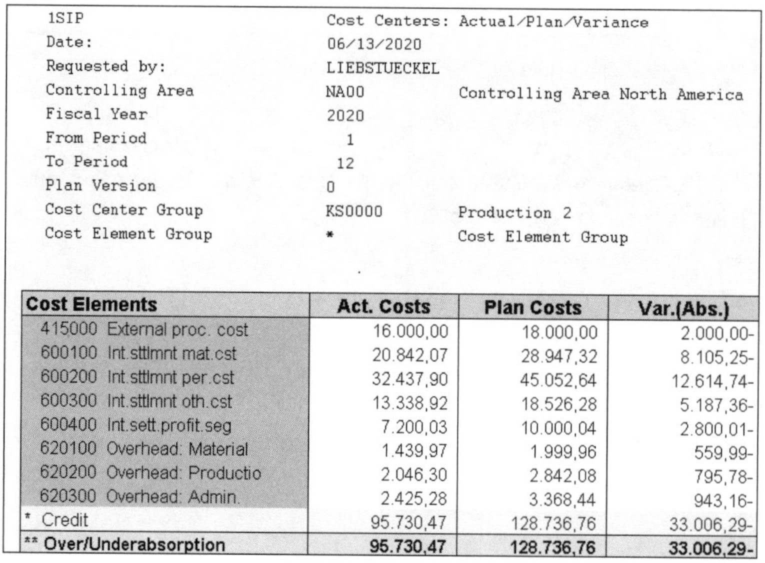

1SIP	Cost Centers: Actual/Plan/Variance	
Date:	06/13/2020	
Requested by:	LIEBSTUECKEL	
Controlling Area	NA00	Controlling Area North America
Fiscal Year	2020	
From Period	1	
To Period	12	
Plan Version	0	
Cost Center Group	KS0000	Production 2
Cost Element Group	*	Cost Element Group

Cost Elements	Act. Costs	Plan Costs	Var.(Abs.)
415000 External proc. cost	16.000,00	18.000,00	2.000,00-
600100 Int.sttlmnt mat.cst	20.842,07	28.947,32	8.105,25-
600200 Int.sttlmnt per.cst	32.437,90	45.052,64	12.614,74-
600300 Int.sttlmnt oth.cst	13.338,92	18.526,28	5.187,36-
600400 Int.sett.profit.seg	7.200,03	10.000,04	2.800,01-
620100 Overhead: Material	1.439,97	1.999,96	559,99-
620200 Overhead: Productio	2.046,30	2.842,08	795,78-
620300 Overhead: Admin.	2.425,28	3.368,44	943,16-
* Credit	95.730,47	128.736,76	33.006,29-
** Over/Underabsorption	95.730,47	128.736,76	33.006,29-

Figure 8.36 Cost Center Report

You can create planned values for the performing cost center and planned values for the receiving cost center. Thus, you can assign planned values for both the performance of the service by the performing (plant maintenance) cost centers and also for the consumption by the receiving (installation) cost centers. The assignment of planned values thus includes the entire plant maintenance activity.

The prerequisite for cost center planning is a *planner profile*, which is created in controlling customizing using the function **Define User-Defined Planner Profiles**. Planner profiles are planning layouts containing data entry forms for different planning options. For example, you can define whether you want to plan at the yearly or monthly level or whether Excel integration is active.

8.3.3 Budgeting by Using Investment Management Programs

Investment management is an area within SAP S/4HANA that supports you in carrying out investments in the true sense (purchasing assets, investing in research and development) but also in plant maintenance programs. The term *investment* is thus understood both in the sense of accounting and also in the sense of any measure that results in costs and should therefore be monitored (for example, plant maintenance projects.)

To budget your investments, projects, and measures, investment programs are available to you via Transaction IM01 (Create Investment Program). An investment program shows the planned or budgeted costs in the form of a hierarchical structure as so-called *program positions* (Transaction IM11 [Create Investment Program Position]). This structure can be arbitrarily defined and is independent of other organizational concepts in the SAP system (for example, business areas, plants, etc.) Within the hierarchy of the investment program, you can plan budgets either from the bottom up or from the top down (Transaction IM32 [Original Program Budget]). Finally, the lowest program position in the hierarchy can be assigned to individual tasks: internal orders, WBS elements, and plant maintenance orders.

Figure 8.37 shows the relationship between investment programs and plant maintenance orders: Plant maintenance orders, like WBS elements or controlling internal orders, can be assigned to an investment management program position and thus to the underlying budget.

The assignment of a plant maintenance order to a position is carried out manually within an order (Transaction IW31, menu path **More · Goto · Investment Program**; see Figure 8.38). However, this assignment can also be done automatically using an assignment key, which you can maintain in customizing.

You allocate the budgets of the investment programs in full and annually using Transaction IM32 (Change Original Program Budget) (see Figure 8.39).

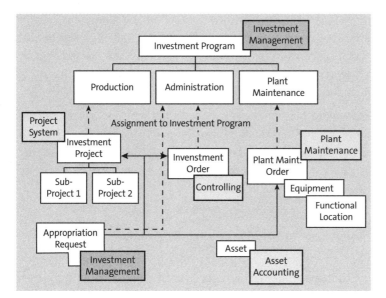

Figure 8.37 Investment Program: Overview

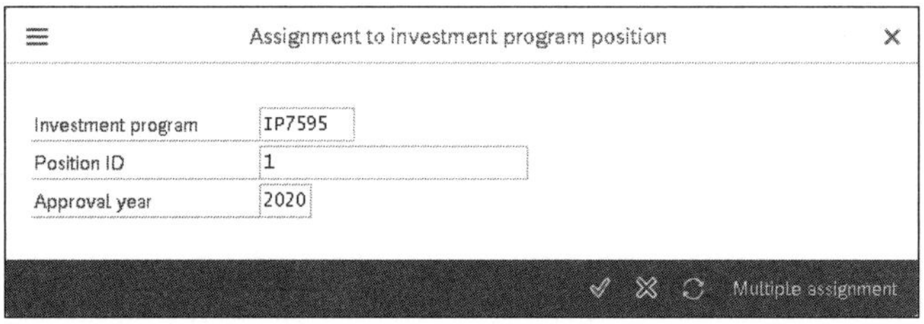

Figure 8.38 Investment Program: Order Assignment

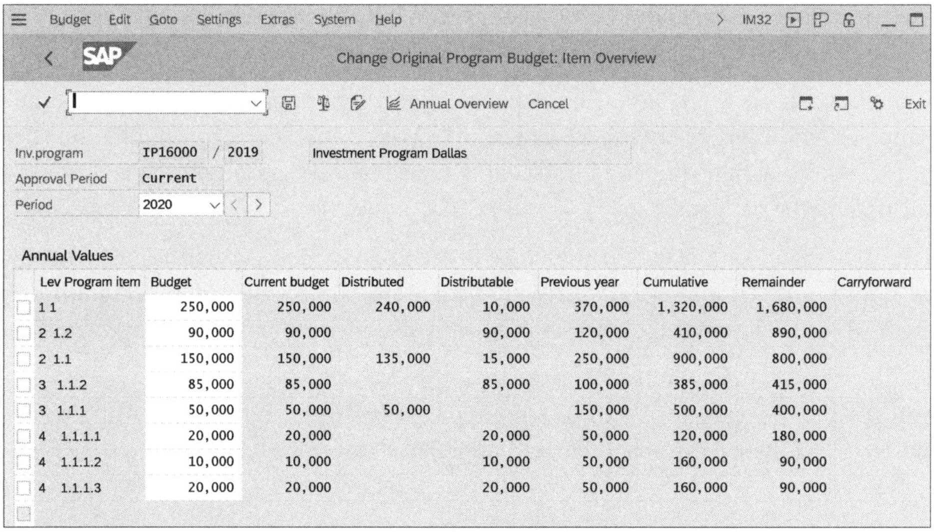

Figure 8.39 Transaction IM32: Investment Program: Budgeting

Costs charged to the order then appear in the budget overview for each program item.

Figure 8.40 (Transaction S_ALR_87012824 [Budget Availability in Program]) shows an investment program with several program items with assigned budgets. The ongoing plant maintenance tasks are then reflected in the allotted orders or in the remaining availabilities.

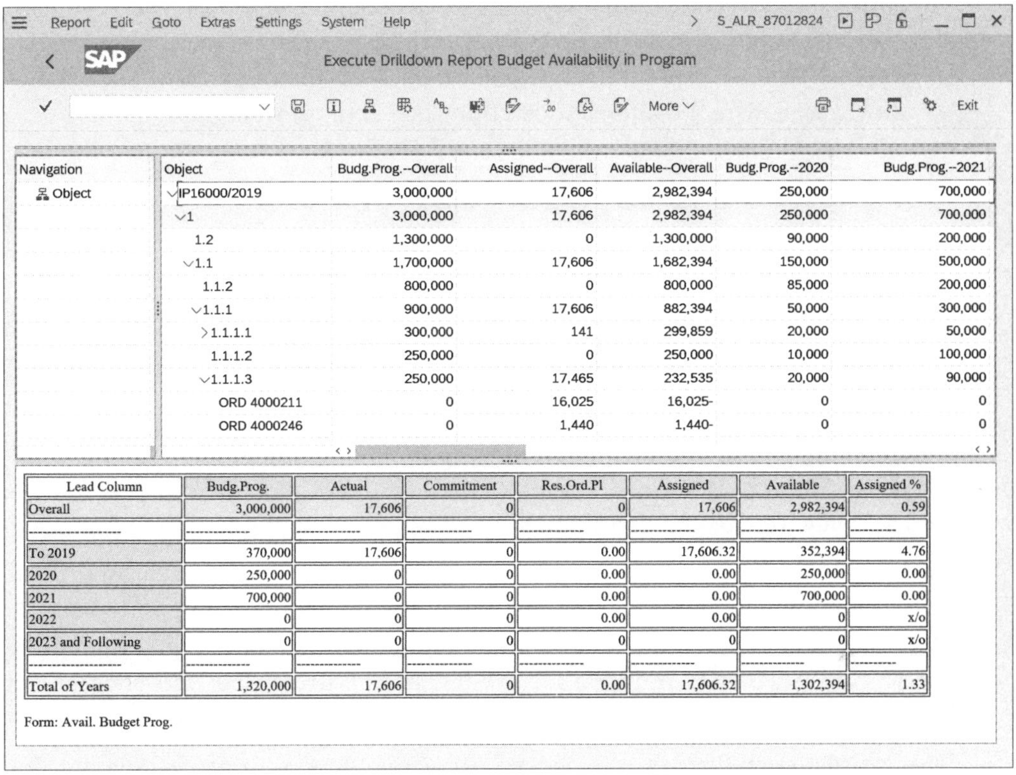

Navigation	Object	Budg.Prog.--Overall	Assigned--Overall	Available--Overall	Budg.Prog.--2020	Budg.Prog.--2021
⚇ Object	⌄IP16000/2019	3,000,000	17,606	2,982,394	250,000	700,000
	⌄1	3,000,000	17,606	2,982,394	250,000	700,000
	1.2	1,300,000	0	1,300,000	90,000	200,000
	⌄1.1	1,700,000	17,606	1,682,394	150,000	500,000
	1.1.2	800,000	0	800,000	85,000	200,000
	⌄1.1.1	900,000	17,606	882,394	50,000	300,000
	>1.1.1.1	300,000	141	299,859	20,000	50,000
	1.1.1.2	250,000	0	250,000	10,000	100,000
	⌄1.1.1.3	250,000	17,465	232,535	20,000	90,000
	ORD 4000211	0	16,025	16,025-	0	0
	ORD 4000246	0	1,440	1,440-	0	0

Lead Column	Budg.Prog.	Actual	Commitment	Res.Ord.Pl	Assigned	Available	Assigned %
Overall	3,000,000	17,606	0	0	17,606	2,982,394	0.59
To 2019	370,000	17,606	0	0.00	17,606.32	352,394	4.76
2020	250,000	0	0	0.00	0.00	250,000	0.00
2021	700,000	0	0	0.00	0.00	700,000	0.00
2022	0	0	0	0.00	0.00	0	x/o
2023 and Following	0	0	0	0	0	0	x/o
Total of Years	1,320,000	17,606	0	0.00	17,606.32	1,302,394	1.33

Form: Avail. Budget Prog.

Figure 8.40 Investment Program: Budget Availability Report

As a result, even in the budgeting process with investment management budgets, monitoring for adherence to budgets is carried out in the context of normal reporting at program item level, which is not active availability control.

Behind the program items, a "real" investment measure can exist that generates an asset under construction. However, this does not have to be the case. You can also create program items simply for statistical reasons in budgeting. From a plant maintenance perspective, you could use the program items for real investment measures, but you could also set them up to manage your plant maintenance budget. Thus, you could budget all your plant maintenance activities together here.

To enable you to budget your plant maintenance tasks using investment management program items, you must execute the following functions in customizing:

- With the customizing function **Define Transfer of Project or Investment Program**, you must control for each order type whether you want to budget with WBS elements or investment programs; you cannot do both at the same time.

- With the customizing functions **Define Relevant Fields for Assignment of IM Program** and **Assign IM Assignment Keys to Order Types**, you must define, for example, whether the cost center of the reference object or the responsible work center should be used for the automatic determination of the program item.

[!] **Passive Availability Control Using Investment Programs**

Program items can be used as a simple tool for budget monitoring, but note that program items only provide passive budgetary control. Passive budgetary control means that the system will not warn you when the budget is exceeded. You must check adherence to the budget yourself via reporting.

The next budgeting method, budgeting using WBS elements, is different.

8.3.4   Budgeting Using WBS Elements

WBS elements were already discussed in the context of project-oriented plant maintenance in Chapter 6, Section 6.9.1, as part of the project system (PS) in SAP S/4HANA. WBS elements are normally used to define the construction planning, organization, and control of a project. You can also use WBS elements to carry out pure budget planning and control; in this section, we'll look at them from that perspective.

To use WBS elements, use Transaction CJ01 (Create Project) to define a project (for example, plant maintenance budgeting) and then use Transaction CJ11 (Create WBS Element) to create several levels of WBS elements as a basis for a budgetary structure. The following are possible criteria you can use for orientation:

- **Asset-related**
  For example, each top-level functional location has a budget.

- **Work center-related**
  For example, mechanical workshop, electrical workshop.

- **Activity-related**
  For example, for maintenance, repairs, overhaul.

Budget planning is then normally done in a top-down manner and assigned to the WBS elements of each budget on an annual basis using Transaction CJ30 (Create Original Budget) (see Figure 8.41).

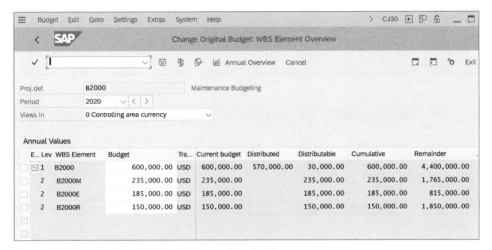

Figure 8.41 Transaction CJ30: WBS Element Budgeting

If you want to distribute budgets on a system basis, you should then enter the WBS element responsible for the budget into the master record of the technical object (see Figure 8.42).

Figure 8.42 Functional Location: WBS Element Assignment

Once you have completed this and set up customizing accordingly, the WBS element is automatically transferred to the order, and thus, the order is assigned to the WBS element. The assignment can be seen in the order on the **Additional Data** tab (see Figure 8.43), where you can also perform a manual assignment or change an existing one.

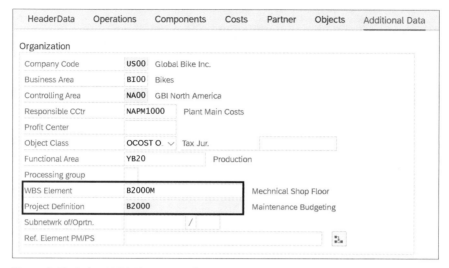

Figure 8.43 Order: WBS Element Assignment

[+]   Changing WBS Assignments Automatically

Assigning orders to WBS elements automatically can be customized by using customer exit **IWO10010** with a custom assignment routine. Depending on the technical object, for example, you can find the right WBS element here for the order type and maintenance activity type. This automatic assignment saves the user time-consuming manual assignment, thus increasing acceptance.

The budget availability check of WBS elements involves both an active and a passive availability check:

- **Active availability check**
  Active availability check means that, for each actual posting (for example, time confirmation, goods issue), the system checks whether the WBS budget is sufficient. Depending on the settings in the budget profile, a warning or error message may be issued.

- **Passive availability check**
  Passive availability check means that the system provides you with sufficient reporting options to check your budgets. Costs charged to the order then appear in the budget overview for each WBS element.

Figure 8.44 (Transaction S_ALR_87013557 [Report Budget/Actual/Variance]) shows a WBS with several elements to which budgets were assigned. Ongoing plant maintenance tasks are then shown in the actual costs and/or the remaining availabilities.

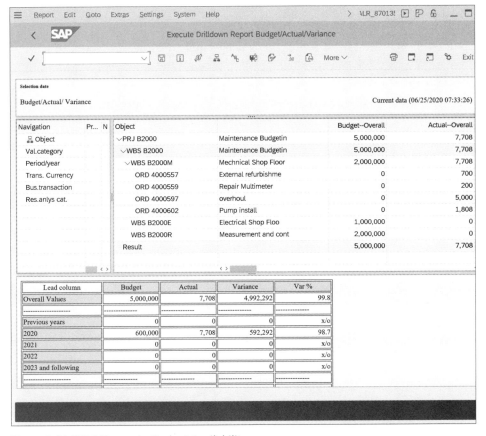

Figure 8.44 WBS Elements: Budget Availability

Behind the WBS elements, either an actual plant maintenance project exists or you can use the elements for purely budgeting purposes in order to manage the ongoing budget. Thus, from a plant maintenance perspective, you can budget all plant maintenance activity using WBS elements.

To budget with WBS elements, the following prerequisites must be satisfied:

- You have assigned your technical objects (equipment, functional locations) a WBS element in the master record.
- You have used the customizing function **Define Transfer of Project or Investment Program** for each order type with an assignment with an "X" to ensure that the WBS elements will be transferred from the master record into the order.
- You have used the customizing function **Maintain Budget Profile** to create a budget profile and assign your WBS elements.
- You have used the customizing function **Define Tolerance Limits** to define the limits for your controlling area and your budget profile at which warning messages and error messages will be generated, thus activating the active availability control.

Active Availability Check with WBS Elements

WBS elements can be an attractive tool for budget monitoring because you have active the availability check, the activation of which prevents the order budget from being exceeded due to actual postings.

With reporting tools, you also have the option of a passive availability check.

Let's come to the last option for managing a plant maintenance budget—maintenance cost budgeting (MCB), a process that was developed especially for plant maintenance.

8.3.5   Maintenance Cost Budgeting

Maintenance cost budgeting (MCB) is a process developed by SAP especially for plant maintenance and its budgeting requirements. However, MCB is not integrated into SAP S/4HANA, which instead uses the SAP Business Warehouse Business Planning and Simulation platform (SAP BW-BPS; see Figure 8.45).

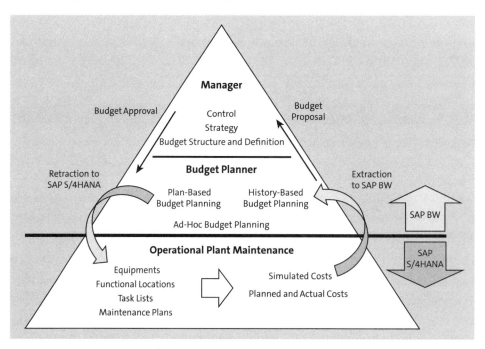

Figure 8.45 Maintenance Cost Budgeting: Overview

MCB is Not Integrated into SAP S/4HANA

You can use MCB only if you have installed SAP BW and have configured SAP BW-BPS. You cannot use MCB with the standard SAP S/4HANA Asset Management component.

Maintenance cost budgeting provides two processes for budget planning—a history-based process and a planned data-based process. Both processes have different planning scenarios, primarily based on the type of data provision:

- **History-based budgeting process**
  For history-based budgeting processes, two kinds of scenarios exist: In a history-based scenario, you can use the actual historical costs of previous periods as the basis for planning; in an ad hoc scenario, you can use freely entered data for budgeting. In the latter scenario, the determination of the data as a basis for planning takes place outside the SAP system (e.g., in Excel tables).

- **Planning data-based budgeting process**
  In the case of a planning data-based budgeting process, we distinguish between a maintenance task list scenario, a maintenance plan scenario, and an ad hoc scenario. The ad hoc scenario, as in the history-based process, is used for free entry of data. Here, too, the determination of the data as a basis for planning takes place outside the SAP system (for example, in Excel tables.) The maintenance task list and maintenance plan scenarios, on the other hand, are based on cost simulation from maintenance task lists or maintenance plans stored in SAP S/4HANA Asset Management.

In customizing, you can set up which of the budgeting processes may be used. Scenarios can also be used in combination.

> **Transferring Actual Costs and Simulated Costs Automatically**
>
> Maintenance cost budgeting supports you in your budget planning by providing history-based actual costs and simulated costs from maintenance task lists and maintenance plans.

Maintenance cost budgeting supports both top-down budgeting and bottom-up budgeting (see Figure 8.45) The manager plans the strategic budget for the area and sends a budget draft to the responsible budget planner (top-down budgeting process.) The planner plans the budget based on historical or simulated data and then sends it back to the manager for approval (bottom-up budgeting process.)

The definition is carried out using report and budgeting groups, with which you create a hierarchy within plant maintenance budgeting that makes it possible for you to map the desired process of budget planning and approval.

> **Simplify Budgeting with Predefined Reports and Budgeting Groups**
>
> Therefore, using the definition of report and budgeting groups, maintenance cost budgeting supports you in the budgeting process (for example, reporting and approval paths).

The budgeting itself then takes place in a special web user interface (see Figure 8.46). Depending on authorization, budget planners and managers can plan or even approve the budget for their areas.

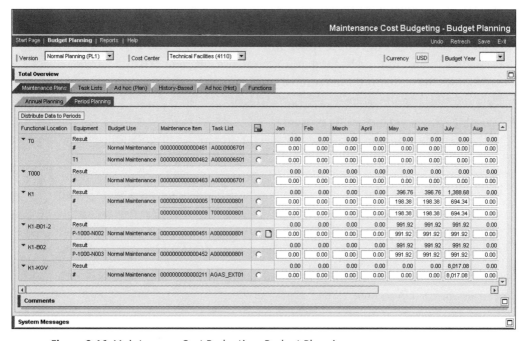

Figure 8.46 Maintenance Cost Budgeting: Budget Planning

Maintenance cost budgeting also provides the option of breaking down the budget into categories or by use; a budget category is the differentiation of the budget relative to the planning of plant maintenance tasks. In the standard configuration of budget planning, a budget proposal is broken down into three budget categories, which are shown separately, as follows:

- **Preventive**
  Costs from regularly recurring plant maintenance tasks planned based on maintenance plans

- **Planned**
  Costs from irregularly recurring plant maintenance tasks that are planned using maintenance task lists or individually in orders

- **Unplanned**
  Costs resulting from an unplanned plant maintenance task, for example, from repairs during machine downtime due to damage

Representing Budgets by Budget Categories

Budget categories can be adapted in customizing to your company-specific needs. Depending on the settings, you can then automatically determine and assign them based on common properties (for example, maintenance activity type, order type) during the data extraction.

The categorization by budget use, on the other hand, concerns the business side of a plant maintenance task. Differentiating by budget use involves the classification of the budget relative to the business process to which a plant maintenance task belongs. In addition to the budget category, this differentiation enables further grouping of the budget proposal by the type of activity, for example:

- Repairs
- Cleaning tasks
- Inspection or maintenance tasks
- Overhauls
- Downtimes

Representing Budgets by Budget Use

Budget uses can be adapted to your enterprise-specific needs in customizing. Depending on the settings, you can then automatically determine and assign them based on common properties (for example, WBS elements or cost center) during the data extraction.

As mentioned at the start of this section, SAP BW-BPS is the technical platform for MCB. As described in Section 8.2.4, InfoCubes and queries are needed for this purpose. For all the other functionality of SAP BW, SAP also provides the business content needed for MCB. Table 8.4 lists the InfoCubes delivered by SAP.

Name	Description
Simulated plant mainte-nance costs 0PM_C05	This InfoCube provides data for simulated plant maintenance costs. The calculation of maintenance plans and plant mainte-nance task lists takes place during the transfer.
Budget for maintenance 0PM_C06	This InfoCube is used to plan the plant maintenance budget. The data is loaded from the InfoCubes maintenance orders: costs and settlements (0PM_C01) and simulated maintenance costs (0PM_C05).

Table 8.4 InfoCubes for MCB

Name	Description
Budget for maintenance 0PM_MC01	This MultiProvider unites data from the InfoCube maintenance orders: costs and settlements (0PM_C01) and budget data for maintenance (0PM_C06), making it possible, for example, to compare current budget planning with historical actual costs.
Budget for maintenance 0PM_C25	This InfoCube is used as an InfoProvider to provide budget data.

Table 8.4 InfoCubes for MCB (Cont.)

Based on these InfoCubes, the queries listed in Table 8.5 are delivered in the MCB business content.

Name	Description
Budget proposal by budget category	Use this query to display your budget proposal broken down by budget categories.
Budget proposal (periodic)	Use this query to display your budget proposal broken down by periods.
Budget proposal (objects)	Use this query to display your budget proposal broken down by your technical objects.
Budget proposal (simulated costs)	Use this query to compare your budget proposal with simulated costs.
Budget comparison (actual costs)	Use this query to compare your budget proposal with actual historical costs.
Budget comparison (planned costs)	Use this query to compare your budget proposal with historical planned costs.
Budgetary control (budget)	Use this query to carry out budgetary control. The budget proposal is compared with the actual costs incurred in the current period and the remaining budget.
Budgetary control (planned costs)	Use this query to carry out budgetary control. The budget proposal is compared with the actual costs incurred in the current period and the remaining planned costs.
Actual cost comparison (plan data-based)	Use this query to compare your budget proposal for the planned data-based budgeting process with historical actual costs.
Actual cost comparison (history-based)	Use this query to compare your budget proposal for the history-based budgeting process with historical actual costs.

Table 8.5 Queries for MCB

You have the option of performing a quasi-active availability control. In the order, you will find the ⑤ button, with which you can check the assigned budget for maintenance costs online in maintenance cost budgeting. A dialog box shows the result of the check (see Figure 8.47).

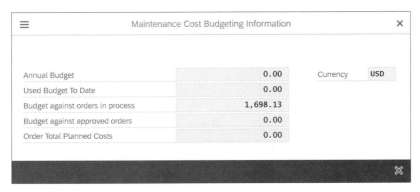

Maintenance Cost Budgeting Information			
Annual Budget	0.00	Currency	USD
Used Budget To Date	0.00		
Budget against orders in process	1,698.13		
Budget against approved orders	0.00		
Order Total Planned Costs	0.00		

Figure 8.47 Order: Budget Information

Due to the flexible options to classify your budgets using budget categories and budget use according to your own needs, you can budget all your plant maintenance activity using maintenance cost budgeting.

You must satisfy the following prerequisites to work with maintenance cost budgeting:

- You have installed at least SAP BW-BPS 3.52.
- In customizing for SAP BW-BPS, you have used the function **SAP NetWeaver · Business Intelligence · Settings for BI Content · Planning Content · Product Lifecycle Management · Budget Planning for Plant Maintenance and Customer Service** to make settings for the central attributes of budget planning, for the budgeting process, and for the individual planning application.
- In the SAP BW content, you have created the report and budgeting groups.
- You have defined the variables for budget planning (for example, planning scenario, budget category, budget use).
- You have set whether you want to work on the basis of equipment and/or functional locations.
- You have determined the content of the start page.
- You have activated the business function LOG_EAM_CI_4 for SAP S/4HANA.
- You have used the customizing function **Define Budget Check for Order Types** to define for each plant and order type that a budget check using Maintenance cost budgeting is permitted.

8.4   Summary

In this chapter, SAP tools were discussed concerning how to obtain information and for budgeting. For obtaining information on your plant maintenance activities you have the following options:

- SAP List Viewer, where a lot of standard reports are offered as part of SAP S/4HANA Asset Management
- QuickViewer, with which you can create your own reports without programming
- The logistic information system, which is a tool for obtaining plant maintenance key figures
- SAP Business Warehouse, which is the strategic SAP tool for analyses
- SAP Lumira, discovery edition, where you can graphically present your key figures

Table 8.6 summarizes the budgeting procedures with their most important properties.

	Budgeting by Order	Budgeting by Cost Center	Budgeting by Investment Management Item	Budgeting by WBS Element	Budgeting with MCB
Integrated into SAP S/4HANA	Yes	Yes	Yes	Yes	No
Application area	Individual order	Planning for cost center	Investments, ongoing plant maintenance	Plant maintenance projects, ongoing plant maintenance	All plant maintenance plans
Active availability check	Yes	No	No	Yes	Yes
Flexibility of the budgeting object	None	None	In certain cases	In certain cases	Flexibly adjustable
Top-down and bottom-up	No	No	Yes	Yes	Yes

Table 8.6 Comparing Budgeting Procedures

Chapter 9

New Information Technologies for Plant Maintenance

Modern communication technologies, such as the Internet, mobile solutions, and cloud technologies, have become established in plant maintenance, as in almost every other area. This chapter describes the prerequisites, options, and limitations associated with these and other technologies when deployed in plant maintenance.

For a long time now, the Internet, along with modern information and communications technologies (ICT), has defined everyday communications within a company. While these new technologies have been rather neglected in plant maintenance for a long time, the trend now also extends into this area. Plant maintenance forms have become the core of many Industry 4.0 projects when it comes to connecting the operation level and administration level and exchanging data.

Therefore, this chapter will introduce you to some of the new technologies provided by SAP. In particular, this chapter describes the options available to you in SAP applications, how you can use them, the prerequisites associated with them, and how business processes change under their influence. The chapter will focus primarily on mobile SAP solutions for plant maintenance and new technologies in the user interface, but this chapter will also provide an overview of SAP Intelligent Asset Management, which contains the asset central foundation, SAP Predictive Maintenance and Service, SAP Asset Strategy and Performance Management, and SAP Asset Intelligence Network. The cloud solutions of SAP Intelligent Asset Management expand the functional scope of SAP S/4HANA Asset Management.

9.1 New Technologies in the User Interface

On the following pages, some new SAP technologies for the user interface are introduced. Chapter 9 provides additional options for designing your own user interfaces, such as GuiXT and SAP Screen Personas. This section will start by covering SAP 3D Visual Enterprise Viewer, move on to discuss the ten most important SAP Fiori apps for plant maintenance, and then discuss quick views.

9.1.1 SAP 3D Visual Enterprise Viewer

With SAP 3D Visual Enterprise Viewer, visualization functions for technical objects, spare parts, and instructions are available in SAP Business Client as well as on mobile devices (such as tablets or smart phones). 2D and 3D model views and animated scenes support you in tasks such as the provision of spare parts and the execution of maintenance. Only the 2D images and 3D scenes that are published within a company are available for the display.

With the integration of SAP 3D Visual Enterprise Viewer in SAP Business Client, you have the following options:

- **Display graphics**
  You can graphically display pieces of equipment and functional locations by calling a 2D image or a 3D scene of the technical object from the master data of the technical object (see Figure 9.1).

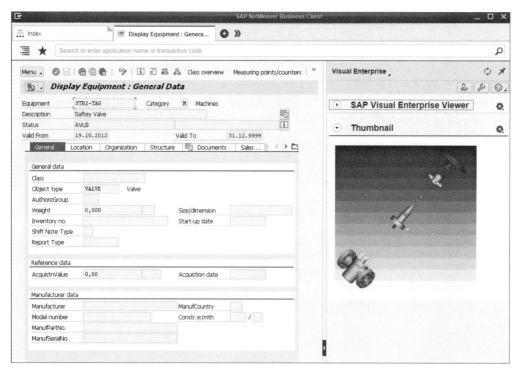

Figure 9.1 3D Model

- **Select spare parts**
  You can use 2D or 3D images to select and determine the required spare parts. The system calls a 2D image or 3D scene of the relevant spare parts in a dialog box. You now have the option of selecting one or more spare parts in the image and of transferring them to the spare parts list. The various display functions, such as disassembling or rotating the model, can assist you in selecting the right part (see Figure 9.2).

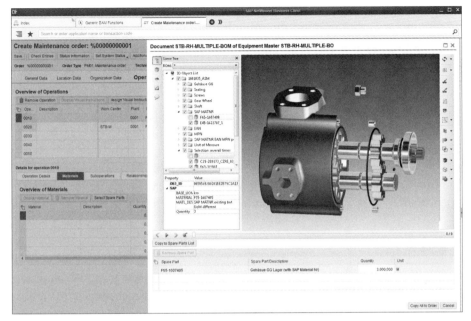

Figure 9.2 Active 3D Model

- **Animate maintenance task lists**
  SAP 3D Visual Enterprise Viewer helps you perform plant maintenance tasks with visual instructions. Visual instructions may be, for example, animated 3D scenes that visualize the individual steps of the plant maintenance task at the operation level (see Figure 9.3).

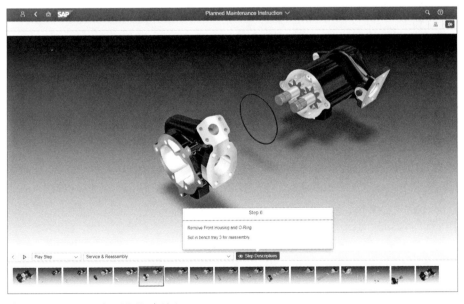

Figure 9.3 Interactive 3D Task List

SAP 3D Visual Enterprise Viewer on a Mobile Device

The biggest advantage of SAP 3D Visual Enterprise Viewer for technicians is that it can be installed on a mobile device. While working on-site, a technician benefits greatly by being supported visually on damage repair or maintenance procedures.

To fully utilize the functions described here, you must first fulfill the following prerequisites:

- You have installed SAP 3D Visual Enterprise Viewer locally.

- You have activated the business functions LOG_EAM_SIMPLICITY, LOG_EAM_SIMPLICITY_2 to LOG_EAM_SIMPLICITY_8, and LOG_EAM_VE_INT.

9.1.2   SAP Fiori

In Chapter 1, Section 1.7.3, SAP Fiori was introduced as the new SAP user interface technology which enables users to access SAP systems. SAP Fiori can be used across multiple devices; that is, not only can you access SAP systems via your desktop, but you can also access SAP systems via mobile devices such as smartphones or tablets. Thus, SAP Fiori is an alternative to SAP GUI, SAP Business Client, or other mobile SAP solutions.

In the following sections, the most important SAP Fiori apps for plant maintenance purposes are introduced.

Set Up SAP Fiori Launchpad?

If you need information on how to set up SAP Fiori launchpad, how to configure the SAP Fiori apps for plant maintenance, and how to customize SAP S/4HANA Asset Management to use the Fiori apps, delve into my book *Configuring Plant Maintenance in SAP S/4HANA*. Everything is described in detail there.

Report and Repair Malfunction

The Report and Repair Malfunction app is an extensive SAP Fiori app with many detailed functions; this app covers almost the entire order cycle. You can use it to report problems with a technical object, plan the necessary work order operations, and confirm the work carried out. Three tiles are available for this app (see Figure 9.4):

- **Report Malfunction**
  This tile is used for creating malfunction notifications.

- **Manage Malfunction Reports**
  This tile provides a list of malfunction notifications that have already been created.

- **Repair Malfunctions – My Job List**
  This tile contains a list of all tasks (notifications, orders, operations) assigned to you or your team.

Figure 9.4 Report and Repair Malfunction: Tiles

You can use the **Report Malfunction** tile (see Figure 9.5) to map complete notification and order processing, as follows:

- Assign the relevant technical object by using the type-ahead search or barcode reading.
- View details of the technical object by navigating with associated apps.
- View a list of all the malfunction reports that have recently been created for the relevant technical object.

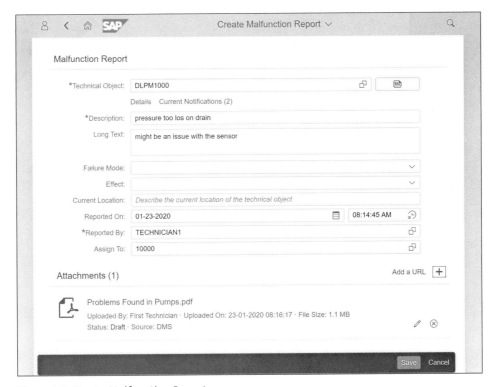

Figure 9.5 Create Malfunction Report

- Add pictures and long texts describing damage.

- Plan operations and assign them to a technician.

- Plan spare parts by barcode reading, from the parts list, or from the material where-used list (see Figure 9.6).

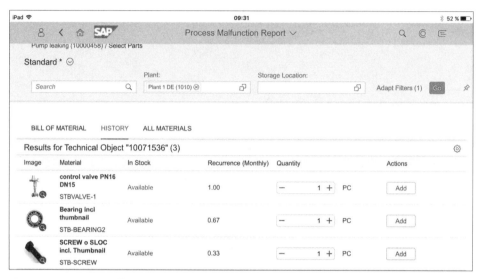

Figure 9.6 Report Malfunction: Plan Spare Parts

- Attach a URL to provide further information about the technical object or damage.

- Check material availability (available-to-promise [ATP] check).

- View whether the quantity of spare parts you need is available in the storage location or plant.

- Release the order.

- Start working and pause your work whenever needed. You can document why you had to pause your work by selecting a reason such as **Waiting for Parts** or **Waiting for Approval** (see Figure 9.7).

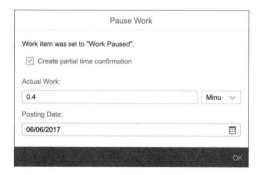

Figure 9.7 Report Malfunction: Pause and Confirm

- Enter time confirmations (partial and final confirmations).
- Issue the spare parts in the required quantity from the storage location.
- Enter technical feedback (e.g., malfunction duration, cause of damage, or fault data).
- As a lead technician assigned to process the entire malfunction report, complete and close the malfunction report.

You can view a list of malfunction reports that have already been created by launching the **Manage Malfunction Reports** tile (see Figure 9.8). This tile allows you to do the following:

- Get a quick overview of malfunction reports and their current status.
- Narrow down the scope of the list by using filters.
- Personalize the list by choosing which columns should be shown and how table entries should be sorted.
- Save the combination of filters and table personalization as a variant.

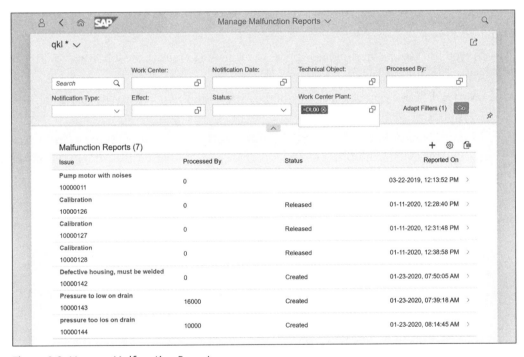

Figure 9.8 Manage Malfunction Reports

You can view a list of the work items assigned to you or your team by launching the **Repair Malfunctions– My Job List** tile (see Figure 9.9). You can get a quick overview of all work items assigned to you or to your team, as well as display all the jobs of your work center that haven't yet been assigned to a technician. This list has the same filter, sort, and save opportunities as the previous tiles.

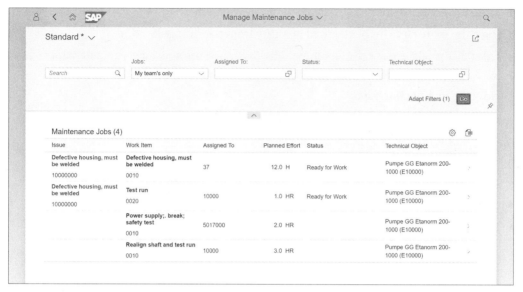

Figure 9.9 Repair Malfunctions: My Job List

If you run the app on a mobile device (smartphone or tablet), the following additional functions are available:

- Use the camera to take a picture of the damage and attach it directly to the notification.
- Use a barcode scanner to record the number of the technical object to be repaired, to add the material number of a required spare part, or to confirm an order via barcode (see Figure 9.10).

Figure 9.10 Report and Repair Malfunction: Maintenance Order Barcode

Request Maintenance

There are two tiles available for the Request Maintenance app: **Monitor Maintenance Requests** and **Request Maintenance** (see Figure 9.11).

Figure 9.11 Request Maintenance: Tiles

By choosing the **Request Maintenance** tile, you can use this app to create a mainte-nance notification. You can submit information such as **Technical Object**, **Description**, and **Effect** on production (see Figure 9.12).

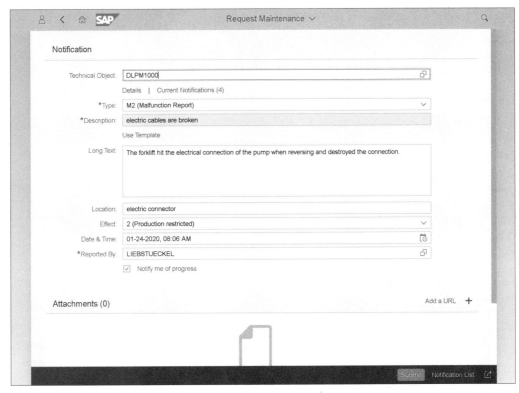

Figure 9.12 Request Maintenance

Here, too, you may attach pictures or other documents that are automatically saved as document management system (DMS) documents in the backend system. Activating the **Notify me of progress** checkbox will keep you informed about the progress of the maintenance work until it's completed.

By launching the **Monitor Maintenance Requests** tile, you can do the following:

- Get a quick overview of maintenance requests and their current status by viewing a list of notifications.

- View the date monitor symbols to quickly detect time issues and monitor the progress of the notifications (see Figure 9.13).

- Narrow down the scope of the list by using filters.

- Personalize the list by choosing which columns should be shown and how table entries should be sorted.

- Save the combination of filters and table personalization as a variant.

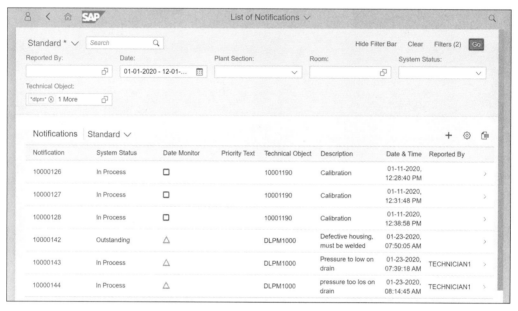

Figure 9.13 Monitor Maintenance Requests

Maintenance Planning Overview

The Maintenance Planning Overview app gives you support in planning, scheduling, and executing your maintenance work. It allows the monitoring of important, time-critical process steps such as work that hasn't yet been assigned, missing spare parts, or overdue orders. The information is made available in graphic and tabular forms.

The Maintenance Planning Overview app shows details such as the following (see Figure 9.14):

- Outstanding notifications that haven't become an order yet

- Purchase requisitions to be released or purchase orders for non-stock material required for spare parts in maintenance orders

- Approved purchase requisitions for non-stock materials for which a purchase order hasn't been created yet

- Non-stock materials ordered but probably not available for the date required

- Released maintenance orders with end dates in the past but not finally confirmed yet

- Finally confirmed maintenance orders that haven't been completed, technically or business-wise

Figure 9.14 Maintenance Planning Overview

Maintenance Scheduling Board

With the Maintenance Scheduling Board app, you can visualize maintenance orders, order operations, and suboperations on a timeline in your work center (see Figure 9.15). Other actions you can take include the following:

- Assign operations to another work center or person.

- Postpone the orders or operations.

- Check whether there are relationships among operations and whether these relationships are currently violated.

- Dispatch order operations and suboperations.

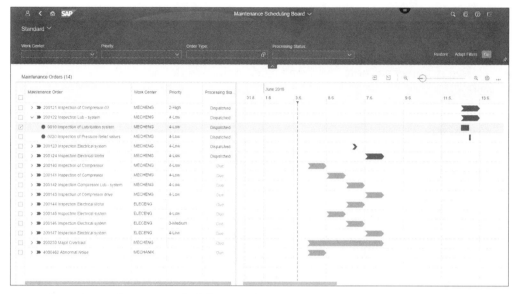

Figure 9.15 Maintenance Scheduling Board

Manage Work Center Utilization

The Manage Work Center Utilization app allows you to analyze and manage the utilization of your work centers. Being the maintenance planner, you can use this app to analyze the workload for work centers. The utilization is based on the operations that are assigned to your work centers and for which capacity is required in the next four calendar weeks (see Figure 9.16).

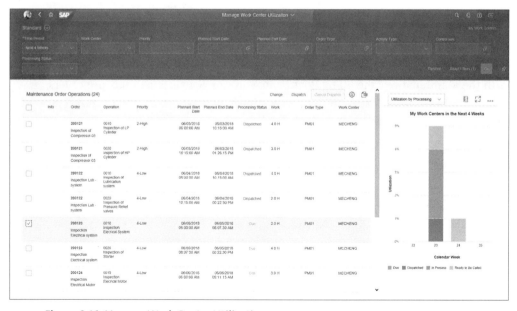

Figure 9.16 Manage Work Center Utilization

This app allows you to do the following:

- Display a list of all operations that are currently assigned to your work centers, including the most important information, such as the associated maintenance order, the priority, and the planned start and end dates.

- View a list of maintenance orders that have at least one operation in your work centers.

- Use filters to narrow down the list of operations (e.g., work center or order type).

- Move order operations to another date or work center to level work center utilization.

- Change the available work center capacity per day for a selected target week.

Technical Object Damages

With the Technical Object Damages app, you can see which damage occurs how often and which part of the object causes the damage. This app allows you to do the following:

- View the amount of damage in tabular form or graphically (see Figure 9.17).

- Filter the damage based on various criteria, for example, maintenance plant, object type, construction type, and catalog profile.

- Display the damage by the code groups of the object parts (see Figure 9.18).

- Identify the functional location where a piece of equipment has been damaged.

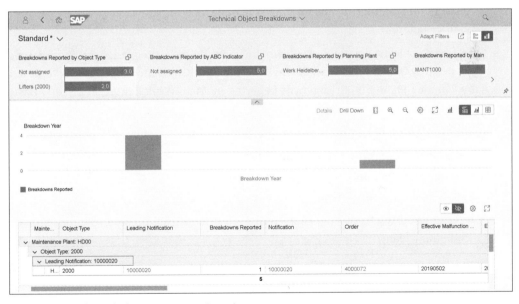

Figure 9.17 Technical Object Damage: Overview

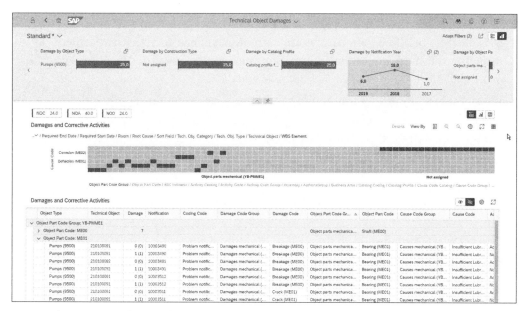

Figure 9.18 Technical Object Damage: Object Parts

Analytical List Page for Technical Object Breakdown Analysis

The Analytical List Page for Technical Object Breakdown Analysis app enables you to point out the causes of particular breakdowns more precisely. Determining the amount of damage of a certain type as well as the categorization of the duration of various different failures will enable you to calculate more precisely the period of two consecutive failures.

Technical objects deliver breakdown incident figures categorized as **Breakdowns Reported by Object Type**, **Breakdowns Reported by ABC Indicator**, **Breakdowns Reported by Planning Plant**, and **Breakdowns Reported by Main Work Center** on a yearly basis (see Figure 9.19).

The aggregation of breakdown causes supplies information such as the following:

- Number of breakdowns per equipment per year
- Duration of failures
- Period of consecutive failures
- Aggregated key figures per characteristics (e.g., construction type, ABC indicator, or planning plant)

This set of information permits particular breakdowns and calculates periods of maintenance to be analyzed more precisely.

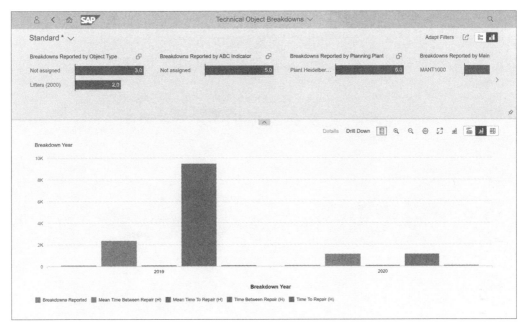

Figure 9.19 Breakdown Analysis

The Analytical List Page for Technical Object Breakdown Analysis app shows the classic maintenance key performance indicators (KPIs):

- Number of downtimes
- Time to repair (TTR)
- Time between repairs (TBR)
- Mean time to repair (MTTR)
- Mean time between repairs (MTBR)

Further details can be analyzed, such as for which equipment or functional location, when, and within which notification a downtime was posted. In addition, downtimes can be categorized into object type, planning plant, year, or work center.

Actual Maintenance Cost Analysis

The Actual Maintenance Cost Analysis app supports you in monitoring and evaluating the actual costs from current maintenance orders (see Figure 9.20). Here, actual material, labor, corrective, and preventive costs for a selected time period can be seen and may be used for further analysis. This app allows you to do the following:

- Set one or more filters.
- Switch between chart view and table view or use both.
- Display time series in a line chart.

- Change chart types, customize the chart settings, and use the drilldown option to change the chart grouping dimension.

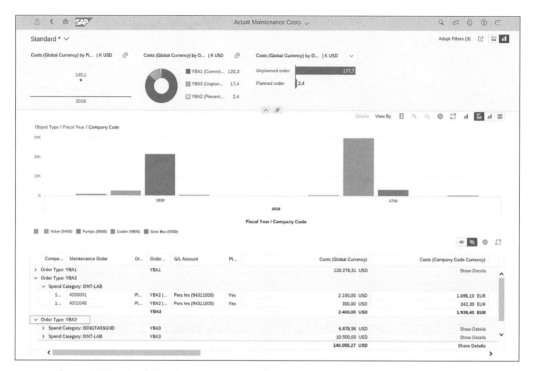

Figure 9.20 Actual Maintenance Cost Analysis

Find Maintenance Objects

There are several apps to search for SAP S/4HANA Asset Management objects (see Figure 9.21), as follows:

- Find Technical Object
- Find Maintenance Notification
- Find Maintenance Order Confirmation
- Find Maintenance Order
- Find Maintenance Order and Operation
- Find Maintenance Task List
- Find Maintenance Task List and Operation

All of these are dynamic apps, which means there is a selection bar, and depending on the selection criteria entered, the list of displayed objects is dynamically adjusted.

Figure 9.21 Find Objects

All these apps behave in a similar way, so let's explain some functionality by using the Find Maintenance Order and Operation app as an example (see Figure 9.22). This app allows you to do the following:

- Filter maintenance orders and operations by various predefined parameters, such as type, status, and priority.
- Select **Adapt Filters (2)** to determine your own selection criteria.

- Select {gear} to determine the view settings (columns to display, sort order, filter, grouping) (see Figure 9.23).

Use predefined links to start a new transaction (e.g., create a new order, display master data, view a list of materials issues).

- Select **More Links** to create your own new links (see Figure 9.24).

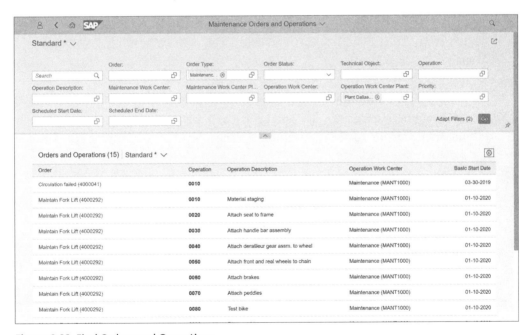

Figure 9.22 Find Orders and Operations

Figure 9.23 Determining View Settings

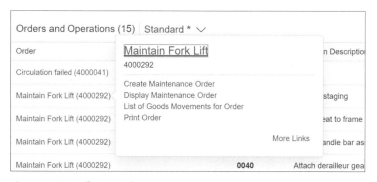

Figure 9.24 Defining Links

- Select 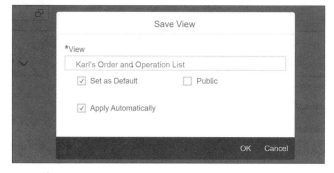 to send an email with a link to your list using your standard email client.
- Save your selection and display settings as a user variant by selecting an option from the **Standard *** dropdown (see Figure 9.25). The next time you start the app, the user variant will be used.

Figure 9.25 Defining User Variant

Monitor Material Coverage

Although the Monitor Material Coverage app belongs to the area of material requirements planning (MRP), it's also quite useful for the material coverage of spare parts. You can monitor all the materials in selected areas of responsibility (see Figure 9.26), specify a shortage definition to determine which types of material have shortages, and use the default filter **Time till Shortage** to check the coverage of materials within a specific time frame. This app provides you with information you need to enable an appropriate and timely reaction to a shortage situation to avoid malfunctions.

With this app, you can do the following:

- Select a shortage definition depending on how you want the system to calculate the material shortage.
- Open a quick view for the material or display a list of vendors.
- Personalize the layout and save it as a variant.

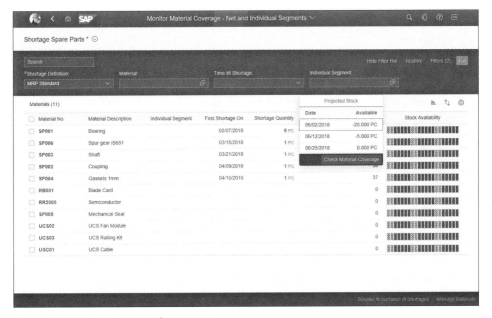

Figure 9.26 Monitor Material Coverage

9.1.3 Quick Views

Quick views enable you to display critical information on assigned equipment, functional locations, material, and long texts in orders, notifications, task lists, and maintenance plans on the SAP web user interface (for example, SAP Business Client) without having to navigate to the respective object. Quick views provide previews of objects and display critical information when you move your mouse cursor over an object. Furthermore, you can also use the links in quick views for navigation.

[!]

Quick Views versus QuickViewer

To dispel an obvious confusion: The quick views mentioned here are not the same as the QuickViews generated by using Transaction SQVI [SAP QuickViewer] and described in Chapter 8, Section 8.2.2, which you can use to generate your own lists. Unfortunately, SAP chose these two similar terms for two completely different functions.

You can configure individually which information is supposed to be available for which users in quick views and suppress what quick views are displayed. The following quick views are available in plant maintenance:

- **Technical object**
  - Quick view for the parent technical object on the **Structure** tab
  - Quick view for installed equipment on the **Structure** tab
- **Order**
  - Quick view for the assigned notification in the **General Data**, activity data, and object list
  - Quick view for the technical object in the **General Data**, activity data, and object list
  - Quick view for the task list in the **General Data**
  - Quick view for material in the activity details
  - Quick view for entered long texts in the activity data and details (**Material** tab)
  - Quick view for the user status in the activity data
- **Notification**
  - Quick view for the assigned order in the **General Dat**a (see Figure 9.27)
  - Quick view for the technical object in the **General Data**
  - Quick view for the task list in the **General Data**
  - Quick view for actions on the **Actions** tab
  - Quick view for entered long texts
  - Quick view for the user status in the task data
- **Task list**
  - Quick view for material in the activity details
  - Quick view for the technical object in the activity data and details
  - Quick view for entered long texts
  - Quick view for the technical object in the **General Data** in the task list with the **Task List for Technical Object** category

- **Maintenance plan**
  - Quick view for the maintenance plan in the **General Data** of the maintenance item
  - Quick view for the technical object in the **General Data** of the maintenance item
  - Quick view for the assigned task list in the **General Data** of the maintenance item
  - Quick view for the technical object in the item details

To be able to use quick views in plant maintenance, the business function Simplified EAM Applications (LOG_EAM_SIMPLICITY_3) must be enabled.

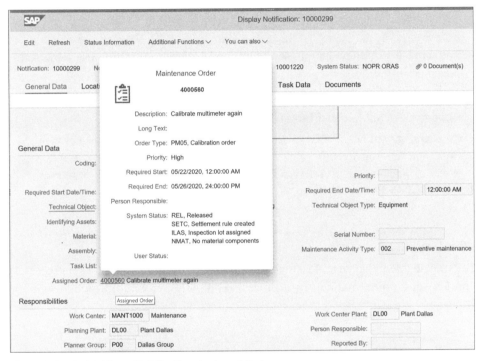

Figure 9.27 Quick View: Notification Assigned Order

9.2   Mobile Maintenance

Before introducing the technological characteristics of mobile maintenance at SAP, let's first establish a basic understanding of the topic of *mobile maintenance*—for example, what actually differentiates a process with mobile maintenance from a process without mobile maintenance, which scenarios you can implement, and other aspects. Then, we'll discuss SAP Work Manager, SAP Asset Manager, and the use of RFID technology.

9.2.1 Fundamentals of Mobile Maintenance

This section presents some of the fundamentals of mobile maintenance: What does mobile maintenance mean, and what do business processes supported this way look like? It also provides some application cases and highlights the advantages associated with mobile maintenance.

What Is Mobile Maintenance?

In SAP, mobile maintenance means the following statements are both true:

- In order to perform a maintenance task, a technician requires information stored in the SAP S/4HANA system to be made available to him or her on site on a mobile device.

- The actual data gathered is entered on site and transferred to the SAP S/4HANA system.

[!]

Mobility Does Not Replace, but Supplements, SAP S/4HANA

SAP's strategy was not, and is not, to replace SAP S/4HANA Asset Management with a mobile version. You won't be able to fully process any business processes with SAP mobile maintenance apps. SAP regards mobile maintenance as part of a business process and as the technology for supporting maintenance processing.

What Does a Business Process Look Like?

SAP mobile maintenance represents not an entire process, but rather, a subprocess. If you look at a typical maintenance process both with and without mobile support, you'll see some significant differences (see Figure 9.28).

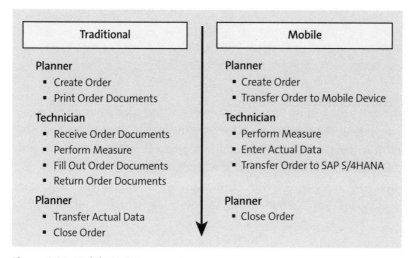

Figure 9.28 Mobile Maintenance Process

The mobile maintenance process differs from the traditional process as follows:

- You do not print any documents.
- You do not transport any documents to and from the maintenance location.
- You do not have to archive any physical documents.
- You do not separate data entry from the process.
- Instead, the order data is available in electronic form on-site.
- You enter the actual data (also in electronic form) shortly after you perform the maintenance task.
- The data is transferred to the backend system (SAP S/4HANA Asset Management).

[!]

Electronic Data Exchange Instead of Gaps in Integration

The key difference between business processes with mobile support and conventional processing is the continuity of electronic data exchange at the planning and execution stages. No gaps arise in integration.

What Are the Advantages of Mobile Maintenance?

Regardless of the details in your company, the general advantages associated with such a working method are evident:

- Less manual effort is required to enter data (the information is not handwritten first and then written in electronic form later but is in electronic form from the outset).
- Entering data on-site in electronic form and transferring it electronically to the SAP S/4HANA system reduces both the risk of transmission errors and the error rate.
- All in all, the data is of a higher quality.
- Consequently, you should receive fewer complaints from sold-to parties as a result of incorrect order settlements.
- Eliminating the need for manual document transport reduces the lead time (technicians do not have to collect or return their order documents).

Another important advantage derives from the access to electronic documents: While carrying out maintenance tasks on-site, with a tablet, the technician has access to all necessary electronic documents (such as instruction manuals, drawings, etc.) needed to perform tasks. This could also be documents of the SAP 3D Visual Enterprise Viewer (Section 9.1.1), from a file server, or from a DMS. The technician may refer to the whole lot of electronic data/documents from case to case just on-demand without having to get back to a planning office to pick them out of relevant files.

Which Variants Are Available?

You must distinguish between offline and online scenarios for SAP's mobile solutions (see Figure 9.29, shown here in the context of the SAP NetWeaver platform).

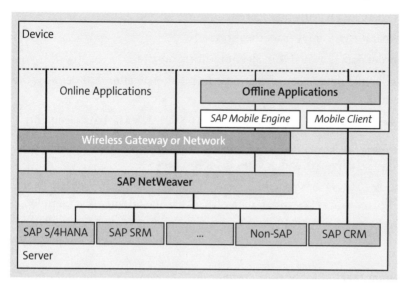

Figure 9.29 Online and Offline Scenarios

For online scenarios, you use the mobile device to contact SAP NetWeaver directly, and you transfer the data to the backend system immediately (for example, SAP S/4HANA), or vice versa. You send data online from SAP S/4HANA to a mobile device; and a typical scenario would be not only for paging a user, for instance, but for all SAP Fiori apps as well. The latter may also be used for mobile maintenance, although an online connection to the server has to be established.

For offline scenarios, you transfer the data from the backend system to a mobile device. The data is available offline and locally for further processing. Once you have finished entering the data, you transfer the data back to the backend system. Typical scenarios involve SAP Work Manager and SAP Asset Manager, which will be discussed in more detail in Section 9.2.2 and Section 9.2.3.

Which Application Cases Exist?

Real-life projects have demonstrated a wide range of different application cases in which mobile scenarios were implemented successfully, including the following examples:

- Frankfurt Airport, which inspects its fire shutters (subject to compliance regulations), checks the condition of its parking facilities, monitors its emergency escape routes, and approves the cleaning services of external companies

- RheinEnergie, which supports its metering point operations and network operations, including the removal/installation of measuring points and periodic counter readings

- KUKA, which supports its service employees when they perform initial operations, correct malfunctions, and carry out maintenance tasks on robots

- Roche Diagnostics, where safety aspects are a major concern and GMP-relevant maintenance orders are processed

- DB Railion Deutschland, which uses mobile technology for maintenance commissioning and preliminary claims recording for its freight cars

- E.On, which deploys mobile technology for sales order processing, inspection, and meter management (installation, removal, meter reading, collection)

- National Grid, a U.S. utility company that uses a mobile process for its complete order processing

- Infraserv, which supports their technicians in maintenance and service work in the areas of heating, air conditioning, ventilation, and plumbing

- GWG, a public utility housing enterprise in Wuppertal, Germany, which has implemented mobile property management and mobile apartment inspections

- Voest Alpine, which uses mobile technology to monitor their technical systems and record malfunctions

A list of all existing and possible application cases would be endless, but I hope this brief list has provided some insight into the many possible uses.

> **Individualization in Mobile Maintenance Projects**
>
> Each mobile maintenance project proceeds in a different manner and far more individually than standard SAP plant maintenance projects. In particular, the functions and the interface design of frontend systems are usually customized to the specific needs of the company.

Which Devices Are Considered?

Another question you must answer when planning a project for mobile maintenance is the use of mobile devices. The market for suitable mobile devices is large, heterogeneous, and particularly transparent. In the course of time, three types of devices have become widely accepted:

- Notebooks (for extensive mobile solutions)

- Tablets (for example, iPad or Galaxy Note)

- Smartphones (for example, iPhone or Android devices)

A wide range of factors will determine the best device or device type for you. When choosing a device type, you should answer the following questions, in particular:

- Which processes do you want to support, and which functions do you require to do this?
- How much information do you want to process locally (main memory)?
- Do you require online access? Should the device be equipped with a cellular radio or a wireless local radio network (WLAN)?
- Which screen size do you require (from a smart phone format through to the notebook format)?
- Do you require a graphic-enabled device (because, for example, you want to view documents or connect a geographic information system [GIS])?
- Which equipment must a device have (keyboard, touchscreen, barcode reader, RFID scanner, stylus, and so on)?
- What are the environmental requirements for the device (dust, impact, ex-protected, humidity)?
- What is a tolerable device weight for your technicians?
- What is your budget?

[!]

Choosing a Device

Several criteria (for example, functions, storage space, peripheral equipment) are significant when choosing from the wide range of device types available (in particular, tablets, smartphones, notebooks, and tablet PCs).

9.2.2   SAP Work Manager

SAP now offers a wide range of mobile solutions (see Figure 9.30), starting with SAP Cloud for Customer for the management of customer information such as leads or opportunities, SAP Inventory Manager for recording goods issues and goods receipts, and SAP Manager Approvals.

Two apps are available for plant maintenance, as follows:

- SAP Work Manager
- SAP Asset Manager

SAP Work Manager is an older mobile SAP solution for maintenance. It was not developed by SAP but supplemented the SAP portfolio when Syclo was acquired in 2011. This section will focus on SAP Work Manager, while the next will discuss SAP Asset Manager

Figure 9.30 SAP Mobile Apps: Selection

Local Layouts

Depending on your choice of mobile device, a variety of layouts are available for the respective hardware conditions. Figure 9.31 shows three screenshots from SAP Work Manager on an Android smartphone: on the left, you see the entry menu with the available functions, in the middle, an order list, and on the right, an order operation list.

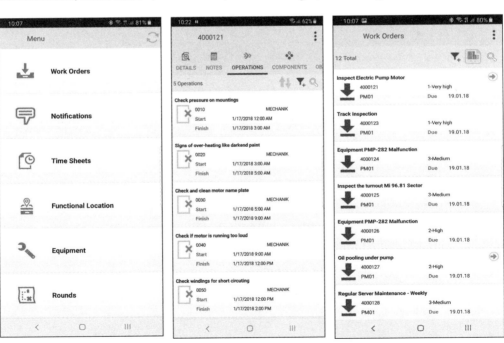

Figure 9.31 SAP Work Manager: Smart Phone Layout

In comparison, Figure 9.32 presents the layout of the SAP Work Manager on a tablet. Due to the size, more information can be seen here. This one shows an order list on the left and a complete order with details on the order header and the notification on the right.

Figure 9.32 SAP Work Manager: Tablet Layout

Basic Functions

If you have fulfilled the technical prerequisites, the following basic functions are available:

- **Order processing**
  - Show order list.
  - Display operations for the order.
  - Enter new operations for the order.
  - Display object list for the order.
  - Display material list for the order.
  - Display message about the order.
  - Add new components.
  - Record material issue.
  - Technically complete the order.

- Create orders.
- Change orders.
- Delete orders that haven't yet been transferred.

- **Notification processing**
  - Show notification list.
  - Show notifications.
  - Create notifications.
  - Change notifications.
  - Delete notifications that haven't yet been transferred.
  - Complete notifications.
  - Display, change, record tasks.
  - Display, change, record actions.

- **Time recording**
  - Add time confirmation.

- **Equipment** and functional locations
  - Display master data.
  - Display classification.
  - Display documents.

Special Functions

SAP Work Manager also has some useful special functions, as follows:

- **Mobile push alert**
  You can configure SAP Work Manager so that messages and orders with priority 1 are automatically pushed to devices, and a special message appears.

- **Inventory processing with availability check**
  A material withdrawal is integrated in SAP Work Manager, but not complete inventory management. If necessary, SAP Inventory Manager has to be installed also. A complete inventory management and various availability checks will be available there.

- **Geographic information**
  SAP Work Manager has the ability to localize and visualize technical objects or orders based on geographic information in a geographic information system—similar to geographic information within SAP Asset Manager (see Figure 9.33).

> **Note**
> SAP Work Manager does not (yet) have a function for electronic signatures.

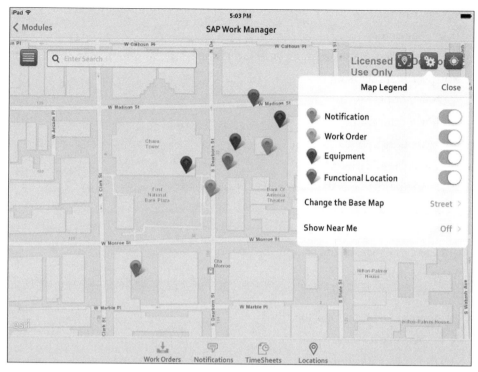

Figure 9.33 SAP Work Manager: Geographical Information

- **Start/stop function**
  In addition to using the standard time confirmation, you also have the option of using the start/stop function, for example, pressing the start button at the start of the job to let the time run. You can use the hold function (see Figure 9.34), to interrupt a job and complete it using the TECO (technical completion) function. SAP Work Manager now calculates the time required and generates a corresponding time confirmation.

Figure 9.34 SAP Work Manager: Start/Stop Function

- **Transfer function**
  The transfer function is available in the same window in which you forward an order originally assigned to you to a colleague, for example, because you're currently unable to process this order due to lack of time.

- **Notes feature**
  The **Notes** function is available for the order (see Figure 9.35), for each work order, for each material component, and for each notification. There is a status history where

you can enter notes. In the backend, these notes are transferred to long text, or a new note is created as an object service.

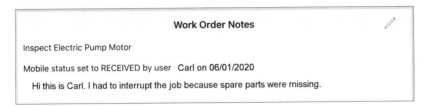

Figure 9.35 SAP Work Manager: Notes Function

- **Timesheet**

  Times can be entered in the timesheet, and various selection criteria can be installed to display which times were booked in which periods. Figure 9.36 shows such a timesheet with a daily overview and feedback from SAP Work Manager on a tablet.

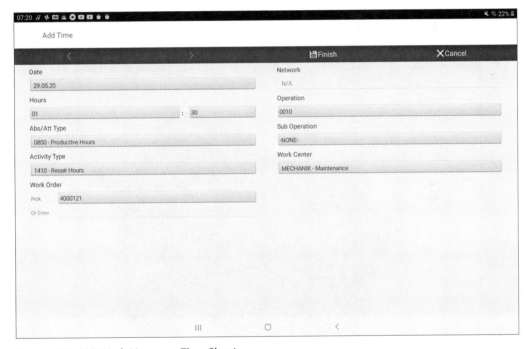

Figure 9.36 SAP Work Manager: Time Sheet

- **Barcode**

  SAP Work Manager has a barcode functionality you can access via 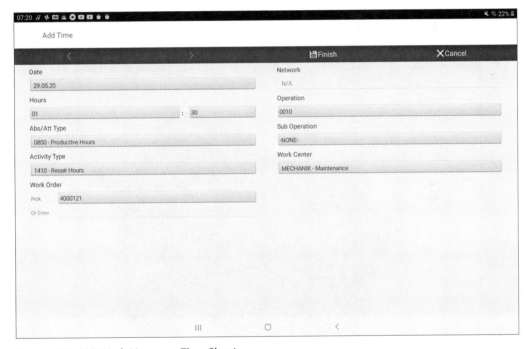 that allows you to read, for example, the barcode of equipment for which you want to create a new order.

- **Speech recognition with Siri**
  Speech recognition via Siri is an excellent option for avoiding the need to manually enter data, and texts in particular (for example, confirmation texts or damage descriptions for new orders to be created), especially for the iPhone, where entering text is somewhat laborious. You can enter your data into SAP Work Manager via speech. Siri and other speech recognition tools could be a great help to reduce effort.

- **Graphic representation**
  As in SAP Business Client, SAP 3D Visual Enterprise Viewer is integrated into SAP Work Manager. You have options as follows:

  - Show graphics: Display 2D images or 3D scenes for equipment and functional locations.

  - Select spare parts: Call up 2D and 3D images to assist in selection and determination of the required spare parts. You can mark one or more spare parts in the picture and add them to the spare parts list. The various display functions, such as disassembling or rotation of the model, are helpful in the selection (see Figure 9.37).

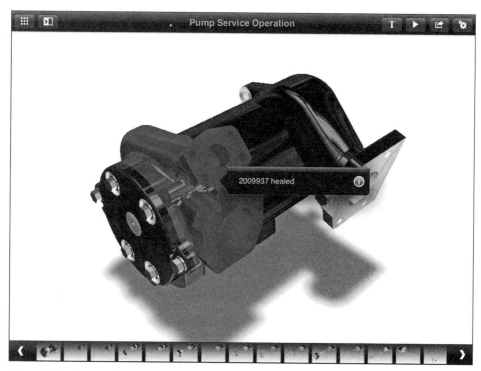

Figure 9.37 SAP Work Manager: 3D Model

- Animated task lists: Visualize work instructions, for example, as 3D scenes where you can follow each step of maintenance work in process (see Figure 9.38).

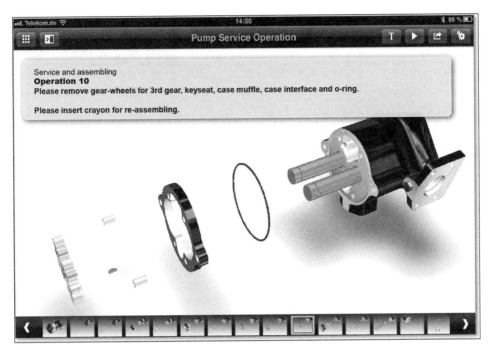

Figure 9.38 SAP Work Manager: Animated Task List

Rounds

Previously, there were two different apps for maintenance: SAP Work Manager and SAP Rounds Manager. However, the functionalities of the SAP Rounds Manager app have been integrated into the current version of SAP Work Manager.

This functionality is aimed at companies who perform performance-based or condition-based maintenance (see Chapter 5, Section 5.5 through Section 5.8) and want to record the required counter readings or measured values for this purpose. The values can be entered in list form or individually. Then, they are temporarily stored on the mobile device until the next synchronization takes place.

Rounds have the following features in detail:

- Display the entry list (see Figure 9.39 left)
- Create a new list of measured values
- Delete the list of measured values
- Create a new measuring point (equipment, functional location)
- Display the list of measuring points (see Figure 9.39 middle)
- Record measured values and counter readings (see Figure 9.39 right)

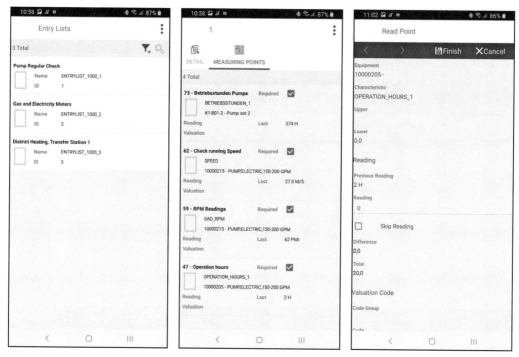

Figure 9.39 SAP Work Manager: Rounds on a Smartphone

Due to their size, tablets can provide a better overview of entry lists. Figure 9.40 shows rounds on an iPad with an entry list on the left and the recording of counter readings on the right.

Figure 9.40 SAP Work Manager: Rounds on a Tablet

As mentioned before, SAP Work Manager is an older mobile SAP solution for maintenance. The end of SAP's maintenance time window for SAP Work Manager is foreseeable.

9.2.3 SAP Asset Manager

In contrast, SAP Asset Manager is the newest SAP solution for mobile maintenance. This was initially developed specifically for iOS devices to implement a more user-friendly native interface for the frontend and so that the end user can set up and use the app more easily. SAP Asset Manager was also designed from the outset to integrate modern technologies such as the Internet of Things (IoT) and predictive analytics.

Before we discuss the functional scope of SAP Asset Manager, Table 9.1 contains a list of how the two mobile solutions differ in terms of technology and distribution.

Scope	SAP Asset Manager	SAP Work Manager
Backend	SAP ERP, SAP S/4HANA	SAP ERP, SAP S/4HANA
Devices	iOS, Android	iOS, Android, Windows
Range of functions	■ Currently limited ■ Considerable functional expansions planned in subsequent releases ■ Integration of IoT and predictive analytics ■ User-friendly, modern frontend	■ Mature and final developed product ■ Only a few further developments in subsequent releases
Deployment	Cloud	Cloud and on-premise
Connection	Online and offline	Online and offline
License model	Subscription	Subscription and purchase
Platform	SAP Mobile development kit on SAP Cloud Platform	Agentry on SAP Mobile Platform or SAP Cloud Platform

Table 9.1 Technical Comparison of SAP Asset Manager and SAP Work Manager

Local Layouts

Depending on whether you're using a tablet or smartphone as a local device, different layouts are available that are adapted to the various hardware conditions.

Figure 9.41 shows three screenshots from SAP Asset Manager on an Android smartphone: on the left, there is the entry menu with functions available; in the middle, an order list; and on the right, the order details.

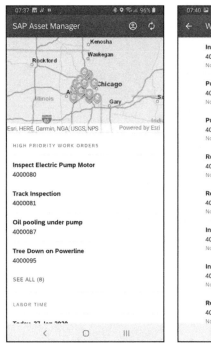

Figure 9.41 SAP Asset Manager: Smartphone Layout

In comparison, Figure 9.42 shows the layout of SAP Asset Manager on a tablet. Due to the size, you can, of course, view more information here. Unlike SAP Work Manager, you can't display an order list on the left and details of an order to the right. Unfortunately, you have to jump to the order detail; in doing so, the list vanishes.

Figure 9.42 SAP Asset Manager: Tablet Layout

Basic Functions

SAP Asset Manager currently has the following functionality (version 2005 [May 2020]):

- **Order processing**
  - Show high-priority work orders
  - Show order list
  - Show order details
  - Change orders
  - Change order status
  - Create follow-up order
  - Create new order
  - Display operations for the order
  - Create new operations for the order
  - Display spare parts for the order
  - Create new spare parts for the order
  - Display notification about the order
  - Display and enter malfunction start and end
  - Display documents for the order
  - Display object lists
  - Add new object list entries
  - Delete orders that have not yet been transferred
  - Return of issued parts
- **Notification processing**
  - Show notification list
  - Show notification
  - Create new notification
  - Change notification
  - Add notification item
  - Add, change, and display tasks
  - Add, change, and display activities (actions)
  - Create order for notification
  - Delete notifications that have not yet been transferred
  - Complete notification
- **Timesheets**
  - Show existing time sheets
  - Add time confirmation to a time sheet
  - Clock in and clock out time capture

- **Measuring points and counters**
  - Display list
  - Install and dismantle counters
  - Change counter
  - Take counter reading
- **Inspection rounds**
  - Filter measurement points
  - Link measurement documents with work order or operations
  - Take measurement readings
- **Equipment and functional locations**
  - Display list
  - View details
  - Install and dismantle equipment in functional locations
  - Display classification
  - Display documents
  - Display measuring points and measurement documents
  - Display guarantee
  - Display business partners
  - Display checklists
  - Assign and manage local objects in offline mode
  - Display Serialized parts
  - Display bill of material
  - Display linear asset management data

[»]

Additional Information

For more information on SAP Asset Manager, see the *SAP Asset Manager User Guide*, Walldorf 2020, to be found at *http://s-prs.co/v518007*.

Special Functions

Some useful special functions are also included:

- **Map**
  You can view a map showing the location of any chosen object at any time (see Figure 9.43). A color distinction is made between whether it's equipment (yellow), functional location (red), notification (green), or order (gray).

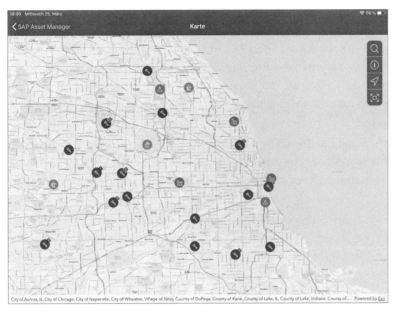

Figure 9.43 SAP Asset Manager: Map

- **Urgent job request**

  You can configure SAP Asset Manager so that a push message appears on the technician's device when an urgent order has to be carried out. The technician has the option of accepting or rejecting the order. The location of the order, including the time and distance, is also displayed (see Figure 9.44).

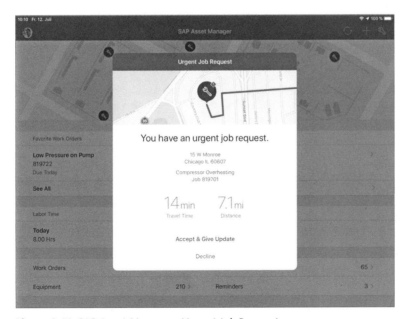

Figure 9.44 SAP Asset Manager: Urgent Job Request

- **Crew management**

  With crew management, you can manage your teams and vehicles. Crew management extends the core application of SAP Asset Manager via the following functions: adding, removing, and selecting technicians and vehicles; recording odometer readings; reporting; and checking and approving crew time. The prerequisite is that the add-on component for crew management is installed.

- **Business partner**

  Orders, equipment, or functional locations can be linked to a business partner. A business partner could have the role of a customer, supplier, or employee. If business partners are assigned, they are displayed on an overview and a detail screen.

- **Routes**

  If the field operations worker add-on component is installed, you can display the routes assigned to a technician (see Figure 9.45). You can also display the route data (e.g., length and duration), the stops of the route, and which technical objects are to be processed at which stop.

Figure 9.45 SAP Asset Manager: Routes

- **Notes and reminders**

  The notes function is available for notifications and orders (see Figure 9.46). You can enter free text there. In the backend, this free text is then created in either the long text or a note as an object service. The reminders serve a similar function, in which the technician can write a reminder. However, they are then independent of a notification or order and can be called up directly from the main menu, while the information can always be assigned directly to a notification or order and can only be called up from there.

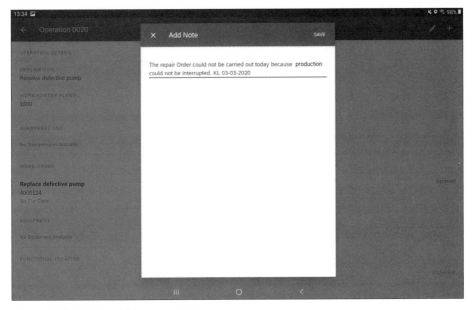

Figure 9.46 SAP Asset Manager: Note

Future Functions

Version 2005 of SAP Asset Manager has not yet reached the functionality of SAP Work Manager. However, there are many development points on the roadmap, a selection of which follows:

- Connection to SAP Geographical Enablement Framework
- OCR and RFID connection
- Support of SAP 3D Visual Enterprise
- Creating reservations
- Creating purchase requisitions
- Management of non-stock materials

Probably, SAP Asset Manager will have reached or overhauled SAP Work Manager in one of the next releases.

> **Roadmap**
>
> Access to the roadmap for SAP Asset Manager can be found here: *http://s-prs.co/v518002*.
>
> Please note that a login is necessary for access to this content.

Another special function of mobile solutions may be of outstanding and pioneering importance: the RFID technology, supporting all mobile solutions.

9.2.4 RFID

RFID stands for *radio frequency identification*, which is a procedure for automatically identifying an object, animal, or person. In addition to allowing for the identification of objects without contact, RFID is also used to automatically enter and save data.

- **RFID components**
  An RFID system is comprised of a transponder, which is on or in the object (and known as an RFID tag, see Figure 9.47), and a reader for reading the transponder ID. In our case, the latter would be the RFID function of the mobile device.

- **Storage capacity**
  The storage capacity of an RFID chip ranges from 1 bit to several kilobytes. The volume of data required on the tag (for example, equipment number, maintenance date, and time) determines what variant you choose.

- **Range**
  Depending on the technical equipment, transponders have a range of between a few centimeters and 10 meters.

[+]
> **Safety Due to Short Distances**
>
> If you use RFID tags with a low range, the data can only be read from a short distance, so you can be reasonably sure that the technician has completed the work.

- **Writability**
  Transponders come in two types: non-writable and writable transponders. For writable transponders, you must distinguish between non-volatile storage (that is, the data is preserved even without a power supply) and volatile storage, which requires a permanent power supply to preserve the data.

Figure 9.47 Barcode and RFID Tag

We won't discuss RFID technology in any greater detail here. If you want to learn more about RFID technology and some of its general uses, please refer to the extensive reading material on this subject. Instead, we'll simply provide some specific examples of using this technology in SAP's plant maintenance system.

The following RFID scenarios are possible for mobile plant maintenance:

- **Scenario 1 (order processing)**
  In this scenario, you cannot modify any orders on the mobile device. You cannot process orders or enter confirmations until the reference object's RFID tag has been read. If several orders are assigned to the same reference object, you can select one order from the list.

- **Scenario 2 (maintenance history)**
  In this scenario, you can write the confirmation data to the RFID tag of a technical object, so the confirmation data is available the next time the technical object is processed.

- **Scenario 3 (reference data transfer)**
  In this scenario, you can use the data that was read from the RFID tag of a technical object when you create a notification or order.

If a mobile solution and RFID technology are used in a typical business process, the process may look like Figure 9.48.

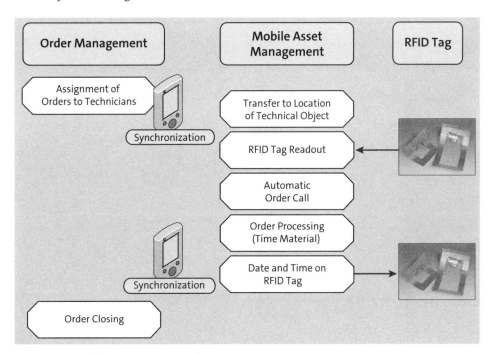

Figure 9.48 Order Management with RFID

[+]

Using RFID Where It Makes Sense

What does the RFID function contribute to mobile maintenance?

- RFID can be used to uniquely identify an object.
- When the RFID tag for a technical object is read, the stored data is displayed.
- Associated orders are released and displayed; that is, the technician cannot start work until he or she has "logged on" to the technical object.
- When you create a notification or order, you read the data from the RFID tag of the technical object, and the new document receives an error-free assignment to the technical object in question.
- For the confirmation, the data is written to the RFID tag and, therefore, considered to be evidence of having performed the work.

9.3   SAP Intelligent Asset Management

SAP Intelligent Asset Management is the solution package for a number of SAP offerings regarding the plant maintenance area. This includes the ERP systems (SAP ERP, SAP S/4HANA) as well as the mobile solutions (SAP Asset Manager, SAP Work Manager). In addition to these traditional applications, there are cloud solutions for plant maintenance which are only available in the cloud and not on-premise (see Figure 9.49).

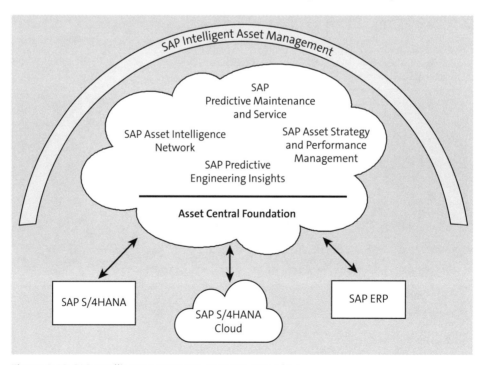

Figure 9.49 SAP Intelligent Asset Management: Overview

These cloud solutions include the following applications:

- SAP Asset Intelligence Network for exchange of asset information and documents with producers, suppliers, and service providers.
- SAP Predictive Asset Insights includes SAP Predictive Maintenance and Service for visualization of machine data in order to derive appropriate maintenance measures and SAP Predictive Engineering Insights for creating physics-based digital twins of industrial assets based on real-time and predictive engineering analysis.
- SAP Asset Strategy and Performance Management, delivering segmentation criteria for technical assets by risk, criticality impact, and environmental factors, so that individual maintenance strategies can be deduced for the respective object or type of object.
- Asset central foundation forms a common data basis for all applications within which data objects from all different SAP systems are pooled, and interface connections to various IoT solutions are offered.

9.3.1   Asset Central Foundation

Asset central foundation offers a joint database for SAP applications, a couple of integrations to the SAP backend (SAP S/4HANA, SAP ERP) as well as to the IoT solutions, and basic functionality for structuring and administrating technical assets. There are two different kinds of interfaces, as follows:

- Synchronization, i.e., bidirectional interfaces allowing differentiation of data administration while ensuring their consistency among several systems.
- Replication, i.e., data is copied by the leading system to the asset central foundation. Subsequent changes in original data are transferred as well.

The following maintenance objects feature an interface between SAP S/4HANA and the asset central foundation (see Figure 9.50). Each entry also specified if it is a synchronization ($\leftrightarrow$) or a replication ($\rightarrow$) interface:

- Equipment ($\leftrightarrow$)
- Functional locations ($\leftrightarrow$)
- Equipment classes ($\rightarrow$)
- Documents ($\leftrightarrow$)
- Material classes ($\rightarrow$)
- Notifications ($\leftrightarrow$)
- Orders ($\leftrightarrow$)
- Business partner ($\rightarrow$)
- Task lists ($\rightarrow$)
- Maintenance plans ($\rightarrow$)

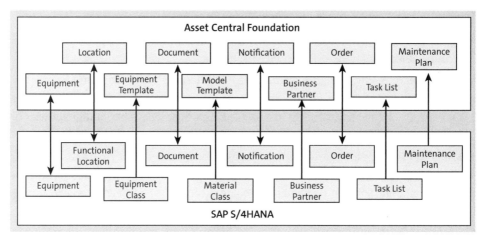

Figure 9.50 Asset Central Foundation Interfaces

Figure 9.51 shows an example of an equipment master record in SAP S/4HANA synchronized with the asset central foundation. Data is shown in a separate tab.

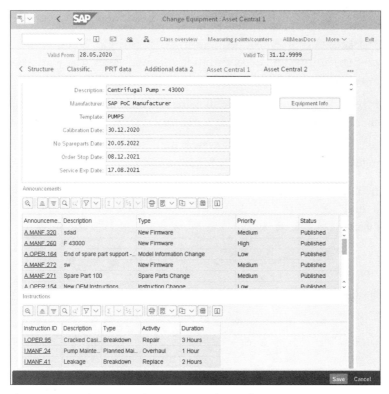

Figure 9.51 Equipment with Asset Central Foundation Data

Figure 9.52 shows an asset hierarchy with an equipment master record in asset central foundation.

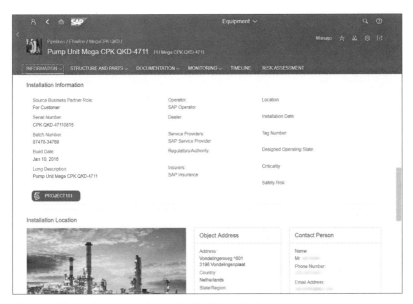

Figure 9.52 Equipment in Asset Central Foundation

9.3.2   SAP Asset Intelligence Network

SAP Asset Intelligence Network is also an IoT application and is integrated into SAP Cloud Platform. The intent of SAP Asset Intelligence Network is to support the exchange of information between manufacturers, service providers, and operators of technical systems and to create a global directory of system data with general definitions (see Figure 9.53).

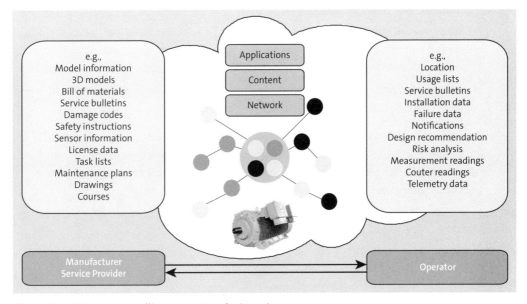

Figure 9.53 SAP Asset Intelligence Network: Overview

[»]

Note

For more information, see SAP SE (ed.), *Application Help for SAP Asset Intelligence Network*, Walldorf 2020 *http://s-prs.co/v518003*; and Seidl, M., *Intelligent Asset Management*, Walldorf 2019.

Information entered by a manufacturer or service provider for the operators could include, for example, model information, bills of materials, task lists, or drawings, whereas an operator can provide information such as location data, operating times, counter readings, error data, or notifications for manufacturers or service providers.

[+]

Central Information Platform for Everyone Involved

With a central information platform, manufacturers and service providers reach numerous operators at once and do not have to provide the information individually for each operator, and operators obtain information from numerous manufacturers and service providers via a central platform without having to acquire the information specifically from each manufacturer or service provider.

Consequently, actual data confirmed by an operator reaches all manufacturers and service providers so that they, in turn, also do not need to collect the information individually from each customer.

SAP Asset Intelligence Network consists of three components:

- Applications are provided for joint use of master data (models, equipment, spare parts) as well as for executing certain functions (i.e. improvement requirements or obsolescence management).
- Standardized content is offered which could be used by business partners jointly. Shared equipment and models are recorded, and by doing so a uniform definition is accepted.
- A network serves the purpose of connecting a number of business partners enabling intra-corporate and cross-company cooperation.

You access SAP Asset Intelligence Network via SAP Fiori launchpad (see Figure 9.54 for an operator's view). This capability provides you with an overview of the current functions and the respective key performance indicators (for example, the number of pieces of equipment).

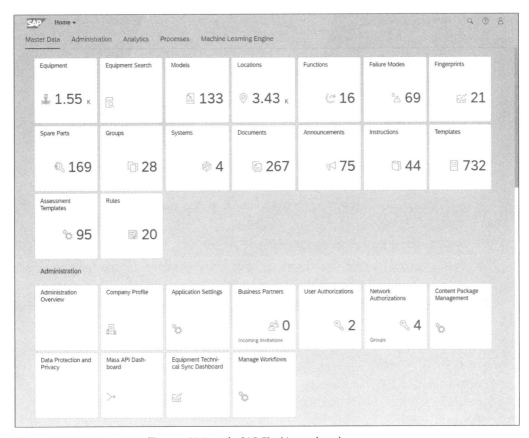

Figure 9.54 SAP Asset Intelligence Network: SAP Fiori Launchpad

To begin with, there are general functions (such as authorization, user administration, company profile, sites) by which you define the basic access to SAP Asset Intelligence Network. This section will give you a short overview of the application (e.g., which master data and which business processes there are). Then it will explain a few important apps in detail (such as the management of models or equipment), and finally, it will show you how SAP Asset Intelligence Network is integrated with SAP S/4HANA.

Master Data Overview

You can access the following master data:

- Templates for metadata maintenance, which means attributes and groups of attributes in regard to a model, a piece of equipment, a location, a system, or a spare part.
- Models (a directory of the models/construction types of the manufacturers)
- Equipment (individual objects of the operators)

- Locations, meaning virtual installation positions (simplified functional locations) within which equipment is installed or could be installed

- Systems, i.e., equipment which is logically or technically linked (control systems, transmission systems, brake systems)

- Templates (templates for models)

- Business partners (contact persons of manufacturers, service providers, or other operators)

- Attachments (documents such as drawings or images)

- Instructions (task lists and maintenance plans)

- Announcements (announcements of manufacturers and service providers for operators)

- Spare parts which may be installed in equipment

- Damage codes (the manufacturer may release damage codes for the operating company or the operator defines their own damage codes)

- Grouping of several objects to a master group (such as fleet, training, failure mode and effects analysis (FMEA), organization, spare part kit

Processes Overview

Besides master data, there are applications available for initiating and performing business processes, accessed by clicking on **Processes** at the top of the screen shown in Figure 9.53):

- Performance improvement, meaning improvement requirements of operators to be met by manufacturers as well as improvement suggestions and troubleshooting manufacturers provide for their customers.

- With the aid of app *search* you may look for error codes or information in equipment or models.

- Obsolescence management, meaning graphic representation for expiration dates of manufacturer support for a model or equipment.

- Requirements, meaning model requirements directed to the manufacturer in order to obtain recommendations for models or equipment.

In the following, I'll acquaint you with a couple of selected apps.

Business Partner App

The *Business Partner* app enables you to display a list of your contact persons of manufacturers, service providers, or other operators (see Figure 9.55). You can also send invitations to business partners and confirm incoming invitations.

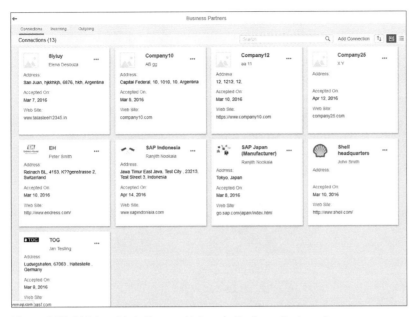

Figure 9.55 SAP Asset Intelligence Network: Business Partner App

Models App

A model is a neutral definition of a technical object that has been provided by the manufacturer and defines all maintenance data and specifications with regard to a new product or an existing product. If you want to stay with the SAP S/4HANA Asset Management terminology, models are similar to construction types. The model overview (see Figure 9.56) is comprised of all models provided by the manufacturers and service providers.

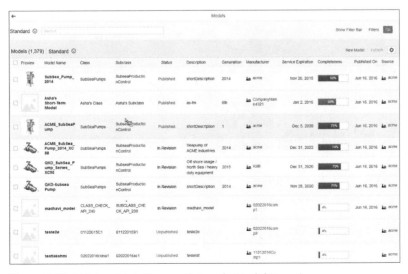

Figure 9.56 SAP Asset Intelligence Network: Model Overview

You can then display the corresponding details, such as model data, instructions, spare parts, attachments, announcements, or measuring points (see Figure 9.57).

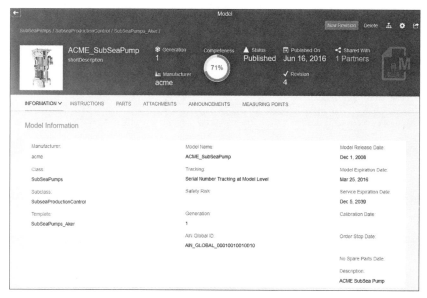

Figure 9.57 SAP Asset Intelligence Network: Model Detail

Equipment App

Like in SAP S/4HANA Asset Management, you could—being the operator—manage individual objects as equipment. You can also create your equipment using a model template. You can then also add specific information to the model data (e.g., location, installation data, or operating times) (see Figure 9.58).

Figure 9.58 SAP Asset Intelligence Network: Equipment

Spare Parts App

For each type of equipment, you may also set up a list of potential spare parts, including information like manufacturer and supplier (Figure 9.59).

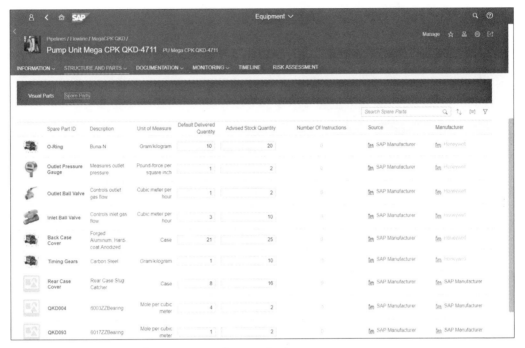

Figure 9.59 SAP Asset Intelligence Network: Spare Parts

Instructions App

Instructions are descriptions of steps to help you perform certain tasks. The manufacturer or service provider provides the operator with these instructions. Instructions include installation procedures, procedures for planned maintenance work or inspections, procedures in the case of failures, and disposal procedures. The instructions in SAP Asset Intelligence Network correspond to those in SAP S/4HANA Asset Management.

An instruction is comprised of information such as the following (see Figure 9.60):

- The steps to be performed
- The required spare parts and production resources/tools
- The models affected
- The announcements published by the manufacturer
- The severity (low, medium, high)

Figure 9.60 SAP Asset Intelligence Network: Instructions

Attachments App

You manage all files belonging to a model, a piece of equipment, or an instruction as attachments, including:

- Image files like images from SAP 3D Visual Enterprise Viewer
- Drawings like CAD design drawings
- Documents like certificates or process instructions

The Attachment app (see Figure 9.61) enables you to display existing documents, upload new documents, or locally download existing documents.

Figure 9.61 SAP Asset Intelligence Network: Attachments

Announcements App

The Announcements app includes information sent by the manufacturer to the operator. In SAP Asset Intelligence Network, the following announcement types are available:

- Change of instructions (when instructions were changed)
- Service bulletin (when recurring problems emerge for this model)
- Recall (when an operator is asked to return the equipment due to safety problems)
- New guidelines (when new guidelines are published for the use of models)
- New model (when a new model is available)
- Change of attachment (when an attachment for a model was changed)
- Change of spare parts (when spare parts were changed)
- Change of model information (when information for the model specifications was changed)

Performance Improvement App

If you encounter problems during the operation of your equipment, you can open an improvement case to obtain proposals or problem solutions. Improvement cases enable you to involve all stakeholders in order to develop a proposal or solution in collaboration with them, including internal stakeholders (for example, from construction) and external stakeholders (for example, operators or service providers).

The following parties are involved in the workflow:

- The requester who requests a proposed solution
- The reviewer who reviews the improvement case sent by the requester
- The provider of a proposed solution who proposes a solution for the improvement case

SAP S/4HANA Integration

If you are a user who only wants to display information on your equipment in SAP Asset Intelligence Network but does not want to store documents there, the interface from SAP Asset Intelligence Network with SAP S/4HANA Asset Management is probably sufficient for your purposes.

This interface enables you to display information on equipment from SAP Asset Intelligence Network as a side panel (see Figure 9.62).

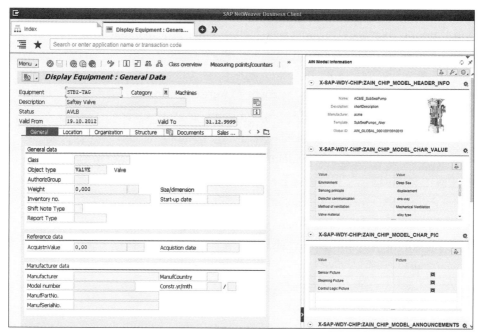

Figure 9.62 SAP Asset Intelligence Network: SAP S/4HANA Integration

SAP Ariba Integration

There is also an interface between SAP Asset Intelligence Network and SAP Ariba: Now you can transmit material from the SAP Asset Intelligence Network spare part list to SAP Ariba's shopping basket and proceed with further procurement processes (see Figure 9.63).

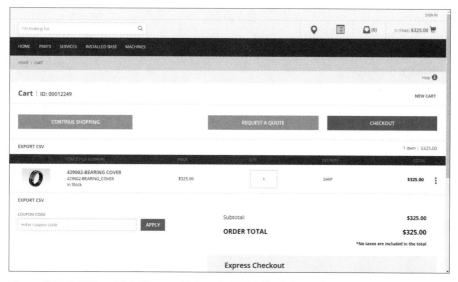

Figure 9.63 SAP Asset Intelligence Network-SAP Ariba Integration

9.3.3   SAP Asset Strategy and Performance Management

SAP Asset Strategy and Performance Management is a cloud solution that allows you to assess your asset reliability as well as assigning the assets with the help of evaluation tools like FMEA (failure mode and effect analysis) to a category in the risk and criticality matrix. The intention is to match each technical object or group of technical objects with appropriate maintenance strategies:

- Run to failure
- Preventive maintenance, time-based or performance-based
- Predictive maintenance
- Condition-based maintenance
- Reliability-based maintenance

Further Reading

For more information, see SAP SE (ed.), *Application Help for SAP Asset Strategy and Performance Management*, Walldorf, 2020: *http://s-prs.co/v518004*; and Seidl, M., *Intelligent Asset Management*, Walldorf, 2019.

This section will give you an overview of the SAP Asset Strategy and Performance Management cycle, and then will walk you through the six steps of the cycle in detail.

SAP Asset Strategy and Performance Management Cycle Overview

The cycle of SAP Asset Strategy and Performance Management could be described as follows (see Figure 9.64):

- Definition of systems and asset to analyze
- Identification of critical assets

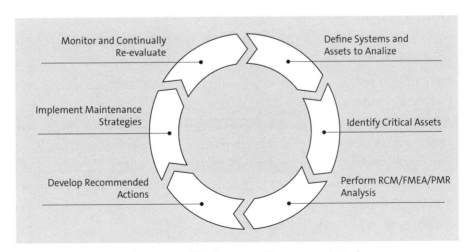

Figure 9.64 SAP Asset Strategy and Performance Management: Cycle

- Performance of FMEA analysis
- Development of recommended actions
- Decision on appropriate maintenance strategies and implementation
- Monitoring and follow-up of decisions taken

Defining Master Data (Step 1)

The master data needed for SAP Asset Strategy and Performance Management is initially the same as for SAP Asset Intelligence Network:

- Templates for metadata maintenance, which means attributes and groups of attributes in regard to a model, a piece of equipment, a location, a system, or a spare part
- Models (a directory of the models/construction types of the manufacturers)
- Equipment (individual objects of the operators)
- Locations, meaning virtual installation positions (simplified functional locations) within which equipment is installed or could be installed
- Systems, i.e., equipment which is logically or technically linked (control systems, transmission systems, brake systems)
- Templates (templates for models)
- Business partners (contact persons of manufacturers, service providers, or other operators)
- Attachments (documents such as drawings or images)
- Instructions (task lists and maintenance plans)
- Announcements (announcements of manufacturers and service providers for operators)
- Spare parts which may be installed in equipment
- Damage codes (the manufacturer may release damage codes for the operating company, or the operator may define their own damage codes)
- Grouping of several objects to a master group (such as fleet, training, FMEA, organization, spare part kit)

Above this, there is additional master data needed for the SAP Asset Strategy and Performance Management cycle:

- Evaluation templates are needed for assessment of equipment, locations, and groups. The types are risk and criticality matrix templates, questionnaire templates, FMEA analysis, checklist templates, and RCM evaluation template.
- Damage categories like security of people, environmental requirements, breakdowns, financial consequences, and others.
- Scales and answers as a basis for valuation.
- Dimension and questions as a basis for valuation.

Identification of Critical Assets (Step 2)

Valuation and checklist templates serve as a basis for risk and criticality assessment, which could then be carried out for equipment, locations, groups, and systems. The assessment identifies impact, dimension, and scales (Figure 9.65).

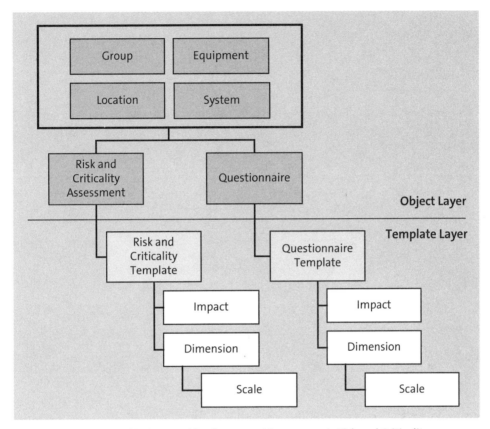

Figure 9.65 SAP Asset Strategy and Performance Management: Risk and Criticality Assessments

Figure 9.66 shows an assessment carried out this way with referential object (equipment) questions, answers, and scales of the answers. As a result, the object for which the questionnaire was carried out will be assigned to the criticality matrix, in reference to the following questions (see Figure 9.67):

- How strong is the effect of the error (on the environment, people, production, finance)?

- What is the level of risk in case of breakdown (actual, existing, initial, reduced risk)?

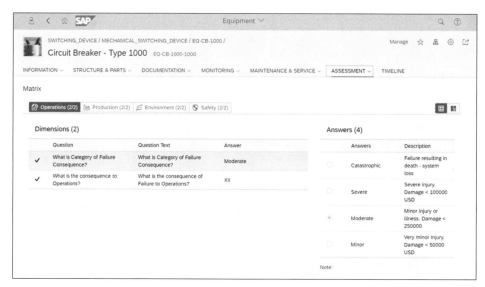

Figure 9.66 SAP Asset Strategy and Performance Management: Assessment Result

Figure 9.67 SAP Asset Strategy and Performance Management: Criticality Matrix

How is the criticality calculated? Criticality is a function of risk. The risk is normally calculated by *probability of break down x consequences of breakdown*. The higher the risk, the more critical the equipment. Criticality is determined by threshold value defined in an evaluation template.

The result is a list of objects indicating the following (see Figure 9.68):

- Which object shows which criticality
- How high the breakdown risk is estimated
- A recommendation of measures to be taken

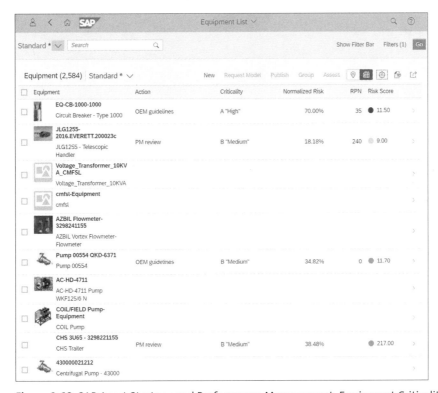

Figure 9.68 SAP Asset Strategy and Performance Management: Equipment Criticality List

Performing FMEA Analyses (Step 3)

FMEA is an acknowledged method for analyzing potential reliability issues to be able to take reasonable steps and reduce errors. It is used to identify types of breakdowns, their causes, and effects on technical objects.

- Identify and recognize potential issues, including causes and effects.
- Evaluate and prioritize the errors identified.
- Propose appropriate measures for eliminating or reducing errors.

You may determine a certain strategy for maintenance on the level of the particular damage code. Certain damage codes could be assigned to models, equipment, locations, spare parts, and groups. They are based on a subcategory and consist of various categories and types. Maintenance strategy is determined by damage code as well as by combined cause/effect scenario. This is why one damage code may have more than one maintenance strategy, depending on the causes and effects assigned to it.

For each technical object, you can display the following indicators (see Figure 9.69):

- RAMS key figures (reliability, availability, maintainability, security)
- Classical plant maintenance key figures (MTTF, MTTR, MTBF)

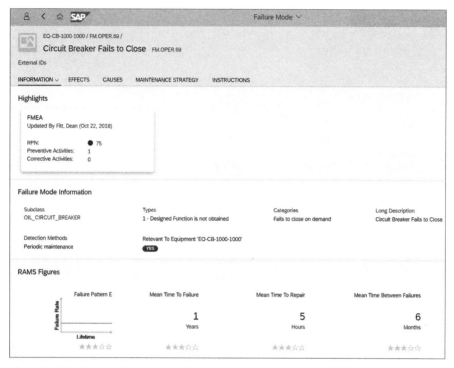

Figure 9.69 SAP Asset Strategy and Performance Management: FMEA Analysis

Developing Follow-Up Activities (Step 4)

The heart of the action is instructions. An instruction is a collection of steps intended to support a user to accomplish certain tasks. In SAP Asset Strategy and Performance Management, the manufacturers release instructions for the operator. Instructions assist and facilitate maintenance of equipment.

- Instructions describe how maintenance is to be carried out.
- There are different kinds of instructions, such as breakdown repair, installation operation, and planned maintenance.
- Instructions can be assigned to certain models, equipment, or groups.
- Failure modes can be assigned to breakdown instructions.
- You may establish the number of steps, duration, criticality, safety guidelines, production resources and tools, and required and spare parts.
- In addition, you may determine prerequisites, the steps themselves, and review.
- You may add various documents. If an animated 3D file was added, the end user may display the sequences.

Figure 9.70 shows this kind of instruction, a maintenance instruction with an animated 3D model.

Figure 9.70 SAP Asset Strategy and Performance Management: 3D Model-Based Instruction

Figure 9.71 shows a risk and criticality assessment of equipment, the outcome of the FMEA analysis, filled-in checklists, the RCM result, and instructions.

Figure 9.71 SAP Asset Strategy and Performance Management: Risk-Assessed Equipment

How to Implement a Maintenance Strategy (Step 5)

Even today, it's still a manual process to assign the right maintenance strategy to a technical object and decide if you want to adopt, e.g., a breakdown-related strategy (run to failure) or if it might be worth it to consider predictive maintenance. This means you will have to decide manually—on the basis of available information—and implement the subsequent changes manually in the SAP system.

The SAP roadmap contains the *Maintenance Strategy Workbench,* which is meant not only to support you in decision making but also to bring about the changes in the SAP system automatically or at least semi-automatically.

Monitoring and Evaluation (Step 6)

In order to review the effects of your decisions and measures, there are, among other things, analytical SAP Fiori apps available:

- Maintenance Planning Overview
- Maintenance Scheduling Board
- Technical Object Damages
- Analytical List Page for Technical Objects Breakdown
- Actual Maintenance Cost Analysis

Also, you may use all of the controlling instruments described in Chapter 8, Section 8.2, such as standard ALV list, LIS analyses, and SAP Business Warehouse queries.

The next two sections will introduce SAP Predictive Asset Insights, including SAP Predictive Maintenance and Service for visualization of machine data in order to derive appropriate maintenance measures as well as SAP Predictive Engineering Insights for creating physics-based digital twins of industrial assets based on a real-time and predictive engineering analysis.

9.3.4   SAP Predictive Maintenance and Service

SAP Predictive Maintenance and Service is an IoT application (Internet of Things) in the cloud, but is also has an on-premise version. SAP Predictive Maintenance and Service is based on an SAP HANA database. This section introduces the cloud version.

The purpose of the application is as follows:

- To visualize current machine data by direct access and thus improve the visibility of machinery
- To support condition monitoring by extended analytical functions, models of engineering, and machine learning
- To be able to forecast as well as simulate the behavior of machines on the basis of this model

Further Reading

For more information, see SAP SE (ed.), *Application Help for SAP Predictive Maintenance and Service – Cloud Edition*, Walldorf, 2020, *http://s-prs.co/v510805*; and Seidl, M., *Intelligent Asset Management*, Walldorf, 2019.

SAP Fiori launchpad as the entry point offers all functions of SAP Predictive Maintenance and Service on tiles (see Figure 9.72).

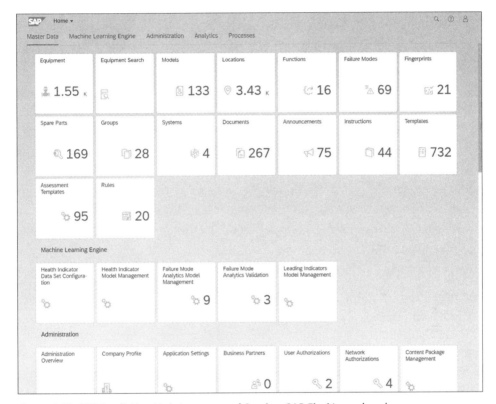

Figure 9.72 SAP Predictive Maintenance and Service: SAP Fiori Launchpad

The following sections will introduce you to the master data of SAP Predictive Maintenance and Service, which is similar to that of other applications, supplemented by SAP Predictive Maintenance and Service-specific master data such as fingerprints and rules. A couple of important analyses (such as indicator diagrams and failure mode analyses) and functions (such as equipment explorer and work activities) are explained.

Master Data

To start with, the master data needed for SAP Predictive Maintenance and Service is initially the same as in all other applications of SAP Intelligent Asset Management:

- Templates for metadata maintenance, which means attributes and groups of attributes in regard to a model, equipment, a location, a system, or a spare part
- Models (a directory of the models/construction types of the manufacturers)
- Equipment (individual objects of the operators)
- Locations, meaning virtual installation positions (simplified functional locations) within which equipment is installed or could be installed
- Systems, i.e., equipment which is logically or technically linked (control systems, transmission systems, brake systems)
- Templates (templates for models)
- Business partners (contact persons of manufacturers, service providers, or other operators)
- Attachments (documents such as drawings or images)
- Instructions (task lists and maintenance plans)
- Announcements (announcements of manufacturers and service providers for operators)
- Spare parts which may be installed in equipment
- Damage codes (the manufacturer may release damage codes for the operating company, or the operator may define their own damage codes)
- Grouping of several objects to a master group (such as fleet, training, FMEA, organization, spare part kit)

Additional functions here are fingerprints and rules:

- A fingerprint is a summary of snapshots within a certain time frame (type, date and time, description, condition of equipment, documents). It describes a referential status of a single piece of equipment which might be used for further process steps, such as for equipment documentation. Fingerprints provide support in defining the normal, referential, and error status of equipment. At a later time, these states could be used for recognizing deviations from the normal state as well as for planning measures to return to the normal state.
- Rules are defined for either a model or equipment. Based on these rules, certain events are triggered; for example, you may send emails with certain tasks to responsible users.

Indicator Diagram

An indicator diagram serves to present you with a graphic view of one or more types of equipment over time. You may determine indicators, time intervals, and other options.

Figure 9.73, for an example, shows the development of the input temperature and oil level and storage temperature for a 4-week period.

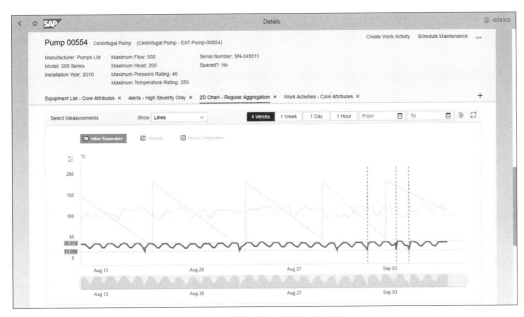

Figure 9.73 SAP Predictive Maintenance and Service: Indicator Diagram

Such a connectivity could also be achieved with SAP Asset Manager and the indicator development be displayed there (see Figure 9.74).

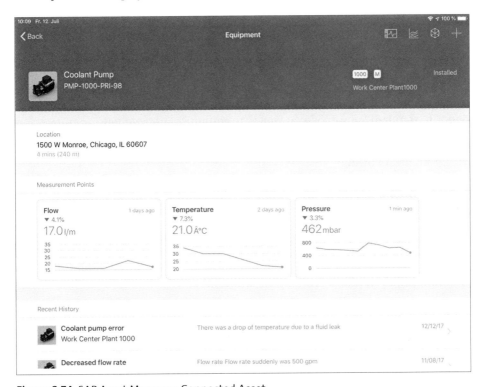

Figure 9.74 SAP Asset Manager: Connected Asset

Equipment Explorer

If you need to get an overview of the actual condition of all equipment as well as the indicators' latest measured values, the functionality of the equipment explorer will help you further (see Figure 9.75). In particular, you will find out where the predefined indicator is to be found: a green, a yellow, or a red field.

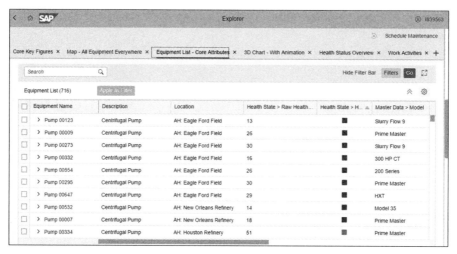

Figure 9.75 SAP Predictive Maintenance and Service: Equipment Explorer

Failure Mode Analyses

Failure mode analyses use machine learning to convert human knowledge comprised of message text to knowledge about the nature of failures and assign them automatically to an error code.

Failure mode analyses extract themes by frequently used words in message texts assigned to standard failure codes as well as to equipment and models.

In SAP Predictive Maintenance and Service, you can display all failure mode analyses arising from the following:

- Equipment with the KPIs MTTR, MTBF, and MTTF
- Models with the KPIs MTTR, MTBF, and MTTF

Figure 9.76 presents an example. It shows a failure mode analysis of the most common damage codes in the course of a year. The graphical depiction shows a comparison of this equipment data and the average equipment model data with the classical indicators MTTR, MTBF, and MTTF

Work Activities

From various applications, you can create a new work activity (similar to a notification; see Figure 9.77). A list will give you an overview of all defined work activities (see Figure 9.78).

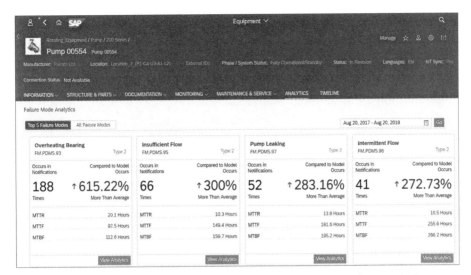

Figure 9.76 SAP Predictive Maintenance and Service: Equipment Failure Analysis

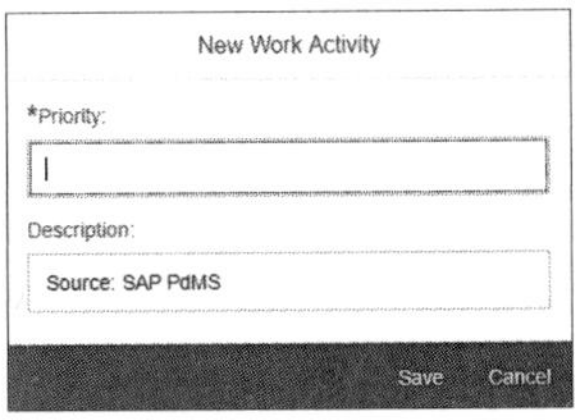

Figure 9.77 SAP Predictive Maintenance and Service: New Work Activity

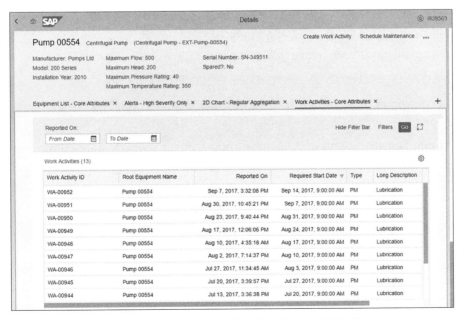

Figure 9.78 SAP Predictive Maintenance and Service: Work Activity List

563

Machine Learning

Let's now look at the application of machine learning in SAP Predictive Maintenance and Service. One approach deals with failure mode analysis, as follows:

- The first step is the assignment of each equipment model to potential damage codes along with configuring the *notification language*.

- Various algorithms are inserted, such as the *latent Dirichlet allocation* or *ensemble technique*, in order to get the characteristics of the notification texts analyzed.

- The machine learning engine assigns the notification texts to the characteristics found in failure mode analysis and suggests an appropriate damage code to each notification.

Another approach is prediction: Here, the aim is to calculate the condition of a piece of equipment (health) out of which the occurrence of errors could be deduced.

First, you have to define the datasets, which involves determining in which way and for which period of time indicators should be aggregated.

Next, mathematical-statistical models are applied to calculate health and to develop projections:

- Anomaly detection with *principal component analysis (PCA)*
- Distance-based failure analysis using *earth mover's distance (EMD)*
- *Logistic regression for failure prediction (LOR)*
- Anomaly detection using *interquartile range (IQR)*
- Failure prediction using *automatic failure prediction (AFP)*
- Anomaly detection using *automatic anomaly detection (AAD)*
- Anomaly detection using *multivariate autoregression (MAR)*
- Failure prediction using *tree ensemble classifier (TEC)*
- Anomaly detection using one class *support vector machine (SVM)*

Possible outcomes could be health scores (see Figure 9.79) or forecast categories, for example.

For the time being, the usage of machine learning is still in the early stages. It remains to be seen how it will be used and if there are sufficient cases of application in practice.

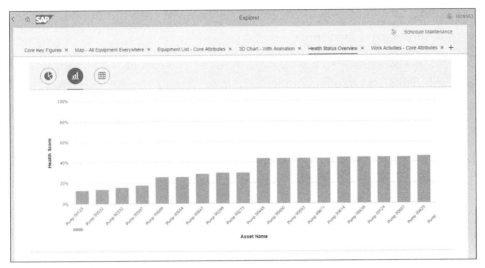

Figure 9.79 SAP Predictive Maintenance and Service: Health Status Overview

9.3.5   SAP Predictive Engineering Insights

SAP Predictive Engineering Insights is a cloud IoT application and is built on an SAP HANA database. The purpose of the application is as follows:

- To get a real-time overview of equipment (location, alerts, key metrics; see Figure 9.80)

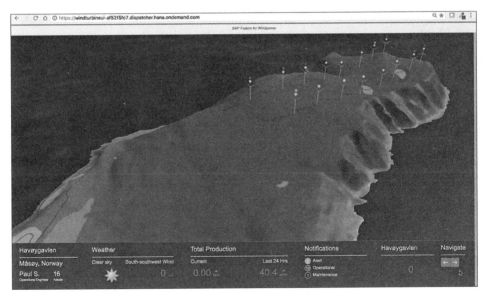

Figure 9.80 SAP Predictive Engineering Insights Equipment Overview

- To analyze asset health with help of physical and virtual sensors

565

- To analyze vibrations with spectrograms and frequency spectra
- To perform what-if simulations

The following sections will introduce you to the master data of SAP Predictive Engineering Insights. Then you'll learn about a couple of important analyses (such as structural and vibration analyses) and what-if simulations.

Master Data

The master data needed for SAP Predictive Engineering Insights is initially the same as in all other applications of SAP Intelligent Asset Management, but there are only three of them:

- Templates for metadata maintenance, which means attributes and groups of attributes in regard to a model, a piece of equipment, a location, a system, or a spare part.
- Models (a directory of the models/construction types of the manufacturers)
- Equipment (individual objects of the operators)

Structural Analysis

SAP Predictive Engineering Insights uses data from physical sensors on a piece of equipment as input for simulating the stresses and strains on a digital representation of the equipment. Figure 9.81 shows how real-world equipment works together with its digital twin.

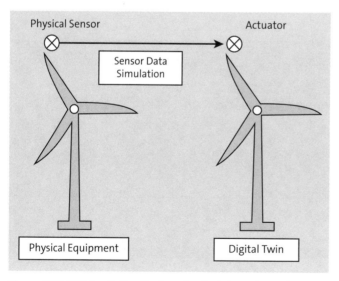

Figure 9.81 SAP Predictive Engineering Insights: Physical Equipment and Digital Twin

The physical sensors transmit data about the external forces in real time. The solution uses data from the physical sensors as an input for an actuator on the equipment's digital twin. The actuator is a component that grabs data from a physical sensor to prescribe the motions of a digital twin. SAP Predictive Engineering Insights uses data from physical sensors as input for an actuator on the digital twin. The actuator stimulates the digital twin of an item of equipment with motions that correspond to those of the physical equipment.

Vibration Analysis

Vibration analysis is a condition-monitoring technique for detecting developing faults in advance of their manifestation and predicting failure.

To analyze emerging malfunctions, you can add spectrograms and frequency spectrums. Whereas a spectrogram shows how the spectrum of frequencies for a selected indicator varies over time, a spectrum shows the frequency for a selected indicator at a particular point in time.

What-If Simulations

You can run what-if simulations of different usage scenarios to decide which best suits your specific needs (see Figure 9.82).

Figure 9.82 SAP Predictive Engineering Insights: What-If Simulations

---

Further Reading

For more information, see SAP SE (ed.), *Application Help for SAP Engineering Insights enabled by ANSYS*, Walldorf, 2020 *http://s-prs.co/v518006*; and Seidl, M., *Intelligent Asset Management*, Walldorf, 2019.

9.4   Summary

This chapter introduced some new information and communication technologies for plant maintenance purposes.

SAP 3D Visual Enterprise Viewer offers visualization functions for technical objects, spare parts, and instructions that are available in SAP Business Client as well as on mobile devices (such as tablets).

SAP Fiori was introduced as the new SAP user interface technology, which enables all users—professional users as well as casual users—to access SAP systems. The most important SAP Fiori apps for plant maintenance purposes were introduced, such as Request Maintenance, Maintenance Planning Overview, and Actual Maintenance Cost Analysis.

As mobile solutions for plant maintenance, *SAP Work Manager* and *SAP Asset Manager* were introduced. SAP Work Manager is the older mobile SAP solution for maintenance, and the end of usage time frame is foreseeable. In contrast, SAP Asset Manager is the newer SAP solution for mobile maintenance and represents the strategic direction.

SAP Intelligent Asset Management summarizes SAP's various cloud solutions for plant maintenance, which are only available as cloud editions but not on-premises:

- *SAP Asset Intelligence Network* for exchange of asset information and documents with producers, suppliers, and service providers
- *SAP Predictive Maintenance and Service* for visualization of machine data in order to derive appropriate maintenance measures
- *SAP Predictive Engineering Insights* for managing digital twins and performing what-if simulations
- *SAP Asset Strategy and Performance Management*, delivering segmentation criteria for technical assets by risk, criticality impact, and environmental factors, so that individual maintenance strategies can be deduced for the respective object or type of object
- *Asset central foundation* as the common data basis for all applications within which data objects from all different SAP systems are pooled and interface connections to various IoT solutions are offered

For the time being, the usage of all SAP Intelligent Asset Management applications is in the early stages. It remains to be seen how it will be used and if there are enough cases of applications in practice.

Chapter 10
Usability

It is a widespread prejudice that usability is not a major feature of the SAP system. This chapter, hence, intends to show the possibilities the SAP system offers to improve said usability. In several empirical laboratory tests, we set up real-world conditions to find out whether improved usability has an impact on the time taken for processing business processes—and if so, how.

There is a reason for placing this chapter in a prominent position at the end of the book. Being particularly important in not only one regard, many companies, however, are paying too little attention to usability, not realizing which benefits they are missing out on.

Some common judgments by self-appointed experts, and an even more common prejudice among those without firsthand knowledge of the SAP system, include the following:

- SAP has not given much importance to usability.
- SAP takes too long to process business transactions.
- The screens are overloaded with information.
- SAP is not usable at all.

All I can say is "That's right!":

- Many companies use standard settings, standard screens, and standard processes when implementing SAP systems and expect their end users to work with these.
- Many companies do not pay much attention to this aspect when implementing SAP systems.
- Many companies do not make ample use of the fine-tuning options the SAP system provides by default—if they even know about them.

Therefore, a particular concern of this last chapter is to explore the possibilities for enhancing usability and to introduce the results from several laboratory tests conducted at our university under real-world conditions.

Perhaps this chapter will help dispel the prejudice that the SAP system is not user-friendly.

For a clearer understanding, let's explore the following four questions:

- What is meant by usability?
- How can usability be measured?
- Does usability mean the same as user acceptance?
- Why is usability so important in plant maintenance?

This chapter will then describe the individual tuning measures and point out where and why they can improve usability. Finally, I'll introduce our laboratory test and its results, which are central in answering the following question: How much can the processing time for a business process be reduced if tuning measures are applied?

10.1 Basics

This chapter offers both an introduction to the topic of usability and answers to a few fundamental questions in this context. What is usability anyway? What are the criteria for usability? What is the difference between user acceptance and usability? Why are these topics of crucial importance for plant maintenance?

10.1.1 What Is Meant by Usability?

Usability refers to the user-friendliness that a user experiences when interacting with a system. A system has high usability if its operation is easy and in accordance with the user's requirements and the tasks to be performed.

In a standardization context, usability is typically also referred to as the *ergonomics* of a software product. In the DIN EN ISO 9241 standardization series, in Part 110 (Dialogue Principles), usability is defined as the product of *effectiveness*, *efficiency*, and *user satisfaction*. Whereas hardware ergonomics refers to the adaptation of tools to the movement and perception apparatus of humans (for example, body forces and movement spaces), software ergonomics deals with the adaptation to the cognitive and physical abilities and characteristics of humans, such as their capacity to process information (for example, complexity), as well as software-controlled display features (for example, colors and font sizes).

In DIN EN ISO 9241-110, seven principles have been defined, which we will describe in detail next. Because the standardization texts by themselves do not provide a lot of information, this chapter contains a few examples to illustrate how the relevant principles could be implemented in an SAP system.

[!]
Principle 1: Suitability for the Task

A dialog supports suitability for the task if it supports the user in the effective and efficient completion of the task.

Examples of the suitability for the task in the SAP system include the following:

- A transaction should not require information that has nothing to do with processing the relevant business process.
- In an input screen, the cursor should be placed in the first field to be completed or corrected.
- The sequence of input screens and fields should be designed in such a way as is needed for the logical execution of a business process.

[!]

Principle 2: Self-Descriptiveness

A dialog supports self-descriptiveness if each dialog step is immediately comprehensible through feedback from the system or is explained to the user on request for the relevant information.

Examples of self-descriptiveness in the SAP system include the following:

- Links are formulated in such a way that their targets are clear.
- An application has an online help system providing context-specific information.
- Erroneous entries trigger comprehensible error messages that contain explanatory long texts with regard to how the error can be undone or avoided.

[!]

Principle 3: Controllability

A dialog supports controllability if the user is able to maintain direction over the whole course of the interaction until the point at which the goal has been met.

Examples of controllability in the SAP system include the following:

- Transactions contain buttons or menu functions that enable you to navigate directly to any screen of the process.
- Lists contain buttons that enable you to sort the information in any column according to diverse criteria (e.g., date or quantity).
- If a database request takes too long, it can be cancelled.

[!]

Principle 4: Conformity with User Expectations

A dialog supports conformity with user expectations if it corresponds to the user's task knowledge, education, and experience and to commonly held conventions.

Examples of conformity with user expectations in the SAP system include the following:

- Identical terms should be used to convey identical pieces of information (for example, a general ledger account is always referred to as a GL account).

- Identical buttons should be used for identical functions (e.g., the same icon should always be used to enable the deletion of an entry).
- When a user presses the [Tab] key, the cursor jumps to the next input field.

[!]

Principle 5: Error Tolerance

A dialog supports error tolerance if, despite evident errors in input, the intended results may be achieved with either no or minimal corrective action having to be taken. Errors should be explained to the user so they can be corrected.

Examples of error tolerance in the SAP system include the following:

- Before data is saved, the data is automatically checked for plausibility and for missing or incomplete information.
- In case of an incorrect data input, the cursor jumps directly to the respective field, which is highlighted in color.
- Error messages are not displayed in technical jargon or as a number but, instead, are formulated such that the user understands them.

[!]

Principle 6: Suitability for Individualization

A dialog supports suitability for individualization if the dialog system is constructed to allow for modification to the user's individual needs and skills for a given task.

Examples of suitability for individualization in the SAP system include the following:

- In a customized list, the user can determine which information should be displayed, how it should be sorted, and so on.
- The user can define customized default values in order to avoid re-entering standard information such as plant, company code, and so on.
- The user can set which dialog boxes are to be used in order to support his or her business processes (e.g., warnings prior to saving data).

[!]

Principle 7: Suitability for Learning

A dialog supports suitability for learning if it guides the user through the learning stages, minimizing the learning time.

Examples of suitability for learning in the SAP system include the following:

- Users are introduced to the business process in a "guided tour."
- Alternatively, external tools are provided that demonstrate the processing of a business process to the user.
- Before saving, the system allows for simulated executions or test postings.

The following principle applies in all cases: Usability is highly inconspicuous because it is meant to serve its assigned function and no other secondary purpose. Usability becomes noticeable only if it is missing.

From a superficial point of view, we could maintain that the SAP system meets all criteria of software ergonomics. In addition to the examples previously listed, numerous other examples exist for each of the seven principles, which confirms that the SAP system is ergonomic.

Counterexamples in the SAP System

Why then does the SAP system have the reputation for poor usability? Why do SAP users often feel that the system is all too complicated and difficult? The answer is simple: In the standard version, many examples also testify to the opposite of usability:

- The sequence of screens (dialogs, tabs) does not match the workflow of the user.
- The data required for a business process is spread out over several screens.
- Identical fields have different field labels (e.g., vendor and supplier, general ledger account, and cost element).
- The screens are overloaded with unnecessary information.
- The SAP system still contains a large number of hard-coded lists that cannot be manipulated by the user.
- The design of lists is outdated.
- Lists contain many pages of entries, although all the user wants to see is the orders of his cost center, for example.
- The user has to enter data that is not needed for his of her specific purpose, such as the plant, purchasing organization, business area, or cost element.
- The user has to manually retrieve information from the SAP system, instead of the system presenting the information.
- In certain circumstances, the user has to call more than five subsequent transactions for a business process.
- Almost never can the user simulate or temporarily store data before saving it to the database.
- The user repeatedly has to click away popups.
- The SAP system contains, in some cases, three to four different icons that enable the same function (e.g., deletion of entries).
- Sometimes the pushbutton bar is positioned in the upper area of the screen and sometimes at the bottom, without any recognizable underlying pattern.
- The user abhors the multilevel SAP menu.

These and similar complaints abound and should not be ignored but taken seriously.

> **⊞**
>
> **Counteracting Non-Usability Concerns**
>
> During the implementation phase, be attentive to the concerns of your employees regarding the usability of the SAP system. Do not ignore the topic but do address your employees' concerns and try to find a solution by implementing appropriate measures.

10.1.2   Assessing Usability

To assess the usability of an IT system, we can rely on a qualitative assessment of its users and/or base the assessment on quantitative criteria.

To measure usability by qualitative assessment, different methods, such as surveys, observation, questionnaires, and so on, are used to obtain a subjective evaluation from the users of the system. As you saw in the previous section, usability and ergonomics involve many subjective aspects. Therefore, user assessment also is subjective and varies depending on the user and the situation.

Results obtained from quantitative methods, for which data can be collected, are much more reliable, objective, and stable.

After all, everything is reflected in a single key figure: the *processing time* key figure, which represents the time it takes a user to process a business transaction in the system.

Therefore, the main focus here will be on *processing time* when exploring the possibilities for improving usability (see sections Section 10.2 to Section 10.4), and this key figure will be examined in the laboratory tests (see section Section 10.5).

In addition to the processing time, another key figure that can be used as a measurement of usability is the *control entries* key figure. Control entries are those interactions that are required for controlling the IT system but which do not involve data entry. These interactions include clicking buttons and pressing the Tab and Enter keys.

Other values that allow for assessing usability include:

- The number of screens
- The number of mouse clicks
- The time spent looking at a screen
- The length of the mouse trail

You must decide yourself whether collecting these key figures will add value to your company when assessing system usability.

10.1.3   Why Usability Does Not Mean User Acceptance

Particularly in the IT industry and in IT departments, you often encounter the predominant opinion that improved usability automatically results in an increase in user acceptance. Another assumption states that usability is the only means of achieving the relevant acceptance among users.

In my opinion, both assumptions are not only wrong, but they are serious mistakes. The actions taken to increase user acceptance must consist of both actions taken to increase usability *and* organizational measures (see Figure 10.1).

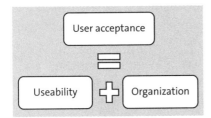

Figure 10.1 User Acceptance

But what organizational measures will help you increase the user acceptance? I have run numerous workshops on *usability* and *user acceptance*, and in each of these workshops, the participants developed organizational measures to increase user acceptance, including some of the following measures:

- Large monitors were taken in use.
- SAPLogon was made available on each computer.
- An intranet help site was set up.
- A small wiki was created.
- Only a small number of options was made available (e.g., for damage codes).
- Key users were selected from the group of participants.
- Participants trained participants (the so-called "Hey Joe effect").
- A hotline was set up that the participants could call at any time (24 hours a day), particularly during the early stages.
- Alternatively, a central email address could be set up which would automatically respond that a service person will call back within a predefined timeframe (e.g., in no more than 30 minutes).
- During the implementation phase, feedback was collected from the participants, and suggested measures implemented as far as possible.
- While in the implementation phase, the participants were regularly presented with the latest status of the system.
- The participants were informed in detail about what was going to happen with the data they had entered.
- The necessity of the respective data entries was emphasized, in particular the correctness of the data.

- Official praise was expressed when, in the preceding year, the number of correct messages exceeded a given figure.

- We had to engage in a great deal of persuasion of the potential users, in particular by demonstrating the benefits and necessity of using the SAP system.

- End users were intensively involved in the test phase.

- The company representatives were regular members of user groups (e.g., in the Plant Maintenance and Service Management work group of the German SAP User Group or in the User Interface work group).

- Immediately after the training, the participants were allowed to sift through what they had just learned. For this purpose, they were given a certain amount of time as well as a test system. In fact, without this opportunity for knowledge consolidation, they would've quickly forgotten much of what they had been taught.

- Handouts were created in the language of the tradesmen.

- The business process was visualized by means of a simple event-driven process chain, and SAP transactions were entered.

- Simple operating instructions were created and laminated, which could easily be placed underneath each keyboard.

- The processes were recorded using the relevant tools (such as SAP Enable Now) and made available to the tradesmen.

- And again and again, it was training, training, training. This measure in particular was regarded as extremely important in all discussions.

[+]

The Right Approach When Training Your Employees

When planning and implementing training, you should employ the following principles:

- Modularize your training. The training of individual modules should take approximately a half day; the absolute maximum is one entire day.

- End-user training should be provided by employees in your company, ideally by the representatives of the user department in the project team.

- For the training, use the system environment and examples of the technical objects that the end users will encounter in their work later on.

- Finally, carry out the end-user training close to go-live; otherwise, your users will have forgotten much of what they learned by the time the system goes live.

This list of measures to increase user acceptance could be continued endlessly, particularly because each company has its own specific organizational measures. Therefore, you should pay heed to the advice in the following text box.

[+]

The Organization Is As Important As Usability

Make an informed decision as to which organizational measures are likely to increase user acceptance in your company.

10.1.4 Why Is It that User Acceptance Is so important in Plant Maintenance?

The aspects of *usability* and *user acceptance* play an important role in all areas of an organization. However, in the technical areas of a company, which include plant maintenance, their role can be substantial.

Usability and user acceptance of the SAP system are more important in plant maintenance than in SAP S/4HANA Finance or purchasing for following reasons:

- **Number of users**
  The first reason has to do with the number of users involved during implementation. During implementation of commercial applications, the number of users involved is relatively small, whereas you will delve much more deeply into a company's operation and work with a much larger number of users during SAP S/4HANA Asset Management implementation. This pattern is especially the case if tradesmen need to generate or confirm orders themselves.

- **Level of training and experience**
  The second reason has to do with the level of training and experience with IT systems. Whereas users from the commercial part of the company already have experience in using IT systems, are well trained, and have used other IT systems previously, in an extreme case, the users you meet during SAP S/4HANA Asset Management implementation might be sitting in front of a computer for the first time, and even using a mouse and a keyboard might be challenging for them. If users from plant maintenance are slightly more experienced, they might know Office applications or computer-based maintenance systems, but generally they will lack experience using integrated business software such as the SAP S/4HANA system.

- **A different approach to handling orders**
  Moreover, the approach to handling orders is different from the one employed in controlling, for example. In controlling, an internal order is considered more in terms of a cost collector, standing order, annual order, lifecycle order, and so on. In plant maintenance, the emphasis is on processing as many activities as possible as measure-related individual orders due to assignment and weak-point analysis reasons. As a result, the number of maintenance orders completed in plant maintenance over the course of one year significantly exceeds the number of internal orders, and these maintenance orders must be easier to handle than controlling internal orders.

- **Equipment of work center**
  In contrast to employees in many other departments (such as controlling or purchasing), employees in plant maintenance often have no assigned work center of their own in which to use the SAP system, for example, in order to print out shop papers or display open notification lists. Instead, several employees have to share a work center. For this reason, as the end of a shift approaches and each employee wants to enter their own confirmations, a high level of usability is required to ensure that the system can be used by one employee after another without any unnecessary delays.

- **Focus on concrete tasks**
  Finally, the concrete tasks assigned to an employee in the company are important: Financial controllers post their items to internal orders or cost centers and analyze them; accountants record received invoices and checks balance lists; purchasers process their purchase orders and check their outline agreements, and every one of them needs an IT system to complete the specific tasks. Every employee enters data into the system and retrieves information from it. However, the tasks assigned to a maintenance engineer basically are comprised of maintenance and inspection and not the operation of an IT system, which is why he or she does not need any IT system to carry out the actual tasks.

These reasons make it an absolute necessity during SAP S/4HANA Asset Management implementation to apply every effort to increase the usability of the system as much as possible. By default, SAP S/4HANA provides many tools to increase usability. The following section will describe these tools from the point of view of plant maintenance.

[!]

> **User Acceptance Is Very important in Plant Maintenance**
>
> The aspects of *user acceptance* and *usability* play such a key role in plant maintenance for the following reasons:
>
> - In plant maintenance, you have a wide variety of users.
> - Many users do not have IT experience or training.
> - Plant maintenance operates from a different philosophy than controlling.
> - The actual job of maintenance engineers consists of maintenance, which means that basically they do not need any IT system.

There's no guarantee that the system will be accepted by the users or be considered user-friendly. However, you can improve the chances by remembering the following principles and making them the benchmarks in all your decisions regarding system characteristics:

- **Keep the system design as simple as possible.**
  While this may sound like a commonly used cliché, our experience has shown that companies do not make use of all options to enhance the usability of the SAP system—either because they do not know about these options or because they decide not to use them for other reasons.

- **Make every effort to increase usability.**
  To achieve this, you will have to invest time and effort in the design of your SAP system.

- **Providing a simple system is difficult and time consuming; providing a difficult system is easy and much less time consuming.**
  Please consider this comparison: Wasn't it easier for you in school to describe a colorful, vivid, and varied painting by van Gogh than an empty inkpot? The same applies to the SAP system. A seemingly perfect system that tries to solve all problems at once, a system that tries to cover all eventualities, is probably so vast and complex that it severely reduces the willingness to accept it. Better to forgo some embellishments, to customize functions, and possibly leave them out altogether to make it easy for users to do their daily job.

- **Prioritize.**
  The following statement was made by a speaker at the end of his presentation, and I agree without reservation:

> **A New Interpretation for the 80:20 Rule**
>
> It is better to have 80% of the system you want with 100% user acceptance than 100% of the system you want with 20% user acceptance.

10.1.5 SAP System Options to Improve Usability

Section 10.2 through Section 10.4 will describe the opportunities SAP offers for simplifying and accelerating business transaction processing in plant maintenance.

These options can be divided into three categories, and you should consider employing them in your company in the order shown here:

- *Category 1*: options available to the users themselves
- *Category 2*: options available to the IT department without programming
- *Category 3*: options available to the IT department including programming

Table 10.1 provides an overview of the measures that fall into each of these categories.

Category	Who?	What?
1	User	■ General user parameters ■ Maintenance-specific user parameters ■ Role menus and favorites menus ■ List variants ■ Personalized input helps ■ Table controls ■ Buttons and key combinations
2	IT department (non-programming options)	■ Transaction variants ■ Customizing ■ Action box ■ SAP Business Client ■ SAP Work Manager ■ SAP Asset Manager ■ SAP Fiori apps ■ GuiXT ■ SAP Screen Personas
3	IT department (programming options)	■ Upstream transactions ■ Web interfaces ■ Customer exits ■ Business Application Programming Interfaces (BAPIs) ■ Classic Business Add-ins (BAdIs) ■ Enhancement points ■ Workflows

Table 10.1 Options to Improve Usability

10.2   User's Options to Improve Usability

In the following sections, I'll describe the options related to category 1 in further detail. You'll learn not only *what* you can do, but also *how* you should do it. Because of the options in categories 2 and 3 require customizing and even programming, only their functions will be described in this book.

Further Information

For more information on categories 2 and 3, check out *Configuring Plant Maintenance in SAP S/4HANA*, SAP PRESS, 2020, *https://www.sap-press.com/5102*.

10.2.1   General User Parameters

From a user's point of view, many entries required by the SAP system remain unchanged over a period of time. This includes information such as the following:

- The user belongs to a specific work center.
- The work center is, in turn, assigned to a specific cost center.
- The user works in a particular plant.
- The user is responsible for a particular functional location.

The use of *user parameters* to prepopulate fields contributes greatly to improving usability. You can access these defaults in Transaction SU3 (Maintain User Profile) or via the menu path **More · System · User Profile · User Data** (see Figure 10.2). Once defined, these fields are then automatically prepopulated with the assigned values when business processes are processed.

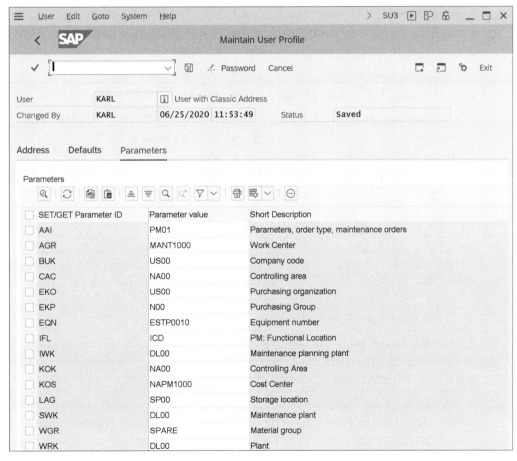

Figure 10.2 General User Parameters

From a maintenance perspective, the following parameters are used frequently:

- AAI: Order Type
- AAR: Work Center Type
- AGR: Work Center
- BUK: Company Code
- CSA: BOM Application
- CSV: BOM Usage
- EKG: Purchasing Group
- EKO: Purchasing Organization
- EQN: Equipment Number
- EQT: Equipment Category
- IFL: Functional Location
- IMD: Measurement Document
- IME: Measurement Recording List
- IP1: Measuring Point Category
- IPT: Measuring Point
- IRL: Reference Functional Location
- ISR: Structure Indicator for Functional Location
- IWK: Maintenance Planning Plant
- KOK: Controlling Area
- KOS: Cost Center
- LAG: Storage Location
- LGP: Storage Bin
- LIS: CATS Profile for List Display
- MAT: Material Number
- MPL: Maintenance Plan
- MPS: Maintenance Item
- MTA: Material Type
- PER: Personnel Number
- PIN: PP Profile/Default Values
- PLN: Task List Group
- QMR: Notification Type
- Q_ALV_GRID_INACTIVE: Deactivates the ALV Grid
- SWK: Maintenance Plant
- VAP: Main Work Center
- WAT: Maintenance Plan Category
- WGR: Material Group
- WRK: Plant

F1 Help Supports You in Finding Parameter IDs

You can save processing time by using parameters to prepopulate fields. You can generally view the relevant parameter ID in the **Technical Info** of the ⌨ F1 help for a field.

10.2.2   Maintenance-Specific User Parameters

In addition to the general user parameters, you can also call maintenance-specific user parameters within the notification via **More · Extras · Setting · Control/Default Values** and within the order via **More · Extras · Settings · Default Values**.

A total of six tabs are available there. On the **General** tab, you can define personal default values for the order type, notification type, planning plant, planner group, and main work center (see Figure 10.3). These parameters have priority over the general user parameters shown above in Figure 10.2. In other words, if you also enter values for the general user parameters, these values are overwritten by the maintenance-specific user parameters.

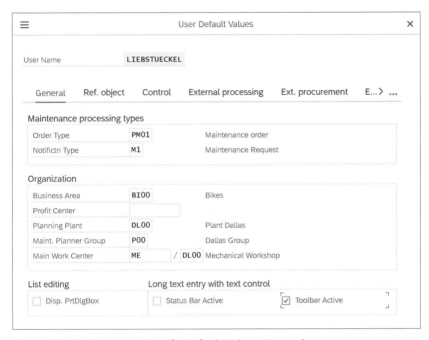

Figure 10.3 Maintenance-Specific Default Values: General

On the **Ref. object** tab (see Figure 10.4), you can define a scenario for the reference object. The following scenarios are available to you:

- O100: **Functional location+equipment+assembly**
- O110: **Equipment+assembly**

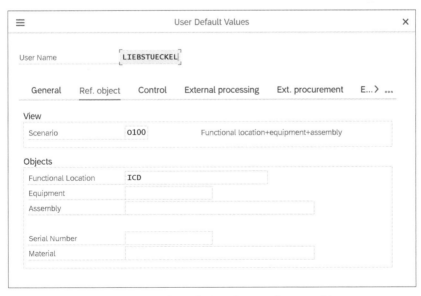

Figure 10.4 Maintenance-Specific Default Values: Reference Object

- O120: Functional location (30-digit)+equipment+assembly
- O130: Serial number+material number+device ID
- O140: Without a reference object
- O150: Equipment only
- O160: Functional location only
- O170: Equipment+serial number+material number
- O180: Functional location 1:1+equipment+assembly
- O190: Physical sample

If you use the **Overview of Notification Type** customizing function to assign a scenario to the notification type and the **Configure Order Types** customizing function to assign a scenario to the order type, the maintenance-specific user parameters override these customizing settings for the notification type and order type. If, however, you use the **Set Maintenance Plan Categories** customizing function to assign a scenario to a maintenance plan category, this isn't overridden. Here, you can also assign a specific technical object, which is also then proposed in the notification and order.

The **Control** tab is available in the order only. Here, you have the option to influence different dialog boxes (see Figure 10.5):

- **Function: Put order in process**
  In this area of the screen, you can influence the **Selection dialog** and therefore override the default setting **Display dialog**.

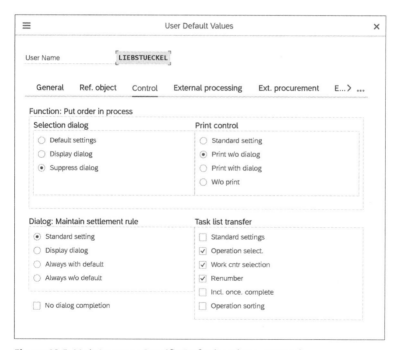

Figure 10.5 Maintenance-Specific Default Values: Control

- **Print control**
  In this screen area, you can override the default setting **Print with dialog**.

- **Dialog: Maintain settlement rule**
  In this screen area, you can override the default setting from the **Settlement Rule: Define Time and Creation of Distribution Rule** customizing function.

- **No dialog completion**
  With this indicator, you can suppress the dialog box for technical completion of the order. Then, the order is always completed using the default values (e.g., the current date and time).

In addition to these default values, you can use this tab to define how task lists are to be transferred to orders:

- **Operation select.**
  Determines whether a dialog box for selecting operations is to appear.

- **Work cntr selection**
  Determines whether a dialog box for selecting work centers is to appear.

- **Renumber**
  Determines whether the operations selected are to be renumbered consecutively in intervals of 10.

- **Incl. once. complete**
  Determines whether a task list can be fully integrated once only (max.).

- **Operation sorting**
  Determines whether the sequence of operations is the same as in the task list.

Then, use these settings to override the default settings from the **Default Values for Task List Data and Profile Assignments** customizing function.

The **External processing** (see Figure 10.6) and **Ext. procurement** (see Figure 10.7) tabs are available in the order only. Here, define personal default values for the procurement of services and materials (e.g., for the purchasing group or material group).

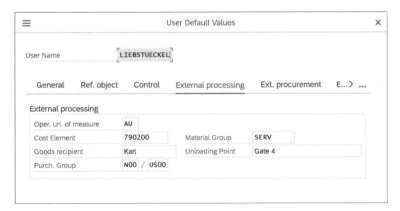

Figure 10.6 Maintenance-Specific Default Values: External Processing

These personal default values override the default values from the **Create Default Value Profiles for External Procurement** customizing function, which are assigned to the plant and order type.

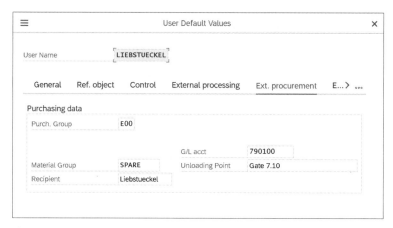

Figure 10.7 Maintenance-Specific Default Values: External Procurement

On the **EAMS Web UI** tab (see Figure 10.8) you define some default settings that come into effect if you use SAP Business Client with its Web Dynpro interface instead of SAP GUI:

- You can determine how the system should react to messages when you perform a specific function in the order (e.g., if you complete orders technically, you want to complete notifications as well).

- If you mark **Hide SF Relationship**, a start-finish relationship can't be selected.

- You can predefine the order type if you use the SAP Business Client **Confirm Unplanned Job** function (see Chapter 6, Section 6.1.2).

- You can predefine the plant and storage location if you post good issues within the Report and Repair Malfunction app (see Chapter 9, Section 9.1.2).

The **Maintenance Plan** (see Figure 10.9) tab is available in the order only. Here, you define personal default values for your maintenance plans:

- For single-cycle plans (Transaction IP41) and strategy plans (Transaction IP42), you can define, e.g., call horizon, scheduling indicator, shift factors and tolerances.

- For multiple counter plans (Transaction IP43), you can define a default value for the operation type (OR- or AND-link).

- If you have activated business function LOG_EAM_CI_10, you can copy maintenance plans. Here, you can define default values for copy options (e.g., scheduling parameters or maintenance items).

Figure 10.8 Maintenance-Specific Default Values: EAMS Web UI

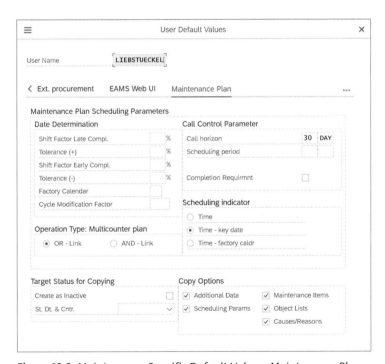

Figure 10.9 Maintenance-Specific Default Values: Maintenance Plan

The **Action box** tab (see Figure 10.10) is available in the notification only.

If you set the **Action box: Table** indicator, the actions which you assigned to the notification type (**Define Action Box** customizing function) are displayed not as a sidebar but as a table in the notification header (see Figure 10.11).

Figure 10.10 Maintenance-Specific Default Values: Action Box

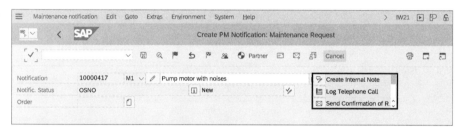

Figure 10.11 Notification: Action Box as a Table

With all these options, the SAP system contributes to both individualization and controllability.

Using Maintenance-Specific Parameters

Using maintenance-specific parameters to prepopulate fields reduces the processing time and enables you to control processing steps.

10.2.3   Roles and Favorites

To create role-based menus, you must call Transaction PFCG. Role-based menus have a much simpler structure than the standard SAP menu, which in plant maintenance, can consist of up to seven levels. Starting a transaction from a role menu is therefore much faster than starting it from a standard SAP menu. If a role menu is assigned to you, the system automatically displays this menu on the initial screen (see Figure 10.12).

A further simplification is provided by favorites, where users add only those transactions they require (see Figure 10.12). Favorites menus can be single-level or multilevel menus. Starting a transaction from a favorites menu is generally much faster than starting it from a standard SAP menu.

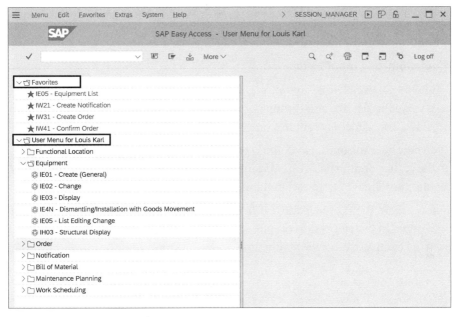

Figure 10.12 User Menu and Favorites

Note the following restriction: Each user creates his of her own favorites menu. In other words, a user can't directly use the favorites menu of colleagues. However, you can use **More · Favorites · Download to PC** or **Upload from PC** to copy favorites menus to another user.

[+]

Use Roles and Favorites Menus

Role-based menus and favorites reduce the launch time of transactions. Favorites menus can be copied to other users by using the download and upload functions.

10.2.4   List Variants

You can save a lot of time by providing your users with the relevant selection and display variants. Chapter 8, Section 8.2.1, introduced you to the options provided by SAP List Viewer.

[!]

Guidelines for List Variants

When creating list variants, you should follow these guidelines:

- Find out what information your users need. Use this information to define selection variants and the appropriate display variants.

> - The selection variants should not contain more than one page of selection criteria.
> - Users should be able to save the most commonly used selection variant as **U_USER-NAME** and to select the most commonly used display variant as a default setting.

10.2.5   Customizing Input Help

An F4 help box usually displays all possible entries. Often, however, this list of all entries is very long (e.g., material groups, object types, or cause of damage) even though the individual user generally requires only a certain number of entries from this list.

Here, you now have the option to define a *personal value list*. To do this, call up the F4 help in the corresponding field (e.g., **Material Group** or **G/L Accounts**), select the entries you require, and choose ★ to assign them to your personal value list.

If you now call up the F4 help for this field, the system automatically displays your personal value list instead of the complete list (see Figure 10.13). You can choose ⊕ to return to the complete value list at any time.

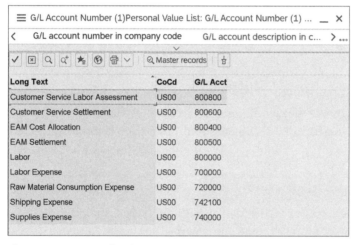

Figure 10.13 Personalized Input Help

[+]

> **Use the Personal Value Lists**
>
> In F4 help, a personal value list saves you time when searching for the correct entry.

10.2.6   Buttons and Key Combinations

Since the mouse was introduced as a control element for computers, opinions have been divided as to whether operation is faster with or without a mouse. If you prefer to use the keyboard instead of the mouse, key combinations and buttons can be helpful.

> [+]
> **Creating Key Combinations**
> Provide important and general valid key combinations for users who prefer the keyboard.

Examples, in plant maintenance and beyond, include the following:

- `F11` **key**
  Use this key to save a document. This function corresponds to the disk icon in the system toolbar.

- `F4`+`Enter` **key combo**
  Use this key combination in date and time fields to copy the current date or time into these fields.

- `F4` **key**
  Use this in general to call up a value list.

- **Clipboard history**
  The commands `Ctrl`+`C` and `Ctrl`+`V` are known and most probably used to copy the last entries. You can also call up the complete clipboard history via `Windows`+`V` and select the desired entry.

- **Share desktop**
  If you no longer see the desktop with the windows open, you don't have to minimize the windows individually to reveal the view of the surface. With the keyboard shortcut `Windows`+`D`, you can minimize it in one go to the taskbar. If you want to restore the old state, press the same combination again, and all windows will be enlarged again.

- **Virtual desktops**
  Smaller windows are a way of not losing track of things on a small display. However, if a large number of programs or windows are to be open at the same time, virtual desktops are the better option. That means you use several screens at the same time, between which you can switch back and forth without any problems. You open the overview with `Windows`+`Tab`. There, it's possible to add further desktops using the plus sign. You can also press `Windows`+`Ctrl`+`D` to create a new virtual desktop and switch directly there. You can assign programs in the task view simply by dragging them onto the miniature of a desktop. If you want to remove a desktop, press `Windows`+`Ctrl`+`F4` while it's displayed.

10.2.7 Table Controls

Table controls are a largely unknown and unused option that end users can use to adjust the SAP system to their requirements. In the past, SAP screens were preprogrammed. In other words, each field occupied a permanently fixed position on the screen. Since then, however, many screens have been provided with table controls, which you can use to define your own screen layout and field sequence.

Examples of table controls in plant maintenance and related areas are provided here:

- Operation list (see Figure 10.14), component list, service specification, and object list in the order
- All partner overviews
- Item, cause, measure, and activity overview in the notification
- Time confirmation, measurement recording, goods movements, and activities in the overall completion confirmation
- Item overview in the maintenance plan
- Operation overview, component overview, maintenance packages, and service specification in the task list
- Collective confirmation
- Item overview for material withdrawal
- Item overview in purchase requisitions
- Item overview in purchase orders

HeaderData	Operations		Components	Costs	Partner	Objects	Additional Data		Location	
General	Internal	External	Dates	Act. Data		Enhancement			Ex. Factor	
OpAc	Work ctr	Plant	Co...	S...	Operation short text			Work	Un	Lo... VI	S...
☐ 0010	MANT1000	DL00	PM01		Switch off and carry out a safety check			0.5 H			
☐ 0020	MANT1000	DL00	PM01		Visual inspection outside: leakage, rust			1 H			
☐ 0030	MANT1000	DL00	PM01		Visual inspection inside: moisture, rust			2 H			
☐ 0040	MANT1000	DL00	PM01		Remove the pump rotor and clean it compl			0.5 H			
☐ 0050	MANT1000	DL00	PM01		Measurement: bearing play			0.7 H			
☐ 0060	MANT1000	DL00	PM01		Exchange: sealing rings to the gearbox			0.9 H			
☐ 0070	MANT1000	DL00	PM01		Safety check and pump in operation			0.2 H			
☐ 0080	MANT1000	DL00	PM01		Testrun			1 H			
☐ 0090	MANT1000	DL00	PM01					HR			

Figure 10.14 Table Control

The following settings are available for all table controls:

- You can use drag and drop to arrange the columns in the order in which you require them most often.
- You can widen or narrow each column so that it accommodates the entry usually made there.
- You can hide fields that you don't need by setting the width of the column to zero.

The most important setting of all is the option to save these settings as a user-specific variant. The upper-right corner of each table control contains the ⚙ icon, which you can use to access a detail screen in which you create your settings as a variant and can therefore override the default settings (see Figure 10.15).

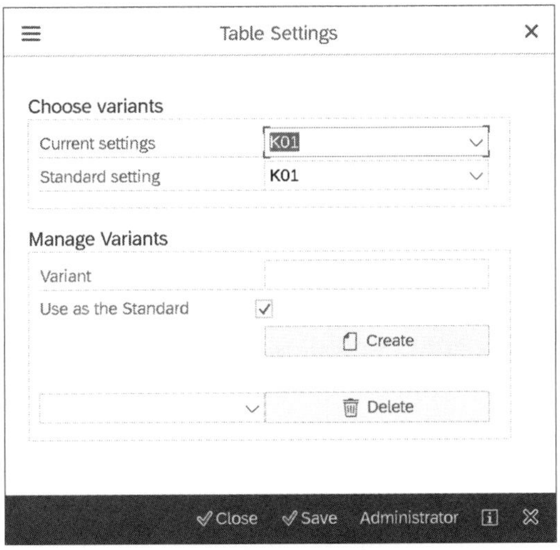

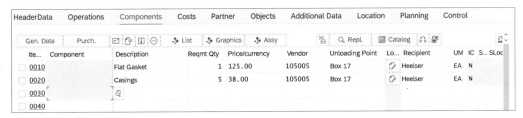

Figure 10.15 Table Control: Save Table Settings

Making Extensive Use of Table Controls

There are individualized table controls and table controls stored as a variant to considerably reduce the time spent making entries and searching for entries in the screen templates, thus making a significant contribution to improving usability.

If you activate business function LOG_EAM_CI_5, SAP S/4HAHA Asset Management makes the following special feature available: Previously, the table controls for the **Operations** overview and **Components** overview consisted of a selection of fields predefined by SAP. The purchasing data was sorely missed. This has now changed. Now all purchasing data can be maintained in both the aforementioned table controls (e.g., vendor, material group, ship-to party, unloading point, or purchasing group) (see Figure 10.16 for the **Components** overview).

Ite...	Component	Description	Reqmt Qty	Price/currency	Vendor	Unloading Point	Lo...	Recipient	UM	IC	S...	SLoc
0010		Flat Gasket	1	125.00	105005	Box 17		Heelser	EA	N		
0020		Casings	5	38.00	105005	Box 17		Heelser	EA	N		
0030												
0040												

Figure 10.16 Purchasing Data in Components Overview

This concludes the description of all the options available within category 1, whereby each user can configure his or her own individual settings.

10.3 Non-Programmer's Options in IT

Let's now take a look at the options available in category 2. In most enterprises, these options are usually the responsibility of the IT department. However, the options contained in this category do not require any programming. The following sections describe the functionality of these options as well as that of those of category 3 (IT including programming), which means that only the *what* will be described.

First, let's look at the approach of creating any number of adjusted variants (known as *transaction variants*).

10.3.1 Transaction Variants

If a transaction—for example, a typical case, Transaction IW31 (Create Order)—is used to process different business transactions and is used by different user groups, adjusting the transaction flow to the respective business transaction or the respective user group make sense. For example, the process of creating an order can differ depending on the user group that creates it:

- Sold-to party or contractor
- Electricians or mechanics
- Planners or technicians

As a result, transaction variants can come in handy to differentiate specific processes for specific users.

Customizing Any Transaction with Transaction Variants

You can create any number of transaction variants for an original transaction. In a transaction variant, you can do the following:

- Hide entire screens.
- Hide individual tabs.
- Disable menu functions.
- Disable buttons.
- Set the field selection control for individual fields (display, required, or hide).
- Prepopulate the field content.
- Modify the column sequence, change the column width, and hide columns for table controls.
- Assign a custom name to the transaction.

Figure 10.17 shows an example of a transaction variant created for Transaction IW31.

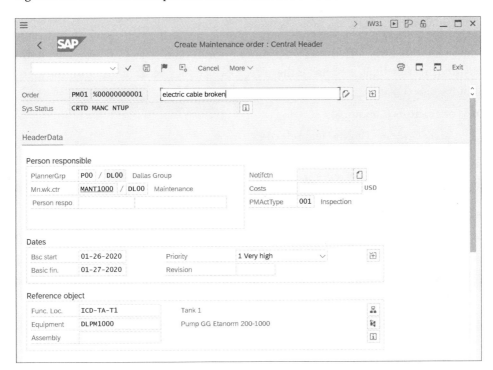

Figure 10.17 Transaction Variant

The following measures have been taken to simplify the screen:

- The initial screen for Transaction IW31 has been skipped.
- The content of certain fields has been prepopulated (for example, **Order Type** and **Priority**).
- Apart from one tab, all other tab have been hidden (for example, **Operations** and **Material**).
- Menu options and buttons have been disabled (for example, **Settlement Rule**, **Schedule**, and **Paging**).
- Subscreens have been hidden (for example, the operation detail subscreen in the order header).
- Some fields have been hidden (for example, **Person responsible**).
- A unique transaction name (here, Transaction ZW31) has been assigned, from which the transaction variant can be called.

The result is a transaction variant whose content has been significantly reduced compared to the original transaction and contains only those screens, fields, and functions that the user needs.

10.3.2   Customizing

Customizing also provides many options in terms of improving usability. The most important of these customizing functions are listed next, along with a description of its function if this is not immediately apparent from its name. The order in which these customizing functions are listed is the order in which they occur in the SAP Implementation Guide (IMG):

- Work centers (Chapter 2)
    - **Work Centers · Define Field Selection**
      Define required entry fields and hide fields.
    - **Work Centers · Configure Screen Sequence for Work Center**
      Adjust the screen layout for work centers.
- Technical objects (Chapter 3)
    - **Configuring the Material Master**
      Adjust the screen layout for material master data.
    - **Material Master Field Selection**
      Define required entry fields and hide fields.
    - **Set View Profiles for Technical Objects**
      Screen layout for equipment and functional locations.
    - **Define Field Selection for Functional Locations**
      Define required fields and hide fields.
    - **Define Field Selection for Equipment Master Record**
      Define required fields and hide fields.
    - **Define Transaction-Based Default Values for Object Types**
      Populate the equipment category or functional location category.
- Work order cycle (Chapter 4)
    - **Define Printer**
      Prepopulate the values for print output.
    - **Send Shop Papers by Email**
      Send shop floor papers using SAP Mail or email instead of printing.
    - **Maintain Settlement Profile**
      Default values for account assignment.
    - **Overview of Notification Type · Screen Areas in Notification Header**
      Reference object of the notification.
    - **Set Screen Templates for the Notification Type**
    - **Set Field Selection for Notifications**
      Define required fields and hide fields.
    - **Assign Transaction Start Values**
      Populate notification type and skip initial screen.

- **Assign Notification Types to Order Types**
  Populate order type for notification type.

- **Define Response Monitoring**
  Propose the service profile and response profile for notifications.

- **Configure Order Types**
  Reference object of the order.

- **Create Default Value Profiles for External Procurement**
  Default values for material and service procurements.

- **Text Types For Purchase Requisitions · Define Text Types**
  Define up to five target text types for purchase requisitions.

- **Create Default Value Profiles for General Order Data**
  Propose values for graphics and scheduling.

- **Default Values for Maintenance Task List Data and Profile Assignments**
  Propose values for external data profiles, graphic profiles, and task list transfer.

- **Define Default Order Types for Maintenance Items**
  Propose the order type for maintenance orders.

- **Define Notification and Order Integration**
  Enter notification and order data in one screen; automatically transfer long text from notification to order.

- **Maintain Default Values for Control Keys for Order Types**
  Propose a value for the control key.

- **Default Values for Maintenance Activity Type for Each Order Type**
  Propose a value for the maintenance activity type.

- **Basic Order View · Define View Profiles**
  Define screen layout for orders.

- **Define Default Values for Component Item Categories**
  Default value for item category for each material type.

- **Activate Default Value for Current Date as Basic Date** Define a value for prepopulating the date.

- **Set Scheduling Parameters**
  Activate automatic scheduling.

- **Message Control**
  Control whether a warning, error, or no message is supposed to be issued.

- **Define Object Information Keys**
  Display object information keys automatically.

- **Settlement Rule: Define Time and Creation of Distribution Rule**
  Create settlement rules automatically.

10

- Define Transfer of Project or Investment Program
  Transfer project numbers or investment programs automatically.

- Define Field Selection for Order Header Data (PM)
  Define required fields and hide fields.

- Define Field Selection for Order Operations (PM and CS)
  Define required fields and hide fields.

- Define Field Selection for Components (PM and CS)
  Define required fields and hide fields.

- Set Screen Templates for Completion Confirmation
  Screen layout for overall completion confirmation.

- Set Field Selection for Completion Confirmation
  Define required fields and hide fields.

- CATS: Maintain Data Entry Profiles and Choose Fields
  Define appropriate profiles for maintenance confirmations.

- Maintenance plans, task lists (Chapter 5)

  - Define Field Selection for Maintenance Plan
    Define required entry fields and hide fields.

  - Define Field Selection for Operation Data
    Define required entry fields and hide fields.

  - Task Lists · Define Profiles with Default Values
    Default values for task lists.

  - Task Lists · Define Field Selection
    Define required entry fields and hide fields.

  - Configure Special Functions for Maintenance Planning
    Enable non-template-based copying.

- Additional business processes (Chapter 6)

  - Create Default Value Profiles for External Procurement
    Propose values for service procurement.

  - Text Types For Purchase Requisitions · Define Text Types
    Define up to five target text types for purchase requisitions.

  - Source Determination and Default Values · For Client or For the Purchasing Organizations
    Set default values and source determination process for external services.

  - Configure Split Valuation
    Define valuation categories and valuation types to enable refurbishment process.

  - Define Serial Number Profiles
    Define serial profile procedures to enable subcontracting process.

– **Set View Profiles for Technical Objects**
Define screen templates to enable calibration of test/measurement equipment process.

– **Define Default Values for Inspection Type**
Define default values for calibration of test/measurement equipment process in quality management.

– **Maintain Catalogs for Usage Decisions**
Set default values for usage decisions for calibration of test/measurement equipment process.

– **Define Follow-Up Action**
Automate follow-up actions like equipment status change or order technical completion.

– **Maintain Revision Type**
Define special type of revision to be able to process maintenance event builder.

– **Define Settings for Shift Note Screen Templates**
Adjust the screen layout and field selection for shift notes.

– **Define Settings for Shift Note Type**
Propose values for categories.

– **Basic Settings for Pool Asset Management**
Propose values for order type, class, and text to enable pool asset management process.

Improving Usability with Purposeful Customizing

Customizing provides many possibilities to enhance the usability of SAP S/4HANA Asset Management. In particular, I want to mention the options for adjusting the screen layout in notifications, orders, and overall completion confirmations.

In addition, you should make specific use of field selection control, particularly for hiding information.

10.3.3 Action Box

When you process notifications, you can use the *action box* to execute follow-up actions that may make notification processing easier for you. After you've executed a follow-up action, it's documented as an activity or measure.

You can start the functions directly from the notification. Then, when you complete the function, the system automatically returns you to the notification. Figure 10.18 shows examples of actions in the action box:

- Entering an internal note
- Documenting a telephone call

- Initiating a telephone call via SAPphone
- Sending an SAP Mail or email
- Posting a goods movement
- Creating a repair order
- Searching the solution database for a problem or solution
- Creating a quality notification
- Generating an 8D report
- Creating a maintenance plan
- Assigning a bill of material (BOM)

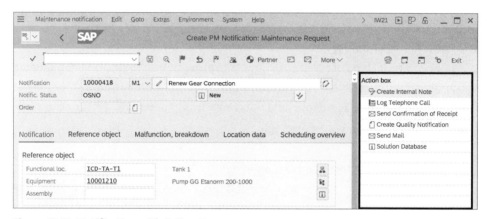

Figure 10.18 Notification with Action Box

As you can see, the action box concerns functions that would normally require you to exit notification processing. Therefore, the action box makes a significant contribution to simplifying a business process.

You can use the **Define Action Box** customizing function to define more functions in addition to those shown in Figure 10.18.

10.3.4   SAP Business Client

In the course of the book, I familiarized you with the handling and functions of SAP Business Client at various points. In terms of usability, SAP Business Client offers you a number of advantages over SAP GUI:

- You can stay in one window and work with several functions (Chapter 1, Section 1.7.2).
- You can perform quick searches in different places You can display context-sensitive information in the side panel.
- In addition to the plant structure, other objects in the Asset Viewer can be called up, such as orders, notifications, maintenance plans, or documents (Chapter 3, Section 3.10).

- You can post orders which have already been completed in a single function. In SAP GUI you would have to follow a sequence of 2–6 transactions (Chapter 6, Section 6.1.2).

- You can use SAP 3D Visual Enterprise Viewer (Chapter 9, Section 9.1.1).

All these are functions that simplify your daily work with the SAP system in terms of usability.

However, configuring SAP Business Client is not that easy. This is why SAP has published a 210-page configuration guide for setting up a workplace in SAP Business Client, made up for a maintenance planner and for a maintenance technician, for example.

SAP Business Client Guide

Download this guide via following link: *http://s-prs.co/v518008* SAP (Ed.): EAM Web UI Implementation Guide – Adapting EAM Web UI, Walldorf 2018.

10.3.5   Mobile Solutions

Chapter 9 discussed SAP's mobile solutions for plant maintenance: SAP Work Manager including rounds (Chapter 9, Section 9.2.2) and SAP Asset Manager (Chapter 9, Section 9.2.3). Regardless of which app you use and regardless of the detailed requirements of your company, the general advantages associated with working mobile in terms of usability are evident:

- There is less manual effort for data entry (not first handwritten and then electronic, but electronic directly).

- The direct electronic recordings on-site and the electronic transmission to the SAP S/4HANA system reduce the risk of transmission errors and thus the error rate.

- The overall data quality is higher.

- As a result, there should also be fewer complaints from the customer due to incorrect order settlements.

- You can choose a device (smartphone, tablet) best suited for your day-to-day business (weight, size, display, data to be recorded, etc.).

- The elimination of manual paper transports reduces the lead time (the technician does not have to pick up or return the order papers).

- Another important advantage results from access to electronic documents: from a tablet, the technician on-site has access to electronic documents (such as drawings or procedural instructions) at any time when performing the maintenance order, which can support the technician's work. These could be documents from SAP 3D Visual Enterprise Viewer, from a file server, or from a document management system. The technician can consult the documents on a case-by-case basis if necessary, without going back to the planning office to get the relevant documents from physical folders.

10.3.6   SAP Fiori

In Chapter 1, Section 1.7.3 , and Chapter 9, Section 9.1.2 , you were introduced to SAP Fiori technology and SAP Fiori apps with regard to the following topics:

- What the SAP Fiori interface is
- What properties it has
- What types of SAP Fiori apps there are
- Which are the most important SAP Fiori apps for maintenance

The question that arises from this information is this: What kind of influence does the SAP Fiori user interface (UI) and working with SAP Fiori apps have on usability? Following are some answers to that question:

- Most SAP Fiori apps require a reduced amount of data—both data displayed and data to be entered—compared to SAP GUI transactions.
- Some SAP Fiori apps combine functions on one screen, which in SAP GUI requires a sequence of several transactions.
- Due to the modern UI, the user also has the subjective feeling of working with a modern system.
- The SAP Fiori interface can be used with any browser (e.g., Edge, Chrome, Firefox).
- The SAP Fiori interface is independent of devices, that is the user can use the device that is best suited for the task at hand: desktop, notebook, tablet, or smartphone. With SAP GUI, only a desktop or notebook can be used.
- Because of the preceding two characteristics (browser-based, any device), the user can also work mobile and isn't tied to a workspace.
- The mobile orientation brings many of the same advantages that were mentioned for the mobile apps:
  - Less manual effort for data entry
  - Reduced risk of transmission errors and reduced error rate
  - Higher data quality
  - Fewer complaints from customers
  - Reduced lead time by eliminating manual paper transports
  - Access to existing electronic documents

You also can create new electronic documents (e.g., photos) and assign them directly to notifications or orders.

10.3.7 GuiXT

GuiXT is an SAP GUI component that enables you to design SAP transactions according to your daily requirements without having to modify the SAP programs or screens. The following options are available:

- Prepopulate fields with values.
- Hide fields and field groups.
- Move fields.
- Add and change text.
- Add field help.
- Add new screen elements (e.g., checkboxes, buttons, graphics, and documentation).
- Adjust table controls.
- Change menu entries.
- Change field labels throughout the system.

Figure 10.19 shows an entry screen for creating an order (Transaction IW31). The screen was customized using GuiXT options in the following way:

- Only permitted priorities, order types, plants, and business areas are provided as radio buttons, which means that you cannot select inappropriate values.
- A context-sensitive image of the technical object is displayed.
- Function keys are provided for related functions (for example, to display the notifications for the technical object).
- Superfluous fields were removed.

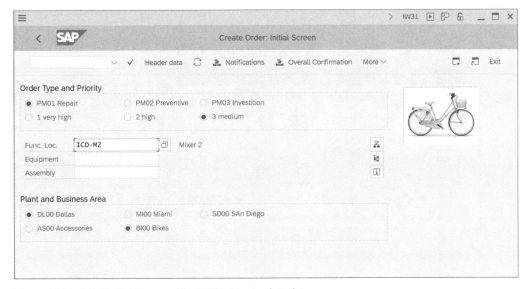

Figure 10.19 SAP GuiXT: Transaction IW31: Manipulated Screen

To activate GuiXT, use the menu path **More · SAP GUI Settings and Actions · Activate GuiXT**. The next time you start Transaction IW31, it will no longer have its standard layout. Instead, it will have the GuiXT-manipulated layout.

[+]
> **Using GuiXT to Adjust Your Screens**
>
> GuiXT can also help you to adjust business transaction processing in plant maintenance to your requirements and to simplify and accelerate processing.

10.3.8   SAP Screen Personas

SAP Screen Personas version 3.0 is currently available, and like GuiXT, it enables you to adjust and redesign the standard SAP screen templates to your own requirements. It is comprised of various functions for changing screens, thus supporting you in your endeavors to improve usability and increase user acceptance.

A modified initial screen for notification creation that contains the user's company logo and provides only those functions that the user requires for daily work in the form of large buttons and graphics (see Figure 10.20) results in much greater user acceptance than the standard initial screen of the SAP access menu.

Figure 10.20 SAP Screen Personas: Modified Initial Screen

Such modified screens are known as *flavors* whereby a specific SAP transaction is personalized in a particular way. Note that a flavor is always linked to one transaction (e.g.,

Transaction IW31). However, you can create any number of flavors for each transaction. After you finish creating a flavor, you can release it for certain users or for all users of your SAP system.

You use a *user interface editor* (UI Editor) to edit the screens themselves. Here, you can edit all the control elements of a screen:

- Titles
- Radio buttons
- Checkboxes
- Function keys
- Input fields
- Dropdown lists
- Field groups
- Texts

Then, depending on the control element, you have the following options (note, however, that not all these options apply to all control elements):

- Completely show or hide individual control elements or entire groups of control elements.
- Define new control elements (e.g., assign a URL to a button).
- Use drag and drop to move individual control elements to the positions that you want them to occupy.
- Change the size of the control elements.
- Assign a new quick info to the control element.
- Change the default value of a control element (e.g., by prepopulating an input field with a particular value).
- Adjust the title and text of a control element.
- Use sticky notes to add additional information to the relevant control element. Unlike quick infos, sticky notes are only displayed when the control element is selected.

Figure 10.21 shows a **Confirmation Cockpit** screen adjusted this way. This confirmation cockpit provides the following functions:

- Single confirmation (Transaction IW41)
- Overall completion confirmation (Transaction IW42)
- Display confirmation (Transaction IW43)
- List of confirmations (Transaction IW47)
- Counter readings and measurement documents (Transaction IK11)
- Material withdrawal for order (Transaction MIGO)

- Entry of technical data for notification (Transaction IW22)
- List of notification items (Transaction IW69)
- List of goods movements (Transaction MB51)
- Technically complete order (Transaction IW32)

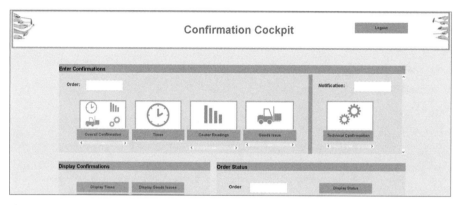

Figure 10.21 SAP Screen Personas: Confirmation Cockpit

[+]   **Additional Resources**

Thanks to Charlotte Papenburg for her bachelor thesis, "Confirmation Cockpit for Plant Maintenance: Concept and Realization Using SAP Screen Personas," (Würzburg, 2016).

The **Storage Location Cockpit** screen (see Figure 10.22) follows a similar approach and can help you perform various detailed tasks, including the following:

- Enter a goods receipt for purchase orders or production orders.
- Enter a goods issue for orders or cost centers.
- Display material stocks overview.

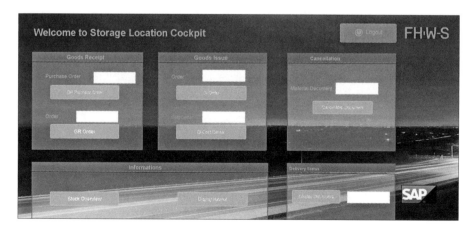

Figure 10.22 SAP Screen Personas: Storage Location Cockpit

- Display delivery status.
- Display material master.
- Cancel material documents.

> **Additional Resources**
>
> Thanks to Daniela Loos for her bachelor thesis, "Storage Location Cockpit: Concept and Realization Using SAP Screen Personas," (Würzburg, 2016).

In addition to individual control elements, you can also change the complete *theme* of the flavor:

- Define your own background screens (e.g., insert logos, display context-dependent images, and define borders and color schemes).
- Adjust the following standard SAP themes: Belize, Corbu, Tradeshow, High Contrast Black, and Blue Crystal.
- Change the color scheme for Belize, Corbu, and Blue Crystal.

You can also integrate Google Maps, which enables you to display the location of the technical objects or orders if they have geodata (see Figure 10.23).

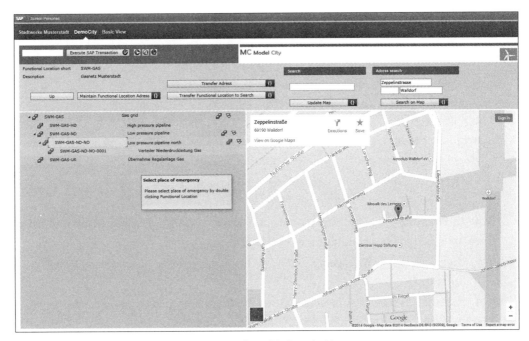

Figure 10.23 SAP Screen Personas: Structure List with Google Maps

[+]
Creating a Web-Like Interface with SAP Screen Personas

SAP Screen Personas provides numerous options for simplifying the interface of the SAP system and giving the users the feeling of working on a web interface and not in an SAP system. Further information is available at *www.sapscreenpersonas.com* and *http://help.sap.com/personas*.

10.4   Programmer's Options in IT

This section provides a very brief description of the functionality (*what*) of the options for category 3 (IT including programming).

10.4.1   Upstream Transactions

When processing business transactions, it's usually necessary to start several transactions in succession. Furthermore, within each transaction, the fields to be entered are distributed across several screens.

The basic idea of upstream transactions is to create a custom transaction containing only one or a few screens. This transaction starts the original SAP transactions in the background and transfers the data. Alternatively, the custom transaction can be used as a cockpit for controlling the original transactions and thus simplifying the process.

Let's explain this further using a real-world example: The business process for calibrating test/measurement equipment is highly complex, requiring several SAP transactions to be called in succession (see Chapter 5, Section 5.6). In the case of an automotive supplier who needed to manage more than 20,000 pieces of measurement equipment per plant, the standard processes were unmanageable. Therefore, the upstream Transaction ZMV01 (see Figure 10.24) was created to do the following:

- The measurement equipment is issued from the warehouse and installed on a functional location (standard Transaction IE4N).
- The measurement equipment on the functional location is dismantled and returned to the warehouse (standard Transaction IE4N).
- The inspection order is generated from the maintenance plan (standard Transaction IP10).
- The measurement results are recorded (standard Transaction QE17).
- The usage decision is made (standard Transaction QA11).
- The inspection order is confirmed (standard Transaction IW41).

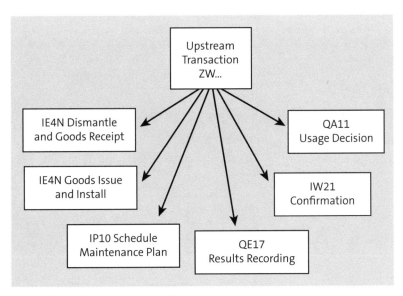

Figure 10.24 Upstream Transaction

Programming Upstream Transactions Often Worth the Effort

An upstream transaction should substantially accelerate business transaction processing. Otherwise, it has failed in its purpose.

10.4.2   BAPI

To simplify the development effort associated with upstream transactions and other custom developments, SAP provides a range of *Business Application Programming Interfaces* (BAPIs). BAPIs can be used for the following purposes:

- Connect SAP systems to the Internet.
- Enable SAP components to communicate with one another.
- Develop upstream transactions.
- Connect third-party software and legacy systems to SAP systems.
- Enable PC programs to be used as a frontend for SAP systems.
- Develop web applications that will communicate with the SAP system.
- Enable workflow applications to communicate across system boundaries.
- Enable WebFlow applications to communicate using the Internet.

You can call the BAPI Explorer in Transaction BAPI (see Figure 10.25).

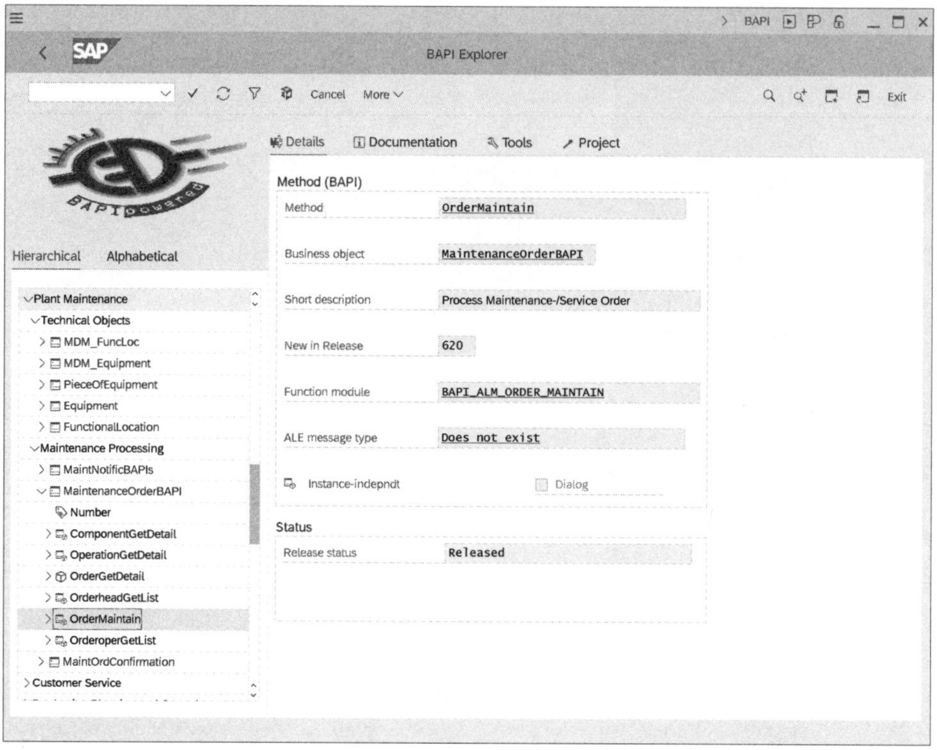

Figure 10.25 BAPI Explorer

In the plant maintenance area, SAP offers BAPIs for the following objects:

- Notifications
- Orders
- Confirmations
- Equipment
- Functional locations
- Material
- BOMs
- Task lists

Navigating through the hierarchy is a simple way of obtaining an overview of all available BAPIs.

10.4.3   Web Interface

A popular way to collect data for the SAP system or to display data from the SAP system without coming into direct contact with the SAP system is to create a web interface.

As an example of a web application, you'll now be introduced to the *EAM app*, which was developed by the Institute for Design and Information Systems (IDIS) at the Würzburg-Schweinfurt University of Applied Sciences, Germany by Florian Wolf, Tobias Schlereth, and Daniel Schwarz, for a well-known customer of the automotive industry.

The EAM app's main functions are displayed in the main menu immediately after you log in to the app (see Figure 10.26):

- **Express Confirmation**
  This function allows you to create completion confirmations for one or more employees involved in an existing order or order operation, all of which can be done on just one screen. Here, you can also perform planned and unplanned material withdrawals, as well as enter downtimes, completion confirmation texts, and causes of damage.

- **Overall Confirmation**
  This function enhances the **Express Confirmation** function to include the recording of measurement readings and counter readings. To provide you with a better overview, the individual functions are spread across several tabs.

- **Technical Confirmation**
  This function contains only the technical aspects of the completion confirmation (e.g., downtimes or causes of damage). It doesn't contain any time or material confirmations.

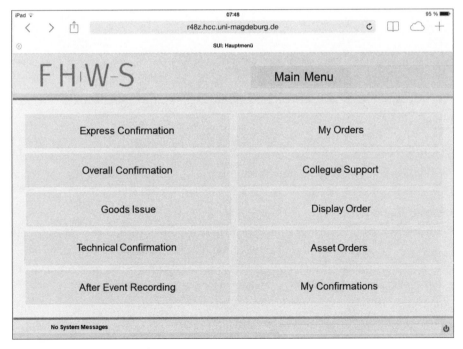

Figure 10.26 EAM App: Main Menu

- **After Event Recording**

  This function (see Figure 10.27) is used to record work that has already been carried out. For example, you can enter an order for a technical object (functional location or piece of equipment) and perform a time confirmation for one or more employees. You can also perform planned and unplanned material withdrawals, as well as specify downtimes, completion confirmation texts, and causes of damage. The following process is associated with transferring such data to the SAP system: notification created → order created → order released → material withdrawal posted → time confirmation posted → technical completion confirmation performed → order and notification completed.

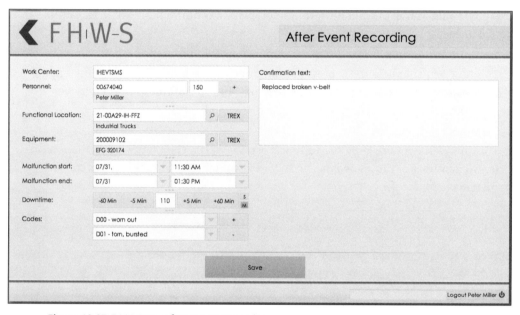

Figure 10.27 EAM App: After Event Recording

- **My Orders**

  This function contains a list of operations currently open or in process for the technician.

- **Colleague Support**

  This function contains a list of operations currently open for the technician's colleagues (i.e., the operations of those personnel numbers assigned to the same work center as the technician). The technician can then assign his colleagues' orders (e.g., if a colleague is ill or hindered in his daily work for some other reason).

- **Display Order**

  This function makes it possible to display a particular order according to its order number.

- **Asset Orders**
  This function enables you to view a list display of all open and completed operations for a functional location or a piece of equipment.

- **My Confirmations**
  This function contains the technician's completion confirmations for a predefined period (e.g., this week) or for any time interval of your choice.

In addition to these functional properties, the following technical properties of the EAM app are also worth noting:

- The EAM app was completely developed as an online scenario. In other words, it has a permanent connection via local area network (LAN), wireless LAN (WLAN), or Global System for Mobile (GSM) communications to the backend system and is able to immediately detect wrongly entered data and output an error message to that effect.

- A BAPI is used to check the validity of the data entered (e.g., whether a valid equipment number or order number was entered).

- A BAPI is used to transfer the data to the SAP system and to post it there (e.g., the OrderMaintain BAPI).

- Because the EAM app was developed for HTML5, you can use it on iPads, iPhones, desktop PCs, industry PCs, Android smartphones, and Android tablets.

- The EAM app can be fully operated using a mouse and keyboard or a touchscreen (e.g., in the case of an iPad).

[+]

> **Web Applications Enjoy High User Acceptance**
> Almost all users are familiar with web applications or apps for their private iPhone, iPad, or smartphone. For this reason, apps are also very easy to learn and use in a professional capacity and are therefore very popular among users.

10.4.4 Customer Exits

You can use *customer exits* to add your own functions to standard SAP applications without modifying the original SAP programs. In standard applications, SAP creates customer exits for certain programs, screens, and menus. Initially, these exits don't have any function. Instead, they serve as a predefined entry and exit point for adding your own additional functions to the SAP system.

You use Transaction SMOD (SAP Enhancement Management) to manage customer exits. You can then view them by entering the following:

- Technical objects: ITOB*, IEQM*, ILOM*, IHCL*, CCM*

- Measuring points/counters: IMRC*

- Warranties: BG*
- Task lists: IAIH*
- Maintenance plans: IPRM*, CI*
- Notifications: QQMA*
- Orders: IWO*, CNEX*, COZF*, IREV*
- Capacity planning: COI*, CYPP*
- Completion confirmations CMFU*, CONFPM*
- Cross-application time sheets (CATS): CATS*
- Information system: MCI*
- Data transfers: IBIP*
- Graphic modules: IMSM*

By way of example, the following are five applications in which data entry was simplified and user acceptance increased significantly as a result:

- **Transfer characteristics**
  Customer exit `IHCL0001` allows you to transfer the characteristic valuation from a material master record to the characteristic valuation of a piece of equipment. If you often add new equipment with reference to a material number, you can simplify the essential maintenance of the classification data by storing information such as performance, type specification, or other technical data once as a classification in the material master and then transferring these characteristics as default values to your new piece of equipment. Ideally, you then no longer have to maintain the classification.

- **Right plant, right storage location**
  Customer exit `CNEX0027`, which, strictly speaking, is part of the project system but can also be used for plant maintenance, supports you in specifying the right plant and the right storage location during material planning. This may be useful, for example, when a spare part is stored in only one plant that all other plants can access. If, within this customer exit, you then program a smart search strategy for your enterprise, you no longer have to worry about having the right plant in material planning for the order.

- **Right task list**
  A significant improvement is also provided by customer exits `IWO10021` and `IWO20001`. The combination of these two customer exits, for example, ensures that the right task list is derived from the damage or cause code in a malfunction report. When the order is created from the malfunction report, the correct operations are already listed in the order. This eliminates the need to find the right task list and include it in the order and therefore accelerates order processing for standardized processes in particular.

- **Right data in notification and order**

  Even though they don't make data entry any faster, customer exits that can run customized data checks when saving orders (IW010009) or notifications (QQMA0014) help to eliminate the need for data corrections. In the notification, for example, you can immediately check whether certain combinations of breakdown and cause codes make sense. These checks help inexperienced users allay their fears about operating the system.

- **Right data in purchase requisitions**

  Customer exits COZF0001 and COZF0002 allow you to automatically prepopulate certain fields for purchase requisitions generated within the order according to your own specifications. For example, you can prepopulate the **Requester** field with the name of the user logged on to the system, or you can automatically enter your department acronym in the **Requirement Number** field. This may not sound like much progress, but if a user has to enter the same department acronym 35 times for 35 non-stock items, it's easy to see why optimization becomes a priority.

The following are some more examples from professional experiences with customer projects:

- You can use customer exit IW010004 to implement order completion checks. For example, one customer wanted to prevent orders from being technically completed if any open purchase requisitions or unconfirmed operations exist or if only some of the objects in the object list have a processing indicator.

- You can use customer exit CONFPM01 to determine your own default values when confirming an order. For example, a customer wanted to prevent the activities of certain employees from being allocated on a cost basis (indicator in the HR master record). Now, if one of these employees enters a completion confirmation, the system proposes an activity type without a valuation.

- You can use customer exit IW010027 to generate your own settlement rule. If you use object lists, you frequently want to proportionally allocate the resulting order costs to the cost centers involved (see Figure 10.28). You can program this customer exit in such a way that the cost centers associated with the equipment are determined from the object list and such that the corresponding entries are configured in the settlement rule and assigned percentages.

- You can use customer exit IW010012 to control priority handling within the order. For example, one customer wanted the system to use the ABC indicator for equipment to automatically determine the priority of an order (e.g., priority 1 is automatically set for "A" equipment).

- You can use customer exit QQMA0001 to define additional fields. One customer wanted to connect his own solution database and also wanted notifications to contain, where applicable, a reference to the solution number, so this customer exit was used to define additional fields in the notification header.

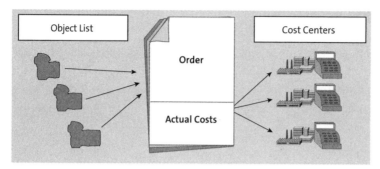

Figure 10.28 Customer Exit Settlement Rule

These examples clearly show the various ways customer exits can be used and also show that, ultimately, there are no limits to your imagination.

> **[!]** **Simplifying the Standard System with Customer Exits**
>
> Customer exits enable you to adjust business transaction processing in plant maintenance to your requirements and to simplify and accelerate processing. However, you need to give considerable thought to whether custom programming really has the desired effect and increases user acceptance.

10.4.5   Other Programming Techniques

For the sake of completeness, let's now introduce you to the other programming techniques for enhancing or changing the standard SAP system without having to modify the system.

BAdIs and Enhancement Points

Business Add-Ins (BAdIs) are used to create predefined enhancement options in SAP's components. Unlike customer exits, however, BAdIs are based on ABAP objects.

You can create BAdIs via Transaction SE19 (BAdI Builder).

The following is a list of examples that demonstrate when new BAdIs (enhancement points) can be used in plant maintenance:

- `EAM_EHP4_CI_SFWS_SC_LIST_ENH` to enhance lists used in plant maintenance (for example, to display maintenance plans, maintenance items, and maintenance packages in multilevel lists)

- `EAM_EHP4_CI_SFWS_SC_INSP_ROUND` to enhance inspection rounds (for example, to activate the production resource/tool as a measuring point)

- `EAM_WS_ORDER_RELEASE_IMPL` for security-relevant enhancements when releasing orders

- `COCF_ES_SN_LIST` to define your own selection options in the list of *shift notes*

SAP Business Workflow

SAP Business Workflow enables you to define business processes that aren't yet mapped in the system. These can range from simple release and approval procedures to more complex business processes such as creating a material master and coordinating the various departments involved. SAP Business Workflow is at its most efficient when a large number of workflows need to be processed repeatedly or the business process requires a large number of processors in a precisely defined sequence.

From a plant maintenance perspective, two workflows are especially relevant:

- **Process a maintenance notification**
  The *process a maintenance notification* scenario is supposed to support users in processing, monitoring, and completing newly created notifications. For example, you can notify specific persons or groups of persons when a new notification has been created or when a notification has been technically completed.

- **Process a maintenance order**
  The *process a maintenance order* scenario is supposed to support users in processing, monitoring, and completing newly created notifications. For example, you can notify the creator of the order when the order has been released or technically completed.

You can call and configure workflows in the SAP menu via **Tools · Business Workflow**. Figure 10.29 shows, for example, Transaction SWDD, the Workflow Builder.

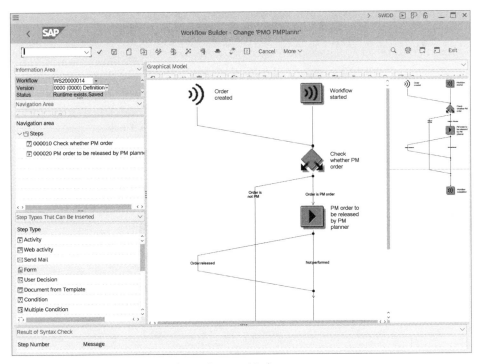

Figure 10.29 Transaction SWDD (Workflow Builder)

Let's now look at tuning measures to find out if they contribute to improving usability and, if so, to what degree. For this purpose, we performed a usability test.

10.5   Usability Studies

To provide quantitative evidence of the effects of tuning measures, we conducted a laboratory test at the Würzburg-Schweinfurt University of Applied Sciences under real-world conditions and involving more than forty test subjects to answer the following question: How does processing time in a tuned system differ from processing time in an untuned system?

Let's start by introducing the test and dealing particularly with the following questions:

- What preparatory measures were taken?
- How was the test conducted?
- What were the results of the usability test?
- What conclusions can we draw from the results?

10.5.1   Preparation and Execution

This section introduces the steps involved in preparing the study—business process selection and tuning measures.

Selecting Business Processes

We first had to select business processes that were a representative reflection of the maintenance process in a company. We ensured that business processes were selected from both plant maintenance and from the area of master data. Business processes involving plant maintenance are often used in daily operations, so they should be given more attention when considering possible optimization measures. We included three such processes.

Business processes involving master data are not as widely used in day-to-day operations, so we included only one such process. Based on these criteria, we selected the following business processes:

- Business process01 (Create Equipment)
- Business process02 (Breakdown Maintenance)
- Business process03 (External Processing)
- Business process04 (Scheduled Repair)

Tuning Measures

After selecting the business processes, we applied the appropriate tuning measures to each business process. To do so, two users were created in the system, who served as sample users for the tuned and the untuned business processes.

For user01, the SAP system default settings, such as SAP standard menu or parameters, were not stored. Moreover, the default SAP settings for the processing of business processes were left in an untuned state.

For user02, on the other hand, a number of tuning measures were implemented that correspond to category 1 in Section 10.2:

- Favorites were created for each business process.
- General parameters were defined (for example, cost center, company code, plant, site plant, planning plant, controlling area, storage location, and so on).
- Maintenance-specific parameters were maintained, including parameters for external processing and procurement, as well as order type, notification type, organization, and reference object.
- Popups were suppressed at specific locations.
- The history was enabled.

In addition, tuning measures were applied to this user's business processes, which correspond to category 2 in Section 10.3:

- The screen layout was simplified in customizing (tabs, field selection upon notification, order, and equipment, among others).
- The **Integration of Order and Notification** option was enabled in customizing.
- A transaction variant was created for order entry.
- External processing profiles were configured in customizing.
- A customized selection variant was defined for selecting notifications.
- Default values were enabled for confirmations (services, backflush).

No measures from category 3 (programming) were applied.

> **[!]**
>
> **The Same Results without Programming**
>
> The following principle was applied: No programming is supposed to take place. The tuning measures are limited to customizing and similar functions and user settings.
>
> In addition, the following principle was applied: The results of a tuned business process and the results of an untuned business process have to be identical.

Selecting the Test Subjects

For the results to be considered representative, we had to find a sufficient number of test subjects with the appropriate qualifications.

- We assumed that five test subjects per business process would suffice.
- To be considered valid from a statistical point of view, the test subjects had to be able to work independently of each other for each business process and user type, so we recruited a total of forty test subjects among information management students.
- For the results to be reliable, the test subjects had to have the same previous knowledge. This condition is best met if none of the test subjects has previous SAP knowledge.

[!] **Suitable Test Subjects**

To ensure that the results were representative qualitatively and quantitatively, forty test subjects who should have no previous knowledge were required to participate in the usability test.

Description of the Business Processes

Because the test subjects were not meant to have any previous SAP knowledge, they needed a proper description of the business processes to be performed.

[!] **Processes Based on Documents Only**

The test subjects were meant to perform the business processes on their own, relying exclusively on the description of the processes.

The description of a business process was similar to the following (an excerpt of business process02: breakdown maintenance for user01):

- *In the SAP menu, use the menu path Logistics • Plant Maintenance • Maintenance Processing • Notification • Create General.*
- *In the screen that opens, click the Notification Type entry field. Then, click on the (F4) help, to select a valid value. In the list displayed, double-click on M1 Maintenance Request. Now press the (Enter) key to confirm your selection.*
- *A screen will open for you to create a maintenance request notification.*
- *In the field highlighted in yellow, enter the text, "defective pump" next to the notification number.*
- *On the Notification tab, in the Reference Object field group, enter the value "P-1000-N003" in the Equipment field. Then press (Enter) to confirm. The system now automatically populates the field for the functional location.*

- *In the Responsibilities field group, enter the value "IO1" in the Planning Group field and the value "A-O1" in the Main Work Center field. Then, press the (Enter) key.*

Recording Tool

Measuring the processing time with a stopwatch seemed too inaccurate and error-prone. We therefore had to find a tool that allowed us to record the activities of our test subjects and to obtain clear readings for the time it took them to complete a business process.

After selecting different tools and testing them internally, we decided to use the keylogger tool *PC Agent* by blue-series.

This software program records a user's activities in the background with a time stamp. The recording files are saved in proprietary format in a previously defined folder as user-dependent items. These files can be converted to many other formats, including to a spreadsheet-readable format.

[!]

Only a Tool Delivers Safe and Objective Results

Using a keylogger tool ensures that:

- Data remains permanently available after completion of the test runs.
- The evaluation can be substantiated with raw data at any time.
- The results are safe and accurate.

Procedure

The tests were carried out in the SAP Laboratory at the Würzburg-Schweinfurt University of Applied Sciences over two consecutive days. On the first day, the business processes *planned repair* and *breakdown maintenance* were performed, and on the second day, the business processes *external processing* and *create equipment* were performed.

The previously created users were assigned to the individual business processes so that which user performed which business process was clearly defined and could be tracked easily, making evaluating and documenting the test easier.

Right before the test, the project team logged on the users to the terminal server and to the SAP system so that the participants could start with their assigned business processes. During logon, the project team also checked that the keylogger software was enabled in the background so that the times and activities of the users were recorded properly for later evaluation.

The subjects received a brief introduction to the SAP system regarding navigation in the system; elements such as the title bar, menu bar, user-defined favorites, the SAP menu, the system toolbar, and the status bar; and direct transaction calls.

Armed with this knowledge and the descriptions of the business processes, each subject performed his or her business process ten times while PC Agent worked quietly in the background.

10.5.2   Results

From the recorded raw data, the average processing time of the five subjects who had completed a business process was calculated. Let's describe the results we obtained, with user01 (untuned) directly compared to user02 (tuned).

Business process01 (create equipment; see Figure 10.30): In this business process (and also in the others), you can clearly observe a steep decline in the time curve, which stabilizes after five to six test runs due to the learning effect. So, we want to calculate the average values of test runs 6 through 10. The average time for test runs 6 through 10 was 1:35 minutes for user01 and 0:45 minutes for user02, resulting in the following relation:

$$M(U) \div M(G) = 2.11$$

In this equation, M(U) = average value of test runs 6 through 10 in an untuned state and M(T) = average value of test runs 6 through 10 in a tuned state.

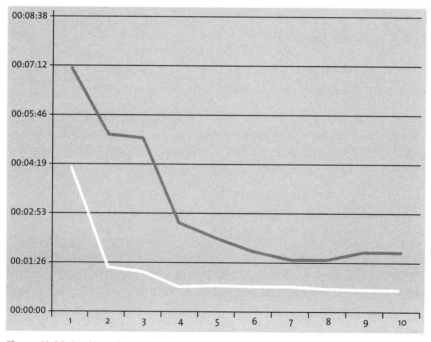

Figure 10.30 Business Process 1: Create Equipment Master

Result for the Creation of Equipment

Business process01 (Create Equipment) takes user01 about twice as long as user02.

Business process02 (breakdown maintenance; see Figure 10.31): The average time for test runs 6 through 10 is 6:28 minutes for user01 and 1:40 minutes for user02, which results in the following relation:

$M(U) \div M(G) = 3.88$

In this equation, M(U) = average value of test runs 6 through 10 in an untuned state and M(T) = average value of test runs 6 through 10 in a tuned state.

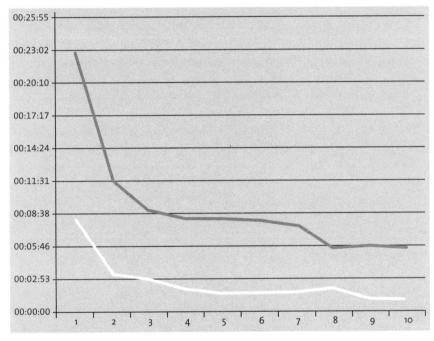

Figure 10.31 Business Process 2: Breakdown Maintenance

Result for Breakdown Maintenance

Business process02 (breakdown maintenance) takes user01 almost four times as long as user02.

Business process03 (external processing; see Figure 10.32): The average time for test runs 6 through 10 is 1:42 minutes for user01 and 12:26 minutes for user02, which results in the following relation:

$M(U) \div M(G) = 3.92$

In this equation, M(U) = average value of test runs 6 through 10 in an untuned state and M(T) = average value of test runs 6 through 10 in a tuned state.

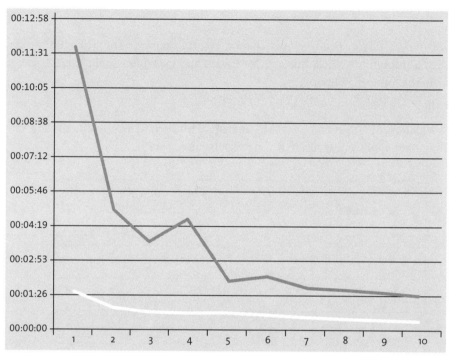

Figure 10.32 Business Process 3: External Processing

[+]

Result for External Processing

Business process03 (external processing) takes user01 almost four times as long as user02.

Business process04 (*planned repair*; see Figure 10.33): The average time for test runs 6 through 10 is 5:53 minutes for user01 and 2:22 minutes for user02, which results in the following relation:

M(U) ÷ M(G) = 2.49

In this equation,M(U) = average value of test runs 6 through 10 in an untuned state and M(T) = average value of test runs 6 through 10 in a tuned state.

[!]

Result for Planned Repair

Business process04 (planned repair) takes user01 almost 2.5 times as long as user02.

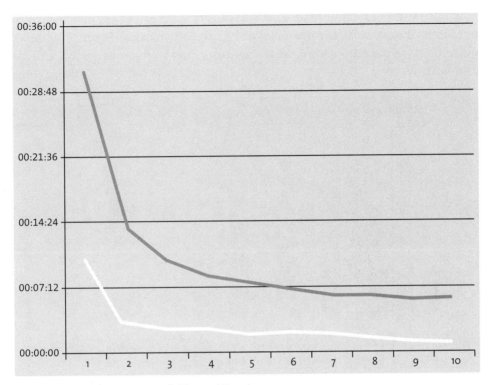

Figure 10.33 Business Process 4: Planned Repair

Figure 10.34 shows a summary of our results.

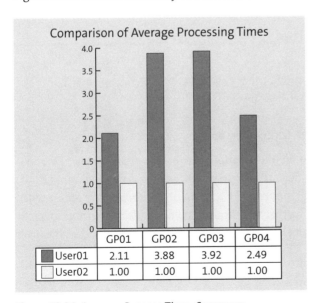

	GP01	GP02	GP03	GP04
User01	2.11	3.88	3.92	2.49
User02	1.00	1.00	1.00	1.00

Figure 10.34 Average Process Time: Summary

In addition to the processing time, another key figure was recorded and evaluated: *control entries* (mouse-clicks, buttons, [Tab] and [Enter] key presses). Figure 10.35 shows the summary of our results. Here, too, the average values for test runs 6 through 10 are displayed.

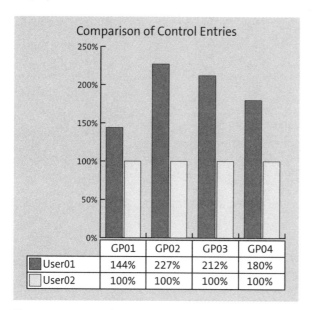

Figure 10.35 Control Entries: Summary

Concerning the control entries, the difference between a tuned and an untuned system is almost as great.

[!]

Result for Control Entries

The untuned system requires 1.5 to 2.5 as many control entries as the tuned system.

10.5.3   Laboratory Test with SAP Screen Personas

A similar second test was performed to determine the impact of SAP Screen Personas on the processing time. The test subjects were to perform various posting transactions (*goods receipt for a purchase order, goods receipt for an order, goods issue for an order, goods issue for a cost center*) and further warehouse functions (*delivery status of a purchase order, display material document*). The five test subjects were to perform the tasks six times with the SAP Easy Access menu and with the SAP Screen Personas Storage Location Cockpit (Section 10.3.8).

Figure 10.36 shows the learning curve of this test in SAP Easy Access and in the Storage Location Cockpit.

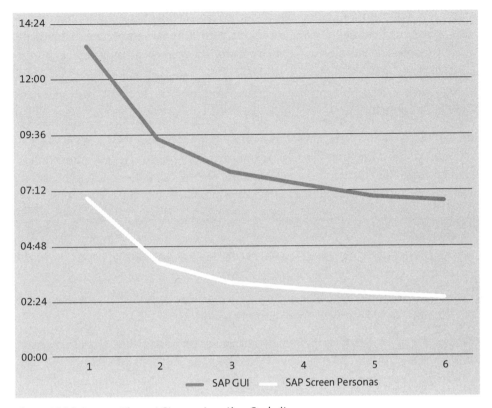

Figure 10.36 Process Time at Storage Location Cockpit

The results show that the processing time in the Storage Location Cockpit is already seven minutes less than in the first test. In comparison, the first test in the SAP Easy Access menu took 13:26 minutes. This data shows that you can reduce the processing time by nearly 50% if you use the warehouse cockpit. The first test indicates an even better relation: an average of 6:46 minutes with the SAP Easy Access menu and an average of 2:34 minutes with the SAP Screen Personas warehouse cockpit show that the processing time can be reduced by more than 60%.

10.6 Summary

SAP offers a lot of opportunities for simplifying the user frontend and accelerating business transaction processing in SAP S/4HANA Asset Management.

These options are divided into three categories:

- Category 1 contains options available to the users themselves, such as defining user parameters, creating list variants, pre-assigning input helps, or configuring table controls.

- Category 2 contains options available to the IT department not requiring programming, such as creating transaction variants, setting up an appropriate customizing, using mobile and SAP Fiori apps, or creating SAP Screen Personas flavors.
- Category 3 contains options only available to the IT department requiring programming, such as developing upstream transactions, web applications, customer exits and BAPIs or BAdIs.

Some of these options were subject to several usability studies conducted by the SAP laboratory at the Würzburg-Schweinfurt University of Applied Sciences. After completion of the usability tests and evaluation of the results, the following statements had been proven sufficiently, resulting in the following statements and conclusions:

[!]
Statement 1

When executing SAP business processes, there is a fast learning effect.

This statement is proven by all learning curves. All test runs yield a processing time which hardly can be improved upon in.subsequent runs.

[!]
Conclusion 1.1

A minimum of training can achieve a lot.

[!]
Conclusion 1.2

Your users should not be discouraged by initially failed attempts and should wait before they complain about the SAP system.

[!]
Statement 2

Tuning measures reduce the number of control entries for SAP business processes.

This statement is proven by all of the statistics, no matter which test run, no matter which business process was performed: with a standard frontend you always had to click the mouse, press buttons, and press the Tab and Enter keys 1.5 to 2.5 times more often than in an optimized frontend.

[!]
Conclusion 2

Check if you have implemented all tuning measures which do not require any programming.

> **[!]**
>
> **Statement 3**
>
> Tuning measures help reduce the processing time of SAP business processes.

This statement is proven by all of the statistics, whether it was the first or the tenth test run, no matter which business process was performed: with an optimized frontend you are always two or four times faster than using the standard frontend.

> **[!]**
>
> **Conclusion 3**
>
> Check if you have implemented all tuning measures not requiring any programming. This can be very helpful.

> **[!]**
>
> **Statement 4**
>
> The level of improvement depends not only on the state of your system before tuning measures are applied but also on the tuning measures you implement.

In the university's laboratory tests, the original state was the SAP standard version; tuning measures were used not requiring any programming. Thereby, an improvement potential of 222% to 396% was fully utilized. If you have already implemented certain tuning measures in your company, your improvement potential might be lower. However, by using additional measures and/or programming, you might even achieve a higher improvement potential than the laboratory tests

And this results in the last and most important conclusion:

> **[!]**
>
> **Conclusion 4**
>
> Never settle for what you have achieved. Improvement potential can always be found.

Appendices

Appendix A
List of Further Sources and Literature

Liebstückel, Karl. *Configuring Plant Maintenance in SAP S/4HANA*. SAP PRESS, 2020.

DIN 31051:2018-09: Fundamentals of Maintenance, issued by Deutschen Institut für Normung (DIN) (German Institute for Standardization), 2018.

DIN EN ISO 9241:2008-09: Ergonomics of Human-System Interaction. Part 110: Dialogue Principles, issued by Deutschen Institut für Normung (DIN) (German Institute for Standardization), 2009.

Kalwachwala, Homiar; Chahal, Sandeep; Cheekoti, Santhosh;; Isacc, Antony Khambhampati, Rajani; Lodha, Vikas; Srinivasan, Syama; Quirk, David, *SAP Master Data Governance*, 2nd ed., SAP PRESS, 2019.

SAP Asset Manager User Guide, Walldorf, 2020. *http://s-prs.co/v518000*.

Road Map Explorer. *http://s-prs.co/v518001*.

Seidl, Markud, *Intelligent Asset Management*, Walldorf, 2019.

SAP SE (ed.), *Application Help for SAP Asset Intelligence Network*, Walldorf, 2020.

SAP SE (ed.), *Application Help for SAP Asset Strategy and Performance Management*, Walldorf, 2020.

SAP SE (ed.), *Application Help for SAP Predictive Maintenance and Service – Cloud Edition*, Walldorf, 2020.

SAP (ed.), *EAM Web UI Implementation Guide – Adapting EAM Web UI*, Walldorf, 2018.

Papenburg, Charlotte, Bachelor Thesis "Confirmation Cockpit for Plant Maintenance: Concept and Realization using SAP Screen Personas," Würzburg, 2016.

Loos, Daniela, Bachelor Thesis "Storage Location Cockpit: Concept and Realization using SAP Screen Personas," Würzburg, 2016.

Appendix B
Overviews

Appendix B contains useful additional information, including overviews of structuring resources, the functions of notifications and orders, options for integrating plant maintenance in SAP, and plant maintenance information system (PMIS) analyses.

B.1 Functional Comparison of Structuring Resources

The following table shows a functional comparison of the most important technical objects.

	Functional Location	Equipment	Assembly
Measuring points and counters	+	+	−
Classes and characteristics	+	+	+
Partner	+	+	−
Address management	+	+	−
Permits	+	+	−
Warranties	+	+	−
Multilingual short texts	+	+	+
Multilingual long texts	+	+	+
Object information	+	+	−
External number assignment	+	+	+
Internal number assignment	−	+	+
Alternative labeling	+	−	−
Document links	+	+	+
Vendor data	+	+	−
Account assignment	+	+	−

	Functional Location	Equipment	Assembly
Responsibilities	+	+	–
Usage history	–	+	–
Usability period	–	+	+
Change documents	+	+	+

B.2   Functions of Notifications and Orders

The following table shows the most important functions of the work order cycle. Assigning a priority helps to plan your project:

- Priority A: function is important. Must be introduced in the first phase.
- Priority B: function has to be introduced at a later stage.
- Priority C: function will not be needed.

Object	Function	A	B	C
Notification	User status			
	Reference objects			
	Priorities			
	Partner			
	Telephone integration			
	Paging			
	Addresses			
	Object parts			
	Damage			
	Causes of damage			
	Measures			
	Activities			
	Notification items			
	Classification			
	Printing			

Object	Function	A	B	C
	Fax			
	Download			
	Breakdowns			
	Approvals			
	Response time monitoring			
	Revisions			
	Solution database			
Order	Reference objects			
	User status			
	Priorities			
	Partners			
	Telephone integration			
	Paging			
	Addresses			
	Printing			
	Fax			
	Download			
	Permits			
	Operations			
	Scheduling			
	Relationships			
	Capacity requirements planning			
	Capacity availability check			
	Reservation of stock material			
	Stock material availability check			
	Ordering of non-stock material			
	Catalog integration (Internet and intranet catalogs, vendor catalogs)			

Object	Function	A	B	C
	Estimated costs			
	Planned/actual costing			
	Order budgets			
	Object list			
	Production resources/tools			
	Production resources/tools availability check			
	Suborders			
	Utilization of production capacities			
Confirmation	Time confirmations			
	Technical completion confirmations			
	Goods receipts			
	Material withdrawals			
	Overhead costing			
	Order settlement			
Immediate repair	Historical orders			
	After-event recording in SAP Enterprise Portal			
	Confirmation of unplanned work in SAP Business Client			
Shift notes and shift reports	Shift notes for work centers			
	Shift notes for technical objects			
	Shift reports			
External processing	External processing via service specifications			
	External processing as a purchase order			
	External processing via work centers			
	Revisions			

Object	Function	A	B	C
Preventive maintenance	General maintenance task lists			
	Equipment task lists			
	Functional location task lists			
	Maintenance strategies			
	Time-based maintenance plans			
	Service-based maintenance plans			
	Single cycle plans			
	Strategy plans			
	Simple multiple counter plans			
	Enhanced multiple counter plans			
	Order maintenance call object			
	Notification maintenance call object			
	Inspection lot maintenance call object			
	"Service entry sheet" maintenance call object			
	Simulation of capacity utilization			
	Simulation of planned costs			
	Automatic deadline monitoring			
Condition-based maintenance	PM-PCS interface			
Refurbishment	Refurbishment of serial numbers			
	Refurbishment of material			
	Production of spare parts			
	Settlement based on standard price			
	Settlement based on moving average price			
	Subcontracting			
Production	Spare part production using a refurbishment order			
	Spare part production using a production order			

Object	Function	A	B	C
Calibration of test/measurement equipment	Test/measurement equipment as equipment			
	Inspection plans			
	Inspection maintenance plans			
	Results recording			
	Confirmation			
	Usage decision			
Pool asset management	Pool asset management requirements			
	Pool asset management planning table			
Project-based maintenance	Work breakdown structure (WBS) elements			
	Networks			
	Manual assignment			
	Automatic assignment			
	Maintenance Event Builder			

B.3   Integration Aspects

The following table is structured in this manner:

- Column 1: Which department is affected?
- Column 2: Which type of information exchange should be used?
- Column 3: Will the information flow from plant maintenance to the department (→), will it flow from the department to plant maintenance (←), or will it flow in both directions (↔)?
- Columns 4 to 6: Does the integration take place within SAP S/4HANA (E), are other SAP systems affected by it (S), and will a non-SAP system be needed (N)?
- Column 7: Which is the relevant application or system?

1	2	3	4	5	6	7
User department	Information	Flow	E	S	N	System
Inventory management; warehousing	Spare parts management	↔	✓			Materials management
	Standardization of spare parts master data (e.g., avoiding duplicates, distribution of master data)	↔		✓		SAP NetWeaver MDM
	Inventory management for equipment	↔	✓			Materials management
	Releasing reservations for stock materials	→	✓			Materials management
	Availability check for stock material	←	✓			Materials management
	Planned or unplanned goods issue	←	✓			Materials management
	MRP for spare parts, including the triggering of procurement orders	←	✓			Materials management
	Serial numbers in warehouse management (WM)	→	✓			Warehouse management, SAP Extended Warehouse Management, and stock room management
	Serial numbers in handling units	→	✓			Materials management
	Refurbishment of spare parts	↔	✓			Materials management
	Management of materials as production resources/tools	↔	✓			Materials management
Purchasing	Triggering of purchase requisitions for materials	→	✓	✓		Materials management, SAP SRM
	Goods receipt of external materials	←	✓	✓		Materials management, SAP SRM
	Triggering of purchase requisitions for services	→	✓	✓		Materials management
	Periodic creation of service entry sheets	→	✓			Materials management

1	2	3	4	5	6	7
User department	Information	Flow	E	S	N	System
	Service entry and acceptance	←	✓	✓	✓	Materials management, SAP SRM
	Integration of spare parts catalogs	←		✓		Open Catalog Interface (OCI) interface
	Goods receipt-based invoice verification	←	✓			Materials management
Production	Assignment of production resources to plant maintenance objects	←	✓			Production planning
	Notification of production in case of continued maintenance activities	→	✓			Production planning
	Data transfer from production systems to trigger malfunction reports or to update measurement and counter readings	←			✓	Process control systems, diagnostics, network monitoring systems, and others; PM-PCS interface
	In-house production of spare parts	←	✓			Production planning
	Service activities, such as modifications, in the context of production orders	→	✓			Production planning
	Usage of plant data collection to confirm plant maintenance orders	←	✓			PDC (production data collection) systems
Quality management	Management of test equipment	↔	✓			Quality management
	Periodic creation of inspection orders or inspection lots	→	✓			Quality management
	Results entry and usage decision for test equipment	←	✓			Quality management

1	2	3	4	5	6	7
User department	Information	Flow	E	S	N	System
Environment, health, and safety	Safety measures as production resources/tools (PRTs)	←	✓			SAP EHS Management
	Safety plan	←	✓			SAP EHS Management
Controlling	Assignment of plant maintenance as a service provider to the cost center structure	←	✓			Controlling
	Assignment of plant maintenance objects as service recipients to the cost center structure	←	✓			Controlling
	Internal orders as account assignment objects	←	✓			Controlling
	Definition of required cost elements	←	✓			Controlling
	Definition of activity types	←	✓			Controlling
	Planning of prices	←	✓			Controlling
	Definition of costing procedures	←	✓			Controlling
	Settlement of plant maintenance orders	→	✓			Controlling
	Allocation of overhead costs	→	✓			Controlling
Accounting	Assignment of plant maintenance objects to asset master data	←	✓			Asset accounting
	Creation or modification of asset master records during the creation or modification of equipment master records	→	✓			Asset accounting
	Assignment of orders to investment programs	→	✓			Investment management
	Creation of assets under construction	→	✓			Asset accounting

1	2	3	4	5	6	7
User department	Information	Flow	E	S	N	System
	Creation or modification of equipment master records during the creation or modification of asset master records	←	✓			Asset accounting
	Capitalization of plant maintenance services in fixed assets	→	✓			Asset accounting
	Definition of required general ledger (GL) accounts	←	✓			Financial accounting
	Invoice receipt (without goods receipt)	←	✓			Financial accounting
Personnel	Assignment of personnel numbers to plant maintenance work centers	←	✓			SAP Human Capital Management for SAP S/4HANA
	Assignment of personnel numbers or positions to technical objects	←	✓			SAP Human Capital Management for SAP S/4HANA
	Planning of personnel numbers in notifications, orders, and order operations	←	✓			SAP Human Capital Management for SAP S/4HANA
	Confirmation including personnel number	←	✓			SAP Human Capital Management for SAP S/4HANA
	Planning of qualifications in order and task list operations	←	✓			SAP Human Capital Management for SAP S/4HANA
	Update of employee time accounts	→	✓			SAP Human Capital Management for SAP S/4HANA
Real estate management	Assignment of functional locations to real estate objects	→	✓			Flexible Real Estate Management
	Data transfer from building control systems to trigger malfunction reports or to update measurement and counter readings, and so on	←			✓	Building control systems, PM-PCS interface

1	2	3	4	5	6	7
User department	Information	Flow	E	S	N	System
	Settlement of plant maintenance orders (for instance, for further clearing in service charge settlement)	→	✓			Flexible Real Estate Management
Construction, network building, or similar	Creation of functional locations, equipment, and bills of materials from upstream systems	←			✓	CAD, GIS, network monitoring systems, or similar
	Triggering of notifications or orders from within upstream systems	←			✓	CAD, GIS, NIS systems, or similar; PM-PCS interface
	Assignment of work breakdown structures (WBS) and/or networks	↔	✓			Project system
	Scheduling of plant maintenance orders for projects	←	✓			Project system
Service and sales	Quotations, sales orders, and invoices for plant maintenance services for third parties	↔	✓			Customer services or sales
	Maintenance of customer data in functional locations and equipment	←	✓			Customer service

B.4   Standard Plant Maintenance Information System Reports

The following table shows the available plant maintenance-related analyses, naming infostructure, available characteristics, and measures.

Standard analysis	Infostructure	Characteristics	Measures
Object class and manufacturer	S062	■ Object class ■ Material ■ Vendor ■ Year of construction ■ Assembly	■ Closed notifications ■ Completed orders ■ Number of actions ■ Processing days ■ Service costs

Standard analysis	Infostructure	Characteristics	Measures
Location	S061	■ Maintenance plant ■ Plant section ■ Location ■ PM planning plant ■ PM planner group ■ Functional location ■ Equipment ■ Assembly	■ Service price ■ Degree of urgency ■ Internal wage costs ■ Internal material costs ■ Internal materials quota ■ Internal staff quota ■ Recorded breakdown duration
Planner group	S061	■ Planning plant ■ Planner group ■ Maintenance plant ■ Plant section ■ Location ■ Functional location ■ Equipment ■ Assembly	■ Orders entered ■ Recorded breakdowns ■ Notifications entered ■ External wage costs ■ External material costs ■ External materials quota ■ External staff quota ■ Planned orders ■ Total actual revenues ■ Total actual costs ■ Total planned costs ■ Planning degree ■ Number of damages ■ Number of damage causes and actions ■ Immediate orders ■ Other costs ■ Unplanned orders
Damage analysis	S063	■ Notification type ■ Functional location ■ Equipment	■ Number of actions ■ Number of damages ■ Number of damage causes

Standard analysis	Infostructure	Characteristics	Measures
Object statistics	S065	■ Object class ■ Material ■ Vendor ■ Year of construction	■ Acquisition value ■ Number of pieces of equipment ■ Number of functional locations with single installation ■ Number of functional locations without equipment installation ■ Number of functional locations with collective installation ■ Number of functional locations
Breakdown statistics	S070	■ Object class ■ Functional location ■ Equipment	■ Actual breakdowns ■ Mean time between repairs ■ Mean time to repair ■ Time between repairs ■ Time to repair
Cost evaluation	S115	■ Order type ■ Plant maintenance service type ■ Functional location ■ Equipment	■ Service costs ■ Internal wage costs ■ Internal material costs ■ External wage costs ■ External material costs ■ Planned orders ■ Total actual revenues ■ Total actual costs ■ Total planned costs ■ Total estimated costs ■ Other costs
Vehicle consumption analysis	S114	■ Maintenance plant ■ Equipment category ■ Vendor ■ Year of construction ■ Equipment	■ Mileage ■ Operating hours ■ Fuel quantity ■ Fuel volume

Appendix C
The Author

Dr. Karl Liebstückel is a professor of information management and business software at the Würzburg-Schweinfurt University of Applied Sciences, Germany. He has more than 35 years of SAP experience and has performed more than 90 industry projects. From 2003 to 2012, he was a member of the board of directors of the German SAP User Group (DSAG) and was its chairman from 2007 to 2012. From 2001 to 2008, he led its Plant Maintenance and Service Management working group. Dr. Liebstückel owns his own consulting company and is the author of several books on the topic of logistics. Previously, he worked at SAP SE for thirteen years in the areas of development, consulting, and training in plant maintenance and service management. His last positions were platinum consultant and global product manager for Plant Maintenance and Service Management applications. You are welcome to contact the author by email at *karl@liebstueckel.consulting*.

Index

T

U

- Set up preventive maintenance, external processing, refurbishment, and more in your SAP S/4HANA system

- Configure notifications, work orders, and completion confirmations with step-by-step instructions

- Customize the SAP Fiori launchpad for plant maintenance activities

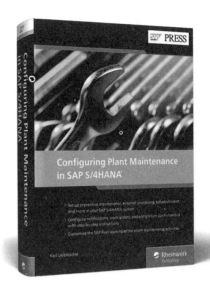

Karl Liebstückel

Configuring Plant Maintenance in SAP S/4HANA

Whether you know it as plant maintenance or asset management, this is the only guide you need to set it up in SAP S/4HANA! Start by planning your plant maintenance implementation, and then jump into configuring the organizational structure and system-wide functions. Use step-by-step instructions to set up your technical systems, from your equipment and fleet to your materials and assemblies. If you're looking to configure breakdown maintenance, corrective maintenance, preventive maintenance, predictive maintenance, or all four, this is the book for you!

763 pages, pub. 05/2020
E-Book: $79.99 | **Print:** $89.95 | **Bundle:** $99.99

www.sap-press.com/5102

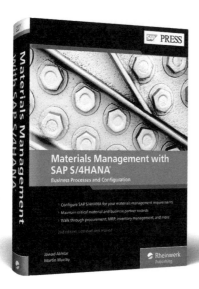

- Configure SAP S/4HANA for your materials management requirements

- Maintain critical material and business partner records

- Walk through procurement, MRP, inventory management, and more

Jawad Akktar, Martin Murray

Materials Management with SAP S/4HANA

Business Processes and Configuration

Get MM on SAP S/4HANA! Set up the master data your system needs to run its material management processes. Learn how to define material types, MRP procedures, business partners, and more. Configure your essential processes, from purchasing and MRP runs to inventory management and goods issue and receipt. Discover how to get more out of SAP S/4HANA by using batch management, special procurement types, the Early Warning System, and other built-in tools.

939 pages, 2nd edition, pub. 06/2020
E-Book: $79.99 | **Print:** $89.95 | **Bundle:** $99.99

www.sap-press.com/5132

- Configure and run MRP Live and classic MRP with SAP S/4HANA

- Evaluate your MRP results with classic transactions and SAP Fiori apps

- Explore planning with demand-driven and predictive MRP

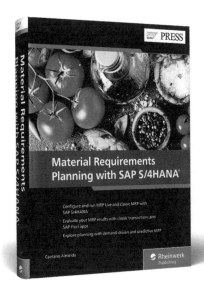

Caetano Almeida

Material Requirements Planning with SAP S/4HANA

With this comprehensive guide, master MRP in SAP S/4HANA from end to end. Set up master data and configure SAP S/4HANA with step-by-step instructions. Run classic MRP, MRP Live, or both; then evaluate your results with SAP GUI transactions or SAP Fiori apps.

541 pages, pub. 07/2020
E-Book: $79.99 | **Print:** $89.95 | **Bundle:** $99.99

www.sap-press.com/4966

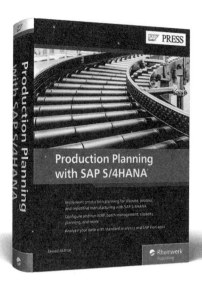

- Implement production planning for discrete, process, and repetitive manufacturing with SAP S/4HANA

- Configure and run MRP, batch management, capacity planning, and more

- Analyze your data with standard analytics and SAP Fiori apps

Jawad Akhtar

Production Planning with SAP S/4HANA

Allocate your materials, personnel, and machinery with SAP S/4HANA! This comprehensive guide will show you how to configure production planning in SAP S/4HANA for discrete, process, and repetitive manufacturing. Next, you'll learn to run those processes using step-by-step instructions. Master production workflows, like batch management, S&OP, demand management, PP-DS, and MRP. With industry examples throughout, this guide is your one-stop shop for PP with SAP S/4HANA!

1010 pages, pub. 03/2019

E-Book: $79.99 | **Print:** $89.95 | **Bundle:** $99.99

www.sap-press.com/4821

- Implement QM with SAP S/4HANA for planning, inspections, and notifications
- Integrate QM processes across your supply chain
- Master batch management, stability studies, quality issue management, FMEA, and more

Jawad Akhtar

Quality Management with SAP S/4HANA

Keep your product standards high with this comprehensive guide to quality management in SAP S/4HANA! You'll learn how to make QM an integral part of your existing supply chain by connecting to materials management, production planning, warehouse management, and other logistics processes. Step-by-step instructions will show you how to both configure and use key QM processes like batch management and audits. Implement quality plans, inspections, and notifications in SAP S/4HANA to be confident in your product's quality!

950 pages, pub. 11/2019
E-Book: $79.99 | **Print:** $89.95 | **Bundle:** $99.99
www.sap-press.com/4824

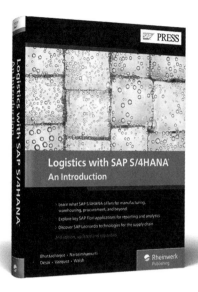

- Learn what SAP S/4HANA offers for manufacturing, warehousing, procurement, and beyond

- Explore key SAP Fiori applications for reporting and analytics

- Discover SAP Leonardo technologies for the supply chain

Bhattacharjee, Narasimhamurti, Desai, Vazquez, Walsh

Logistics with SAP S/4HANA

An Introduction

Transform your logistics operations with SAP S/4HANA! With this introduction, see what SAP has in store for each supply chain line of business: sales order management, manufacturing, inventory management, warehousing, and more. Discover how SAP Fiori apps and embedded analytics improve reporting, and explore the intersection between your supply chain processes and new SAP Leonardo technologies. Take your first look at SAP S/4HANA logistics, and see where it will take your business!

589 pages, 2nd edition, pub. 01/2019
E-Book: $69.99 | **Print:** $79.95 | **Bundle:** $89.99

www.sap-press.com/4785

Interested in reading more?

Please visit our website for all new book
and e-book releases from SAP PRESS

www.sap-press.com